TRUE SCIENCE AGREES WITH THE BIBLE

Jesus said:
"Ye shall know the truth,
and the truth shall make you free"
John 8:32

TRUE SCIENCE AGREES WITH THE BIBLE

by
Malcolm Bowden

Sovereign Publications
Box 88
Bromley
Kent BR2 9PF

First Edition 1998

ISBN 0 9506042 4 0
Published by Sovereign Publications Box 88, Bromley,
Kent, BR2 9PF, England

Typesetting
The 10 point Times New Roman text was set using GST Pressworks Desk Top Publisher 2.03 programme. The illustrations were drawn with GST Designworks 2.02 Graphics programme. The front cover used CorelXara 1.5 graphics programme.

Printed by Bath Press.

DEDICATION
to Barry Setterfield

Barry Setterfield has laboured long and hard in several areas of importance to Christians, in matters doctrinal, theological, geological, astronomical and others. But this dedication is for his original pioneering work in the decrease in the speed of light. For this, he has had little recognition of his wide scientific abilities, his industry and input, and this book attempts, in some small measure, to correct this situation.

NOTES

Unless otherwise noted, all emphasised words or passages within a quotation are made by the author of this book.

Powers of numbers are given as 10^2 and not the more familiar 10².

Figures are given in numerical order in each subsection. Where other figures are referred to in different sections these are given with their specific section and subsection - e.g. Fig. 2.3.5 is in Section 2, Subsection 3, Fig. 5.

REFERENCES

Sufficient letters of an author's name are given to identify him in the reference section. The page number follows a colon. Where he has more than one reference, the particular work is indicated by the year of publication; e.g. [Asp69:123]. Where he has more than one reference in the same year this is indicated by A, B etc.

BA = Biblical Astronomer; Journal of the Association for Biblical Astronomy (See ref. Bouw, G. 1992)

CSM = Creation Science Movement, Box 888, Portsmouth PO6 2YD

E or CENTJ = *Creation Ex Nihilo Technical Journal*, followed by volume(number):page. P.O. Box 6302, Acacia Ridge, D.C., Qld, 4110, Australia.

EB = *Encyclopaedia Britannica,* 15th Ed., 1985 - followed by volume:page.

NBD = *New Bible Dictionary 2nd Ed.*, Inter Varsity Press 1982.

Q or CRSQ = *Creation Research Society Quarterly.* Followed by volume/number:page. P.O. Box 8263, St. Joseph, MO 64508-8263, U.S.A. As a guide, the first volume was produced in July 1964. Volume 34 no.1 in June 1997.

Impact Articles are produced by the Institute for Creation Research, P.O. Box 2667, El Cajon, CA 92021, U.S.A.

SF = *Science Frontiers*: Issue number. Published by W. Corliss (see Appendix 9).

... AND ABBREVIATIONS

c is the symbol used in physics for the speed of light.

CDK stands for *"c* decay" - the decrease in the speed of light.

CONTENTS

SECTION 1 - A SURVEY OF GENESIS 1-11

SECTION 2 - THE CREATION EXAMINED

SECTION 3 - GENESIS 6-11 - THE FLOOD

SECTION 4 - THE AGE OF THE EARTH AND UNIVERSE

Contents

List of Illustrations

Acknowledgements

I would like to thank several friends who commented upon certain sections on which they had specialist knowledge. Three in particular, Bill Cooper, Gerardus Bouw and Brad Sparks, are also acknowledged in those sections that are founded on their work. Pete Williams, a Hebrew scholar, helped with several points regarding translations. Michael Oard, David Cox and Paul Garner commented on parts of Appendix 4 - Geology, but did not necessarily agree with my final conclusions.

Acknowledgements for publications

Fig.3.2.3 - "The frozen mammoths sites" - is based on Walter Brown's *In the Beginning* Fig. 65 with his kind permission.

Fig. 3.5.1 - "Flood stories in folklore" - is based on Byron C. Nelsons chart in *The Deluge Story in Stone* by permission of Bethany House Publishers.

Poor Bill's Almanac in Section 6 is reprinted with the permission of the editor of the Creation Research Society Quarterly.

Foreword

The book *True Science Agrees with the Bible* by Malcolm Bowden is another of his thoroughly researched, highly readable books on the vitally important subject of the Bible and science. When I started to read it, I found it hard to put down since he has included so many fascinating and important subjects in his book, many of which are not discussed in other works.

As the reader will discover, Bowden covers a wide range of material, including a survey of Genesis, archaeological discoveries, the age of the earth, early British Christianity and the founding of Britain, and a critique of Einstein's theories of relativity, just to name a few. Bowden's position on a few subjects may be controversial, but he provides a careful, thorough defense of his acceptance or rejection of the subject in question.

This book contains a wealth of material that will be of interest to scientists, pastors, students, and the average layman. We owe a great debt of gratitude to Malcolm Bowden for the countless hours he has spent in researching this material and assembling it in an enjoyable and easily readable form.

Duane T. Gish, PhD
Senior Vice President Institute for Creation Research
El Cajon,
California 92021

INTRODUCTION

"For the scientist who has lived by his faith in the power of reason, the story ends like a bad dream. He has scaled the mountain of ignorance; he is about to conquer the highest peak; as he pulls himself over the final rock, he is greeted by a band of theologians who have been sitting there for centuries" Robert Jastrow in *God and the Astronomers* (Jas).

....

In writing this companion book to my previous work *Science vs. Evolution*, it is unavoidable that some of the material in that work is repeated in this volume: evidence against evolution automatically supports creation.

The title

Regarding the title of this book, it has unfortunately changed during the course of writing it - "Science Supports Genesis", "Science Supports the Bible", "True Science Supports the Bible" to the present one. It has been referred to in previous writings by these names which might have caused a degree of confusion for which I apologise. The reason for the last change is that for the Christian the Bible needs no "support" from any human studies; it is self authenticating; hence yet another change.

The sections of this book may also need some explanation. To attempt to deal with the wide range of subjects involved in a work such as this in the strict order that they occur in the biblical account, would result in a very uneven progress through the various chapters and verses - some requiring only a brief mention, others taking very many pages. To avoid this and adequately deal with each subject, I have only briefly set out the major comments on the more important verses in Genesis so that they form a basic framework. Minor topics are dealt with in Section 1, but major subjects are examined more fully in the rest of the book.

In the research for this book, the problems that had to be dealt with were much greater than for earlier works. In them, the subject was a false scientific theory that had been closely examined and criticised by many writers. I have been studying, lecturing and writing against evolution since 1969 and can state from experience that *there is not a single piece of evidence that seems to support evolution that cannot be demolished by a creationist expert in that field.* It is this volume of evidence that enables creationists to debate with academics at any level. As a result of this work over many years, the total material available is very great. This was drawn on in the writing of my *Science vs Evolution* to produce a comprehensive book that exposed the fallacies of all the major "facts" produced in its support and many of the minor ones.

Having effectively dismissed evolution as an acceptable theory of how the universe, this earth and man in particular came into existence, it is obviously necessary that this void should be filled with a Biblical alternative that is scientifically sound. There are, however, very few creationist works that attempt to give a fully comprehensive scriptural version of how the processes of Creation and the Flood could have produced the present world as it is found. The subjects that have had to be investigated are very wide and many different viewpoints dealing with the same topic had to be examined and weighed for acceptability. One important area of difficulty is geology and so far no sequence of events that can adequately explain the present strata has been set out by any creationist. In this, and several other subjects, only the most likely views can be provided at this stage.

"True Science"?

The adjective was added to the title of the book to emphasise that where evolution and derived subjects are concerned, much that is accepted as scientifically proven is far from being so. *Every single so-called fact that flatly contradicts Scripture has been shown to be in error.* There is the saying that "All truth is God's truth" and we can therefore expect that as the Bible is God's truth for man's salvation, so this physical world, designed by Him, will not conflict with it.

This is a very important aspect. We have provided rebuttals to many "facts" that appear to contradict Scripture, but there are many more that space prevents us dealing with, and even more will be presented in the future as "clear evidence that contradicts the Bible". The reader can rest assured that eventually every single one will be shown to be only another example of false science that is being promoted to undermine trust in the Bible. Later admissions of error are not given the publicity that the original announcement received.

The authority of the Bible

To some, writing in defence of the Bible might be considered as unnecessary. Charles Spurgeon once said, "Defend the Bible? I would as soon defend a lion!" In fact, the situation is quite the opposite to that assumed, for the detractors will one day have to answer for their stance against God's word. Heraclitus, having presented his case at a trial, concluded: "I will not entreat you: nor do I care what sentence you pass. It is you who are on your trial, not I." This would apply also to those who seek to deride the accuracy and authority of the Bible.

It might be thought that creationists are effectively doubting God's word and need to verify it scientifically. Smith (Smi) likens this to doubting the word of a friend and then going away to check it. He points out, however, that if all scientists accepted the Bible, the whole field would take an immense step forward. What creationists are having to do is to defend the Bible against attacks mounted by its opponents who have managed to persuade some Christians their evidence is sound.

One other major criticism of creationists is that they rigidly adhere to the Biblical account of events and have to interpret all of life from its perspective. This sounds like a charge of "making up one's mind and forcing the facts to fit it". This has also been neatly answered by Smith (Smi) who likens the process to studying a maths book. Presented with a problem that is difficult to solve, the student might try many avenues, but to save time may eventually go to the answers at the back. Knowing this, he can work out what the intermediate steps are, thus achieving a full solution. In the same way, knowing that the Bible is an accurate record by the Author, to save much wasteful speculation, we can go to this and use it to help us in the difficult task of discovering "how the world came about and how it works".

One minister who is a writer of science books on evolution (who shall remain nameless) gave an interview on Premier Radio during which he surprisingly said, "A lot of people write off the creationist position as if it's not based on science. That's not true and I think that there needs to be a great deal of respect between the different camps. Creationists use scientific arguments just as those who take the view that God created but used, say, the Big Bang to do it - also on scientific arguments."

He continued by saying, "Scientific theories are only as good as the evidence on which they are built. It may be that if we had this conversation in ten years time we may be talking about a different scientific theory - that is the nature of science." Now this is perfectly acceptable for most theories, but when we come to the examination of origins, this is effectively beyond the realm of science. Scientists may speculate about this, but usually present their ideas with such assurance to the public that they are taken as "truth". We may therefore legitimately ask: "Why should we believe what you are saying now as being "the truth"if you are going to tell us something quite different as "the truth"in a few years time?" Christians can go to the book written by the One who created the world and read exactly what He did, and *that* record will not change with time.

The Bible has withstood attacks against it ever since it was written and it has yet to be faulted; why should Christians abandon it at the behest of a changeable "science"? There is a saying: "Those who marry the current fashion soon find themselves widowers."

The aim of this book

This work is quite unfashionable for we will be examining a number of subjects and presenting evidence which contradicts views held not only by evolutionists but many creationists also. We must emphasise that few of these originate from this author. In all discussions, there is usually a wide spectrum of views, but often people are familiar with only a few of them. Where the facts seem to be adequately convincing, all that has been done is to publicise the little-known evidence presented by others. We would emphasise that many are highly qualified in their respective fields and it is their case, and not this author's, that deserves careful examination. Occasionally, by linking such evidence together, a new solution to a problem can sometimes be formulated.

What is the aim of the book in general? In view of the complexity of many subjects, it is unlikely that a full scriptural and scientific explanation of all present evidence and past events will ever be available, but we must continually aim for greater clarification. It is hoped that this work will extend the boundaries of our understanding of the Bible in some areas at least and that it will be a source of encouragement to all Bible-believing Christians.

As I have written the book, I have realised how difficult it is for anyone, this author included, to change their mind on any important topic. Arguing by presentation of evidence, convincing to the proposer, is brushed to one side by another. In view of this characteristic that most people possess, all I can do is, like a market stall owner, set out my wares and invite my readers to try the goods on display. Unlike most stalls, however, far from saying the wares should not be touched, we invite them inspect, dismantle and test them to destruction if necessary, in the hope that some of the goods are accepted as being the best quality compared with alternative wares on other stalls.

The style of the book

One correspondent suggested that the book should be written in an academic style, leaving the facts alone to convince the reader. This was given some considerable thought but not accepted. Researching and writing this work has been lengthy but enjoyable. Much has been discovered that was new to this writer, and the keenness to communicate this to the reader, together with an almost irrepressible sense of humour, ruled out any possibility of adopting a detached, scholarly style.

In addition, I am conscious that each book is read by one individual at a time. With all this in mind, a fairly personal style has been used - as though I were speaking to each reader. It will be seen that there is more use of italicised words and phrases and inverted commas than is usual, and these will have to replace the inflections of voice that can carry considerable meaning during conversations between two individuals.

Why Genesis is important

Liberal churchmen deny the historicity of Genesis, considering it as embedding basic truths in a mythological framework. In discounting Genesis in this way, they have removed the whole basis for man's sin, for the advent of death, the special place of man's relationship to the Godhead - and much else. They cannot adequately explain how historically these fundamental facts of life could have been brought about with all the spiritual implications that they have when we turn to the rest of the Bible.

For many years, as a keen but liberal church-goer, I did not believe the Bible as being an accurate record of events. It was only on discovering the scientific evidence that I realised that Genesis was accurate and gave a few lectures on the subject. For well over a year, I was in the unusual position of accepting Genesis as accurate but rejecting the rest of the Bible, until I was converted.

This is the opposite situation to that of many Christians. Some, coming from Christian homes, accept the Bible unthinkingly because their parents believe it. On going to school or, more particularly, to university, they meet a barrage of evolutionary teaching and the Bible is derided. Peer pressure on young people being what it is, few can stand their ground - unless well informed on the subject. Genesis is then accepted as a mythological expression of theological truths but having no basis in reality. They do not realise that they have effectively removed the whole foundation for much of their Christian faith.

If you ask people the question, "What do you think of Genesis?", the replies could be very broadly summarised as follows:

The *non-Christian* might dismiss not just Genesis but the whole Bible as a mixture of myth and truth, only being important in the parts he knows about - usually "being kind to your neighbours".

The *liberal church-goer* will probably say that it is God's explanation of origins put into a story form suitable for the low level of understanding of early people not long emerged from a Stone Age culture. It is just a Jewish adaptation of the Gilgamesh Epic copied from their Babylonian neighbours.

Evangelicals might give two responses. What might be described as a *liberal evangelical* might also consider Genesis to be "a poetic reflection of spiritual events" - or some such view - and will generally accept the basic evolutionary dogma as they are invariably theistic evolutionists. Asked for an explanation of how sin came into the world if it was only populated by clever monkeys who were in the process of evolving into humans, there will be much vagueness and little convincing explanation.

They will often express annoyance that this "hot" subject is raised unnecessarily as being too "divisive" in the church, and that it impedes the more important evangelistic activities. They do not realise that it is a most effective means of alerting the non-Christian to the fact that the real evidence, in a range of subjects, shows that the Bible is accurate. Many have been brought to true faith by this very route. One American evangelist has stated that he far prefers to go into a university campus just after the creationists have lectured there, as he has many more conversions.

Liberal evangelicals also claim that their theistic evolutionary views do not contradict the Bible. Their followers therefore do not have to choose between "science" (i.e. their theistic evolution) and the Bible. This we would dispute. Creationists have long claimed the evidence for their views is far better, and the failure of theistic evolutionists to enter into debate on this important subject surely indicates they are aware of this fact. Readers of books by theistic evolutionists might like to bear in mind that there is no indisputable scientific evidence that supports their stance.

Bible-believing evangelicals will have no difficulty in accepting the full account as given in Genesis and the whole Bible. Despite ridicule regarding Genesis and the Flood, they will hold to their belief in the trustworthiness of the Bible rather than the latest scientific propaganda against it. The liberal evangelical may protest that he too is a Bible-believer - it is just that he has a different interpretation of certain passages. However, he must allow me to make a clear distinction between the two positions. Just how important this distinction is we hope to demonstrate in this book. As one who has been, in turn, agnostic, liberal church-goer and a Bible-believing evangelical, I can speak with some experience of the fundamental differences in these positions.

What is an evangelical?

At this point it is important for those not aware of what an evangelical is, that it should be described, otherwise the position from which this book is written will be misunderstood. A true evangelical Christian is a person who accepts by faith the death of Christ *alone* as sufficient for the forgiveness of his sins and his fellowship with God for all eternity. No other "works" such as baptism, communion, etc. are necessary for his salvation. Above all, he acknowledges that he is unable to earn salvation by his efforts or good works. Good works are undertaken out of love for God and not as a primary condition.

This is only the very briefest of outlines, but it will be sufficient for its present purpose.

This work is therefore written from the position of a Reformed Evangelical Bible-believing "young earth" creationist. If this acts as a trigger for words such as "narrow minded" and "bigoted", then so be it - but it is only fair that the reader should be aware, at the very beginning, of where I am coming from and that there is no hidden agenda.

Miracles in the Bible

To be acceptable to true Bible-believing Christians any proposed model should firstly be in harmony with Scripture. Secondly, it should provide a reasonable explanation of how the universe, with all its amazing complexity, could have come into existence. Any such explanation should not need to recourse to too many miraculous interventions by the creator God simply to explain those features for which we are unable to provide a more "natural" explanation.

It might be thought that in looking for a natural explanation of what might be miraculous events is not unlike promoting a "God of the Gaps"; i.e. the concept that science reigns supreme over an increasing domain and God is banished to an ever diminishing area of activity that science cannot, at that time, explain. This is not so, for we would contend that God is in total control of all activities, whether natural or miraculous.

This does raise the subject of whether we should strive to give a purely mechanistic scenario for all the present phenomena. I would suggest that we should not, and would quote two incidents reported in the account of the Flood.

The first is that when God told Noah that He would be bringing a great flood upon the earth he said that Noah should "bring into the Ark" two of every kind (Gen. 6:19 - 7:4). It is just possible that Noah might have known what each kind would have consisted of but it would have been a major task to have gone out and collected them all. However, in Gen. 7:15 it records that the pairs "came to Noah", clearly under the command of God by His intervention.

The second is that God actually shut the door of the Ark when all the occupants were inside (Gen. 7:16).

Thus, God Himself took an active part in this extraordinary event, and we should not be surprised if He so arranged other events such that no rational explanation could be provided. As we read in Hebrews 11:3: "By faith we understand that the worlds were framed by the word of God, so that the things which are seen were not made of the things which are visible."

There is another important consideration regarding faith in the accuracy of Scripture in which miracles may not be involved. Conditions in the past were most certainly different to today's, and under these conditions certain events may have taken place naturally, but which could not occur today due to the changed circumstances. Seeing that they could not occur today, scientists dismiss them as virtually impossible. Let me give an example.

The Bible records the life span of the early patriarchs as just under 1,000 years, and this has been the subject of much ridicule. They provide a most obvious reason for the rejection of the whole of Genesis - and from this the whole Bible - as a fable rather than truth.

We will be showing that the speed of light was very much faster in the past. This would have affected what are known as the "transport constants": amongst them are viscosity and osmosis. If viscosity was much lower than at present, we have an explanation, amongst many other things, (lower resistance to blood flow, etc.), of the longevity of the patriarchs. A higher level of the earth's magnetic field will also be shown to be conducive to longer life spans.

Now here are two factors that give a perfectly adequate scientific explanation for their long lives. Yet this is not immediately apparent from the Genesis record. It is only by *careful enquiry* that we are able to discover the evidence showing that acceptance of the accuracy of Genesis is far from being the act of "blind faith" that many think it is.

This is an important factor in a person's attitude to the Bible. Either they accept it as accurate or they dismiss it - or parts of it, which is much the same. This is no reason for rejecting the Bible for, if one takes the trouble to conduct further *careful enquiries*, it will always be found that the record is accurate. This rejection on inadequate grounds *by those who do not want to believe it* can be illustrated by a closely parallel situation recorded in the Gospels.

Wilful disbelief

The Jewish leaders frequently "proved" to those who said Jesus was the Messiah that he could not possibly be because He did not come from Bethlehem (Matt. 2:4-6). He was "obviously"from Nazareth, for that was where He had lived before He began His ministry. This charge, *with all the appearance of being correct*, was used to dismiss those who dared to give

Him any support.

It is in the Gospel of Luke that the explanation is recorded, for He was born in Bethlehem during the comparatively brief visit of His parents there for a census.

What is particularly important is that, from the accounts, *not once did the Jewish leaders ever try to find out by careful enquiry* if He *had* been born in Bethlehem. Even when Christ stood before them they never troubled to clear this matter up. More interesting still, and even more important, *He never volunteered the information either; He allowed them to flounder in their disbelief.*

It is suggested that there are similar situations regarding the interpretation of the evidence existing in nature that cannot be easily explained according to present-day knowledge. This is no reason to then reject the Biblical record. Despite this, scoffers will continue to disbelieve the Scriptures and fail to enquire beyond their prejudices.

When, one day, all is finally revealed, God will show that it required one small change, such as the speed of light, to bring about a number of otherwise inexplicable facts that are in the Bible. He will then ask, "Where was your faith?" One can be certain that there will be much guilt and embarrassment when all the facts are finally revealed. As C.S. Lewis has said, "There will be surprises."

Let us then return to this fundamental issue of just how much evidence should be looked for in order to determine the events that resulted in the present conditions. In ranging over several broad subjects, of which creationism is only one, it is possible to conclude that God deliberately does not allow a completely natural explanation to be reached. This is obviously in order that man, in examining any discipline in depth, will ultimately be faced with some phenomena that defy a purely rationalistic explanation. This apparent barrier to full knowledge seems to apply in all areas of life and some of these have been collected and discussed in Section 6.7 - "God's hidden presence".

If any person in search of the truth is fully open-minded (which in practice is almost impossible), he will ultimately have to acknowledge his own ignorance and realise that it is God who is in command of this universe and will not be dismissed from it. His hand can still be recognised by those who have had their spiritual eyes opened so that they can see His handiwork in this wonderful creation.

Therefore, whilst every reasonable attempt will be made to give a scientific sequence of events for the creation of the universe, there are undoubtedly many areas where no fully satisfactory natural explanation can be provided. For the majority of them, this is because we do not have sufficient evidence. In a few cases, the hand of God may need to be acknowledged in the ordering of a number of events, and for this no apology is made.

This approach will no doubt be derided by the sceptical reader, who will consider this an irredeemable weakness that, in his eyes, destroys the credibility of this book. This causes no great personal disturbance for this work is not written to gain the approval of sceptics. As C.S. Lewis said:

> Those who assume that miracles cannot happen are merely wasting their time by looking into the text: we know in advance what results they will find for they have begun by begging the question (Lew:8).

This work is therefore written mainly to encourage Bible-believing Christians, so that they may have full confidence in the accuracy of God's Word - a confidence not just in its doctrine and the faith it teaches, but in its scientific and historical accuracy also.

To those readers who are convinced sceptics, I would pose the following questions:

(i) Is it possible that such a Being as an all-powerful Creator God exists?

(ii) If such a Being exists, would He not be able to suspend or amend the laws that He had created at any time?

(iii) If this is so, what then prevents you from accepting that this God carried out His Great Plan of the Universe exactly as He has portrayed in His book - the Bible?

If (and it is a sincere hope) this book should convince the reader of the Bible's reliability for the first time, then may it be a start to you seeking the Real Truth within His Word and thereby eventually experiencing the ultimate joy - which is to join the many millions of Christians who will "glorify God and enjoy Him forever."

M. Bowden.
Bromley 1998

SECTION 1
A SURVEY OF GENESIS 1 - 11

In this examination, no attempt is made to discuss every verse as Henry Morris has done in his excellent *The Genesis Record* (MorrH77), but we will be dealing mainly with the more scientific aspects.

For some events, a possible natural explanation will be suggested which might be labelled "unsupported speculation" by some. There should be no objection to providing an explanation for a verse where no corroboration can be obtained, provided any such explanation is Biblically sound and in accordance with good scientific principles and evidence. The main purpose is to show that Genesis can be explained, in most of its account, in a perfectly natural way and that it is unwarranted to dismiss it as ancient Hebrew myth.

We will deal only briefly with each main event, referring the reader to the later separate sections where specific subjects are dealt with in greater detail.

The documentary evidence

Before embarking on this huge subject, we should first examine the reliability of the documents from which we draw much of our faith.

Non-Christians might be under the impression that these documents are few, unreliable and differ between themselves. This is not the case.

We will be showing in Appendix 7 the extreme care with which the Jews copied their documents as old ones had to be replaced. The discovery of the Dead Sea Scrolls showed how very little difference there was between these 2,000-year-old versions and the present-day.

Regarding the New Testament, there are claims of some 5,000 NT manuscripts, but many are only a small part of a book. There are about 2,000 manuscripts of the Gospels and less than 100 copies of the whole of the NT in Greek. There are some 14,000 OT manuscripts.

In comparison with this large number of accurately copied documents, those of the Greek and Roman world are sparse. For example, Julius Caesar's *Gallic Wars* was written about 50 BC; the oldest surviving copy was written about 850 AD - some 900 years later and there are only ten ancient copies existing. Similarly, the Roman Tacitus's *Histories* were written 100 AD but the oldest of only two copies existing dates from 800 AD; 700 years later. Yet no one doubts that these are as the authors composed them.

Thus, the documents undergirding the Christian faith are far more accurate and numerous than any others recording historical events. With this assurance, we can examine what they have to say to us today with considerable confidence.

As far as the Greek NT manuscripts are concerned, there are slight differences between them, and comparing them to arrive at what the original manuscript said is known as Lower Criticism. Higher Criticism deals with the meaning and interpretation of the contents of both the OT and the NT, and this has generated a number of heretical views.

SECTION 1.1. GENESIS 1 - 2:3
THE CREATION OF THE UNIVERSE

Day 1 - v 1 "In the beginning, God created the heavens and the earth"

In this majestic statement, God's first act in what might be called His *Great Drama of the Universe* is set out for us. There is no apology or explanation of what he did, and certainly no hint of Him proving His existence.

That there is a supreme and infinite God is abundantly clear to all human beings when they examine the design and workings of nature. At the final judgement no man will be allowed to hide behind the theory of evolution and claim that he was misled by his peers; the evidence is too overwhelming for such a pitiful excuse to be proffered before an Almighty God.

"In the beginning"

This suggests that this was the moment when time - as we know it - was created. God is obviously outside time, and He has no difficulty in seeing the end from the beginning. It is just like a film-maker who can see the whole of a length of film, but it has to be projected only one frame at a time in order for us to understand it. Therefore God has no difficulty in predicting exactly what will happen - for He has foreordained every event. This does not, of course, take away any of our responsibility for our actions.

This seeming contradiction between human free will and God's predestination will be found to be non-existent and they will be seen to be fully compatible when He provides the final picture of all world events. Saint and sinner alike will all agree that His Plan was perfect from the beginning. Furthermore, He is perfect and therefore He has never made a mistake. From this it follows that "this is the best of all possible worlds", even with its pain and suffering. When all is finally revealed, every person will be forced to agree that this was the best possible way in which He could have carried out His amazing Plan.

"God created"

Only God can create a universe out of nothing (*ex nihilo*). Scientists still do not understand the working of the atom, but they know that there is immense power locked up in every one. Some have described the atom as "knots of energy in space".

"the heavens and the earth"

What is intended by the word "heavens"? Does this refer to the spiritual heavens or the starry universe - or both? I would suggest that it is speaking of the creation of matter from which the earth was formed and of the universe of stars and galaxies. Although the word is plural, this is also used to describe the visible "heavens" that "declare" God's glory (Psalm 19:1).

That the spiritual heaven and the angels were created before the physical earth and universe is indicated by God's reply to Job when he asks "Where were you when I laid the foundations of the earth?...when the morning stars sang together and all the sons of God shouted for joy?" (Job 38:4,7). The angels appear to have been watching God's great act of creation. They may have been created only moments before the creation of the physical universe but more likely in another form of time frame.

One of the major problems facing the Christian is that there is a tendency to assume that the life hereafter will be much as we experience it today. I do not think that we can assume any such thing. Time, if it could be called such, will probably exist in a completely different form. This would mean that not only would eternal life be different, but the appalling prospect of eternity in hell of the unregenerate may also be totally different. Irrespective of this, what all objectors have is an inadequate trust in the perfect justice of God, who will finally demonstrate this before an onlooking world that can only agree that he is indeed just and perfect in every single one of his acts and judgments.

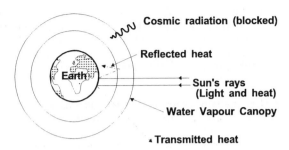

Fig. 1. The Water Vapour Canopy

v 2 "The earth was without form and void"

This is just a description of the earth before God began to shape it and make it a fit habitation for man.

The Genesis record, and indeed the whole of the Bible, makes it abundantly clear that the earth was created in six days and only a matter of a few thousand years ago. Despite this, there have been many attempts to evade this interpretation and we examine the main ones and the motivation behind them in Section 2.1.

v 3 "And God said 'let there be light'"

The precise nature of light is still unknown to scientists. It appears to behave sometimes as a wave and at other times as a particle. Quantum theory attempts to provide an adequate explanation of this phenomenon, but probably no final satisfactory theory will ever be reached.

In the same way that ripples in a pool need water to transmit them across the surface, so light as a wave-form needs a medium in which to travel. This substance is denoted as "aether", and its relationship with light is a fundamental aspect of physics but the theory of relativity denies that the ether exists. We examine the subject of relativity in Appendix 8.

v5 "So the evening and the morning were the first day"

Here we have a clear assertion that the day was a normal one of 24 hours. This is repeated for each of the seven days of creation, and in view of this there should not be any doubt in the reader's mind that only 24 hours was involved. Even though he is unlikely to read Hebrew, it is surely obvious that this was what the writer (Moses) intended to convey in his record of events.

Despite this clear emphasis, there are many sincere Bible believers who nevertheless look for vast periods of time within the creation account. There have been attempts to say that the word "day" can cover far more than 24 hours; even a million years or more for each "day". This distortion of the Hebrew is not acceptable - even to liberal Hebrew scholars as we will see in Section 2.1.

Day 2 - vv 6-8 "God made the firmament, and divided the waters which were under the firmament from the waters which were above the firmament"

In their book *The Genesis Flood* Whitcomb and Morris supported the view that this verse could be interpreted as the separation of a large amount of water that was placed in suspension at a high altitude, called the Water Vapour Canopy (Fig. 1). This would have resulted in a number of beneficial effects during the pre-Flood period, explaining the longevity of the patriarchs and many other aspects. It can also explain several of the changes that were brought about following the Flood. It obviously does not exist today but there are one or two indications that there may have been such a canopy at one time. There are some technical problems with this proposal, however, and the whole subject is examined in Section 3.1.

Day 3 - vv 9-10 "Let the waters under the heavens be gathered together into one place and let the dry land appear.... And God saw that it was good."

The land now appears above the water. It should be noted that it is the water that is "gathered into one place". This suggests that the area covered by the water is much less than that covered by the land as otherwise it would have been land surrounded by a larger area of sea.

This is important as most experts assume that the original land area was about the same as we have today (whether the continents have moved or not). This may have a bearing on the resulting geological theories produced by creationists. For example, in calculating the land area to determine the amount of vegetation that may have existed at the time of the Flood, the present areas are generally used. However, the actual area may have been very much greater before the Flood if the implication of this verse is considered.

It does continue in verse 10 to call the water "seas" - in the plural. It is possible that they were one connected body of water but were positioned in large separate areas, not unlike the Great Lakes of Canada. It does seem clear that the earth was one whole area over which man and animals could travel without crossing large tracts of water.

v 11 "Let the earth bring forth grass... and the fruit tree that yields fruit according to its kind"

The plants are created before there is any mention of the sun. There is, however, some source of light coming from one direction which provides the twelve-hour periods of day and night. Whilst most plants can survive several days without sunlight, it was probably this temporary source of light which provided them with the daily energy they would need for perfect healthy growth. A possible way in which this source of light might have been generated for a while is described in Appendix 1.

In this verse we have the first use of the phrase "according to its kind". This refers to the inability of one *kind* (Hebrew *baramin*) to be changed - i.e. evolve into - a new *kind*. This is the barrier that Darwin had to break through if his theory of evolution was to have any credibility whatsoever. He never did deal with the problem. He knew that there were definite limits to the breeding of any species. He simply brushed the whole problem to one side saying:

> It would be equally rash to assert that characters increased to their utmost limit could not, after remaining fixed for many centuries, again vary under new conditions of life. (Chapter 1, *Origin of Species*).

This was pure speculation and as experiments have never validated this claim, the whole basis of his theory is destroyed.

Linnaeus, the Swedish biologist (1707 - 1778), collected numerous plants and animals from around the world in an effort to classify them so that the limits of each kind could be determined. To a certain extent he was not completely successful. What he called a "genus" (= a "family" today) in the

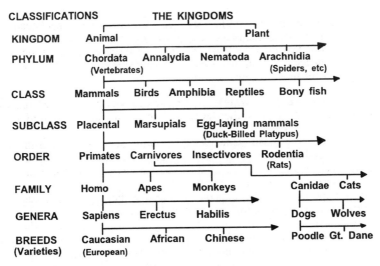

Fig. 2. Classification groups

animal world was probably a *kind*, whilst in the plant world, a kind is probably each of the genera.

What happened historically was that the evolutionists seized upon his classifications and by arranging them in a certain order, made them the basis of the "branching tree" of how the various "species" evolved over millions of years. Fig. 2 gives the way in which animals have been classified into various groups and sub-groups etc.

The kinds (*baramin*)

Regarding these *kinds*, there have been a few cross-fertilisations between sheep and goats, lions and tigers, etc. and it might be thought that these boundaries have been breached. However, the offspring are generally infertile and would have little chance of survival in normal conditions.

In fertilisations generally, the genetic information is not confined to the DNA in the chromosomes only, but is spread throughout the whole of the cell structure, particularly in the cortex or *outer cell membrane*. Broadly speaking, the cell contains the genetic information of what particular *kind* it will be (dog, tiger, horse, etc.), and the DNA controls only the variety of features (size, colour, etc.) that will appear in the animal.

The female's ovum provides the cell genetic information (*kind*) together with its own share of the DNA, whilst the sperm provides only the male's part of the DNA. Thus the *kind* is transmitted through the female line, the male only providing some DNA variety.

Where animals have fertilised across *kinds*, the male DNA has only changed some of the characteristics of the basic type within the cell of the female. The result belongs to the female's *kind* and no viable animal has ever resulted from such a forced union.

Day 4 - vv 14-17 "Then God made the two great lights: the greater light to rule the day, and the lesser light to rule the night. He made the stars

also."

Surprisingly the sun, moon and stars were not made until the fourth day, after the creation of the plants the day previously.

Some contend that God "created" the sun and moon on the first day when He created the heavens, but that He only "made" the sun shine on the fourth day. This we cannot accept. Examination of the context of the words for "create" (*bara*) and "make" (*asah*) show that there is little difference between them. Why should God "create" the fish in the sea but only "make" the beasts of the field? *Bara* cannot mean only to "create from nothing" as this is used for the creation of man but clearly he was made from "the dust of the earth" (Gen. 2:7) and both words are used for the creation of man - vv 26 and 27. Finally, putting the whole subject beyond argument, *the only correct interpretation of the Hebrew is that the sun was created on the fourth day and cannot be interpreted to mean it had been created some time before that day* (WillP). The tense cannot be translated otherwise. Where possible, Scripture should be interpreted consistently, and if this interpretation were to be used for the other days of creation, it would make nonsense of the whole account. Those who claim the sun was shrouded by mist or only shone forth on the fourth day are reading into the text only what they want to see. The importance of this will be seen in Appendix 10.

What is outstanding in this passage is the central place that the earth has in the whole of creation. The creation of the sun and moon are briefly referred to, whilst the immense power contained within the total number of stars is ignored, their creation being mentioned almost as an afterthought.

Despite putting a very bold front on their theories, astronomers really have no satisfactory explanations for very many phenomena they have discovered. In Section 2.2 we show they can neither explain how the stars were formed nor how the planetary system came into being and much else besides.

The overriding importance of the earth in the Genesis account is surely proof that the whole purpose of God in creating the universe was to put man at the centre of a perfect environment and give him every opportunity to be a grateful and willing servant of God. All else in creation was secondary to this main aim. With this in mind, we can then see how serious was the sin of Adam that he, as our federal representative, should then proceed to throw this love and care back into God's face. We can see just how ungrateful his rebellion was by the fact that it brought in its train all the sin and suffering in the world. Man, with his fallen, sinful mind, then proceeds to blame God for being the creator of suffering in this world!

Day 5 - v v20-23 "God created great sea creatures and every living thing that moves, with which the waters abounded, according to their kind, and every winged bird according to its kind."

The sea creatures appear to have been created in fairly large numbers of each *kind*, so that the local environment into which Adam was to be created would be well stocked at that time. God, however, commands the sea creatures to "fill the waters in the seas" and "the birds to multiply on the earth" (v22). There was still a great area that they had yet to colonise.

Day 6 - vv 24-25 "God made the beast of the earth after his kind."

Land creatures were created with immense diversity, but all were later to perish in the Flood except a few of each basic species that survived in the Ark. Of those that emerged, many species appear to have eventually died out for they do not exist today. This was probably due to their inability to survive and raise offspring in the greatly different climatic conditions that prevailed after the Flood. What we have today is only a small selection of the huge variety of animals that God originally created. Even from those that exist today, there is still such a variety that amazes and puzzles biologists. As we look at some of these strange creatures, one cannot help feeling that God does have a sense of humour. The camel and the duck-billed platypus are but two of many animals that may have brought a smile to God's face as He created them.

That God does indeed have the attribute of humour is surely proven in that He must have had it first (as a lesser form of Christian joy?) before He was able to make it part of human nature. We are, after all, made in His image!

v 26 "Let us make man in our image.... So God created man in His own image; in the image of God He created him; male and female He created them."

The fraudulent nature of *all* the supposed "missing links" between man and apes has been exposed in another work (Bow81). The whole theory is based upon a handful of bones - or more often parts of bones - that are presented with a huge fanfare of publicity every time a new discovery is made. In this way the public are, at regular intervals, beguiled into thinking that they are only clever apes, and not created in the image of God.

God made man from the dust of the earth (i.e. the chemical elements he had already created) and He then breathed "life" into his nostrils (2:7). God made all the animals but there is no mention of giving them "life" in this way. From this, what is being referred to here must be spiritual life, so that man may have some degree of communion with a holy and transcendent God; a communion that no animal could ever experience.

Man was given all of the communicable attributes of the Godhead such as love, fellowship with other people, sorrow, perseverance and many others that the reader might like to list at his leisure. Every single one of these gifts was tainted with sin at the time of the Fall. However, it is the Christian's joy to know that he will have a closer communion with God than even Adam could have had during his earthly existence. Indeed, God, being omniscient, knew that the Fall would take place and all the suffering that would follow - for it was all part of His glorious Plan (Bow92).

v 29 "And God said 'See, I have given you every herb that yields seed which is on the face of the earth and every tree whose fruit yields seed; to you it shall be food.'"

There can be no doubt that Adam and all the animals existed on a completely vegetarian diet. Such was the balance of nutrition in the pre-Flood fruits that man could exist in perfect health. This changed after the Flood when Noah and his descendants were allowed to eat meat and fish (Gen. 9:3).

v 31 "Then God saw everything that He had made, and indeed it was very good."

On five occasions God looked over His creation and declared it good. Now at the end of the final day of His creation He declares it to be *very* good. There is a sense of complete satisfaction with His work. It was indeed a perfect world in which He had placed Adam and given him all the advantages that He could, leaving him only one prohibition to test his obedience. Even with all these advantages, Adam nevertheless failed the test. He therefore had no excuse for his wilful act.

What was meant by "perfect"?

There are certain questions that arise when trying to picture what this perfect world was like. Was there any death of animals? Did the world have a time limit? Answers must be speculative but we will examine some topics.

1. Death?

It would appear that Adam had only a natural span of life of about 1,000 years, and to allow man to live for ever, God had specifically placed the Tree of Life in the Garden of Eden (Gen. 2:9). When Adam fell, God banished him from the Garden so that he could not have its fruit (Gen. 3:22-23) and he subsequently lived only (!) 930 years. The tree presumably contained some ingredient that prevented the ageing of the human body.

The perfection of the creation before the Fall also raises the subject of the death of animals and even insects, etc. Were they included in the ban on death in the original creation? Adam had access to the Tree of Life to preserve him from death, but animals had no such resource. It can therefore be assumed that they died after their allotted life-span.

That animals died is also implied in Romans 8:12 where, through Adam, sin first came into the world but this brought about the death of *man* - animals are not referred to. If animals did not die, certain problems would arise. For example, there would have been gross over-population - oysters produce masses of eggs, and within eight years, if none died there would be 10^{80} oysters; enough to fill the oceans.

If there was no death of animals, then even insects in the path of a passing animal would have to be preserved. This is not impossible for God to order, but the situation becomes increasingly difficult to sustain.

2. Food

Man and animals were both vegetarian after creation (Gen. 1:29-30) and this appears to have continued after the Fall to the time of the Flood. That this is a natural (and therefore probably original) state is implied in Isaiah 11:7. Having just listed a number of predators that will peacefully lie down with their prey, he then prophesies that "the lion shall eat straw like the ox". Thus, the picture of final perfection involves the reversion of carnivores to the vegetarian diet they possessed when they were first created.

It seems that man may have retained his dominion over the animal kingdom after the Fall as there is no record of animals becoming a danger to man or even to other animals. This only became an important feature of life after the Flood when God allowed man to eat meat (Gen. 9:3-4). That some animals also became carnivores only after the Flood is indicated when God placed upon them a fear of man (Gen. 9:2) so that man had some protection from them now that they hunted other animals.

3. Population, entropy and a limit on time

God commanded Adam and Eve to "multiply, fill the earth and subdue it." There was obviously a limit, albeit very extensive, on this process. There was, therefore, probably a time limit upon this whole situation, perfect though it was. This limit would also apply to the animal population.

This time limit is also apparent in the many activities that would be taking place.

Entropy is only a scientific word used to describe the "running down" of the universe. This is also known as the Second Law of Thermodynamics; i.e. there is an irreversible decrease in the amount of energy available to do work. When all heat transfers from hot areas to cold areas has been completed, all temperatures will then be uniform and there will be no way that useful energy can be obtained. When the sun has cooled, all life on earth will cease.

All these limits are very lengthy, and there would be ample time for God to see whether Adam (and Eve) truly loved Him and obeyed Him implicitly. Once that was well established, the end could come at any time. As we are all too well aware, Adam failed. However, God was not "caught out" and did not have to devise a "second best" plan. He knew what would happen from the very beginning, for He had already written in the Lamb's Book of Life the names of those to be saved from a sinful world for He had chosen them "before the foundation of the world" (Eph. 1:4).

4. Harmful phenomena?

There is one theological problem that arises from this view that God's original creation was "perfect". Does this mean that there was nothing with any harmful potential in existence anywhere in the universe? Several examples of danger that may have existed at the time of creation could be given (the reader might like to make his own list) but we will consider just two such items - radioactivity and meteorites.

(a) Cosmic rays and radioactivity

Today, we have cosmic radiation coming in from outer space which is very harmful to all life. We receive considerable, but not complete, protection from them due to both the layer of ozone high in the atmosphere which absorbs them and the earth's magnetic field which deflects them. At the time of creation, were these rays in existence but completely prevented from reaching earth by (say) the Water Vapour Canopy? Similarly, were there dangerous radioactive elements in the rocks?

As God declared the world perfect, we would contend that they only became active and dangerous *after the Fall*. If this is assumed, then there is no problem in accepting the normal understanding of God's proclamation. That the world was subjected to "bondage to decay" at the Fall would include the elements that are now radioactive. God had only to alter one or more physical properties of the forces in the atoms to allow the heavier ones to begin to decay by normal processes. We examine this event further when discussing polonium haloes in Section 4.

(b) Meteorites

These are large rocks circling around the planetary system, one of which could strike the earth at any time with catastrophic consequences. Did they exist on the day of creation? We would suggest that they did not.

The astronomer, van Flandern, has proposed that the missing planet, sometimes named Phaeton, exploded and created the belt of asteroids that circle around the planet's original position. However, their total mass is only 1/5 of that of the moon. He proposed that the rest of the planet formed the many meteorites and even comets that now circle in space. It is therefore possible that this explosion took place at the time of the Fall, allowing the pre-Fall period to be "perfect". However, the trajectories of these objects should be examined to see if they could have been achieved within the time frame of 6,000 years since creation.

We would also mention the possibility that it was only from the time of the Fall that the speed of light began to decrease.

....

The sequence may then have been:

Creation to Fall - man had access to the Tree of Life to live for ever. Animals died a natural death. Man and animals vegetarian.

Fall to Flood - man had a natural life span (c 900 years?). Cultivates ground for food. Radioactivity began at the Fall. Possible start to the decrease in the speed of light.

After the Flood - man's life span gradually decreased. Man allowed to eat meat. Animals now carnivorous but given fear of man.

....

Chapter 2:1-3 "Then God blessed the seventh day and sanctified it, because in it He rested from all His work which God had created and made."

There is a natural period of rest on the seventh day that man needs in order to continue with his work for the remainder of the week, but there have been attempts to change the frequency of this rest day.

The battle cry of the French Revolution was the deceptive propaganda slogan of "Liberty, Fraternity and Equality". Yet once power had been seized by the subversive forces behind this clandestinely organised uprising, one of the first acts they brought in was to enslave the innocent citizens they now controlled. Far from giving them the liberty they had promised, they changed the laws to give one day off in ten instead of every seventh day: a 45% increase in the days worked before a day of rest!

However, the law had to be rescinded. It was found that the workers became too exhausted if they worked more than six days without a break. A similar situation has been found in the building industry, where weekend working has been found to be ultimately less productive due to the fatigue of the workers in the second week. Whenever man thinks that he knows better than the ways ordained by God in His goodness, one can be sure that problems will inevitably follow.

SECTION 1.2 GENESIS 2:4-25
THE SECOND ACCOUNT OF CREATION

This second account of the creation process has been claimed by those who wish to discredit the Bible as being the work of a separate author to that of chapter 1. Jean Astruc, a pupil of Voltaire, noted that chapter 1 uses the Hebrew *Elohim* for "God", whilst chapter 2 mostly uses the Hebrew *Jehovah*. On this basis alone, he claimed that there were two separate accounts of creation that had been combined into one record by Moses.

Such a proposition drove a wedge into the acceptance of the reliability of the Biblical record, for it assumed that there were two separate (and slightly different) accounts of creation, and that Moses just put them both down when writing Genesis. This dividing up of Genesis did not stop there, for in 1780-83, Eichorn published a book in which he divided up Genesis and much of Exodus into Jahwist and Elohist documents that had been put together by Moses. He later changed this to the more popular view that a compiler had used the two sources "J" and "E". Thus was born the Documentary Hypothesis that was extended in the late nineteenth century by other scholars to include J, E, P and D sources. This became known as the Graf-Wellhausen theory, named after the two men most involved with concocting this speculative view of the Bible.

This whole theory has been discredited by more than one able Bible-believing scholar, one such being the "incomparable" Robert "Dick" Wilson. Another critic is Archer who amply rebuts the whole basis of the theory in his *A Survey of Old Testament Introduction* (Arch). Despite such evidence, it is still taught in theological colleges as a "proven fact" of how the Bible "developed", for it fits the evolutionary framework to which all science and history must conform in today's teaching.

The explanation of why two different words for God are used in the Hebrew is that the accounts are from two different viewpoints. In the first chapter, God is a creator and sovereign over all, and the vast scale of creation is recounted in its stages. Therefore *Elohim*, signifying God's majesty and sovereignty, is the appropriate word. In the second chapter, God is in a more personal and covenantal relationship with man, and therefore *Jehovah* was more suitable. This second account is centred on the importance of man in God's creation.

vv 5 -6 "For the Lord God had not caused it to rain on the earth... but a mist went up from the earth and watered the whole face of the ground."

There was no rain in the pre-Flood period. The vegetation was watered by a mist which provided adequate water for the vegetation. Even today, some forms of desert ecology use stones placed around the roots of plants. These become very cold in the cloudless nights so that when the moisture content of the air increases in the heat of the morning, the moisture condenses on the still cool stones and drips into the ground to water the roots.

Alternatively, it has been suggested that the mist was from jets, the "fountains of the deep", produced by the high pressure in the earth's interior. This would have resulted in lush vegetation like a rain forest.

The irrigation of the Garden, however, was much more peaceful for it was by the river that "went out of Eden to water the garden" (v 10). This must have been a fairly large river for it divided into four rivers. These were given different names, Pishon, Gihon, Hiddekel and Euphrates, but it should not be imagined that the present day Tigris and Euphrates are the original rivers flowing from Eden. The Flood so completely changed the face of the earth, generally covering it with huge depths of sediments, that no landmarks of the original country would have survived.

Having said that, it is remarkable that the description of these rivers is in the first person (vv 10-14), as though the author is describing what existed at the time he was writing. This suggests that this is a first-hand account written perhaps by Adam for his posterity, that has been handed down to later generations and incorporated in the full account by Moses with little change. The reference in this same chapter to Cush and Assyria may be names that were reused by the post-Flood patriarchs reminding them of the pre-Flood lands.

Holy ground?

It is not impossible, however, that God reformed the land and settled Noah over the same site where Eden was originally positioned, and reused the name Euphrates for one of the great rivers in the area. This is not as fanciful as might be thought, for God has a special interest in certain areas which form part of the history of mankind.

The clearest example of this is the place where Abraham intended to sacrifice his son. For this, God specifically sent him to the "land of Moriah" (Gen. 21:2). It is here that he was prepared to sacrifice Isaac. Many hundreds of years later, Solomon "began to build the temple of the Lord in Jerusalem on Mount Moriah" (2 Chron. 3:1). Clearly, Abraham's sacrificial site was on one of the mounts that form Jerusalem. Thus, on the very spot that Abraham was willing to sacrifice his favourite son, the continual animal sacrifices of the Temple pointed towards the One whose sacrifice would be the culmination of them all. As we know, His actual death took place "outside the city wall" where the criminals were crucified.

Whether this centre of religious interest may also have some relationship to the original position of the Garden of Eden must be left to speculation only.

The centre of the earth?

There is yet another point about the geographical position of Jerusalem. A study by Andrew Woods divided the whole of the earth's land surface into small equal areas which were then analysed by computer to see which of them has the smallest total distance to all the others - i.e. what point is in the effective centre of the earth. The result was that the area that might be called the Bible Lands was the centre of the earth. This was the area bounded by Jerusalem, Babylon, Ararat and Memphis in Egypt.

This is a subject of a complete Memorandum by Woods (WooA), and in the synopsis in the *ICR Impact* No. 2 it is suggested that as God instructed Noah to "fill the earth", He is hardly likely to have landed him in some remote corner of the new earth surface. The "Fertile Crescent" was only a short distance from the Ark's landing point, and Noah and his descendants would have been able to quickly settle in this fertile area and build their cities.

The precise centre is actually Ankara in Turkey which forms an almost perfect square with Jerusalem, Babylon and Ararat. In the *Impact* article this is considered adequately near enough to the centre to prove the point of the investigation. It is possible, however, that Jerusalem or the Fertile Crescent may well have been the very centre at that time. Large land movements, as an aftermath of the geological forces released at the time of the Flood, may have subsequently slightly altered this original centre to its present position.

Religious centre of the world

It is surely not coincidental that Jerusalem is also the centre for the three great religions of the Western world - the Muslims (apart from Mecca), Jews and Christians - and each have their "Holy Days" on Friday, Saturday and Sunday respectively. God has some very intriguing ways of organising the people of the world! No doubt each reader will have his own views on the purpose of God in arranging this close and problematic relationship.

v 17 "... of the tree of the knowledge of good and evil you shall not eat for in the day that you eat of it you shall surely die."

Here is the great order by means of which God was to ensure the obedience of Adam and Eve. It should be noted that it is only when there is the possibility of failing a test that there can be any proof of continued obedience. God set Adam a simple test to check whether he was truly obedient or not. This is an important aspect of God's plan for mankind (Bow:92).

vv 18-19a "And the Lord God said 'It is not good that man should be alone. I will make him a helper comparable to him.' Out of the ground the Lord God formed every beast and every bird of the air..."

This verse appears to show that the animals were created *after* he had created Adam on the sixth day, which would contradict the account in chapter 1. However, Hebrew only has the perfect tense ("made") and does not have a pluperfect ("had made"). Therefore, this passage can equally be translated "*had* made" - i.e. the account recalls that they had been created previously but now God was going to bring them before Adam (Whit69:97).

v 19b "God... brought them to Adam to see what he would call them."

In Western society, a name is normally given to a child in order to distinguish it from others and there is little interest in the meaning of the name. In Eastern societies it is quite different. The name is meant to give an indication of the nature of the person. This can be seen in the range of names given to God in the Old Testament.

Adam's intelligence

We will show below why Adam probably had a very high level of intelligence. With this, he would be able to look at an animal and then discern very quickly what its particular and peculiar attributes were and name it accordingly. (This is not to say that intelligence and discernment always go together; those with high intelligence do not necessarily possess wise discernment and sound judgement!)

Adam's intelligence before the Fall would have been of a very high order. We tend to think that Adam's abilities were not too dissimilar from those we now possess after the Fall. It was following the Fall that *every one* of man's attributes were degraded to a lower level than before. Thus did man become "totally depraved", i.e., every single attribute he possessed was affected by the Fall, but not to a depth that would have prevented society from functioning. It did later get worse, and man's behaviour became such that God swept the population aside and began again with Noah and his family.

There is an important aspect of Adam's level of intelligence before the Fall. His mind was as yet unaffected by the Fall and there is the possibility that he was also able to think very much quicker than we can today. This would have been due to the much higher speed of light at the time of creation - a subject dealt with more fully in Appendix 1. If the speed of light was much faster, then electron and ion movement would have been faster. This would have meant that electrical impulses, ion exchanges, etc. would have been much faster, from which thinking would have been quicker.

It has been said that intelligence is the ability to see patterns in what appear to be random events or data. The faster a person can check through a number of possible links between isolated items of information in an intelligence test, the quicker he will reach the correct pattern and the higher will be his score. There are some who may dispute this interpretation of intelligence, but it is the standard assumption in most intelligence tests. This outline is given to indicate that Adam was probably vastly more intelligent than even the greatest brain that has ever lived.

The theological consequence of this is important. Far from the eating of the forbidden fruit being just a minor infringement of God's instructions, *Adam would have been fully aware of just how serious his rebellion against God really was by his action*. In no way would he be allowed to shift the blame, even though he immediately tried to. He had to take the full responsibility of disobeying God, and as he was the federal head and representative of all mankind, we have had to carry that burden also. It should not be assumed that any other person would have done any better. Despite being given a perfect setting, we would all have taken the same decision as Adam did had we been in the same circumstances.

Innate knowledge

Whilst dealing with Adam's intelligence, we might briefly consider what he might have had implanted within him when he was first formed by God.

It is obvious that God must have given Adam many mature abilities such as speech, mathematical ability, etc., as well as a general knowledge of the many ways in which the world operates. With this, He would have been able to converse with Adam from the beginning. It is a moot point whether Adam would have been given any special knowledge of medical herbs, etc. for cures that might have been needed after the Fall.

This implanting of innate information within the human brain might be paralleled with that in birds for nest building and direction finding.

Man has an innate ability to use not only the language of his group but, surprisingly, to create one also. This was found amongst a group of deaf children in Nicaragua where the staff knew no sign language so the children were left to themselves. They soon developed their own sign language which they gradually improved until it became very sophisticated with structure, grammar and consistency. A child could watch a surrealist cartoon and describe its plot to another child. However, any child joining the group older than five would have to struggle to learn it much like an adult learning a foreign language (*The Times* 5.2.96).

This does raise the interesting question of what abilities and information there may exist in mankind - sometimes without the individual being aware of it - and what has to be "learnt" by means of committing to memory or practising many times in order to master a particular subject or skill.

We all know of gifted people who obviously have a natural talent for (say) playing the piano, or making rapid arithmetic calculations. These must be an innate ability placed within these particular individuals. It is interesting to read that when Moses was constructing the Tabernacle, God had "called Bezalel... and filled him with... knowledge and all manner of workmanship... to design artistic works, to work in gold and silver and bronze" and furthermore he had the ability to teach others these skills (Exodus 35 :30-35).

In a similar way, when Solomon was constructing the Temple, he sent for Huram to come from Tyre for he was "filled with wisdom and understanding and skill in working with all kinds of bronze work" (1 Kings 7:14).

God has given individuals various specialist skills for carrying out His work. In the secular world, they are all too frequently assumed to be due to the person himself and are used for self-aggrandisement; they do not realise that it is an unearned gift.

"Idiot savants"

This subject leads on to that of "idiot savants". They are those unfortunate people who have been born mentally defective and often have to be cared for in an institution, yet some possess a particular ability to a very high level. One of the more usual is an ability in arithmetic. Such people are able to find square roots of large numbers, and multiply others, all with amazing rapidity.

Yet they are quite unable to explain how they go about getting these remarkable results. One. when asked, said that you have to get the numbered "tiles" to slip easily into the right order! Others might have gifts of music or drawing, etc.

One intriguing case was a teenager who was able to say what the day of the week would have been for any date in the past; i.e. that it was (say) Tuesday on a specific date centuries ago. He was questioned by psychologists and they said that of the various ways of calculating this information, he did not apparently follow any of them. Indeed, he was not able to do even very simple arithmetic, so how he was able to give the correct day was a complete mystery.

Thus, many have innate abilities that have been given by God and for which they have had to do nothing. As Christians, we should recognise that any such gift is for the use of God in His Church and for spreading the Gospel. Yet how many people look upon the gifts they possess as something that they should be praised for and take great pride in exhibiting before others, but never acknowledge the source - or rather Person - who initially gave them their gift?

v 21 "... the Lord God caused a deep sleep to fall on Adam, and he slept. And He took one of his ribs, and closed up the flesh in its place. Then the rib... he made into a woman."

This is a most surprising account of how God created a female as an "helpmeet" for Adam. We look at this incident in Section 2.4.

SECTION 1.3. GENESIS 3 - 6:4
THE FALL AND ITS EFFECTS

There are many expositions on the Fall, and it is not intended here to enter into the very great significance that there is in the three questions that Satan put to Eve. It is noted, however, that the whole basis of Satan's temptation is to reveal to Adam and Eve some "special knowledge" that he claims God has been withholding from them. This is nothing less than the charge of *gnosis* which is the name given to the "secret knowledge" known only to those initiates into a special group. This is the hallmark of a multitude of secret groups who claim to have special revelations of what Truth really is. From denominations who claim that they possess the secret "knowledge of the truth handed down verbally from the Early Fathers" to cabbalistic, mystical groups, alchemists, Freemasonry and all other clandestine organisations, they partake in some form or other of this basic gnostic heresy. It is this gnostic basis of the Fall and of all modern political and economic systems today that has been fully exposed in Alan Morrison's excellent book *The Serpent and the Cross* (MorrisA).

In contrast to this secret knowledge, the True Christian faith is completely the opposite, for it is open to all who care to listen. There are no hidden secrets and people are free to attend all their services of worship and public meetings to inspect the basic tenets of the movement. Indeed, Christians are only too keen to publicise what they believe, so that others may believe it also. All that is needed is a desire to discover what God's requirements are for today's fallen mankind. That this is not sought for is due to man's pride in still continuing to ignore God and "doing his own thing" - just as Adam did.

The results of the Fall

Adam was our representative, and when he fell he took all future mankind with him. Every part of us is less perfect than it was in the original creation. As Adam was also given dominion over the animals, then they too became subject to imperfections. We now have pain, death and destruction, but not necessarily disease or prey and predators.

Having been banished from the perfection of the Garden of Eden, it was a completely different situation that Adam now found himself in. Where before he could simply pluck fruit from the trees, he now had to work with hard labour to gain food. He had to dig, plant and reap "by the sweat of his brow" just to survive. It was made more difficult due to the thorns and thistles that now came into prominence in the plant kingdom (v 18).

These changes did not involve anything new to be created; this had all been completed during the first six days. What God did was to alter that which He had made in the first place. Probably, knowing Adam would indeed fall, He had already built into the creation the potential for just the variations that He knew would be needed for this change of circumstances.

As just one small indication of the way in which a simple change can have a desired effect, it is a fascinating fact that thorns begin as leaves but they do not reach full development. No new creative power is called into operation, merely the stunting of growth of a normal leaf to produce the thorns referred to in verse 18.

There are many other changes that would probably have to be made. Certain bacteria and viruses may have had their characteristics changed so that they now attacked the health of plants and animals including man. The talons and teeth of lions and tigers may have been part of their anatomy since creation or they may have been changed at this stage. However, they were still herbivores for only after the Flood were man and animals allowed to eat meat. They would then be able to use their fangs and talons for hunting forays.

This does raise the question of the hunting instincts of animals. Were they given them as they emerged from the Ark or possibly some time later when the number of animals had grown?

How God made the many necessary changes in the whole of the environment is not revealed in Scripture. However, it does not take much imagination to see that He could carry this out with no major disruption of the ecology or of the organisms involved. By numerous but comparatively small alterations He could bring in a new set of living conditions for all life on the earth.

At the Fall, man lost his intimate contact with God and proceeded to go his own way. Predictably, the inherent sinfulness of mankind when free of God's restraining hand resulted in great lawlessness before the Flood swept that evil generation away.

Genesis 5 - The early patriarchs

This chapter gives the long ages of the early patriarchs. There are people who have a growing interest in the Christian faith but find these long ages stretch their tentative acceptance of the reliability of the Bible beyond breaking point. We would ask any reader with such reservations to withhold judgement until the end of the book, We hope to show that there is good evidence that the perfect conditions on earth in which God placed Adam, not those present today, were well able to result in such long lives.

The sons of God, the daughters of men and the giants

In chapter 6:1-4 there is the strange account of "sons of God" taking "the daughters of men" as wives. There were also "giants on the earth in those days" and more appear to have resulted from the "daughters of men" bearing them from their union with the "sons of God". What is this all about?

There are some who suggest that the descendants of the "sons of God" are the giants who were the forefathers of Goliath of Gath (whom David slew) and his brother and sons (2 Sam. 21:18-22). They lived at a time long after the Flood, and unless they passed their characteristics through one of the wives of Noah's sons, there was no genetic connection between them. It is more likely that Goliath and many other "mighty men" were the result of extraordinary mutations, hormonal imbalances or extremes of variability, a number of whom may have been related to each other, sharing these particular features. Their gradual demise is recorded in the Bible. We can still today have giants, in this case mostly because of hormonal excesses that stimulate the body to grow much larger than normal.

Regarding the "daughters of men" and the "sons of God", some have interpreted this as being angels (fallen sons of God) cohabiting with "daughters of men" (humans), the resulting offspring being the depraved ancestors of those whose crimes would eventually prompt God into sweeping them away in the Flood.

Calvin, in his examination of this passage, dismisses this interpretation as an "absurdity" and asserts that the sons of God were those descendants of the chosen godly line of Seth who should have kept themselves separate from the ungodly descendants of Cain.

Unfortunately, these two lines eventually began to intermarry. The "sons of God" saw the beauty of the "daughters of men" and married them - ignoring the fact that they were marrying godless women. This mixing of the two separate lines eventually brought about the wholesale corruption of the world. Only the line to Noah was kept free from intermarrying with the descendants of the murderer Cain.

In this, there is a lesson for us even today. Firstly, the Christians should keep themselves "unspotted from the world" (James 1:27). Secondly, a Christian should only marry another Christian (2 Cor. 6:14). When this rule is ignored, the Christian spouse can suffer severe heartache, and it can be the root of much stress in the marriage. They will be unable to share their many spiritual experiences with their partner and the raising of the children can also become a problem.

SECTION 1.4. GENESIS 6:5 - 9: THE FLOOD

The picture presented in the Bible is one of widescale corruption and violence. This is too similar to the present times to provide the Godless man with any comfort, hence his rejection of this account of God's violent solution of the problem. As a result, secular propaganda ridicules this event and the "animals in the Ark" is a constant subject of mild amusement. We would mention that there are no grounds for translating the name of Methuselah as "When he dies - judgement".

The "fountains of the deep" were probably great waterspouts rising high into the air as the crust of the earth cracked and allowed this water under very high pressure to escape.

The "windows of heaven" would refer to the collapse of the Water Vapour Canopy, triggered by the entry of volcanic dust into the canopy around which the vapour could condense. This is treated in greater detail in Section 3.1.

It should be noted that eventually the fountains and windows were "stopped". This suggests that there was some water left in these reservoirs. We will be seeing that there is still an enormous amount of water inside the earth. There has also been found a considerable quantity of water droplets very high in the atmosphere. Even more recently, as we will discuss in Section 3.2, large icy cometesimals are still striking the atmosphere and bringing in a massive amount of water.

The world-wide Flood

One of the major attacks that liberal Christians make upon the record of the Flood is that it was only a local event. There are numerous replies to this such as:

(i) The Bible is emphatic that "the waters prevailed exceedingly on the earth, and *all* the high hills under the whole heaven were covered" (Gen. 7:19).

(ii) There are many other scriptures that confirm the Genesis account. Gen. 10 describes how all nations came through Noah and his three sons. 1 Pet. 3:20 says that only "eight souls were spared", etc.

(iii) If it were local, Noah had only to move to another part of the globe. He had no need to build a huge Ark to accommodate two of every kind of animal.

(iv) A local flood does not last for a whole year.

(vi) Many very high mountains have sedimentary strata at the top, showing that they were under the sea at some stage. That they may have been thrust to a higher elevation after the Flood does not alter the fact that they *were* covered by water when they were deposited.

Many more reasons could be given and it would be very difficult to explain them all away.

The Bible cannot make it clearer that it is describing a world-wide Flood and those who maintain that it was only a local flood have no right whatsoever to then claim that they are Bible believers in any meaningful sense. To maintain their position, they have to blatantly "wrest the Scriptures". They usually resort to saying that it contains spiritual truths couched in myth, but that ignores the clear evidence that it is an actual record of historical events.

The Ark

The size of the Ark was enormous. Using a cubit of about 18 inches (450mm), the Ark was approximately 450 ft (137m) long, 75 ft (23m) wide and 45 ft (14m) high (Fig. 3). Vessels of this size were not made until 1884. It was a box-like construction and not streamlined to move through the seas; it merely had to survive the tempests of the Flood. This box structure was also very stable and if the heavy animals and storage were placed in the bottom of the vessel it would have been almost impossible to overturn.

The ratio of the length to breadth of the Ark is 6:1 and it is only after years of trial and error and many experiments that ship designers have found this to be the most suitable ratio. The seaworthiness of the Ark has been recently checked using sophisticated computer programmes. It was found to be as good as, if not better than, modern ships and that it was able to withstand waves 100 ft (30m) high (Hong).

The Flood

We have already mentioned the fact that God brought the animals to the Ark and then shut the door when all were inside. The world-wide cataclysm was then begun.

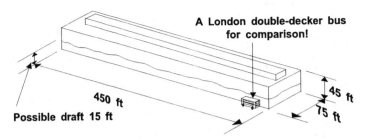

A London double-decker bus for comparison!

450 ft

45 ft

75 ft

Possible draft 15 ft

Fig. 3. The dimensions of the Ark

There is little indication in the Bible on just what started the Flood. It is possible that it might have been triggered by the impact of a meteorite as will be considered in Appendix 5. Whatever started it, the throwing of volcanic debris high into the atmosphere would have provided the material needed for the water vapour to condense around, thus starting the forty days of torrential rain. Most of the water of the Flood, however, would have come from the interior of the earth and we discuss in Appendix 4 its importance in forming the geological strata.

There were only two of each "kind" of "unclean" animal in the Ark, and therefore all the wild animals we have today were descended from them. It would seem to be a repeat of the original population of the earth by the various "kinds" (*baramin*) in Genesis 1. Similarly, all the various human races are descendants of the eight people in the Ark. Each of the races are only a specific selection of the range of variations that the human species can produce - a subject considered in Section 3.6.

Also in the Ark would be air-breathing dinosaurs. These would not have to be full-grown specimens but only young ones that would have many years of breeding before them. On coming out of the Ark, the climatic conditions would have been so different that some might have died out in one or just a few generations. Others might have lived for many generations and provided the folk stories of great "dragons" that lived in earlier times.

There are obviously many unknowns regarding the housing, feeding and cleaning of this huge floating menagerie and in the events following the landing of the Ark. The account of the Ark has therefore become the butt of ridicule of many anti-creationists. One American magazine appears to be devoted solely to this purpose. Many of their objections can be easily dismissed, but some are valid and require an answer.

It is always easy to ignore criticisms if one's readership is sympathetic to your views. However, I have found that one of the most convincing demonstrations of which side has the better arguments is the way in which they deal with the criticisms of the opposition. If one listens carefully to the majority of debates on *any* subject - not just evolution vs. creation - it will be found that rarely does one side give an adequate rebuttal to the opposer's criticisms. A few may be partially dealt with and the rest ignored, most of the time being taken with restating the evidence that supports their case and the weaknesses of the opposition - not in answering their criticisms. In view of this we will try to give reasonable answers to our critics in Section 5. Woodmorappe has also given a very full answer in his *Noah's Ark* (WoodJ).

The landing of the Ark

The Ark is said to have "rested" (Gen. 8:4) on the mountains of Ararat. This is usually taken to mean that it grounded on the mountain, yet two and a half months later the tops of the mountains were seen (v 5). Furthermore, God would hardly have allowed the Ark to ground on the top of a high mountain where cultivation would be impossible.

The Hebrew for "rested" is *nuwach* and has a wide variety of meanings, amongst them "cease", "be quiet", "be at rest", etc. It has been suggested (Q15/3:161) that the Ark actually "rested" from its journeyings over the Ararat area and the mountains protected it from turbulence as it gently moved out and settled in an area suitable for Noah's family to start living in. It is significant that the very earliest farming settlements recorded by archaeologists have been found around the Ararat area (Q17/1:8).

In addition, cereal crops have been associated with many settlements of very early man. In a "Stone Age" Late Palaeolithic site in Egypt, grinding stones for grain were found (Q17/1:3). This period is said to be that of the "hunter-gatherer" before the farming "revolution" began in the Neolithic period that followed. Therefore the concept of man going through a stage of hunter-gatherer before eventually cultivating plants is unfounded. The two methods of obtaining food existed at the same time. There are many hunter-gatherer tribes still today.

The search for the Ark

There have been many expeditions to the Ararat mountains, but no convincing evidence has been produced that would confirm its location. There is another site 17 miles away in the foothills of Ararat where a boat-shaped formation has been claimed to be the Ark, but reliable creationist geologists who have visited the site say it is only a geological formation.

There is an interesting confirmation from early records of the Flood and the landing of the Ark on Ararat. Watson, in a fascinating article (Q18/1:33) on the records of many ancient writers, quotes Josephus who said:

> All the writers of barbarian histories make mention of this flood and of this ark; Berosus the Chaldean [said] "It is said that there is still some part of the ship in Armenia, at the mountain of the Cordyaeans, and that some people carry off pieces of the bitumen"... Hieronymus the Egyptian and ... a great many more, make mention of the same. Nicolaus ... speaks thus "There is a great mountain in Armenia ... upon which it is reported that many who fled at the time of the Deluge were saved; and that one who was carried in an ark came ashore on top of it; and that the remains of the timber were a great while preserved. This might be the man about whom Moses, the legislator of the Jews, wrote."

That the remains of the Ark existed on Ararat appears to have been an accepted fact by many of those historians nearer to the Flood. Who knows if it may yet be discovered at a time when Christianity is being persecuted? This would give assurance to those that need it and disturb their persecutors. However, whilst "the Jews require a sign and the Greeks seek after wisdom" (1 Cor. 1:22), those with a secure faith should not ultimately depend upon the presentation of physical proofs, for it is sufficient for them that "The Spirit bears witness with our spirit" (Rom. 8:16).

The emergence from the Ark

Noah, his family and all the animals emerged from the Ark to find that the world was a totally different place to that which they knew when they entered it. The landscape was unrecognisable, the weather conditions had changed and rain was now a regular occurrence.

Noah sacrificed to God in thanksgiving and God gave him the sign of the rainbow as a promise never to inundate the world again (Section 3.3). Such were the changes in conditions that Noah unwittingly became drunk as he did not realise the effect that the new conditions would have upon the wine he made (Section 3.4).

With the speed of light higher than today, this would have resulted in rapid growth of vegetation and many other physical and metabolic activities (Appendix 1).

The Fertile Crescent

Archaeologists have for many years admitted that the earliest known centre of civilisation was in what they refer to as the Fertile Crescent - the land of the Tigris and Euphrates that constitutes Iraq today. This confirmation that the earliest civilisation was in the area recorded in the Bible is a witness to its accuracy. There have been attempts to claim that there were even earlier centres of civilisation elsewhere but these have little support. The Fertile Crescent covers a huge area of many thousands of square miles that would have contained many cities - all united in one language.

There is a minor point about the direction taken by Noah in reaching this low-lying fertile area. Ararat is to the north of the plain, the plain itself running north west - south east. The most obvious way of reaching this area would have been to get to the northern end and then travel south-east to populate it. But we read in Genesis 11:2 that "as they journeyed *from the east*, they *found* a plain in the land of Shinar and dwelt there." They appear to have landed at Ararat and then travelled much further to the east of the plain in fairly hilly country, entering Shinar "from the east". This seems an unusual route but does fit the Biblical record of events.

Ice Age(s)?

There is evidence of an Ice Age shortly after the Flood waters subsided. Secular geologists claim that much of Europe and North America were covered by a huge glacier that formed the landscape, creating wide valleys, etc. Some creationists agree but others contend that much of the evidence could be interpreted as the activity of fast-flowing water during the Flood. We deal with this in Appendix 4 on Geology.

SECTION 1.5. GENESIS 10 - 11
THE TABLE OF NATIONS

We have a very full record in the Bible of the early descendants from Noah and his sons. These were to become separate nations as they spread over the face of the earth. These genealogies have been the subject of much investigation, and in Section 3.6 we present some of the findings of those who have examined the evidence in depth. It is a fascinating subject to see how our ancestors can be traced back to these patriarchs.

That Europeans come from the line of Japhet seems certain. We have extended this examination in Section 3.7 to include some evidence for the ancestry of the British and then further to trace when Christianity first came to our shores. In researching this subject, several important facts came to light which it was felt should have much wider publicity than they have received so far. Whilst not an essential part of supporting the Biblical record, it has been set out in that section as it was felt that it would be of great interest to many readers.

The Tower of Babel

As man became more advanced in his civilisation and able to undertake larger projects, he desired to make a huge structure as a symbol of his greatness - in his own eyes.

It is thought that the Tower may have been like a ziggurat, with many steps to the top. Some have suggested that it may have been for positioning a table or instrument with the signs of the Zodiac for astrological purposes, but there is little support for this. Others have suggested that the Flood was so strong in their minds that they built their own "mountain" in order to avoid any similar future calamity.

There are about 32 sites of ziggurats in the Mesopotamian area, but two of them are the more likely location of the Tower of Babel.

Babylon, founded by Nimrod (Gen.10:9-10), was a large city with a ziggurat. Unfortunately, the original structure has long since gone but an early king claimed he was rebuilding an older one that had been destroyed. This was later destroyed also and rebuilt by Nebuchadrezzar II (c 580 BC). This was described by Herodotus in 460 BC from which an idea of these constructions can be drawn. It measured 300 ft (90m) square and 108 ft   (33 m) high. There were five platforms, but others had seven and were as high as they were wide. The top structure was usually a cubic temple (NBD:111).

Glazed brickwork was used with different colours at each platform. The top structure Herodotus saw was inhabited by a chosen woman and furnished with a couch and table. The god Marduk was said to descend and "commune with mankind". A typical ziggurat is shown in Fig. 4.

In 1899 Koldewey excavated Babylon and in the oldest area found a series of arches and a well. He conjectured that this may have been the remains of the Hanging Gardens of Babylon built for Queen Semiramis - one of the Seven Wonders of the World that the Greeks listed (Cer:197).

The other more likely site is only seven miles (11 km) south-west of Babylon at Birsippa or Birs Nimrud. The *Encyclopaedia Britannica* (EB 2:396) notes that the tower was burnt in an extremely hot fire probably due to the use of bitumen and reed matting used in the core. Many ziggurats were built with bitumen ("slime" in the AV.) as stated in Gen. 11:3.

These ziggurats were built and rebuilt by various kings to their god Marduk and appear to have similar dedications, but one old Biblical chronology reference chart of 1890 (Hull) quotes *The Borsippa Inscription* of Nebuchad-nezzar in Smith's *Bible Dictionary* that says;

> A former king built it (they reckon 42 ages) but he did not complete its head. *Since a remote time people had abandoned it, without order expressing their words* [i.e. their language was confused].

This same reference work noted that Birsippa means "Tower of Tongues". It is therefore possible that these ruins may be the remnant of the original Tower of Babel.

What is concerning is that these two interesting pieces of information were not quoted in any of the references that I consulted, not even the *New Bible Dictionary*, that should have mentioned them. Why is it that modern works

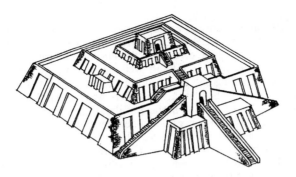

Fig. 4. A typical ziggurat

fail to give such information? One has the impression that there has been a continual filter such that only evidence that is supportive of the liberal viewpoint is promoted by those who write the textbooks for future historians.

The Dispersion and the Stone Ages, etc.

As men dispersed across the face of the earth, they would remember the story of the Flood that they had heard from their fathers. These would be repeated down the ages, and eventually these "folk stories" would be recorded by anthropologists who studied their culture. This story of a Great Flood was found so frequently and from around the whole world that it was noted by many experts. We deal with this subject in Section 3.5.

As men moved away from Babel they would only have natural tools and implements, such as stones, wood, bones, antlers etc. to utilise. As they discovered and then developed local deposits of metal, their use of them resulted in them progressing from a "stone age" to a "bronze age", "iron age", etc. as classified by archaeologists. However, each "age" was only a reflection of what they could find in each area, and not a world-wide progress of uniform development over thousands of years. Consequently, we consider that progress through these "ages" would be rapid and at different rates. As they varied in different areas at the same time, they cannot be used as a reliable means of dating and will not be used in this work.

The account of Job

The earliest written book of the Bible is that of Job. He lived in the "land of Uz" (Job 1:1), south-east of the Dead Sea where later the Edomites lived (Lam. 4:21). They were an ungodly people and therefore Job is unlikely to be the Edomite Jobab (Gen. 36:33-4) but more likely Jobab the son of Joktan who was the brother of Peleg (Gen. 10:29). His long age of 140 years after his trial places him in this period when the life spans of the patriarchs were reducing rapidly

This book is remarkable, for some descriptions seem to be eyewitness accounts of major upheavals given as confirmations of the speaker's reliability. He records features of the creation of the earth and the universe that is the same as Moses was to write in Genesis many years later. God seems to have created the angels first and some of the stars also before the foundations of the earth (38:7). One of his friend's speeches implies the long life-spans of the patriarchs for he says that compared to them "our days are as a shadow" (8:9).

There are several accounts of geological events such as the opening of the land for the overflowing water (38:25). Even more violent is the overturning of the mountains, shaking the earth such that its "pillars" tremble (9:5-6).

Although he lived in what is a desert area today, Job often refers to the sea and both its great flooding and drying up in 12:15 and 14:11. He also may be referring to the Ice Age when he says that there was ice and that "the waters of the sea harden like stone and the surface of the deep is frozen" (38:29-30).

He also describes what appears to be a decadent human group that lived "in caves of the earth and the rocks" (30:6). This may have been the Neanderthal men who have been found in many areas of Europe and elsewhere around the world. It is this author's opinion that they were decadent descendents of modern man who suddenly disappeared from history. Examination of their skeletons showed that many suffered from osteo-arthritis, rickets and syphilis. This suggests they lived under difficult conditions, and it is possible that there may have been promiscuity that allowed the syphilis to eventually wipe out the whole race of Neanderthal men and women (Bow81:163f).

Sodom and Gomorrah?

Whilst there have been claims that the location of these cities has been discovered, we have not been able to obtain any reliable information on them. We therefore await further evidence that may be forthcoming in due course.

Recent history

Having traced the early history of man, we enter into the later times of recorded events of other nations where dates can be cross-checked and an increasingly reliable chronology be set out. We deal with the Egyptian and Israeli records in Section 3.8 as these can shed light on the early history of these two nations.

Regarding the New Testament, although there is controversy about many of the dates and events in that period, they are generally within a few years. It is the Old Testament and the Genesis account in particular that are so frequently dismissed and it is these that we have sought to defend.

In 1 Kings 6:1 there is a clear dating of the beginning of the building of the Temple by Solomon which was 480 years after the Israelites came out of Egypt, *i.e.* the Exodus. As the Exodus is dated by several Biblical chronologists at c 1445 BC, we have used this date as a basis and dates in the Bible can be worked out from this event. There are, however, many problems with providing a framework of major dates for the whole Bible but we present a possible chronology in Section 3.9.

We will therefore draw a line across the historical record at this point, and proceed to deal with the many subjects raised above that require further investigation and explanation.

SECTION 2
THE CREATION EXAMINED
Section 2.1
"LONG AGE" THEORIES

There are several interpretations of the early chapters of Genesis that claim the period of creation was not in six days nor was it about six thousand years ago. Proponents of these views vary in what the time spans were, but they usually agree that it was probably to be reckoned in millions of years - usually in conformity with the times claimed by (or, rather, needed by) evolutionists. These are the immense periods of time invariably attached to the geological column.

The main versions of Long Age interpretations are the Gap theory, the Day-age theory and Wiseman's theory, which will now be examined.

A - The Gap Theory

This is the proposal, accepted by many sincere Christians, that the correct translation of verse 2 in chapter 1 should be "and the earth *became* without form and void". This view proposes that there was a first creation which lasted for millions of years. However, due to Satan's rebellion, God destroyed all life forms, thus making the earth "become" a void. The remains of the organisms that were annihilated in that first judgement are claimed to be the fossils that are now to be found in the various rock strata beneath out feet.

Charles Lyell had written his *Principles of Geology* in the 1830's, in which he had claimed that examination of the geological strata showed that it must have taken in the order of many thousands, if not millions, of years for the various layers to have been laid down. Christians realised that this neatly undermined the credibility of Genesis which gave only six days as the period during which God created the heavens and the earth and a date for creation at about 4000 BC.

As I have pointed out (Bow82), Lyell admitted that he wrote this work specifically to undermine a literal belief in Genesis. It provided the huge time spans needed by the theory of evolution.

Gradually Lyell's view became more accepted by scientists and a few churchmen, until it began to predominate. This forced those who believed the Bible was God's word to re-examine it to see if there could be any accommodation between the Biblical account and the new "scientific" viewpoint. The Gap theory arose which sought to pour all the necessary "millions of years" into the gap which was held to exist between verses one and two, when their translation was reconsidered.

This view was first propounded in 1814 by Dr Thomas Chalmers mainly to combat the long ages proposed by Hutton and later Lyell. It later achieved both publicity and respectability by being included in the footnotes to the *Scofield Reference Bible* in 1909.

There are today some in the U.K. who still hold to this theory, whilst acceptance of the view is much more widespread in America. There are, however, a number of objections to it, from both a spiritual and scientific point of view. The most thorough critical examination of the theory to our knowledge is that set out by John Whitcomb (Whitco65) and the following is a brief review of his main arguments.

(i) There is no record of the important subject of the "original" creation of the earth; only one verse refers to it. Surely more space in the Bible would have been devoted to this period and its cataclysmic end. In addition, if Gap theorists assume that this first destruction resulted in all the fossils in the geological column, it reduces Noah's flood to a local flood that left little trace.

(ii) All the original animals and men would have been destroyed and fossilised. They therefore had no relationship to those living today. Yet many fossils are virtually identical to those living now. Did God have to create them twice over?

(iii) Fossils of men show that man lived in that first creation. Yet they could not have had a soul as this is only recorded in the following verses describing the creation of Adam.

(iv) If Satan fell to earth and millions of animals became fossilised remains, then the earth was a graveyard inhabited by an evil spirit. God's evaluation of His creation in Genesis 1:31 that it was "very good" could hardly be applied to such a situation if Adam was walking over the bones of dead men and animals.

(v) Romans 5:21 states that "sin reigned in death", Romans 6:23 says "the wages of sin is death" and I Cor. 15:21 says "by man (Adam) came death". Now the creation until Adam's sin was perfect, but when he sinned then death entered into the now fallen world for the first time. Yet the Gap theorist would contend that there had been an earlier creation that God had destroyed, and therefore death had already occurred once before. This contradicts the Bible passages that death first entered the world when Adam sinned. This and (iv) above are surely the most important and obvious Scriptural objections to the theory.

The whole theory hinges upon the translation of certain Hebrew words;

(a) "*Hayetha*" may be either translated "was" or "became". Five times in the first five books of the Bible it is translated "became", and examination of the context of these passages makes it clear that it is describing a change of state. This is felt to be adequate to use it in this context.

However, 258 times it is translated "was", and Hebrew scholars agree that there is no warrant in the context of verse 2 that it should be translated "became". In addition, to translate it correctly as "become" it should be followed by "*lamedh*" (="to"), as is done in a number of verses. To ignore these points and nevertheless translate it as such is to unwarrantably force onto the word the meaning the Gap theorist wants, simply to support his case.

It can be very deceptive to translate the Bible in such a very amateurish way simply to bolster a case. It requires considerable study to grasp the full meaning of a word and its context. We will later examine another example where Hebrew scholars are united on the meaning of a word (*yom* = "day") that differs from the interpretation placed upon it by those who seek to discover long ages in Genesis.

(b) "*tohu wa bohu*" - waste (or without form) and void. These two words are used for divine judgement in Isaiah 34:11 and Jeremiah 4:23 and it is contended this interpretation should be applied here also. "*Tohu*" is also used twenty times on its own and often implies an evil sense.

However, "*tohu*" does not necessarily infer evil. For example, in Job 26:7 it says, "He stretches out the northern (skies) over empty space (*tohu*)", in which there is no hint of evil connotation. In other places it refers to wilderness or desert.

Isaiah 45:18 says that "He did not create it (the earth) to be empty (*tohu*), but to be inhabited." This is said to show that the first creation was not *tohu*, but that it later became so - between verses one and two. But it can quite legitimately be taken to mean that he did not intend it to remain in a chaotic state but within a period of six days populated it with teeming life.

Thus, the better meaning of "*tohu*" is "emptiness" rather than "destruction", and the implication of the judgemental destruction of an evil condition must be obtained from the context; an implication which is not present in verses 1 and 2, and is only there to those who wish to see it.

(c) "Darkness" is often used in the context of sin and evil, which can be implied in verse 2.

However, darkness itself is not necessarily evil, for in Psalm 104:19-24, we read, "You bring darkness, it becomes night", and later (v24) God is praised for the many and varied features of His wonderful creation, of which one is the night. So again, the context determines what should be implied in a word.

(d) "*Barah*" = "created" (out of nothing) and "*asah*" = "made" (from existing material).

Verse 2 says that God *made* the earth "void", i.e. He did not create it, but reformed an existing habitation to become a wasteland.

The fundamentally different meanings of these two words is often referred to by Christians in their examination of Genesis, and considerable meaning is read into the text on this basis. Such a distinction may not, however, be fully justified, for they appear to be used almost interchangeably in this description of creation.

For example, as we have already pointed out, He "created" the great sea monsters (v21), but he "made" the beasts of the field (v25). Surely there could not have been any great difference in the way that God made these two kinds of creatures. Again, in verse 26, God said, "Let us *make* man in our image", but then we read (v27) that God *created* man. Other examples could be given showing that these two words are used in this chapter with the same meaning for both. Therefore, no great weight can be placed upon the word "*asah*" to mean that something already populated was *made* void. It can also be translated as *created ex nihilo.*

(e) "*Maleh*" (v28) can be interpreted "replenish" as God's instruction to Adam after an initial inhabited world had been swept away. But the correct translation is "fill", with no inference of populating the world a second time.

A more positive piece of evidence regarding the correct interpretation of this verse is that in Exodus 20:8 in the fourth commandment. It adds, "For in six days the Lord made the heavens and the earth... but he rested on the seventh day. Therefore the Lord blessed the Sabbath day and made it holy." This passage clearly states that the creation of the heavens and the earth were within the six days of creation described in Genesis 1. Gap theorists would place it in some unknown time before then.

The evidence set out above should be sufficient to answer the case presented by those who hold to the Gap Theory. This theory has been examined in some depth as, somewhat surprisingly, there are still many who hold to it, as mentioned above. Why this theory and others like it should have been "invented" in the first place and held so strongly is an important question that we will discuss at the end of this section.

B - The Day-Age Theory

This proposes that the "day" (*yom*) in Genesis 1 really refers to a long period for each day of creation, thus stretching the time from the creation of the earth to that of mankind from anything between many thousands of years to many millions. In support of this an appeal is made to the translation of Genesis 2:4 "in the *day* (*yom*) that the Lord made the earth and the heavens". We will examine this question of the translation of "*yom*" later.

Another passage referred to very frequently is 2 Pet. 3:8: "With the Lord a day is like a thousand years, and a thousand years is like a day." From this it is considered acceptable to translate "*yom*" as a long period of time, perhaps even the specific period of a thousand years for each day.

However, the context in this passage is quite different. Peter is pointing out that God is very patient, and His view of time is quite different from ours, for He is prepared to delay the day of judgement in the hope that some will be saved. To quote this passage in support of a long-age creation is to force it to apply to a quite separate circumstance that it cannot sustain. There seems to be an element of clutching at straws when the passage of Peter is used in support of such a position.

C - Wiseman's "Days of Revelation" Theory

There are other theories that have been propounded, such as that by P.J. Wiseman (Wisem). He proposed that the six days of Genesis 1 were six days of 24 hours during which God recounted to Adam the sequence of events that took place when He was creating the world that Adam could now see before him. This had taken millions of years, but it was over a period of six days that He gave Adam a stage of the story each day.

This is also a very fanciful theory, which has many of the same problems that face all Long Age theories such as we have discussed above.

General difficulties

Those who seek to stretch the time span of Genesis 1 to many thousands or millions of years generate for themselves great physical and spiritual problems. To give a few examples:

Physical problems

One physical problem is that on the third day we read of the creation of plants, but it is not until the fourth day that the sun was created. If each of these "days" were very long periods of time, how could the plants grow without the sunlight they would have needed?

Also on the subject of the creation of the sun and stars on the fourth day, were they not existing for many thousands of years until that "fourth day"? Was there no twelve hours of light and twelve of darkness until then?

The insects and bees, etc. would have been created on the fifth day as those that were "creeping things". How would the plants, created on the third day, have been pollinated if there were huge spans of time in each "day"?

The reader might like to list other problems arising from long periods between each day of creation.

Spiritual problems

One spiritual problem is that if man evolved from apes over millions of years, there would have been thousands of similar "apes" that would have looked like a man. Did God select one (or several?) member(s), make him in his image (whatever that might mean in this interpretation) and breathe into him (*and her!*) the "breath of life"? It is only some such sequence of events that could have taken place, which makes nonsense of the whole of the Genesis account of the creation of man and his wife.

More important, the account of the Fall of Adam is removed from being a central action that affected the future of the whole of mankind, and the need for a perfect man (i.e. Christ, who was both man and God) to come to earth to rectify this situation and restore the communion of God with man. This is a crucial factor that is subtly destroying the roots of the Christian faith - often without Christians who accept this view realising how their foundations have been removed.

With all these somewhat artificial interpretations of what should be the clear understanding of the Genesis account of the time taken for the creation of the universe, much depends upon the interpretation of the word "*yom*" for the period of a day in the Hebrew, to which we will now turn.

The translation of "day" (*yom*)

Crucial to all these proposals is how the word "*yom*" is translated. Is it justifiable to render this "day" as a long period of time as it is legitimately translated in "the day of the Lord"? Invariably, the "day is like a thousand years" passage referred to above is quoted.

In order to determine the opinion of those who were well learned in Hebrew, David C.C. Watson wrote to Prof. James Barr of the Oriental Institute of Oxford University and received the following reply.

23 April 1984

Dear Mr Watson,
Thank you for your letter. I have thought about your question and would say that probably, so far as I know, there is no professor of Hebrew or Old Testament at any world-class university who does not believe that the writer(s) of Gen. 1-11 intended to convey to their readers the ideas that (a) creation took place in a series of six days which were the same as the days of 24 hours we now experience (b) the figures contained in the Genesis genealogies provided by simple addition a chronology from the beginning of the world up to later stages in the biblical story (c) Noah's flood was understood to be world-wide and extinguish all human and animal life except for those in the ark. Or, to put it negatively, the apologetic arguments which suppose the "days" of creation to be long eras of time, the figures of years not to be chronological, and the flood to be a merely local Mesopotamian flood, are not taken seriously by any such professors, as far as I know. The only thing I would say to qualify this is that most such professors may avoid much involvement in that sort of argument and so may not say much explicitly about it one way or the other. But I think what I say would represent their position correctly. However, you might find one or two people who would take a contrary point of view and are competent in the languages, in Assyriology, and so on: it's really not so much a matter of technical linguistic competence, as of appreciation of the sort of text that Genesis is.
Perhaps I might mention that I have another book coming out soon

Escaping from Fundamentalism, SCM Press London, which has some discussion of these questions. Westminster Press in Philadelphia are doing the American edition, perhaps with a different title, I don't know. It comes out in this country on 1st June.

Thanks again for your letter and all good wishes.

Yours sincerely,

James Barr.

This is a quite surprising letter. From the title of his book it is clear that Barr is not a creationist, yet he states that all professors known to him, who would have the same non-fundamental view of Genesis, nevertheless consider "*yom*" in Genesis to mean a 24-hour day, the Flood was world-wide and all animal and human life perished in it. A similar exercise of asking the same question regarding "*yom*" was carried out by Dr J. Howitt who circulated several universities around the world. He received seven replies and all agreed that it should be translated as "day" as commonly understood (Creat).

Another point is that had Moses wished to infer an indefinite length of time, he would have used the Hebrew word "*olam*" as in Joshua 24:2, "from ancient times" (Q17/1:82). Instead he used the very clear word "*yom*" for one day of 24 hours.

From this it is evident that those who claim that "day" can refer to long periods, and quote the "thousand years" passage in Peter referred to above are making a "translation" with no knowledge of Hebrew and are relying on a particular idiomatic use of "day" in English colloquialisms.

There is therefore no warrant for this interpretation whatsoever, and it is to be hoped that this evidence will be pointed out to those who still use this passage in Peter. It is unwarranted to distort the Scriptures in this way in order to maintain credibility with scientific colleagues, and God is not honoured in so doing.

The Early Fathers' views of Genesis

There was little dissension in all Jewry or mainline Christianity that Genesis was an accurate record of creation in a six-day period at about 4,000 BC. Hutton's views differed but it was not until Lyell published his *Principles of Geology* in the 1830's that doubts began to be seriously entertained.

Almost all of the early Fathers in church history accepted Genesis and the six days of creation as historical. There has been an attempt, however, to claim that they interpreted it far more allegorically than had been thought.

This attempt is made in Forster and Marston's book *Reason and Faith* (For89A) in which they assert that the early church Fathers did not take the Genesis account of creation literally but allegorically; i.e. the "days" were not 24 hours, etc. The authors list seven names that allegorised "days" to mean "millenia", but then they admit that "Whether or not the 'days' of creation were themselves literal is seldom discussed" (p205) - which negates their argument. They refer to Basil (326-379 AD) in rather more detail, saying he "claims to take it all literally" but that he "actually adopts a complex interpretation".

Similarly they say that Chrysostom "appears to take the 'days' literally", but then quote a rather vaguely worded passage he wrote about Adam's rib. One quotation from each of Origen and Augustine is given with the implication that they also allegorised Genesis. Following this, they boldly claim, "Naive literalism was never a part of Christian orthodoxy" (p.207), and this claim is made several times throughout the remainder of the book.

But is their summary of Basil reliable? An examination of Basil's writings (Wat) makes it abundantly clear that he interpreted Genesis in its normal literal sense. He made comments such as:

> God made everything... in a short time... So let us pass by all figurative and allegorical interpretation... [on "evening" and "morning"] - This is to be understood as the duration of one day and one night [and that some interpreters] have taken refuge in allegories.

For good measure, to ensure that his readers were quite clear what his position was he said:

> Those who do not accept the Scriptures in their ordinary, common meaning, say that "water" is not water but something else; plants and fishes they interpret as they please;... twisting it from the obvious sense as do the interpreters of dreams.... As for me, when I hear the word "grass" I think of grass, and the same with plant, fish, wild beast, domestic animal. I take everything in the literal sense, for "I am not ashamed of the Gospel".
>
> It seems to me that certain people have tried by alteration of the sense, and figurative interpretations out of their own imaginations, to attribute to the Scriptures a spurious "depth". But that is to make oneself wiser than the oracles of the Holy Spirit, and under the pretext of "exegesis" to force personal ideas into the text. Therefore let us take these oracles *as they are written"* (Wat.; also Q27/4:138).

No-one reading his works could possibly claim that he was other than a *sensible* literalist in his approach to Genesis, yet Forster and Marston would have their readers believe that Basil interpreted Genesis allegorically. They also claim that Augustine was not a literalist, but we have only to quote one passage in his *City of God* to demolish this argument:

> Let us omit the conjectures of men who know not what they say, when they speak of the nature and origin of the human race... they are deceived by those highly mendacious documents which profess to give the history of many thousand years, though reckoning by the sacred writings we find that not 6,000 years have yet passed.

An examination of the works of Origen, Calvin and others who are quoted as open to a non-literal view will refute this claim. *To allegorise a passage is not to deny that it was a historical event.* All these bear witness to the falseness of their claim that "Naïve literalism was never a part of Christian orthodoxy". I have emphasised the word "sensible" when referring to Basil's literal interpretation of the Bible, for what the authors have done is to point out that no Christian ever takes *every* passage in the Bible in a strictly literal sense (e.g. the trees of the fields do not clap their hands - Isaiah 55:12). From this they use the following fallacious line of reasoning:

(a) No Christian, including creationists, takes the *whole* of the Bible literally - some passages have to be taken allegorically (agreed).

(b) Therefore, when creationists claim to take the Bible literally, they do not, for even they have to accept some passages allegorically.

(c) As it can be seen from (b) that creationists are inconsistent interpreters of the Bible, we can ignore their claim that Genesis is literal and interpret it allegorically.

It is not difficult to see the huge flaw in this line of thinking, which is the inference of the word "whole" before the word "Bible" in (a). When creationists say they believe the "whole" Bible, they do *not* take the obviously *allegorical* passages as *literally true*. Those sections that are meant to be taken as true, whether historically or theologically, are accepted as such. Literalists are emphasising the fact that they do *not* indulge in "picking and choosing" what passages they accept as true *and what they allegorise*. What should be clearly understood by sensible Christians to refer to the accuracy of the Bible has, by inference, been extended by Forster and Marsden to include obvious allegories so that they can then ridicule the whole position of creationists who refuse to interpret Genesis as an allegory.

Genesis is a clear statement of fact and for these authors to attempt to discredit those who accept Genesis as Moses obviously intended, is to grossly mislead readers who follow them unthinkingly. It requires only a modicum of common sense to see which passages should be taken as allegories - they are comparatively few and very obvious to the majority of sensible Bible-believers.

David Watson has pointed out that allegory can only be used when the readers can apply a picture with which they are familiar (e.g. harvest time) to illuminate a situation that is less understood (e.g. the end of the ages). The familiar can be used to illustrate the less familiar.

This is not the case with Genesis. This record of creation is the only account of a unique event, and the readers have no other picture or experience to draw upon. It is provided for the information of future generations of mankind, none of whom could have been present when it took place. If it is an allegory, what was the original concept it was meant to illustrate? It bears no resemblance to the Big Bang!

In a letter defending their position, Marston said they "assume that the compiler [!] did not intend literality in either chapter (Genesis 1 and 2) and there is no contradiction between them" (Marst). He later adds, "I do believe it is absurd to suggest that the compiler put together two contradictory 'literal' accounts without realising their contradiction." The essence of this argument is that no sensible compiler would have put two contradictory accounts together and yet believed that both were to be understood literally. Therefore he must have only considered that they were two equally valid *allegories* about the same event.

As we have maintained, there is no conflict between Genesis 1 and 2, which negates this argument. Regarding their reference to the "compiler" they obviously ignore Christ's many pronouncements that *Moses* was the writer of the Pentateuch (the first five books of the Bible) - not some anonymous "compiler".

Regarding Exodus 20:11, they admit that "it plainly says" that "in six days the Lord made the heavens and the earth, the sea, and all that is in them, and rested on the seventh day", but later (p216) state "It is not a sign of spirituality or desire to honour God to take as much literally as possible"!

"Bible-believers"?

This question of just how much of the Bible should be taken as an accurate account and what should be taken as an allegory is an important distinction for Christians. Many sincere Christians claim they are true Bible-believers but nevertheless do not take the accounts in Genesis of creation and the Flood as literal. In view of this, are they right to claim this title? I would suggest not, for the simple reason that where the Bible *can* be taken literally - including the miracles - then it should be understood in this way. It will be found that those who read Genesis allegorically are almost invariably supporters of evolution.

In a letter Marston wrote in *The English Churchman* (1.10.93) he complained about a review David C.C. Watson had made in a previous issue. He commented:

> *Christians in Science* (CIS) has no commitment to any specific scientific theories, only to the acceptance of the truth of the Bible and its view of God as creator as accepted by evangelicals and Bible-believers throughout history."

Watson, in the same issue replied:

> The Editorial Board of *Science and Christian Belief* includes a number of distinguished academics who are well known as evolutionists and (some) even as anti-creationists; and in the 80 pages of this April issue I have found not a single sentence that allows credibility to the creationist model. I am forced to conclude that Dr. Marston's use of the phrase "Bible-believing" is very different from my own and from that of most ordinary Christians.

In this same letter, Marston says he is "puzzled that young-earthers like Watson so often cite James Barr as *the* [emphasis his] authority on interpreting the Hebrew of Genesis, when Barr's motive was to attack evangelical views of the Bible". Surely the fact that Barr is an evolutionist gives added support to creationists when he admits that the writer of Genesis intended a period of 24 hours. Marston has completely missed - or deliberately ignored - this very obvious and important point. This is just one example of the level of argument he uses and many others could be quoted.

We have examined Forster and Marston's views on this subject at length in view of the confusion that is arising in evangelical circles as to what a "Bible-believer" really means. There is an extremely simple way to determine just where any professing Christian stands on this issue. One has only to ask them whether they believe that the universe was created in six days a few thousand years ago as recorded in Genesis. Any tendency to prevaricate or qualify their answers will tell the enquirer all he needs to know.

Several evangelical Christians have expressed their concern about *Reason and Faith* which espouses evolution, coming as it does from those who claim to be Bible-believers. Much more could be written in criticism of this work and others by the same authors (For89B, For95) but we will leave it to the reader to judge whether they are "wresting the Scriptures".

The rise of Long Age theories

It is not difficult to understand why these theories were so readily invented and accepted many years ago and should still be in vogue even today.

In the late nineteenth century, the rising theory of evolution demanded millions of years for the idea to be viable, and this requirement had already been "proven" by Lyell. This presented a major problem to Christians in a wide range of professions. They would want to maintain that the Bible was an accurate record, but would also want to avoid ridicule by their colleagues for believing in a creation only six thousand years ago. Peer pressure and the desire to be professionally accepted were just as powerful then as they are today.

For those whose livelihood depended upon a scientific profession in which "millions of years" was the accepted norm, then the pressure to conform was considerable; to not comply was to risk ridicule, reduced prospects of promotion and even dismissal. Those in scientific employment, such as at universities, etc., where young-age views would be strongly discouraged, were far more likely to espouse a Long Age interpretation.

It was for this reason that the Scriptures were searched for some way in which "millions of years" could enter into the picture. This gave rise to the Gap theory, treating Genesis as an allegory, and the other interpretations discussed above. These were seized upon as solutions to their dilemma, despite the weak Scriptural support they had.

These Gap-type theories were first proposed in order to have the best of both worlds, but since then there has developed a considerable body of respectable scientific evidence indicating that the earth is young, and this is held by many Bible-believing scientists today. The problem for them is that, depending on their position in their organisation, they may prefer to keep this aspect quiet for, if known to the hierarchy, their status or even their livelihood may be affected. With such a prospect, who would place his family responsibilities and social standing at risk for what can so easily be dismissed as an unorthodox view held by a "cranky minority" that should not be investigated too closely?

Being in independent employment in a field that has no connection with creation, no such pressures or decisions have ever had to be faced by this writer. In view of this, those who face this dilemma, far from being criticised, have my full sympathy.

These Long Age theories will, no doubt, still be promoted by some. Those whose professional position might be under threat will continue to hold to it - or at least profess it and even open-minded believers in the Bible will find a change of conceptual thinking ("paradigm") just as hard as others.

It is therefore hoped that those who can make this very difficult paradigm shift will do so. They will then join their many Christian brothers and sisters in accepting the clear Scriptural record of a six-day creation that took place only a few thousand years ago, leaving the Gap theory and all other Long Age theories to be quietly laid to rest.

SECTION 2.2
ASTRONOMICAL ANOMALIES

When we look up at the starry sky on a dark night we are presented with such a spectacle that there must be few who do not have a sense of awe and wonderment. This is so obvious that God challenges Job, and us, to see His hand in its creation when He says, "Can you bind the beautiful Pleiades? Can you loose the chords of Orion? Can you bring forth the constellations in their seasons?" (Job 38:31-2).

Such is the beauty and complexity of the various astronomical bodies that we can only give a brief summary of the strange nature of some of the observations made. A true explanation of how they could have come into being by natural means has consistently puzzled astronomers. Any such questioning, however, is confined entirely to professional circles, and even here the discussion is carefully limited and controlled lest it becomes too radical for comfort, as we will see when we deal with the opposition faced by the astronomer Halton Arp. Meanwhile, the public are fed a grossly simplified picture of "how the universe came into being" that is contradicted by the normal laws of the mechanics of moving bodies.

We will examine a number of topics that demonstrate very clearly that any mechanistic (i.e. non-miraculous) explanation of the formation of the planetary system, stars and constellations is unsatisfactory. There are too many strange features that could not have been formed by a simple mechanical sequence of events.

In order to appreciate what follows, we will set out briefly some of the major features of particular members of the observed universe around us as presented by popular astronomical writers such as Patrick Moore.

The Orthodox View

Our sun is one of a number of millions of stars all clumped together to form our GALAXY. There are many hundreds of thousands of similar galaxies now found, most of them being shaped like a disc with a thickened centre. A number also have bands of stars in spiral arms curved round the outside making them look like a spinning catherine wheel firework.

The light from a star can be split up by a prism into a spectrum and the light analysed. If you heat different elements up they emit light with specific wavelengths that enable the element to be identified. Thus the components of a star can be identified by a SPECTROSCOPIC ANALYSIS.

Light is not the only thing that can be examined, as it forms just a narrow band of possible emissions that range from the very energetic cosmic rays (high frequency and short wavelengths) to very long radio waves and even the 50 cycles per second mains frequency. These all travel at the speed of light, and so the shorter the wavelength, the higher the frequency. Knowing one measurement, say the wavelength, you can obtain the frequency by dividing it into the present speed of light (299,792.458 km/s) and vice versa. Fig. 1 gives the full range of measurable wavelengths and frequencies as a reference.

Incoming radio waves and X-rays from space can now also be measured and plotted, very high levels coming from some regions where there is no obvious visible object.

When astronomers looked at the light from distant galaxies, they found the same pattern of light in the spectral analysis that they expected, but, very significantly, the whole set of frequencies was shifted by the same amount towards the red (lower frequency) end of the spectrum. This became known as the RED-SHIFT, and the amount of red-shift for thousands of galaxies has been measured.

Now light from an object can be given a red-shift by moving the object away from the observer very rapidly, at some fraction of the speed of light. This movement away from the observer results in a lowering of the frequency (DOPPLER EFFECT) which is a similar effect to what is heard (at a much lower frequency) when a siren on a car goes past you. The pitch (frequency) falls as it moves away from you.

When the red-shift on many galaxies had been measured and compared with their (assumed) distance from us, it was found that there was a simple ratio between them - their distance was proportionately related to their speed of recession. This ratio was known as the HUBBLE CONSTANT. From this, the degree of red-shift was interpreted as a measure of the distance of a galaxy from us. If we imagine a balloon with many specks of dust randomly distributed within it, and the balloon is expanding, then each speck will be moving away from all the others as the whole space increases uniformly in all directions as the volume increases. This is the picture that this red-shift presented to the astronomers - everywhere they looked at distant galaxies, they were rushing away from us.

If the distance of these galaxies is known, and the speed that they are moving away from each other has now been measured, it is a simple calculation to work out how long ago they started as a small clump of material which then exploded to produce the universe with receding galaxies we have today. The time when the primordial matter exploded has been calculated as having occurred 20 billion years ago - 2×10^{10} years ago (2 with ten noughts behind it!).

This is the main evidence that forms the basis of the BIG BANG THEORY, from which was later produced a scenario of how the universe, and this earth in particular, developed. After the explosion of the primordial material out of which the whole universe was formed, the dispersion was fairly uniform to begin with, but gradually material collected together to form stars, which in turn collected to form galaxies, and later groups of galaxies and super-galactic groupings. Stars were said to obtain their heat by nuclear energy and eventually expanded into red giants that finally collapsed into white dwarfs.

For our own local star (the sun), various ways in which the planets could have formed been proposed. The most well known theory is that of Laplace's "nebular hypothesis". This suggests that a cloud of gas around the sun flattened into a disc due to the rotation which then by gravitation formed local masses that became the planets.

Another theory suggested that a passing star drew out a filament of material from the sun. This cigar-shaped mass then broke up and collected into lumps which eventually cooled to form the planets.

The earth is claimed to have been formed 4,500 million years ago, giving adequate time for it to cool to give a hard crust on which the evolution of life would take place.

....

What has been set out above is the general picture still propagated today. The problem, however, is that on closer inspection, contradictory evidence builds up until, just like the theory of evolution, common sense declares that the whole scenario must be discounted. The mass media, however, continues to churn out the same old dogma and little publicity is given to fundamental

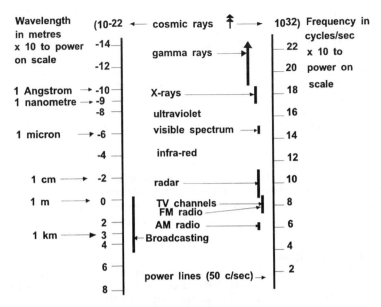

Fig. 1. The electromagnetic spectrum

contrary evidence.

There are a number of areas that show how inadequate the evidence is in support of the above "tidy" scenario, and we will examine some of the contrary facts and the ramifications that flow from them.

1. THE PLANETARY SYSTEM

There have been a number of theories that attempt to explain how our planetary system could have been brought into existence by purely mechanistic means. Mulfinger examined four theories of how the universe came into existence and eleven theories about the planetary system - and showed that all could be heavily criticised (Mulf).

One of the more complete attempts is by Fred Hoyle (Hoy) but how successful he was in proving his ideas we will examine later. Before we begin to discuss the subject of our planetary system, however, we need to keep in mind just how sparse the universe really is. Illustrations in books usually show the planets greatly enlarged compared to their distance from each other and from the stars, etc. This gives the impression that they are relatively close together. The actual distances between planets are immense compared with their diameters.

To present the true relationship, we will give a scaled version of the system, which, to fully appreciate, needs to be paced out or the distances to be roughly estimated. If we imagine the **Sun** as being a 6 inches (150mm) diameter ball, then on this scale, **Mercury** is 21 thousandths of an inch (0.5mm) in diameter and is 21 ft (6.4m) away. **Venus** is only twice that size and 39 ft (12m) away. The **Earth** is about the size of Venus (0.04 ins or 1mm diameter) and is 54 ft (16.5m) away. Surprisingly, **Mars** is smaller, about the size of **Mercury** but 27 yds (25m) away. These are all virtually just grains of sand. The largest are

Jupiter and **Saturn**, about 0.6 ins (15mm) in diameter (about the size of a marble) and 93 and 171 yds (85 and 156m) away. **Uranus** and **Neptune** are 0.2 ins. (5mm) diameter and 344 and 540 yds distant (314 and 494 m). **Pluto** would be 720 yds (658m) away. These are huge distances compared with their diameters.

Even more surprising is that the nearest **star** would be about the same size as the sun but 2,500 miles away! The whole picture gives one a concept of the vastness and emptiness of space. The earth is minute compared with the sun and very far away from it, yet the sun supplies all the great heat we receive that is so necessary for life to exist.

PROBLEMS WITH THE PLANETS

The main problem facing any scientific theory of how the planetary system formed is that there are a number of very unusual features about it. Just how varied the different planets and their moons are is rarely referred to in books on astronomy, and some of these factors are considered below. Fig. 2 sets out some of this data.

(a) Their composition

As we have mentioned, Laplace proposed that the planets condensed from a flat disc around the sun. Astronomers are aware that this does not work but it is still presented in popular books and newspaper articles.

One difficulty with this theory and others like it that derive the planets from a central source is that the planets are all completely different in composition.

Mercury is cratered rock with a very thin atmosphere. **Venus** is similar but has an atmospheric pressure ninety times higher than ours. The **Earth**, in contrast to all the others, has an abundance of minerals and an atmosphere, suitably arranged for the maintenance of life. **Mars** is like **Mercury**. **Jupiter** may have a rock core, then metallic hydrogen (due to the pressure) becoming liquid hydrogen nearer the surface and then hydrogen gas. The surface has several bands of gases rotating in *opposite* directions around the equator. **Saturn** has a rock core and metallic hydrogen and helium, with liquid hydrogen, methane and ammonia. **Uranus, Neptune** and **Pluto** seem to have rock cores with ice coverings of various solidified gases.

With such a wide range of constituents, it is difficult to see how they could have all originated from the same source.

(b) Speed vs orbit

Each of the planets is travelling around the sun at just the precise speed that it must have in order to maintain its present fairly circular orbit. If any one of them increased their speed slightly, they would have to move out to a more distant position. If fast enough, they would gradually spiral off into space as the centrifugal force would be greater than their gravitational attraction to the sun. Conversely, if any one were to be slower, then it could spiral towards the sun to a lower orbit, or, if slow enough, pulled into it by gravitation.

(c) Angular momentum

If a top is spun, or a weight is swung on the end of a chord, they are said to possess angular momentum (spinning energy). Similarly, the planets have a total mass that is circling the sun. The angular momentum of each of them can be calculated and added together. The sun has a much greater mass than all the planets combined, but strangely, it is only turning slowly. Its angular

PLANET	DIAMETER Km	DISTANCE FROM SUN Mill Km	ROTATION PERIOD ROTN ORB Hr-Dy-Yr		TEMPERATURE °C	TILT°	COMPOSITION	MOONS
SUN	1.39 Mill	-	-	-	5,500	-	Hydrogen	
MERCURY	4,878	57.9	58.6D	88D	+427 to -183	-	Cratered rocks, thin air, He,H,Ox,Na,K	
VENUS	12,014	108.2	243.2D RETRO	225D	Clouds -33 Surface +480	3 RETRO	Cratered rock, 90xearth At. Press.	
EARTH	12,714	149.6	23.93H	365.2D	22	23.4	Rock, thin atmosphr, Ox,N	1 (Synch)
MARS	6,794	227.9	24.62H	687D	-23	23.98	Cratered rock, v thin atmos.	2
ASTEROIDS	940 Max	21-876	-	-	-	-	Rocks	-
JUPITER	143,844	778	9.67H	11.86Y	-150	3	Rock core? Met., Liq. and gas H	12 Pro 4 RETRO
SATURN	120,536	1,427	10.23H	29.5Y	-180	26.7	Rock core, Met.+Liq,H, Meth, Amm	17 Pro 1 RETRO
URANUS	51,118	2,870	17.2H	84Y	-214	82 RETRO	Rock core, Liq+gas-water,Amm,Meth	17
NEPTUNE	50,538	4,497	16.1H	165Y	-220	28.8	Rock, Ice+gas H2S, Methane	7 Pro 1 RETRO
PLUTO	2,324	5,900	6.38D	248Y	-220	57.5 RETRO	Methane ice	1 RETRO

Fig. 2. Planetary data

momentum is very small for it is less than 2% of the total angular momentum of the whole planetary system. The question then arises, if the sun is turning so slowly, where did the planets get their angular momentum from? As we will see, Fred Hoyle attempted to solve this problem.

Furthermore, the sun's axis is tilted at 7° to the orbits of the planets. What could have caused this and how could the sun have given off material to make the planets at a different angle to its spin?

(d) The moons

There are a large number of moons circling the planets, most of them in the same direction as the planets are circling the sun (prograde). It is sometimes suggested that the moons are captured by the planets but van Flandern has said, "Gravitational capture of one body by another is virtually impossible under ordinary circumstances." (Fla:262)

An examination of Fig. 2 will show that there are a number of moons that are circling their planets the wrong way round (retrograde). The following are of particular interest:

Jupiter has 12 prograde moons and 4 retrograde. Io, a prograde moon, is gradually coming closer to Jupiter (Hec). This indicates that it could not have existed for very long, otherwise it would have fallen into Jupiter many years ago. This again indicates that the planetary system is young.

Neptune has 7 prograde and 1 retrograde - Triton. This large moon is also spiralling towards Neptune (Hec).

Uranus has 15 moons and 10 complete rings on its equatorial plane, but this is tilted almost horizontally, i.e. at right angles to the ecliptic (its orbit around the sun) (Fla:298). There is no easy explanation of how this system could have arisen naturally. In addition, its magnetic pole is at 60° to its axis of rotation.

Saturn really requires a chapter of its own to do full justice to the many interesting features of its rings and moons.

For many years astronomers wondered what these rings consisted of. The advent of powerful telescopes showed that they were composed of thousands of lumps of rock reflecting the sun's light. There are several features that do not fit conventional theory. For example, Phoebe is the only moon that orbits prograde but spins retrograde.

There are also two outer moons, Epimetheus and Janus, orbiting the planet on slightly different orbits. Every four years, as one overtakes the other, they actually switch their orbits perfectly and the inner one takes the position and speed of the outer one and vice-versa! How could these two moons have been so carefully positioned to have carried out this complex manoeuvre for billions of years?

When this information is dealt with in textbooks (e.g. MooreP), the fact that these moons are retrograde may be far from apparent. For the prograde moons, almost all of them rotate around the planet on a plane that is only a few degrees from the "equator" of the planet, and this would be shown in a table as say "6° tilt" etc. Any moon on an orbit at right angles to this plane would of course be at 90° - but none are.

Retrograde moons are also provided with the angle of tilt of their plane of rotation but in this case it might be tabled as "175°". What this is in fact, is a *retrograde* moon at an angle of 5° to the equatorial plane of the planet, but this is somewhat hidden by describing it as being at an angle of 175°. We will see that this method of minimising the fact that the motion is (inexplicably) retrograde applies to the rotation of the planets also.

There is often much talk about planets "capturing" moons, but van Flandern maintains that this is almost impossible (Flan). As a moon approaches a planet, its orbit will be bent by the gravitational attraction, but it will then continue into outer space, for there will be no adequate force that can change its approach orbit into a circular one around the planet. Its velocity is usually too great for it to be "captured" so easily, much the same as comets continuously orbit the sun.

Our moon

The origin of our moon has been a consistent puzzle for astronomers. One survey of several ideas eventually proposed that the Accretion Theory of the moon "from a cloud of planetesimal debris that was trapped in orbit around the earth" was the most likely, but admitted that this had only been adopted "as alternative hypothesis have been found implausible" (Kaul).

(e) The rotation of the planets

All the planets circle the sun anticlockwise viewed from our north pole. All the planets also rotate on their axis in the same anticlockwise direction (prograde) except three which are retrograde.

Venus (at 2.7°) and Pluto (58°) are spinning slowly backwards, whilst Uranus is spinning on an almost horizontal axis. The angle is usually given as 98° from the ecliptic (the planet's path around the sun). This is more than a right angle so it is theoretically spinning slowly backwards, although really it is on its side.

As with the retrograde motion of the moons, this retrograde spin is not highlighted and only described as "the angle of tilt" from the plane of the orbit of the planet around the sun. This is usually a few degrees - 23.4 for the earth. For Uranus this angle is given as 98° and for Venus it is given as 177° - i.e. retrograde and 3° (180 - 177) tilt.

One baffling fact (to conventional astronomers) is that the moons of Uranus circulate precisely on the plane of the planet's ecliptic ("equator") and not near the sun's ecliptic as most others are; i.e. they are also at right angles to Uranus's orbit around the sun. The planet *might* have been rotated on its axis, but not its moons with it. This planet and its moons must, therefore, have been created complete with their "inexplicable" orbits.

No attempts have been made to explain how these three planets and various moons could have these unusual spins and orbits if they all came from the same source that all the other planets came from. What could have produced these spins without pulling their orbits wildly out of shape or sending them into space? No explanations are given. Indeed, one has only to examine any popular book on astronomy, particularly regarding the planetary system, to see that there is little attempt to explain how it could have arisen naturally.

Astronomers are discovering many strange phenomena through their instruments and their growing bafflement becomes increasingly obvious to anyone with even just a slight knowledge of the subject. The reader might like to open any book on astronomy and see if it presents any reasonable theory of how the present universe could have originated.

Comets and cometesimals

The subject of comets is more fully discussed in Section 4 as the existence today of "short-term comets" indicates the young age of the universe.

Cometesimals are comparatively small comets that are striking the earth and were only discovered in the early 1980's. They consist of frozen water that hit the earth's atmosphere at the surprising rate of about 20 every minute (Berg). They weigh about 100 tons and are about the size of a house. This represents a huge amount of water entering the earth, but it may be balanced by the water that leaves the atmosphere. The heat of entry rapidly vaporises them and they do not reach the ground. However, it is possible that a very large one may have had a catastrophic effect as we will suggest when discussing the rapid destruction of the woolly mammoths.

It has also recently been found that there is a considerable amount of water at a height of 70 km (*Science* 13.2.98).

Hoyle's "explanation" of the planetary system

Laplace's theory of how the planets came into existence is only one of many that has been used to present what appears to be a satisfactory explanation for public consumption, but as we have said, they all have many difficulties.

In an effort to deal with the problem, Fred Hoyle wrote *The Cosmogony of the Solar System* (Hoy) in which he sets out a possible sequence of events by which the planetary system may have been produced.

I have a great respect for Hoyle, for he is fearless in promoting a number of ideas that have upset several established scientific dogmas. As a result he has been almost completely ostracised by his peers (Bow91:175). This book, however, does him little credit. He tries to present a viable scenario of mechanical events, but in order to finish with the present arrangement, time after time he has to call upon a particularly unusual sequence of incidents in order to obtain the desired result. He considers that the sun was spinning and sent out a thin disc of material. This condensed into lumps of matter, and these lumps gradually bumped into each other to form the planets. He assumes they are ice particles, but when considering the formation of the earth, they strangely become iron lumps in order to explain our iron core.

He tries to explain how most of the angular momentum is in the planets and not in the sun. To do this he has to assume that the part of the total mass of the primordial solar nebula that eventually produced the planetary system was much greater than the present mass. He arrives at this conclusion by a series of intricate arguments and finds that it is nearly four times the present mass of the planets. This excess mass, in the form of hydrogen and helium, was then evaporated into space due to the escape velocity of Uranus and Neptune being sufficiently low, all having to take place in a specific sequence to get the present situation accounted for.

In order to then give the planets the majority of the angular momentum, he speculates that there was a thin layer of material that enabled this matter to be spun faster than the sun by means of a "torque transmitter" that was "probably magnetic in its nature" (p20). This process required the nebula to have a magnetic intensity that exceeds "about 100 G". He considers this is reasonable as some sunspots have an intensity up to 2,000 G.

There is no evidence that this "thin conducting layer" exists or has ever existed. He makes no reference whatsoever to Saturn's rings or how *any* of the moons of the planets were formed or how they are found circling their planets - in both directions in some cases. These are serious omissions, and suggests that he found them too difficult to explain, even using the strained methods he employs.

These examples, and others in the book, pile speculation upon guesswork upon suggestion until the credibility of the more critical reader reaches breaking point. It is almost painful to watch him trying to wriggle out of the many dilemmas that our planetary system presents him with.

This book is an attempt by one of the most able astronomers to provide an acceptable explanation of how our planetary system came into existence. If this is the best that the profession can do after many years of exploration of the sky and theorising, then I would suggest that they have failed badly in their endeavour.

2. THE MEASUREMENT OF DISTANCES

So confident are the pronouncements of astronomers about the immense distances to the stars and galaxies that it is generally accepted that they are well proven. There are, however, many assumptions in the methods used, and a degree of circular reasoning.

The distance to the nearest stars can be measured by parallax, but only 6,000 are near enough to be measured in this way. If a photo of the stars is taken when the earth is on one side of the sun, and six months later when it is on the other side, then the two photos can be compared. The nearer stars will be in a slightly different position compared to the many stars in the far distance. Using the distant stars as a fixed background, the amount of "movement" (a small angle) can be measured. As the diameter of the earth's orbit is known, by triangulation calculations the distance to the star can be worked out. This is indicated in Fig. 7.10.3.

Measuring the distance to stars and galaxies much further away is difficult. It was noticed that certain stars varied in their brightness (cepheid variables) and that their average brightness was linked to the frequency of the variation. By measuring the frequency of a cepheid variable its average brightness could be determined, and this was then compared with how bright it appeared in our telescopes and a measure of its distance could be given. One problem is that the nearest cepheids are beyond the range of using the parallax method, and their distances had to be estimated by statistical methods (Stei79:158).

There are other means of estimating distance but with all these methods that rely on measuring the relative (apparent) brightness of an object the main problem is that the light can be greatly reduced by an unknown amount of intergalactic dust. This could greatly affect any conclusions regarding distance.

A number of the furthest galaxies for which distances had been estimated were found to have a red-shift of the spectral lines. This was correlated with their (estimated) distance by Hubble to obtain the Hubble Constant of measurement. From this, knowing the red-shift of a galaxy, the distance could be calculated with some accuracy, *if the assumptions were correct.*

Contradicting this assumption is Tifft's discovery that spiral galaxies have higher shifts than elliptical ones even in the same cluster, and that dim galaxies have higher shifts than bright ones. The shift has also been found to change even within a ten-year period (E8/2:230). Even some stars in our own galaxy have "excessive red-shift". All this indicates that red-shift has little connection with distance from the earth.

Even clearer evidence that red-shift is not due to distance alone will be examined when we consider the work of Halton Arp later.

3. THE FORMATION AND AGE OF STARS

There is no adequate explanation of how stars could have formed from the Big Bang. When material is moving apart at high speed, there is little tendency to form into the huge mass that a star possesses. The process by which stars could have formed is a major problem to astronomers. Various theories have been proposed but all are basically flawed in some way.

The amount of light coming from a star (luminosity) and the temperature (determined by its colour) have been plotted and the result is known as the Hertzsprung-Russell diagram (Fig. 3). This is claimed to demonstrate the way in which stars grow from the "mainstream" line of them into red giants and then collapse into white dwarfs. The whole theory is based upon nuclear energy, with the helium and hydrogen gradually being used up. However, if nuclear energy is providing the energy, then we should be receiving three times as many neutrino particles from the sun than has been found - which is a problem for astronomers. We will see that the sun is shrinking at a rate that is more than enough to generate the enormous heat it radiates. From this, it has been shown that the present arrangement of the mainstream stars and red giants in the Hertzsprung-Russell diagram can be adequately explained by various stages of contraction of different forms of stars (Q30/2:71-76).

It has not been proven that the neutrinos recorded actually come from the sun, but even if they are all generated by the sun it only indicates that some of the energy may be nuclear. Most or all of the energy is probably coming from the sun's contraction, as we will see in a later section.

Black holes

According to Relativity theory, stars larger than three times the size of the sun should eventually collapse into a black hole. This is so dense that even light cannot escape from it. The problem is that none have been identified with any certainty, and they are far fewer than theory predicts. There is much talk about their characteristics as though they were a common feature of the sky, but the evidence for their existence is very slim. If the theory of relativity is incorrect, then the justification for their existence disappears. However, this is so fiercely defended that there is little hope of their demise within the foreseeable future. In addition, they make imaginative subjects for writers and the public are kept entertained by space-ship odysseys involving them, so one can expect them to "exist" for many years yet.

4. THE BIG BANG

We have outlined the Big Bang (BB) theory above, and will here give some of the evidence that contradicts it. Naturally, this gets little publicity in the popular press.

1. Cosmologists say that as the universe expanded, each photon of energy radiating from the BB lost energy, such that its energy now is only sufficient to register the very low 3°K radiation.

But for the light from distant galaxies to be only Doppler shifted to give their measured red-shift, these photons of light must *maintain* their energy. Akridge has pointed out that this involves two contradictions.

(i) If the BB photons lose energy due to expansion, then *all* photons must lose energy as they travel through space; you cannot differentiate between those photons from the BB and those from distant galaxies.

(ii) Cosmologists cannot have their explanation of the 3°K radiation and at the

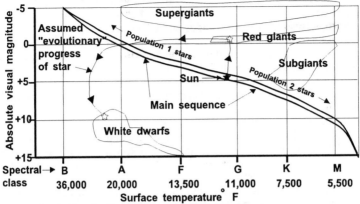
Fig. 3. The Hertzsprung-Russell diagram

same time use the red-shift as a measure of distance. Akridge gives a neat illustration of this (Akr82).

Take a galaxy that is 100 million light years (MLY) away from us. Its light is just now reaching us. If the star was rushing away from us, the Hubble constant will tell us how much its wavelength would be reduced due to Doppler red-shifting, and it comes to 0.5%.

However, if the universe is expanding, the Hubble constant will also tell us how much the expansion of the universe had reduced the energy of these photons during their 100 MLY travel, and it comes to 0.5% also.

Thus, *the red-shift has two possible explanations:* recessional Doppler shifting or expansion of the universe; *and they cannot both be operating at the same time to give the measured results.*

To put it another way; either the galaxy is 100 MLY away from us, or it is rushing away from us; but not both at the same time!

This presents cosmologists with a major dilemma, and we would consider this a major objection to the BB theory that deserves to be more widely known.

2. When we look at distant galaxies, if they are as far off as astronomers say they are, then, in view of the time taken for their light to reach us, we are seeing them as they were millions of years ago. But they are not randomly arranged in space but are grouped into clusters, these into superclusters, and these again into "walls" of galaxies. Astronomers admit that they cannot explain how these large groups could have formed so quickly after the initial Big Bang.

3. Knowing the rate of expansion, it is possible to calculate how long ago the BB occurred. There have been many widely varying estimates of this value - from 2 to 20 billion years. The problem is that some galaxies appear to be older than the universe!

4. If the universe had expanded 0.1% faster than it has, it would be expanding 3×10^3 faster than it is at present. If it expanded 0.1% slower, it would have reached only 3×10^{-6} of its present radius before collapsing. No stars could have formed in such a universe for it would not have existed long enough to have formed stars (Q19/1:28). This suggests that the BB has been very "fine tuned".

5. We examine below the evidence that red-shifting of spectra is no indication of recession velocity of a galaxy. This would completely destroy the whole Big Bang theory. No wonder one expert admitted that:

> Any suggestion that the simple interpretation of the red-shift might be wrong or at least incomplete, sends shivers down the spines of conventional cosmologists (E8/2:230).

Furthermore, studies of the red-shift of galaxies show that they have changed in the brief space of ten years which is inexplicable by orthodox theories.

6. The amount of variation in the 3° Kelvin background radiation is too small to account for the collection of the expanding matter into stars and galaxies. This is also discussed later. In Section 4, The Age of the Earth and Universe, we will show that the most likely explanation of the 3°K radiation is the heating of the intergalactic dust.

Even secular cosmologists admit that the BB theory is unable to overcome many of these objections, but that it is still held to because there is no other theory around that they can adopt in its place. That the universe was created is barely considered, and then only to be dismissed as "unscientific".

5. HALTON ARP AND RED-SHIFTS

Quasars, Redshifts and Controversies is the title of a very interesting book by Halton Arp (Arp), an astronomer with an international reputation. His main work was the study of a number of galaxies that do not conform to the normal patterns, and this drew him to examine their relationship to quasars. This is the shortened name given to quasi-stellar objects which are very bright bodies that are said to be near the edge of the visible universe. If the red-shift is an indication of both distance and movement away from us, then they are receding from us at phenomenal speeds.

He noticed that these quasars were often near galaxies, and he found that this nearness was so frequent that it was well above a random event; i.e. there was a very definite connection. On close study of many photographic plates he not only established this as a fact but very surprisingly found with a number of them a wisp of material between the galaxy and the quasar, thus establishing a very definite physical connection. Even more surprising was that in some of them the relationship of the quasars, galaxy and connecting material looked as if the quasars had been ejected by an explosion near the centre of the galaxy, sending a narrow jet of matter in one direction. In some cases, there was another "reaction" jet of material in precisely the opposite direction.

In addition, the red-shifts of some of these quasars were at specific and regular steps of values. They should have a smooth distribution of red-shifts if this was indicative of their varying distances from the earth, and therefore these stepped series of red-shifts is unexpected. Setterfield, however - an Australian creationist - has written a paper (to be published) explaining this in terms of the quantum jumps in the atom.

This discovery is very similar to the findings of Varshni regarding an even clearer series of stepped red-shift values of many galaxies that is discussed in Appendix 10. Both of these discoveries are but another embarrassment to orthodox astronomy.

Opposition to Arp

These findings by Arp of the connections between quasars and galaxies with differing red-shifts considerably upset the senior astronomers of the day, for they presented two problems. Firstly, they had no explanation of how these quasars could have come into being by an explosion in the centre of a galaxy.

Secondly, and far more revolutionary, was the fact that these quasars, with their large red-shifts, had always been interpreted as "being on the edge of visible space". Yet here was Arp saying that they were physically connected to galaxies with a much lower red-shift. This totally destroyed the idea that red-shift was a measure of distance. It was obviously due to some other factor in these cases at least, and probably the same cause could explain the red-shift in all other galaxies.

The reason that his ideas received so much vilification and blockage was that his evidence cut the ground from under the Big Bang theory - if red-shifts were *not* due to the recession of the galaxies, then the universe was *not* expanding, and the Big Bang would lose its basic evidence and all credibility.

Such was the inertia of the rolling scientific bandwagon riding high on this major subject of the Big Bang that Arp's evidence could not be allowed to take root and flourish. It was duly crushed under the very considerable weight of the academic juggernaut.

Word of his discoveries soon circulated on the scientific grapevine and when he presented a paper on the subject, he was a subject of ridicule by one opponent even before he had spoken. After that the opposition was quickly marshalled. He was denied access to telescope time, he had difficulty in getting his papers published, a confirming study by other astronomers was never published, etc. etc.

He co-authored a paper with Professor Oort (of "cloud of comets" fame; see Section 4.11) in which he put some of his evidence, but this was omitted when the paper was eventually published. He was unable to use an X-ray map of ejected quasars in his book as he had been specifically warned that he could not use it "without permission". Arp eventually moved to Europe to continue his work and wrote his book in order to present his evidence and his side of the controversy.

Fred Hoyle supported Arp, and a paper by Hoyle on the same subject was not accepted by many universities. Arp was dining at Hoyle's university in Cardiff, and when he mentioned Hoyle's name to his neighbour, the latter furtively dropped his voice and said, "He is a great scientist who was treated very badly round here." Arp said he would never forget "the fearful whisper in which it was spoken, as if we were in some kind of occupied territory" (Arp:170).

In reading of this controversy it becomes apparent that Arp was not subjected to some local opposition, but found that all the normal avenues of promoting his discoveries were suddenly closed to him on an *international* scale. He is denied telescope time in Hawaii and elsewhere. All the international journals suddenly, as if on a signal from a central control, refused to publish his papers. This is but one more example of the total grip that the established (evolutionary) controllers of the scientific world have upon *all* the outlets available to those working in this field.

Arp indeed contends that with such a stranglehold to enforce rigid adherence to established views, "the truly most creative and important achievements in science will not take place within the universities or institutions at all" (Arp:169). The only problem with this thought is that in many subjects, particularly astronomy, expensive and sophisticated equipment is essential - well beyond the finances of any small independently- minded establishment. In addition, there is the problem of circulating any new and interesting information. How will these new revolutionary discoveries reach the general scientific community if they are denied access to the international journals?

Having said this, there is an increasing number of scientists, medics, etc. who are first publishing their papers on the World Wide Web internet system rather than applying to reputable journals. One reason is to establish their precedence in making any important discovery. Another is that their papers are not subjected to any "establishment censorship" and therefore they are free to publish "controversial" results. In many fields of research there is a growing use of this means of circulating important results, and those in positions of influence over the more orthodox channels have, as yet, been unable to exert any control. This may well be an important channel allowing considerable flexibility.

Arp, like so many others, appears to be unaware of just how well entrenched and all-pervasive the opposition is to anyone who would criticise subjects even remotely connected with the theory of evolution. In his case it was the red-shift and its effect upon the Big Bang theory. This is the atheist's loudly proclaimed starting-point of the universe that was to then "evolve" over billions of years. It must not be criticised too vigorously in public and will be defended with fearful tenacity behind the scenes.

Science, scientists and "Truth"

Occasionally, after a lecture against evolution in which I have exposed many fraudulent claims perpetrated under the guise of "science", I have been criticised for implying that all scientists lack integrity. This is both ridiculous and strongly denied. The vast majority of scientists pursue their calling with zeal and passion in their search for truth. What I do maintain, however, is that should *any* scientist discover anything that has the slightest implication of contradicting evolution, no matter how remote his field may be from that subject, he will find that he will meet considerable opposition to the presentation of his evidence. We would cite the world-wide opposition to Arp's discovery that threatened the Big Bang theory as a classical example of such forces in action. We will meet it again when examining the shrinking of the sun, relativity and the work of Harold Aspden.

6. THE RIPPLES IN THE BACKGROUND RADIATION

It has already been noted that as the universe expanded from the Big Bang, there are no adequate forces that can explain how stars, galaxies or galaxy clusters could have been formed. All around the sky a very uniform temperature of 3° Kelvin has been measured. Zero Kelvin is equal to -273°C. It is thought that this is the present temperature of the Big Bang as it expanded and cooled down from its original very high temperature, and so it is called the "echo of the Big Bang". The problem is that this temperature is so very uniform wherever the astronomers point their instruments, and there is not sufficient variation to account for the clumping of the expanding material into stars and galaxies.

In 1992, a huge blaze of publicity was given to the discovery of what were claimed to be "ripples" in the measurements of the 3° K radiation. It was presented as the first item of news on the TV, with the news presenter gravely announcing it in hushed tones usually reserved for a declaration of war! It was hailed as the "discovery of the century" and the theory that the universe had been created from the Big Bang was now "confirmed". It was even called the "Holy Grail" of scientific exploration. In this authoritative way the subject was presented to the public.

The scientific basis for such a sweeping claim was a little less reassuring. The Big Bang theory had been under increasing pressure from scientists for many years (Nar). Indeed, an earlier TV programme had set out some of the contradicting evidence and the views of some dissenting experts. It was being seriously questioned whether the theory was correct, particularly in view of the uniformity of the background radiation. However, many very important names in the scientific world had been in the forefront of propagating this theory, and the thought that it might be publicly criticised appears to have galvanised considerable activity. If the Big Bang theory were to be discredited, there was no other viable theory ready to take its place, and defenders of the theory were desperate to discover some variations in the radiation.

To get beyond the interference on earth, the COBE (Cosmic Background Explorer) satellite was launched to search for these "ripples". The raw results, however, did not immediately show any variations, so the information was subjected to a complex computer programme that removed the "noise" and should leave only the signal from space. It was only after being subjected to this procedure that these faint ripples were obtained. This news was then spread like wildfire around the globe, even before the full scientific details had been published in a professional journal where it could be criticised by other experts. When this happens, one can be fairly certain that the public are being subjected to pre-emptive propaganda.

Just how big were these ripples? The precise temperature measured is 2.735 Kelvin. The variations from this value were a mere *thirty millionths of a degree!* This is an incredibly small variation and could be explained by other causes. In fact it is just about the limiting accuracy of the recording instruments.

These small variations could easily be due to the presence of intergalactic dust of which there are varying amounts. This could affect how much radiation is received from any particular area, giving the appearance of ripples in the amounts received.

Another explanation could be that it is an inbuilt feature of the programme used to reassess the results; i.e. the variations are only a product of the computer programme. The procedure relies on subjecting the data to many variations to try and discover if there is a basic underlying pattern in the data received.

That the production of these results is simply due to such a procedure is quite possible. Only the year before, there had been another blaze of publicity given to the discovery of a planet said to be circling a star. This was a discovery that has been eagerly awaited for many years. Such high hopes were later dashed, for it was admitted that the existence of the "planet" was due to a fault in the programme used to analyse the results. The programme used to remove the "clutter" from the signal could have itself produced spurious minute variations of temperature.

To return to the COBE results, there are many variations that could arise, and one creationist referred to some 40 such instrumental factors. When some of these had been roughly estimated, the resulting confidence level fell to only 11% (Q30/4:217).

These minute variations in the radiation are claimed to be just large enough to allow the theoreticians to explain the condensing of the expanding matter into stars and galaxies, etc. However, some say that they are not sufficient. With such a huge burst of publicity for the so-called "discovery" of the variations, one has the impression that the whole problem is now solved; this is far from the truth. In the same issue of *Nature*, one commentator, under the heading "Big Bang Brouhaha", advised "caution in accepting the data" (Nat92). A few pages further on, Silk gave a review of the results that strongly suggested that the evidence was epoch-making. Yet, having noted that there are several theories "lurking in the wings", he says at the end of the article:

> So far there is no self-consistent set of initial conditions that matches the observed Universe both on large and small scales (Sil).

One must question what is happening if "initial condition" theories do not match observations. Surely theories should *start* from observations, not the other way round. Perhaps scientists have taken a wrong turning in that there was no Big Bang "initial condition" to start with.

The real cause of the radiation - heating the dust

If the BB did not occur, what could have caused the radiation observed? That it is the "echo" of the BB has been shown to be unsustainable without using an artificial and unrealistic model of the universe (Akr81). There is a most obvious and convincing explanation. The stars are continually radiating energy, and this is absorbed by interstellar gas and dust which re-radiates it at a very low temperature. Using reasonable assumptions, calculations show that our galaxy would have warmed the gas and dust to the observed temperature within about 6,800 years if the starting temperature was zero Kelvin. We refer to this again in Section 4 - "The age of the earth and the universe".

Cosmologists agree that this is a possible explanation, but to accept it would ruin their present theories and they would be left with no means of forming stars and galaxies.

With all the objections given above there is yet another factor, for which there is no evidence, that is needed by modern cosmologists. In order to explain many astronomical observations, there has to exist an enormous amount of what is called "cold, dark matter" - CDM.

Cold dark matter (or "missing mass")

CDM is a very mysterious material. Being cold, it does not radiate heat and therefore cannot be detected even with very sensitive heat detectors. Because it is dark, it cannot be seen. Finding it, therefore, is somewhat of a problem - to put it mildly.

Even though it has never been detected, it is badly needed by cosmologists in order to explain several phenomena they find when they look at the surrounding universe. They need it to be part of the process of condensation of the Big Bang's expanding matter to stars, etc. Also, there are stars and galaxies that should be separated by vast distances, and yet are much nearer to each other and more stable than can be accounted for. To give the impression to the public that they have an explanation for everything they can see, the experts have had to assume that there is a massive amount of this invisible material that attracts the stars and galaxies and keeps them together.

This "cold dark matter" is spoken about with such certainty that one is led to assume that it really exists - all they have to do is to find it!

The most surprising (dare I say, amusing?) aspect of this whole saga is that the quantity of CDM required by the astronomers to give the results they require is no less than ten times as much as all the material in the known universe! That they have had to postulate the existence of so much matter and yet have never been able to show that it even exists strongly suggests that their fundamental ideas of how this universe operates have taken a very wrong turning at some stage in the past.

Bouw examined 14 different explanations for this problem, but all were badly flawed (Q14/2:108). In view of this, it might be suggested that they admit their errors and accept that the universe is as they find it because God made it that way. This is unlikely to come to pass as there are too many reputations riding on the crest of this particular wave and all the many "benefits" - such as high salary and prestige - that flow from it.

6. SETI - (Search for Extraterrestrial Intelligence or Life)

There has been a considerable investment of time and money in looking for evidence of life other than on the earth. Many years ago there was high expectation that life had existed on Mars simply because straight lines had been seen on its surface and interpreted as "canals"! Millions have been spent in sending satellites to other planets to see if there is any form of life existing on them. None has ever been found.

In late 1996 there was much media attention to the meteorite that was supposed to have come from Mars containing traces of primitive life. This is so speculative that we will not waste time or space upon it. That the rock was found several years ago but the announcement was only made when NASA badly needed additional funding has not gone unnoticed by commentators.

In what might be seen as an act of desperation, a search for life on planets that circle other stars is being made. The argument used is that there are many billions of stars in the known universe and of these a small percentage must (?) have planets going round them. Of these a small percentage "must" have a planet at the right distance to support life. Of these a small percentage "must" have the right constituents for life to form. As the number of stars we started with are many billions, there "must" be perhaps several thousand planets on which life could have evolved and therefore there is a high probability of life on another planet.

The weakness of this argument is obvious; by making the percentages sufficiently small, it can equally be "proven" that there is *no* possibility of life existing elsewhere. The percentages are pure guesswork and no scientist who values his reputation should stoop to such arguments.

There are two methods being used to find extraterrestrial life. The first is to detect some form of message being transmitted to us by other living creatures. The skies are searched for a regular pattern of signals that could only be from an intelligent being. None have been found.

The second is to find a planet orbiting a star that might be able to support life. This is done by finding a star that "wobbles" very slightly due to the motion of the planet around it and this is very difficult to detect. In a TV *Horizon* programme (11.3.96) on the subject, only three stars had shown this - 51 Peg(asus), 47 Ursa Majoris and 70 Virginis. Only the latter appears to have its planet at the right distance that would allow water to be in its liquid form. Too close would boil it off; too far and it would freeze. However, water has never been found outside this earth apart from trace amounts.

We would mention that even these three stars may be a product of the method used. The six-monthly wobble of one pulsar star was found to be due to the movement of the earth around the sun that had not been allowed for. The very minute movement of these three stars could be due to an unknown factor affecting the results. Of course, even very thin evidence that a planet *might* exist is given much publicity, and the "instant pundits" will be wheeled on to the TV programmes to pronounce that it *might* have other living beings upon it.

On the *Horizon* programme, a NASA administrator spoke hopefully of our great-grandchildren knowing that there were other beings, but it was all wishful thinking. One could not help feeling saddened that these people should waste their lives looking for something that is not there. In all of 35 years of searching, no evidence of other life has been found. The American Congress stopped funding SETI in 1993.

It is an interesting self-contradiction that the materialist scientists ignore the evidence for design, order and intelligence that surrounds them on this earth, claiming it is due to chance; yet they are seeking the slightest regularity of patterns in signals from outer space to state that there is extraterrestrial intelligent life "out there".

We have made the categoric statement that there is no other life in the universe for three reasons:

The first is that there is little probability of a planet circling a star at just the right distance and with all the elements suitable for the generation of life. We will be discussing in a later section the very critical position this earth is relative to its distance from the sun. We are also the only one of the planets with such an abundant supply of the necessary elements. The chances of this happening elsewhere are extremely remote - even given the huge number of stars there are. Few stars (if any) have planets around them and the majority are unsuitable due to their high emissions of lethal x-rays.

The second is the very great hurdle that has never been overcome by atheists (materialists, humanists) even for this planet, which is that life could not have formed from simple chemicals. We have shown in another book the immense improbability of even a small protein being derived from the various amino acids by chance, and that Richard Dawkins's so-called "computer proof" has a major flaw deliberately built into its programme to achieve the rapid results he wanted (Bow91:107).

The third reason is theological.

The crucial theological aspects

Firstly, there is no indication in the Bible that God has created any other living beings into which He then "breathed" His spirit. We are unique in that we have a relationship to God Himself.

Secondly, if there is life on another planet that is comparable to humans in its complexity and refined sensitivity, then there is the possibility of sin entering in. This would raise the question of God's purpose in creating life. Would He make many centres of life, and are we the only one that rebelled against Him?

To answer this, we would point out that it was sufficient for Him to have only *one* representative for all mankind - Adam. He was tempted into rebellion and brought about the Fall of man, and we have all followed after our earthly father. Would Christ have to go to the Cross on every planet that had human-like life forms for their salvation? Such a suggestion is patently ridiculous.

In a similar way, God has created this *one* earth on which he is playing out His "Great Drama of the Universe". He has no need to make more than one "experiment"; He has this one under full control, and it is all going according to His perfect plan.

It is for these reasons that the search for extraterrestrial life is so unproductive, and those who work upon such programmes will one day realise what a futile waste they have made of the one and only life God has given them.

SECTION 2.3
WERE THE PLANETS ALIGNED
AT CREATION?

There has been some interesting data forthcoming from computer calculations of the position of the planets in past ages. Computers have been
programmed with the information of their present positions, orbits and speed,
and then the "clock" is run backwards to see where they were in earlier years.
Of course, much depends upon the accuracy of the data fed into the computer,
for it requires only a small error of the speed, or an assumption that present
speeds and orbits have been maintained over vast periods of time, for the
relative positions of the planets to become increasingly inaccurate as the time
is taken further back. The greater the period of time, the greater the effect any
small error will have, making the results useless and misleading.

In 1980, Gene Faulstich, an American student of Biblical chronology, wrote
to Owen Gingrich, Professor of Astronomy at the Center for Astrophysics,
Harvard University Observatory, asking:

> I am looking to employ an able astronomer to calculate as near as
> can be, the time of the conjunction of the new moon over Jerusalem
> (which according to my calculations occurred on the first day of
> Spring), in the year 4001 BC. I would also like to know if there
> were any unusual planet arrangements at the time. Can you possibly
> put me in touch with someone?

Faulstich centred on the vernal equinox because in the Talmud Joshua is
quoted as saying, "In Nisan the world was created" (Rosh Hashana 10B). He
places the vernal equinox on March 21st Tuesday at 6pm. This was the
beginning of Day 4 of creation - using the Jewish start to their day in the
evening.

Gingrich replied as follows:

> It is, of course, difficult to calculate accurate planetary positions as
> early as 4,000 BC because there are no observations to control
> accuracy; nevertheless, it is easy to get them within a degree from a
> straightforward computer programme we have here. According to
> these calculations for the year 4,001 BC, the conjunction of the
> moon and sun did not occur until the third day after the vernal
> equinox, and of course the first visibility of the crescent would be a
> couple of days later than that. I find the following rough geocentric
> longitudes:
> Sun 2°
> Moon 355°
> Saturn 85°
> Jupiter 28°
> Mars 344°
> Venus 343°
> Mercury 344°
>
> Sincerely Yours,
> Owen Gingrich (Faul81)

This alignment of three planets and the moon with the earth is most
surprising. To check this information I asked the Royal Greenwich Observatory for their views and they agreed that Gingrich's figures were "probably
about right", but added:

> If you consider heliocentric co-ordinates then there does seem to be

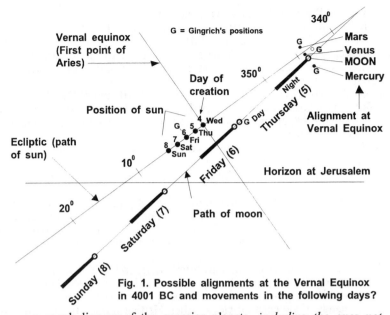

Fig. 1. Possible alignments at the Vernal Equinox in 4001 BC and movements in the following days?

a rough line-up of the superior planets, *including the ones not known to the ancients.* I find it difficult to see the significance of any such alignment with what I assume you are taking as the Creation. If it is to be regarded as significant in terms of the Creation then surely the alignment would have to be "perfect" or of no significance whatsoever.

We have referred to the problem of the "error in an assessment for a year that far back in time", whilst Gingrich notes that his was "within a degree" of accuracy. Is it not possible that the planets *were* in line and that it is the inaccuracy of the computer programme that places them slightly out of line?

Regarding the precise positions of the planets, days of creation and dates, etc., this is not always clear from Faulstich's descriptions and three significantly different situations were obtained from publications he has issued. On checking his latest series of alignments with Gingrich's co-ordinates it was found that they differed considerably and there were internal inconsistencies within his articles in dealing with the movements of the planets, moon and sun, etc. It was therefore decided to ignore Faulstich's sequences, to start with Gingrich's values and see what the situation was about that time.

Using the vernal equinox as a reference point, Gingrich's angles were scaled from it. These are shown with a small G in Fig. 1.

Relative to a line to the vernal equinox, each 24 hours the moon moves 12.2°, the sun moves 1°, Venus moves 0.55° and Mercury and Mars remain virtually stationary. It was noticed that if the moon was taken back 12.2° (one day) further, then it would be almost in alignment with Mars, Mercury and Venus. As the positions of these bodies were only accurate "to within a degree", then it was possible that when they were created, they *were* in line.

We have therefore constructed Fig. 1 to show the possible relative positions of these bodies at the time of creation on the fourth day (which we will assume to be Wednesday) and subsequent days.

Although Gingrich said that the moon was at 355° at the vernal equinox, this may have been at the end of that day. Taking the moon back 12.2° from 356° places it in alignment with the planets. Thus, allowing for astronomical inaccuracies, we would suggest that a possible sequence of events is as follows.

Day 4 - Wednesday evening (Thursday begins) At the end of Day 4 - at 6 pm (our time - dusk) the new Jewish Day 5 began. Moon, Mars, Mercury, Venus and Earth all created in perfect alignment. Sun created in line with the vernal equinox.

Day 5 - (Friday begins) - Moon moves 12.2°. Venus begins to move away from Mars and Mercury.

Day 6 - (Saturday begins) - Moon moves further 12.2°. Adam and Eve created.

Day 7 - (Sunday begins) - Moon now sufficiently past the sun to begin to show a thin crescent of light of the new moon. This signalled to Adam the beginning of the week and the sun and moon would be used as an astronomical clock "for signs, and for seasons, and for days, and years" (Gen. 1:14).

This is surely a surprising alignment and suggests that this may well have signified the date of creation. Although Jupiter was not involved, God appears to have positioned several planets in a special alignment visible from earth like the "hands of the celestial clock" when He first formed them. From this point onwards they would start to move as they ticked out the "signs, seasons, days and years."

Bouw's alignments

Faulstich's claim has been examined by Gerardus Bouw (Bou93A) but he did not criticise the basic data. Bouw pointed out that Jewish scholars say that the date of creation was the first day of autumn not the first day of spring of that year. This would have been on the 21st October at 7.00 am He therefore investigated the positions of the planets around that time and found some other alignments.

Somewhat surprisingly he does not refer to the date of 21 October as having any significant alignments but found two separate alignments of planets two weeks earlier. However, they could only have been seen when looking down on the orbits of the planets and the earth was not included in either of the two lines. There would therefore have been no spectacular alignments visible from the earth at that time.

FAULSTICH'S DATING METHOD

The reference to the work of Faulstich raises a most interesting proposition that initially seemed to hold great promise of obtaining an accurate dating method that could cover the whole of the Biblical chronology.

The Jewish method of dating their year was by means of an *observed* calendar. (We, by contrast, use a *calculated* calendar.) The Jews started the year when the first thin crescent of the new moon appeared after the time when the green ears of barley had matured in the spring (Deut. 16:9). If the new moon appeared before that time, then an additional month was added, and the next new moon was taken as the start of the new year. The months were alternately 29 and 30 days long as the period of the moon from one new moon to the next is 29.53 days. Using this method, the year was always adjusted to the seasons, the extra days being added automatically to keep them in step. (Our calendar has an extra day added each leap year to keep the year in step with the seasons.)

Faulstich used a computer programme in which were entered the known periods of the planets, moon and sun. It then printed out the number of all the days, when there was a new moon, the day of the week, the year, etc., going back to 10,000 BC and up to 3,000 AD. This gave a framework from which all other dates, days of the week and starts of Jewish New Years could be determined.

The periods used were the 24-hour day, the seven-day week, the 29.530587 lunar month and the 365.242199-day apparent year. All these figures are not multiples of each other and only coincide once every 2,395 years. Thus, if two of these values are known, the possible dates they could apply to would be widely spaced and easily pin-pointed. It is rather like two clocks running at slightly different rates, one correct and one slightly faster - say, gaining one minute each day. Knowing what they each say it should be possible to know what the day is by the difference between them as this will increase slowly each day.

(Whilst on this subject, it has been noted that with the different periods of the lunar month and the year, these almost coincide every 606 months. With thirteen intercalated months in that period to keep the year in step with the seasons, this means they will virtually coincide every 49 years. It has been suggested (Q19/1:72) that this is the basis for the Jewish Year of Jubilee - Seven Sabbaths of years (Lev. 25:8). However, having said that, there is considerable dispute between Jewish scholars, even today, on whether the Jubilee took place every 49 or 50 years.)

From the basic data given above, Faulstich constructed a chronology of events in the Bible. He used certain events that occurred on, say, the Sabbath that was also a particular date in the Jewish calendar. He claimed that this gave him many "spot points" in his chronology which he could then fill in and provide a complete chronology covering every day in the history of the Jews.

Unfortunately, a number of statements and assumptions in his writings were unacceptable to this author, and efforts to clarify these in correspondence failed to result in satisfactory replies. What looked as if it might be an interesting method of dating could not be adequately supported.

SECTION 2.4
THE CREATION OF EVE FROM ADAM'S RIB

In Genesis 2:21-23 we have the account of how God made Eve from Adam's rib. This is certainly one of the more difficult passages for some Christians to accept, and it is hoped that what follows will give them a clearer and more acceptable understanding of what probably took place in this miraculous event.

In the late 1970's I met Dr Wilder-Smith when he gave me a fascinating account of how God could have easily created Eve from Adam's rib. He had briefly referred to it in his book *Basis for a New Biology* (Wild76:207) and there was a more detailed account by Koontz in the CRSQ (Koo).

When God created Eve, we read that he caused a "deep sleep to fall on Adam" (Gen. 2:21). This was no ordinary sleep, but one that God made very "deep" during His "operation". To create Eve He took one of Adam's ribs and closed the flesh over its place. Why did He use a rib?

In the body, the numerous cells have a wide range of functions, and are specially designed for their role. For example, nerve cells have to carry information over long distances and interact with many other nerves. They therefore develop a very long thin structure with many branches that connect through synapses with other nerves. Similarly, blood cells not only lose their nucleus but are shaped to give a large surface area to allow the oxygen to enter and be released quickly. Glandular tissue has several sets of chromosomes due to repeated chromosome reproduction. Many other examples could be given as all cells are highly specialised in their design for their particular function.

Every cell has the same information in its DNA, but in those that have a very specialised function, much of this information is "switched off" and not used, allowing the others still active to control the development of the cell.

Of all the many cells in the body, the bone marrow cells in the ribs are amongst the most undifferentiated. This means that God would have to do less work in "switching on" unused sections of the DNA chromosomal chains than for a specialised one.

There are 46 chromosomes in the human cell arranged in 22 pairs. Both members of each pair are the same shape except the sex cells. In these, the male has an X and a Y chromosome whilst the female has two X chromosomes. If the male Y chromosome is suppressed, then the X has only to be duplicated and we then have two X chromosomes - the identical female equivalent of Adam.

Most readers will be familiar with the recent development of "cloning" a variety of plant or animal. For example, they have cloned rubber plants so that they all grow to an identical height, position of branches and leaves, quality and quantity of rubber, etc. With identical trees, the tapping of the rubber can be carried out by machines.

The method is to remove the nucleus of a cell that has been fertilised and replace it with another nucleus of the desired type. This can be repeated in other cells using the nuclei from a stock set of cells from one plant or animal. The resulting offspring will all be identical in the same way as identical twins and triplets, etc.

Without being disrespectful, it could be said that, in a not dissimilar fashion, Eve was a perfect reproduction, or "clone", of Adam, but the female "version" of him!

One question occasionally asked is why a man has nipples when he has no use for them. The answer is that forming of the sexual organs is identical in both sexes for a long period of the development of the human foetus, and it is only in the late stages that they differentiate into the very specific organs of the two sexes. By that time the nipples have appeared in the male foetus but are not developed further.

By taking a part of Adam and using it to form Eve, Adam was presented with a wife who was a perfect match for him. This would give added significance to Adam's joyous exclamation;

This is now bone of my bones and flesh of my flesh. She shall be called Woman because she was taken out of Man (Gen. 2:23).

In this exultation, he used a play on the words for man ('ish) and woman ('isha) that indicates their oneness. The play on words may have been by Moses - unless Adam spoke Hebrew! However, many languages have similar-sounding names for man and WO-man.

Gender roles

In this creation of Adam first and the forming of Eve from part of him, we see the order of responsibility that God had set out for the family and the organising of society. The strongly patriarchal hierarchy in the Jewish society of the Old Testament is but a continuation of this God-ordained order. We also see it continued in the New Testament. Here, it is not so much with modifications but more corrections from the excesses of traditions allowed by the OT Jewish religious leaders. Such a patriarchal society is anathema to today's "politically correct" agitators, who seek to not just equalise but reverse this order to achieve a social organisation that completely contradicts God's provision.

There is strong pressure to reverse these roles to correct the "imbalance" that is claimed to exist in today's society. Boys are trained to take lessons in cooking whilst girls are taught handiwork, carpentry, etc. All this is against the natural inclinations of the vast majority of children and as it is against the instincts implanted in them by God, such efforts must eventually fail.

This subject is very clearly set out in an interesting article by Powell (Pow). She gives the results of research by a number of secular workers, some of whom adopt the feminist approach but have to admit their puzzlement with what they discovered. We summarise some of the points she reports.

(i) Boys have a natural tendency towards aggressiveness, visual-spacial and mathematical abilities and are better at the manipulation of objects. They prefer activities like riding and climbing and are "chauvinistic" in seeking to establish their masculine identities. Males have a better organisational ability, a greater tendency towards competition and dominance and to seek authority, status and a position of recognised achievement. This enables them to obtain high positions, even in countries which have a policy of "equality" such as Russia, China and Israel.

(ii) Girls are better at auditory skills, and have a greater sensitivity to taste, smell, temperature, touch, social stimuli, etc. and tend to fantasise. Women are unhappy with competition and the adversarial approach to solving problems. They are reluctant to assume leadership which is why the feminist movement is often troubled by positions of authority due to "women's reluctance to vest power in the hands of women." Career women tended to deal with social, family and personal issues in their profession.

(iii) "men who fail will give the excuse, 'Success is not worth the effort', while for women it appears to be more of a 'self-evident truth'."

(iv) The main role that men are suited for is as provider/protector to their family unit, whilst for the female it is as the "caretaker". The women in the Israeli "kibbutzim" gradually reverted to their natural roles even though pay was not an issue and the leaders were intent on eliminating gender differences. Equality of pay in Australia resulted in lower employment of women due to employers finding that men were more dedicated to their careers and achieving success. The most significant contribution to criminality is the absence of a father.

All this evidence, collected at considerable cost to the public purse, only presents truths that are so very obvious to all sensible people, particularly if they are parents. The fundamentally different sexual characteristics of children are so deep-seated that it requires considerable effort and dedication to make any modest change. The unrelenting propaganda from powerful pressure groups does have some effect, but left alone, most children will revert to their natural instincts and become the moderately competent parents of the next generation. Some, however, will have been so badly affected that when they become parents, it will result in yet another generation who will be inadequate parents in their turn.

Regarding this pressure to "equalise" (!) the sexes, a letter in the Daily Telegraph (14.1.97) told of a professional career women who was;

> determined that her young daughter should not be gender-prejudiced [what a delightful word!] by buying her dolls and bought her cars and lorries instead. One day she discovered the girl wrapping them up in pieces of cloth and chatting fondly to them while tucking them up in her cot.

There are many successful women who are dedicated to a career, and there are obvious overlaps where some men are less ambitious than some women. This does not alter the fact that *generally* the natural instincts that are present in the vast majority of men and women around the world are as set out above.

We will not go any further into what might be for some a most contentious subject, but simply say that the reason for this attack upon the family and distortion of the "gender roles" is fundamentally an attack upon yet one more of God's many directives that He has provided for the benefit of mankind.

No Christian would want to see women "chained to the kitchen sink" but would want to see them take their rightful role in society. Christianity has placed women on a higher level of social standing than any other faith - even those nations that have aimed at "equality". Who has not seen pictures of Russian women shovelling concrete on a freezing building-site and not felt that they were demeaned and little different from being slaves of an inhuman system?

In contrast, this writer has always had a very high regard for the Dutch people, and it is a fact that they have a higher percentage of evangelical Christians than most other nations. Not unconnected with this, a far higher proportion of their women are happy to be "homemakers".

Only when both men and women undertake their God-given role will the majority of them have that deep sense of fulfilment that is God-ordained.

What the relationship should be between a man and woman, particularly within a family, is beautifully described by Matthew Henry in his well-known exegesis of this passage describing Eve's creation in Gen.2:21-23, when he says:

> The woman was made of a rib out of the side of Adam: not made out of his head to rule over him, nor out of his feet to be trampled

upon by him, but out of his side to be equal with him, under his arm to be protected, and near his heart to be beloved.

In modern ears this will sound patronising, but it simply encapsulates the God-ordained relationship that is emphasised throughout the whole Bible. What woman does not look for some degree of protection from the rigours of the world? What man does not want to fulfil his role of sharing his life with a loving partner and providing for the whole family?

Having said that, I can see the faggots being stacked in preparation.....

SECTION 3.1
THE WATER VAPOUR CANOPY THEORY
AND THE AGE OF THE PATRIARCHS

In Gen. 1:6-7 we read, "Then God said, 'Let there be a firmament in the midst of the waters and let it divide the waters from the waters.' Thus God made the firmament, and divided the waters which were under the firmament from the waters which were above the firmament; and it was so."

What happened at this point?

The Water Vapour Canopy and its possible effects

A theory of water above the earth was first suggested by Isaac Vail in 1874 (Q12/1:52). The canopy idea was taken up in American creationist circles and several CRSQ articles were written on the subject. Whitcomb and Morris set this out in *The Genesis Flood* (Whitc69), and Dillow's *The Waters Above* (Dill) deals with the Water Vapour Canopy (WVC) in some depth.

The usual interpretation is that this water vapour layer was, by divine fiat, lifted up over the present air level that we have today, thereby increasing the pressure at sea level. It is suggested that the canopy was effective in preventing the harmful cosmic radiation from penetrating to the earth's surface where it would damage all living tissues in some degree, depending upon its strength. The canopy would also have created a very uniform climate around the world, giving lush vegetation even in polar areas, which would account for the presence of coal at the South Pole and in land near the North Pole. (That it may have moved there with moving land masses - plate tectonics - is an alternative explanation.)

The ages of the patriarchs

In Genesis chapters 5 and 11, the Bible gives an account of how long all the patriarchs lived, from Adam to Abraham, and how old they were when they had their son who was to carry on the inheritance. All these repetitions of ages and births may seem a little boring and for many they represent only a Jewish myth; a myth, they would claim, perpetuated by a small religious race simply to give importance to their ancestry by exaggerating the age to which their forefathers lived. However, for those who believe that the Bible is an accurate record of history, the ages form the basis of Biblical chronology which gives the time scale of the Bible and man's progress on this earth.

Archbishop Ussher

It should be noted that the Bible is very careful to give the age of the patriarch at the time of the birth of the son who would continue in his inheritance. This is surely evidence that God expected the reader to work out from this how many years had elapsed since the dawn of creation. Archbishop Ussher's date of 4004 BC is remarkably close to the conclusions of many other more recent scholars who base their calculations on the Massoretic text of the Old Testament. This subject is discussed in Section 3.9 where the chronology of the Bible is examined.

One of the most striking charts to come from the Bible is the plotting of the life span of each of the patriarchs as shown in Fig. 1. In this, the patriarchs are simply placed in their order and their age plotted. It becomes immediately apparent that something drastic must have happened during the life of Noah. Up to his time, almost all the ages are just under 1,000 years, but subsequently all the life spans of his descendants decrease along a falling curve to the

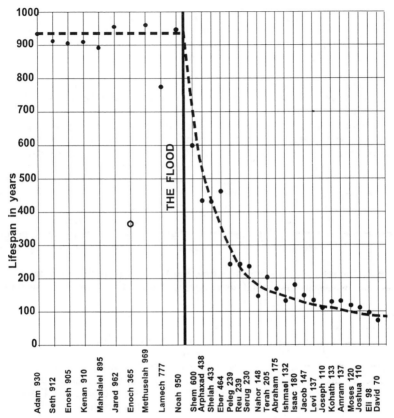

Fig. 1. The life-spans of the Patriarchs

present life expectancy of about 70 years.

The most obvious incident is of course the Flood, which involved vast changes of the earth's form and climatic conditions. But what factors were there that could have actually shortened the life expectancy in such a drastic fashion?

At the time of Noah's Flood, this canopy descended as torrential rain providing some of the flood water, although most of this would have come from the earth's interior - "the fountains of the deep". With the canopy removed, it is considered that the cosmic radiation was now free to reach the earth and as a result the general life expectancy began to decrease.

When a population is exposed to radioactivity, it can damage the cells of all organisms. Cells are at their most vulnerable when they are dividing and the chromosomes become visible just before they divide. It is for this reason that pregnant women and young children should not be subjected to X-rays, due to the many rapidly developing cells they have. As an indication of the damaging effects that X-rays can have, radiologists have a life expectancy of 60.5 years. against the average of 65.7 years for doctors not exposed to these rays

(Dill82:166 and Q15.1:29). Another example is that several researches have shown that Downe's syndrome children are born to older women, not because they have "tired eggs", but because they have been subjected to a higher number of X-rays over a longer period of time than average (Men).

It should be explained that X-rays are part of the electromagnetic spectrum which includes light and radio waves, etc. Their relationship is set out in Fig. 2.2.1.

In addition to damaging cells, radiation can alter genetic information in the chromosomes. These create harmful mutations and render the organism less fit to operate in the world. This genetic damage can be transferred to following generations, rendering them all less fit and prone to disease, and this "genetic load" gradually increases over the generations. It is for this reason that marriages between closely related people, such as brothers and sisters, etc. is forbidden in society. Any offspring from such a union would be likely to have a "double dose" of the same damaged genetic material and be that much less fit by deformity, mental retardation, etc.

There is a sharp drop to the time of Arphaxad, then another at the time of Peleg "when the earth was divided". This phrase may refer to language differences but physical changes that might affect life-spans could be the dividing of the continents and the impact of an asteroid. This is a matter of ongoing debate.

It can be seen that in Abraham's time it was still permissible to marry a near relative as he married his half-sister Sarah. She was the daughter of his father but not the daughter of his mother (Gen. 20:12).

Cain's wife!

This, of course, deals with the "old chestnut" problem thrown at Bible believers - "Where did Cain get his wife from?" The answer is obvious; he married one of his sisters. They were still both genetically "pure" and there would be no problems of inherited defects arising with their children. It is only when damaged genetic material began to increase after the Flood that such marriages were eventually forbidden in all tribes and specifically by Moses in Leviticus 18:6f.

This theory of the collapse of the Water Vapour Canopy resulting in the sudden decrease in the average life-span of man is very plausible and would explain a number of events that appear in the Genesis account. We will consider some of the problems that the theory has and the suggested solutions to them but will first examine some of the many effects that the presence of the canopy and its later removal would have had.

1. WHERE WAS THE CANOPY?

There is the question of what the "firmament" is that Genesis 1:7 refers to, for it says that the waters were divided above and below it. In this context the "firmament" would be the air surrounding the earth, with the WVC sitting on top of it. This is supported by 1:20 in which we find the birds are to "fly across the face of the firmament of the heavens".

But in 1:14 we find the sun and moon are also "*in* the firmament of heaven". This suggests the firmament is the whole of the universe and to contradict the interpretation that it was only the air above the earth.

However, if this assumption is made, the problem then becomes even more difficult, for it would mean that the upper layer of the divided waters was outside the furthest galaxy. This water could not have then descended as rain from "the floodgates of heaven" and some other source for the rain would have to be proposed. This interpretation of Scripture is surely untenable.

The most straightforward understanding is that the word "firmament" is used for both the local atmosphere of the earth, over which the canopy was positioned, and the whole created universe in which the astronomical bodies were placed. The Hebrew allows both understandings [WillP].

2. THE CANOPY IN FOLK TALES

Just as there are many folk stories of the Flood, so are there some accounts of a canopy being formed in the upper atmosphere (Q17/1:65). There are references to "celestial oceans" which provided the rain for the great Flood, and words used for "heaven" sometimes include a word for "water" in its etymology. Dillow gives a number of examples of folk tales in which water from heaven plays a major part in an ensuing Flood

3. THE ELECTROMAGNETIC "WINDOW"

One of the effects of the canopy theory is that the heat from the sun warms up the earth and becomes effectively "trapped" in the atmosphere (the "greenhouse" effect). This would produce a uniform warmth around the earth but preliminary calculations indicate that too much heat would be trapped and the temperature would become too high.

The radiation of the incoming heat rays are concentrated in the 0.2 - 0.9 micron wavelengths but the warm earth re-radiates this energy in the infra-red (8 - 13 microns) wavelengths. What is most remarkable is that it is in just this waveband that *water vapour has a reduced absorption.* Thus there is a "window" in the spectrum that allows some of this excessive heat to escape into space!

Having said this, further investigation indicates that it does not take a very great depth of water vapour to effectively absorb almost all the radiation from the earth (Q29/3:144). Thus the problem may need further examination and it indicates how complex the investigation is. It is nevertheless interesting that the wavelength range emitted by the earth is the very one for which the canopy has the least absorption. This cannot be a coincidence, and this feature must surely have played an important part in stabilising the temperature at earth level in the pre-Flood atmospheric conditions.

The effect of CDK?

A major factor that has never been considered in all these calculations is the difference that the decrease in the speed of light would make. We will see later that this affects what are known as the "transport constants" - viscosity, osmosis, ion and electron movements, etc. The effect that CDK could have upon not just the calculations discussed above but on other problems examined later might be more than adequate to provide a perfectly satisfactory solution.

4. EVIDENCE THAT IT EXISTED

As the canopy does not exist today, it might be thought that the theory behind it is pure speculation with no evidence in its support. Dillow proposes ten "predictions" (Dill82:138) as evidence of its former existence which he examines in some detail. A number can be explained satisfactorily by geologists and others, but as he points out, this one assumption provides an explanation to a large number of surprising facts that cover a very wide range of different subjects.

He makes the interesting suggestion that "the efficiency of any theory is equal to the number of facts correlated divided by the number of assumptions" (p139). i.e. if one assumption correlates many facts it gives the theory a high level of probability. On this basis the Water Vapour Canopy is a reasonable concept, whilst the theory of evolution should be rejected.

We have presented above some of the evidence for its existence such as the "greenhouse effect", longevity of the patriarchs, etc. but we will mention two facts that indicate its former presence.

(a) The high level of Helium3

The cosmic rays entering the earth's atmosphere not only produce radioactive Carbon14 but, by a series of reactions, the stable isotope Helium3. Professor Korff showed that there was much more Helium3 in the atmosphere than could be accounted for at the present rate of its generation. He therefore suggested there was a time "when the earth was warmer, *the earth contained much more water vapour* and [the process] was operating at a much higher rate than at present" (Kor:105).

Furthermore, in the section on astronomical anomalies, we referred to the cometesimals of water that are striking the earth in surprisingly large numbers. It is possible that these may be a remnant of the canopy. However, they are almost certainly coming from much deeper in space than the limited height that the canopy once occupied.

(b) Meteorite distribution

Meteorites are generally only found in the very top layers of the earth's strata. Dillow contends that this could be explained by all meteorites that fell before the Flood were burnt up during their passage through the greater depth of the present atmosphere plus that of the canopy.

What is particularly interesting is that he says that "none are found in pre-Pleistocene strata" (Dill:189) although he does not quote a reference. Even if the level was slightly earlier than this, it would place the pre-Flood/post-Flood boundary at a very late stage in the geological column. This contradicts some creationists who, on other evidence, place this boundary very much lower in the column - as early as the end of the Carboniferous. We consider this further when examining the subject of geology in Appendix 4.

It has been claimed that meteorites have been found in earlier strata, but the evidence in its support is slim. It can therefore be concluded that Dillow's explanation is probably correct and that furthermore the Flood deposits were laid down rapidly, giving little time for any significant number of meteorite impacts in the strata.

However, having said that, the debris resulting from early meteorites would have probably precipitated the canopy as rain - as we will see later.

5. THE CANOPY AND LIFE SPANS

The plot of the life-spans in Fig. 1 shows that something catastrophic happened to the human race, such that there was a rapid decrease in life expectancy - from just under 1,000 years to today's 70. What could have effected this?

NATURAL SOURCES -		MAN-MADE SOURCES -	
(millirems/year)			
A. External to the body			
Cosmic radiation	50		
From the earth	47		
From building materials	3	Medical (X-rays etc.)	61
		Atomic energy	0.2
B. Inside the body		Luminous watches,	
Inhalation of air	5	TV, Atomic waste	2
Natural in tissues	21	Atomic fallout	4
	----------		----
	126		67.2

TOTAL RADIATION = 193.2 millirems/yr

Fig. 2. The present day radiation hazards

a) Cosmic radiation

The agent usually considered to cause the damage is cosmic radiation which is so harmful to life.

However, Dillow shows that the amount of damaging rays reaching the earth *today* is quite small (Dill:167. Q15/1:27, EB26:509) and Fig. 2 gives the amount of radiation we are all subjected to. Of course, the man-made quantities would not have been present at the time of creation, but even with this removed, the level of natural radiation is not excessive.

Research has indicated that exposure to 1,000 rads in a person's lifetime would shorten his life by 11%. From Fig. 2, the average is only 0.193 x 67 years = 12 rads. Thus, from this analysis at least, there is little support for the influx of cosmic radiation causing the decrease in life spans.

Before dismissing radiation as a prime cause, however, we must remember that conditions at the time of the Flood may have been quite different to those today, and we will consider three possible ways in which radiation may have had an important effect on post-Flood longevity.

(i) Increased radioactivity levels

There may have been a release of radioactivity from the collapse of the canopy, which may have been protecting life up to the time of the Flood. Isotopes generated in the upper atmosphere may have descended with the rain of the Flood and been fairly concentrated for many years before eventually being washed away from the land area. Alternatively, or in addition, radioactive material could have been brought up with the mass of chemicals that formed the rocks we have today. When the speed of light was much higher at the time of the Flood, this would have made a difference to the effect that radioactivity would have had at that time, as we will discuss in Appendix 1. All this could have affected the genetic coding of all living forms.

(ii) C14 within the body

Armstrong (Arm) noticed that the ages *decreased* on a roughly exponential curve at the same time that the generation of Carbon14 was *increasing* at earth level also on an exponential curve (see Fig. 4.1). He therefore suggested that the presence of C14 in the body was one of the causes of the decreasing life spans. The decay of the C14 actually within the body would have made it much more potent in affecting DNA molecules and the many other complex proteins that control the immune system and the body's metabolism. This certainly seems to be a very valid explanation and one that would be well worth further investigation.

(iii) The ozone layer

There is yet another explanation we would put forward that would explain why cosmic radiation could have had a major effect after the Flood.

It should be noted that the values in Fig. 2 only apply today. It is possible that not only might there have been a sudden increase in radioactive elements brought down with the canopy collapse, but conditions after the Flood may have been, indeed surely would have been, quite different from those prevailing at present. It is not necessarily correct to carry out calculations using today's conditions as though they applied immediately after the Flood.

Today, there is a very thin layer of ozone that is most important in protecting us from damaging cosmic rays. The small amount of ozone in the Hartley band around the earth effectively blocks all radiation with wavelengths below 295 nanometres (all radiation above the visible spectrum in Fig. 2.2.1), and the shorter the wavelength, the more damaging effect they have.

The importance of the ozone layer in protecting us from the dangerous cosmic radiation is well (over?) publicised in today's ecologically sensitive mass media. If it is as dangerous as we are led to believe, then the very thin layer of ozone is of vital importance to the continuance of life.

This leads to the thought that when the canopy collapsed, this protective layer may not have been in existence and would only have been built up slowly over the years following the Flood. This means that those generations after the Flood would have been exposed to these dangerous radiations and their life-spans would have decreased significantly as the genetic mutations - called the "genetic load" of mutations - gradually built up in the species. Life-spans would have continued to decrease to the new, low stable level of about 70 years that we have today as the generation of the ozone gave increasing protection.

We would therefore suggest that this might have been a major factor in the decrease in the life-spans of the post-Flood patriarchs.

Radiation in space and the Van Allen Belts

Just how much protection we receive from the earth's magnetic field and the ozone layer may not be fully appreciated.

There are cosmic rays in outer space that are lethal to all forms of life. If subjected to 300 rems (a measure of radioactivity), within a few days 40% of people would die. If the level were 500 rems, 50% would die. We are protected by a combination of the ozone layer, the earth's magnetic field and the Van Allen Belts positioned around the equator. The latter extend from 600 miles to about 16,000 miles above the earth.

All the present manned spacecraft orbit the earth well below this limit at about 200 - 300 miles height. Satellites can go to any height but even their electronic equipment has to be protected from damage by the rays.

A major protection is given by the Van Allen Belts. Although they do protect us from radiation, they are themselves extremely dangerous. The *Encyclopaedia Britannica* (v 14 pp 327-8) notes that the cosmic radiation interacts with the atmosphere to produce protons and electrons that are trapped by the earth's magnetic field. They continuously spiral around the earth going from pole to pole, reversing direction each time. As they last about 10 years, the level has built up until it is 10,000 times more powerful than the short-life cosmic rays that generate them. They can penetrate "several centimetres of lead" and even satellites "must be protected otherwise their electronic equipment would be subject to irreparable damage" (EB).

With such barriers, anyone venturing into and beyond the Van Allen Belts would require very substantial heavy protection from both these lethal rays and the cosmic radiation beyond.

Whether radiation, from whatever source, played a major or minor part in reducing longevity, there are other factors that may have had an equally profound effect which we will now consider.

(b) Conditions in Eden

It will be remembered that in Eden there was not only the tree of knowledge of good and evil. The only reason given for sending Adam and Eve out of Eden was "lest he put out his hand and take also the tree of life and live for ever." (Gen. 3:22-24). This suggests that the fruit contained something that would have given him eternal life. He obviously had to eat it regularly for God removed him from the Garden so that he could not obtain the fruit and, eventually, Adam died.

The process of ageing

There is no clear evidence of what causes ageing, but it appears to be a chemical process. We would here note that with all the millions of years at its disposal, evolution has failed to overcome the problem of death, which would have been a major step in the "survival of the fittest". If a complex cell could develop out of a soup of chemicals, such a step should not have been all that difficult.

One cause of death that has been proposed is the cross linkages occurring between large molecules in the cell. As these linkages increase in number and length, the cell function declines.

Further research has shown that there is a more likely cause connected to the replication of DNA molecules. All our cells continually divide and replace other cells that have died. After many divisions, the cells no longer divide, and eventually die. The reason for this is given in a fascinating paper by Dr Crompton (Crom).

The ends of the DNA in a cell are called the telomeres and they act as a healing and protective end to the DNA.

The chromosomes are in parallel pairs but in reverse order, and when the cell is replicating itself, the replication at one of the ends is difficult. When the cell divides, several of the repeated pattern of the telomeres are lost. When they reach a certain low number, senescence sets in and the cell becomes flatter. When there are fewer still, cell-death (apoptosis) sets in.

If the cells do not die, then they may become a benign tumour, and these can in turn become malignant. Crompton concludes that:

> The tree of life could have been an "ordinary" tree whose fruit simply reset the telomeric clock. In our imperfect world, consumption of such a vitamin would be similar to consumption of a potent carcinogen.

(c) Reduced magnetic field

The earth's magnetic field has steadily decreased from an original high level at the time of creation. This would have had two effects.

(i) High magnetic field effects

The cosmic radiation is deflected by the shape of the earth's magnetic field (Fig. 3). When this was high, little radiation would reach the surface of the earth. As its power decreased, so the level of radiation would rise until a large proportion of the rays could reach earth level. The increase might be quite rapid at a certain critical strength of magnetic field, and this possibility is illustrated in Fig. 4.

The decrease in the magnetic field might have had other, possibly more important effects upon the earth's inhabitants - either directly or having a controlling effect upon other major phenomena.

(ii) The healing action of a magnetic field

Experiments on bone fractures have shown that they heal quicker and bones will grow to close gaps up to 3/8 inch (10mm) when they are subjected to a magnetic field (McLeod). However, these appear to be pulsing magnetic fields which would not apply to the earth's magnetic field which is like a permanent magnet that is slowly decreasing in strength. There may be other benefits as yet undiscovered with such a field if it were adequately strong, but there seems to be little research on this in medicine these days.

(d) The importance of oxygen

The present pressure of the air at sea level is 14.7 pounds per sq. inch (101 kPa) (1 atmosphere = 760 mm of mercury pressure = 1013 millibars). As oxygen forms 21% of the air, then its partial pressure is 0.21 atmospheres. If the total pressure is doubled, then the partial pressure of the oxygen is also doubled to 0.42 atmospheres, which is roughly what it would be under a 40 ft. (12m) depth of water vapour in the canopy. Thus, there would be a much higher pressure of oxygen that could be utilised by the body. High pressures with low concentrations of oxygen have much the same effect as low pressures of pure oxygen. However, experience has shown that not more than 2 atmospheres of the present ratios of oxygen and nitrogen could be tolerated by man. This would be the situation for the 40 ft (12m) of water in the canopy discussed earlier.

Oxygen has an extremely important function in the metabolism of the body.

(i) Oxygen in the blood supply

The amount of oxygen carried by the red corpuscles is unaffected by any increase in oxygen pressure, but the oxygen tension in the plasma is affected. After passing through the lungs its tension has dropped to 45mm of mercury (0.9 lbs/si) which is only 5mm more than the 40mm of oxygen tension within the cells (Q15.1:31). If the oxygen partial pressure was higher in the past, this would have had the effect of forcing much more oxygen into the body, with large beneficial results to health. This may have been a major factor in the increased longevity of the pre-Flood population. We will also show later that CDK may have had a similar effect by reducing viscosity.

(ii) Decrease in ageing and increase in healing in the past

It has long been known that oxygen can reduce ageing, give rapid healing of wounds and combat gangrene. Placing senile people and stroke victims in high pressure (hyperbaric) oxygen can give remarkable improvements. Dillow quotes one authority who has had stroke patients carried into the oxygen chamber who were able to walk out after the first treatment (Q15/1:32)

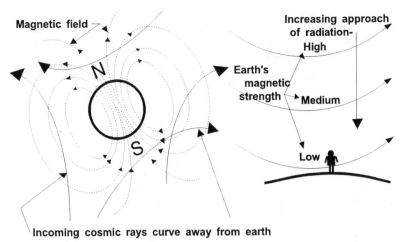

Incoming cosmic rays curve away from earth

Fig. 3. Cosmic ray deflection by the earth's magnetic field

Fig. 4. The approach of radiation

Wounds also heal rapidly. This was discovered when the severe wound of a deep-sea diver under pressurised oxygen was healed in 24 hours. So effective is this treatment for a wide range of illnesses that there are 2,000 chambers in Russia, 800 in China and 30 in the U.K.

There is a growing movement in the American medical profession by qualified doctors who have become disenchanted with orthodox treatments that depend so heavily upon man-made drugs which can have such disastrous "side" effects. A wide range of treatments is now practised by some doctors. Amongst them is the intravenous infusions of very dilute hydrogen peroxide which is an easy and safe way of introducing additional oxygen into the body. The range of illnesses that have been successfully treated is very wide and the method is rapidly gaining in popularity, particularly in America (RefX1). There are a few practitioners in Britain. The ingestion of very dilute amounts of hydrogen peroxide has also been found to be beneficial, particularly with arthritis (RefX2). One other interesting effect is that cancer cannot survive in the presence of oxygen, and one researcher treated cancer in rats simply by adding hydrogen peroxide in their water (Hol). Research on this work was stopped.

All the above only emphasises the important part that oxygen plays in the health of the body. Its reduced pressure after the Flood may have been a major factor, acting with other influences, in reducing life-spans.

We will also be examining another major factor when the subject of the decrease in the speed of light is discussed.

(e) Carbon dioxide

Dillow suggests that carbon dioxide may have been as high as 0.5% and that this could account for increased longevity. Higher pressures of carbon dioxide increase blood supply to the brain and skin. This would have produced more activity in the hypothalamus in the brain that regulates ageing, thus being another possible factor for the long life-spans of the patriarchs. It is likely that the oceans were warmer before the Flood and would not have been able to absorb as much carbon dioxide as today's cooler oceans can. Therefore the pre-Flood atmosphere may have held more carbon dioxide.

He points to the more lush vegetation that used to exist in the recorded past, and the fact that the growth rings on the giant redwood trees are spaced three times the present spacing, indicating a much more rapid growth. He would contend that this was due to the higher level of carbon dioxide. Today, agriculturalists add carbon dioxide to the air in their greenhouses to increase growth.

High levels of carbon dioxide do make breathing more difficult, but in the pre-Flood world, this would have been offset by increase of the partial pressure of the oxygen due to the higher air pressure under the Water Vapour Canopy (Q30/4:197)

Dillow's suggestions may raise more problems than they solve, but it is interesting to see just how many factors might have played a part. It is possible that many of the beneficial conditions due to the existence of the canopy may be the result of more than one factor operating to bring about the events recorded in the Bible.

6. STAR VISIBILITY

If a depth of rain-water of 40 ft (12m) is assumed to be held in the WVC, then there is the question of how much starlight would get through. An analysis of this problem (Q14/3:139) shows that about 255 might be visible on a dark night to Adam, and due to the greater depth of atmosphere that the light had to penetrate, no stars below 8° above the horizon would be visible. Dillow notes that when the canopy collapsed, some 2,500 stars would become visible and the sun's intensity would increase by 23%. In view of this he suggests that this might have given rise to the worship of the sun and stars culminating in the building of the Tower of Babel.

This does at least show that starlight would still have been visible even with a large amount of water in the canopy.

SOME DIFFICULTIES AND POSSIBLE SOLUTIONS

It is obvious that the canopy no longer exists, and therefore any viable model produced must still be speculative. Any such model, even though speculative, is not to be dismissed, for as we have made clear, so long as a reasonable explanation can be provided, then such conditions *may* have existed. There are certain difficulties with the Water Vapour Canopy if it is analysed using present-day conditions and normal scientific methods.

The analysis of atmospheric conditions is extremely complex as witnessed by the numerous formulae that are involved in trying to find a solution even when simplified vertical sections of the pre-Flood canopy conditions are used. There are factors such as absorption and reflection of the sun's rays, re-radiation of absorbed heat to the layers above and below (the air is divided into layers for the computer analysis), increasing pressure with depth affecting the characteristics of the air and water vapour, and mixing, condensation and turbulence can occur. The factors are many and varied and the problem is now examined using computers, but even making many simplifying assumptions, large programmes and many hours of computer time are involved.

We will not examine the subject in great technical detail but discuss some of the main features and problems involved, including reference to certain Bible passages that might otherwise be overlooked.

A) Amount of water in the canopy

The rain fell for 40 days and nights and a rate of 0.5 inch (12mm) per hour is usually assumed, which is a severe torrent. This would give a depth of water of 40 ft (12m) over the earth's surface. This would, of course, be of much greater depth as water vapour in the canopy over the present atmosphere.

There are several problems with this large amount of vapour.

(i) High canopy temperatures

With this amount of water, the pressure would be 2.18 atmospheres (i.e. 2.18 times the present pressure). Dillow used complex computer analyses and produced a viable set of conditions that gave reasonable temperatures at earth level with a higher temperature at the base of the canopy to maintain it in a vapour condition.

Later investigators arrived at results that indicate that only about 2 ft (0.6m) of water could be accommodated without a severe rise in temperature at earth level (Q28.3:122 and 29.3:140). The subject, however, is extremely complex and one investigator admitted that another structure could be conceived that allowed the canopy to hold 40 ft (12m) of precipitable water.

(ii) Energy of the collapse

With a body of water at a very high level above the earth, there is a huge amount of stored potential energy. As the vapour descended as rain, this energy would have to be dissipated in some way. It would be transformed into heat that would raise the temperature of the surrounding air as the droplet's descent was impeded by air friction. The result is that the energy would raise the temperature far too high for life, which is one reason for limiting the depth of water to 2 ft. (0.6m) and not the 40 ft. (12m.) that has been generally used (Q28/3:122).

(iii) Atmospheric expansion

With the reduced load of the canopy, the atmosphere would expand which would cool it. This may have counterbalanced the heat increase discussed above.

(iv) The condensation of the vapour to water would release a large amount of heat into the atmosphere

Dillow adds all these factors for 40 ft of water and finds that the air would reach 2,100°C (p 272) which is far too high.

If 2 ft (0.6m) of water is the largest amount that a canopy could maintain, then only a light rain could have fallen for the requisite 40 days. It could, however, have been concentrated in a fairly restricted area or latitude of the earth to produce the torrent referred to in the Biblical account. This does not accord with the original Hebrew, however, which describes ferocious conditions during the Flood that were much more extreme than the English translations imply (Q17/4:209).

Dillow's suggestion of how this problem could be overcome is that for about a year prior to the date of the Flood, volcanoes had already begun to throw up large amounts of dust which would have cooled the canopy and fine droplets might have formed. When the Flood eventually occurred, much of the heat could have been dumped into the oceans, where their volume would have caused only a small rise in temperature. This is dismissed as "side stepping" and a "weak hypothesis", but what he has done is to offer a solution that God *may* have used to overcome the problem.

It has also been suggested that the "fountains of the deep" may have thrown up huge quantities of water that descended as rain. However, unless well distributed by high winds, the water would probably have descended as almost a solid mass of water rather than rain droplets.

A more scientific solution has been offered by Morton who suggested that the permittivity of the ether was increased sharply at the time of the Flood (Q27/2:60). This would have decreased the speed of light and would also have enabled large amounts of heat as the electrons adjusted themselves to a new position around the nucleus. This would create other problems but he contends that this is the only change that would have allowed the 40 days and nights of rain.

Another factor could have been a huge ingress of ice cometesimals as discussed above. These would have had a considerable effect upon the whole subject of the mechanics of maintaining the canopy and its later collapse.

One aspect that does seem to have been satisfactorily resolved is that of mixing between the canopy and the air below. There would be a temperature inversion at the junction and the canopy could rest in a stable condition over the atmosphere below. Diffusion would also be negligible. Although conditions are quite different, there is a good confirmation of the stability of a canopy in the very pure conditions still existing for 30 miles (50 km) depth below the cloud cover on Venus (Akr79). Dillow also points to the uniformity of the temperature of the cloud cover over the equator and the poles on Venus for which no explanation has yet been found. The atmosphere appears to have some very fast jet streams that maintain this stability (Dill82:283). There is much about meteorological systems that is still little understood.

In these calculations there are several factors usually omitted, mainly because they cannot be allowed for in computer programmes. One such is the significant effect that clouds of mist can have as a reflective layer. This reflects the sun's heat and greatly reduces the heat problems discussed. Another is the possibility of lateral movement of heated layers towards the cooler poles. If these, and other factors, such as the change in permittivity and the cometesimals, are added, it should be possible to produce a viable model of the canopy conditions with far more than 2 ft (0.6m) of water in vapour form.

PETERSON'S ARTICLE

A most interesting article in the CRSQ by E.H. Peterson (Pet) covered a number of events in Genesis.

He points out that Adam and Eve were both naked, and therefore from this the temperature of the air at ground level must have been warm and very stable, probably between 84-94°F (29-34°C). There could have been no high winds that would have caused a "wind chill factor", which reduces a body's temperature to well below the actual still air temperature.

Peterson contends that the reference in Genesis 3:8 to God walking in the garden in the "cool" of the day is a mistranslation of "*ruwach*" which should be rendered "wind" or "breeze". This breeze would occur when the temperature was at its highest and local thermals would be generated and air would be pulled in from the sides thereby creating the breeze. Thus even at the hottest times, there was a cooling wind, giving a continuation of the perfect conditions God had arranged for Adam and Eve.

Adam was instructed to "multiply and fill the earth", which could mean that these ideal conditions existed over the whole earth. This, in turn, suggests that the earth was *not* tilted and therefore there were no large climatic variations of the seasons of the year. That there were differing periods in the year could be seen from the changing of the stellar constellations. That there may have been an original 5° tilt and how and when the earth was tilted further will be discussed in Appendix 5.

The earth was watered by warm streams arising from the earth's interior. There was no rain because of the high pressure generated by the canopy, which gave clear skies.

Peterson notes that there is good evidence that the level of the post-Flood oceans was much lower than at present by some 4-500 ft (120-150m) Possibly relevant to this is the enigmatic passage in Genesis 8:1 where it mentions that "God made a wind to pass over the earth and the waters subsided".

That "God *made* a wind" suggests that it was not a natural wind but a special wind to do a particular work. Peterson proposed that the wind took much of the water from *off* the earth and that the Water Vapour Canopy was replenished, but this is difficult to accept.

Incidentally, we should note that both the "fountains of the deep and the windows of heaven were also stopped, and the rain from heaven was restrained" (Gen 8:2). This suggests that they were not completely emptied. As we shall see, there is still a huge amount of water in the earth's interior, and it is possible that the ice cometesimals may be remnants of the canopy.

Summary

There are many factors that could have been operating in the pre-Flood conditions, and taking these all into consideration it should be possible to eventually produce a viable set of conditions both before, during and after the Flood. Although the theory is treated cautiously by some creationists, we would mention the following few points for further thought:

(a) Without a considerable amount of water in some form in the atmosphere, there is no source for the torrential rain of the Flood. Some have suggested that this could have been provided by volcanoes sending water high into the atmosphere, but this could hardly be classed as "opening the windows of *heaven*".

(b) The presence of the wavelength "window" in the absorption spectrum of water vapour which precisely matches the re-radiation wavelength of heat from the earth suggests that this might have been an important factor in maintaining good conditions at earth level up to the time of the Flood.

(c) To those who doubt the existence of the pre-Flood canopy we would ask:

(i) If there was no Water Vapour Canopy, where did the water go that was raised above the firmament in Genesis 1:6-7?

(ii) Where did the water come from that produced the torrential rain of the Flood? It could not have come from a fountain of water from the earth for the Bible says that it was the windows of *heaven* that were opened.

Although a full scenario cannot be provided, we trust that we have demonstrated that there is some good evidence that supports the theory of a pre-Flood Water Vapour Canopy and that it complies with Scripture.

SECTION 3.2
THE FROZEN MAMMOTHS ENIGMA

Many bones and tusks of woolly mammoths have been found above the Arctic Circle, some in Alaska but mainly in Siberia. There are huge amounts of ivory from their tusks and it has been regularly transported for trading purposes. The most inexplicable feature is that at 49 sites undecayed frozen flesh has been found on carcases ranging from small portions to almost complete mammoths. "Dima" was a complete baby mammoth that had been flattened by pressure, found in an ice lens 6ft (2m) below ground level.

The carcase that has been most fully examined is that from Beresovka in Siberia that had been found protruding from a frozen river bank in 1901. It had been brought to its present location by a landslide of "muck" that had entombed it in a half-sitting posture (Fig. 1). This muck is described as a mixture of sand, gravels and clay, etc., all jumbled into a chaotic mass. Today, the ground defrosts only to a depth of 2 ft (600 mm) in summer.

The slight thaw of the ground in summer had allowed the river to wash away part of the bank which had exposed the carcase. It was thought that it had been visible for about two summers; animals had eaten the back of the body and the face as these were visible and the meat was still fresh enough to be edible. The mammoth was removed from its position and studied carefully. Dillow reports this carcase in his *The Waters Above* (Dill) and in his CRSQ article (v14n1:5-13), but the fullest examination of the whole mammoth problem is by Walt Brown in his *In the Beginning* (BrownW).

The mammoth was found with food in its mouth and 24 pounds (11 kg) of undigested plants in its stomach. It is often reported that it was found with "buttercups in its mouth", but this is not correct. Unchewed bean pods were found in the mouth; the buttercups were found in its stomach, and these were not flowers but seeds.

There are several problems surrounding the death of these mammoths.

Problem 1 - The very sudden death

There were several pointers to the fact that the animal had met a very sudden death:

(i) The bean pods in its mouth were still in their husks unchewed, indicating that it had not had time to swallow its last mouthful.

(ii) The carcase had been very suddenly frozen such that the contents of the stomach had not had time to disintegrate under the corrosive effect of the digestive juices. Many of the plants had very delicate flowers, etc. and these were still preserved despite the fact that the stomach would move mechanically for up to half an hour after death. It was estimated that they would not last more than 2-3 hours, and experiments showed that delicate plants immersed in a mixture of gastric juices became unrecognisable within 5 hours. The effect of gastric juices is reduced as the temperature falls, so in the calculations for the rate of freezing it was conservatively assumed that the contents of the stomach would have to be reduced to 4°C (40°F) within 10 hours.

(iii) When thawed, the meat gave an appearance of freshness, and the dogs were fed on it. Brown could find no evidence that humans had eaten the meat and derided stories that mammoth steaks had been served in restaurants.

There were clear indications that this animal, and several other mammoths at other locations, had died from suffocation.

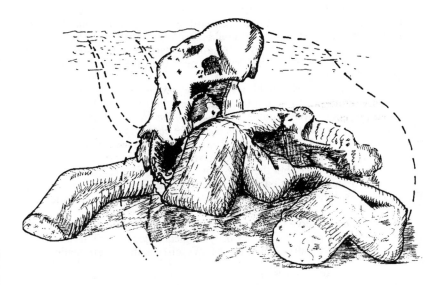

Fig. 1. The Beresovka mammoth

Problem 2 - The warm climate when they died

What is surprising about the 11 species of trees and shrubs and the 50 herbs and grasses found in the stomach is that the majority of them were warm climate plants. For some of the species found, the nearest living counterparts were growing many miles south on the Russian Steppes. Thus, the animal must have been living where it died in a warm climate. Yet, today, in that same location, the temperature for most of the year is well below freezing; about -46°C (-50°F).

In addition, these plants all flower in the summer, so it must have been midsummer when the mammoth died. The hair and skin were the same as those of an African or Indian elephant and lacked the oil-producing gland that would have made the animal less sensitive to cold. There are elephants and, of course, many tropical animals with fur, so this is not indicative of a cold climate. The mammoth, therefore, was not adapted for cold weather despite having a thin woolly fur covering over parts of its body.

Problem 3 - The rate of freezing

It is this investigation that gave the most surprising result. For meat to be preserved, it must be frozen very quickly. If the cells have sufficient time to deteriorate they produce water internally, and when this freezes, the cells are destroyed.

Several calculations were made using complex computer programmes to simulate the rapid rate of freezing that the mammoth would have had to undergo for the contents of the stomach to be preserved against the gastric juices. The standard used was that given above; the stomach temperature had to fall to 4°C (40°F) within 10 hours. It was assumed that the animal was at normal blood heat of 37°C (98.4°F) when it died.

The results of one estimate was that the external temperature must have rapidly dropped to -115°C (-175°F), whilst another gave it as -101°C (-150°F). These are extremely low temperatures not experienced anywhere on the earth today. How could such low temperatures have been produced so rapidly around an animal that had been leisurely eating in the middle of the summer, and killed it before it could swallow the food in its mouth? Furthermore, this was not a brief event, for the average temperature today is still well below freezing and the flesh has been preserved on many carcases over a very large geographical area (Fig. 2).

The "wind chill factor" would have greatly reduced the effective temperature but it is doubtful if it could have produced such very cold conditions as rapidly as the calculations require. There is also the "wind" (Genesis 8:1) that God made to pass over the earth. This may have been a miraculous event as it was specifically "made" by God. It is usually assumed that it was to "asswage" the waters, but this may not have been its purpose; the wind blew and the waters asswaged, but they may not have been connected. This "wind" may have had an important part to play in the post-Flood conditions, but the Bible gives us little information. Creationists might like to consider this further.

We would here observe that despite this great drop in temperature, there is no mention of any glaciers forming or geological evidence of carving of the landscape by great depths of moving ice. We discuss this when dealing with geology.

Problem 4 - The freezing below ground level

There is one aspect that Dillow discusses but does not adequately solve, which is the sequence of events that would result in the present situation.

All his calculations are for the body of the mammoth to be above ground, but it was found frozen just below the original surface of the ground. Let us try to picture the scenario.

The mammoth is standing and is suddenly frozen within a matter of a few hours. It is then buried in a mass of loose muck. But if the mammoth was so quickly frozen, then the surrounding ground would also be quickly frozen solid for at least a moderate depth. The mammoth could not have *then* been buried into it beneath the surface, and frozen muck cannot flow around it and bury it. The muck must have been still plastic.

The reports say that it was buried in a landslide, which indicates that the material was unfrozen at that time. It is difficult to imagine a mammoth frozen by extremely low temperatures yet being inundated by *un*frozen sand and pebbles that must have been near to the animal.

The problem is that the air temperature for a buried mammoth would have to be much lower than the -115°C (-175°F) calculated for a standing mammoth. Dillow examines this but finds that even with a drop to -171°C (-275°F) it would take 11 days to reduce the stomach temperature to 4°C (40°F). He concludes "Mud or ice burial is insufficient" (Dill:395).

Dillow proposed that the muck was covered by water for the period of the Flood, but that the carcase did not defreeze. In order to show this is feasible he assumes that the body was buried under 20 ft of muck (Dill:418). But the Beresovka mammoth was only just below the surface. His sequence would also require these specific areas of mammoth entombment to return to a deeply frozen state after the Flood and remain in this state until today.

The only conclusion is that the carcase was killed by a sudden phenomenal drop in temperature, *and at virtually the same time engulfed in the muck,* the whole mass continuing to freeze rapidly under such a low temperature that the mammoth's stomach was also quickly frozen even though it was below the

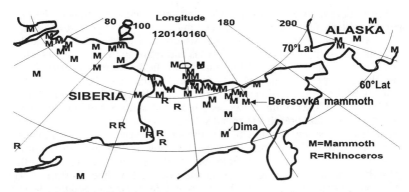

Fig. 2. The sites of frozen mammoths and rhinoceros

surface of the ground.

Problem 5 - The tearing of the mammoths

One feature of some mammoths is surprising. Several of them appear to have been ripped to pieces in some massive accident. The Beresovka mammoth had a broken pelvis and a hind leg that was splintered into pieces. These breakages would have required considerable force. Other bones are reported with flesh still attached to them. One interesting carcase is that of a frozen baby mammoth excavated in Alaska. It is now preserved in a cold chest on display in the American Museum of Natural History, New York. Its trunk had been partially torn from its face and this had been sown back with one leg added to make a somewhat gruesome exhibit (Fig. 3). This tearing of at least some of the carcases only adds to the problems surrounding them.

....

To summarise; there was a warm climate with animals grazing peacefully in the summer or autumn. This was rapidly transformed into a mass of muck that entombed their ripped limbs and rapidly froze them.

Fig. 2. The baby woolly mammoth

Any model must adequately explain the five problems given above.

The evidence shows that the Beresovka mammoth, and others, died by suffocation. This may have been due to the freezing of its lungs or filling them with dust, or by being buried in the muck. The probability is that the suffocation and burial took place almost simultaneously. Then, *in that position*, it was very rapidly frozen. This is a very important feature that most explanations cannot account for.

Is there any way in which these unusual and conflicting conditions could have arisen?

One model proposes that the earth's crust split open at the time of the Flood and the subterranean waters were forced out at very high pressure. They went above the atmosphere, froze into hail which then descended over the land adjoining the split, burying the mammoths and freezing them at the same time.

We could not see any relationship between the proposed crustal split, considered as passing between Siberia and Alaska, and the position of the majority of the carcases along the north coast of Siberia. In addition, a depth of 4,000 ft (1,220m) of muck has been recorded and we would doubt if hail, which would quickly reach a terminal velocity, could churn up the earth to this depth. It would surely first kill all the animals and then cover them all under a solid blanket of hail with little subsequent mixing. Frozen animals might also be expected around the South Pole, but none have been reported. Furthermore, hail formed today has to rise up and down many times in storm clouds with strong upcurrents in them. They grow to a large size by adding a layer of ice around each hailstone every time they rise and fall.

Another model proposed the dumping of ice from a passing satellite over both poles, but, as above, there are no reports of rapidly frozen animals being found near the South Pole as they are in the north. This also does not deal with the five problems we have listed above.

....

Of all the many mysteries found in nature, this is one of the major conundrums facing both evolutionists and creationists. The evolutionist simply avoids the whole subject. The creationist has to find a mechanism that could rapidly produce the conditions as they are found and then fit this into a total world geological and historical scenario that is rational and Scriptural.

So far, no theory is able to fully explain these circumstances. Any proposal that relies upon rapid changes of weather conditions, high winds, etc. to start an ice age cannot possibly bring the temperature down quickly enough to explain the freshness of the meat, the tearing of the limbs and the rapid freezing of the animals despite being covered by the muck.

Dillow's chapter heading dealing with the problem is "The Laughter of the Gods". Certainly, God may well have smiled when He produced the geological and climatic events that resulted in such a seemingly inexplicable set of conditions.

Is there, however, a possible explanation? We would like to propose one suggestion.

A possible solution?
It was during the reading of the comparatively recent discovery of the ice cometesimals striking the earth that the impact of a large cometesimal suggested itself.

We propose that there was a large cometesimal that entered the atmosphere at high velocity. This might have broken up into many smaller units or a string of several large units due to gravitational stresses (Roche's limit) or the mechanical break-up as it struck the atmosphere. There may have been a combination of these extremely cold large and small masses hitting the earth over a wide area. As they had come from outer space they may have been very close to the absolute temperature of -273°C (-460°F). Some of the outer layers of the mass would have been burnt up by the friction of entry into the atmosphere but there may have still been one or more large masses left by the time they reached the ground. The pieces of frozen ice would, therefore, have had a considerable reserve of "coldness" which would allow them to have some rise of temperature yet still be cold enough to deep freeze the animals and the ground around them.

The result would have been the violent destruction of all life on the surface of the earth in the area. The ground would be ploughed up, churning the whole into a mixed mass of smashed animals and vegetation - exactly as found today. The important feature is that the incoming ice lumps would have been very cold still and having churned up the earth for a considerable depth *would have been mixed up with it.* The air temperature would also have been made extremely cold, and this would have "blast frozen" all the animals and the erupting ground. When the disrupted mass eventually stopped moving, the coldness it had experienced and the ice within it would have quickly frozen the whole depth into a solid mass, thus preserving any flesh even though it may have been buried at a considerable depth. Subsequent thawing of some areas in summer periods would allow many animals near the surface to thaw, decay and have their bones washed into vast deposits of tusks and bones - now collected by the locals for export.

This sequence of events would overcome the great problem of how flesh could have been frozen so rapidly that it was preserved, yet be found under considerable depths of soil that would have insulated it from any freezing air temperatures above the surface. The ground is frozen to a very great depth as trees have been found at 1,700 ft (520m) that are frozen and not petrified (BrownW:111).

The heat problem
It has been objected that the energy of the incoming mass would be so great that the heat generated would cause an enormous rise in the temperature, more than sufficient to melt any ice. We would suggest that some of this energy was dissipated in ablation of the surface layers (like the returning spacecrafts), but that the atmosphere would have presented no great barrier to the incoming cometesimal. The main dissipation of its energy would have been in churning up the ground. There should still be sufficient "coldness" in the remaining ice masses to freeze the mammoths even though buried.

This "heat problem" is only another aspect of the paradox facing any explanation. There must have been an enormous dissipation of energy to have churned up the ground to such great depths, *and at the same time* the ground had to be deeply frozen for this same great depth to preserve the mammoths. We would leave it to other experts to see if the energy equations can be shown to support the model we have proposed.

Possible supporting evidence?
Having proposed the above scenario, it was interesting to subsequently read Brown's account of the strange form of ice lenses that are in the muck and usually near the frozen mammoths. This "rock ice" is very unusual as its surface becomes discoloured when exposed to air, indicating that it was buried very rapidly with little contact with the air. It also has small bubbles and particles of soil and plants in it, indicating that it had enclosed at some stage but that it had not been frozen from a liquid state as they would have settled out. Brown contends that this would have been the result of the descending hail that had been greatly compacted when it hit the ground.

He also refers to a particular soil known as "loess" that covers vast areas of the world as well as forming deposits in the muck of Siberia and Alaska known as "yedomas". He proposes that this was the material ripped from the splitting crust by the force of the jets of water. It was thrown high into the air with the water and deposited over large areas of the globe.

The model presented by this writer is not dissimilar, but that the source was an incoming mass of interstellar ice. This would have the necessary energy to churn up the ground for a great depth, and descend with such speed that very little of the main mass would have any contact with air. The loess may have been another of its constituents, and such an interstellar source has been proposed for this soil (BrownW:117). However, it is more likely to be a normal sediment as it has a high salt content and is found in many places around the world.

A salt test?

If the rock ice came from subterranean water, then it should have a moderate salt content. We would propose that very little salt will be found in rock ice if it came from outer space. A very high salt content *has* been found in the lower layers of *some* rock ice (BrownW:135), but there is no mention of this in any of the main deposits. This suggests to this writer that rock ice *has* been tested for salt, but finding none, it has not been referred to. It will be interesting to see if rock ice has in fact been specifically tested for salt; it will determine whether its source was the ocean or space.

When did it occur?

There are many reports of islands composed almost entirely of ivory tusks, and of areas where there are a large number of the bones of different animals jumbled together. These are often on higher ground as though large groups were trying to escape rising water. This might look as if they were victims of the Noachic Flood, but it is more likely that they were washed into these mounds at a later stage. Brown notes that no fossil-bearing strata has been found under the muck, showing that the churning of the ground effectively reached bedrock. In addition, no shells have been found in the muck, indicating that the sea has never deposited any shells in this area.

It is possible that the impact was a post-Flood event, and may have caused the tilt of the earth's axis - a subject examined in Appendix 5. The line of the frozen carcases is roughly along the 70° parallel of latitude - a strike line near the Pole that would produce some tilting of the axis, and if travelling from west to east, may have speeded up the earth's rotation to change it from 360 to 365.4 days in the year. The break-up of an icy body would diffuse the effect over a large area. We have this generalised situation in Siberia and Alaska, and there is no evidence of a specific point of impact.

There will no doubt be many objections to the proposed sequence set out above, but we would suggest that it is the best model available to provide an adequate explanation for the strange mixture of evidence that the frozen mammoths and others animals present to both creationists and evolutionists.

SECTION 3.3
THE FIRST RAINBOW

In Genesis 9:11-17 we read that when Noah came out of the Ark he saw a rainbow, apparently for the first time. God gave it as a reminder (to Himself!) that never again would He bring a world-wide Flood upon the earth and as a token of this covenant between them.

There is always a rainbow when sunshine falls upon raindrops, but you have to be at the right position to see it. It can also be seen in the fine spray of a garden hose with your back to the sun when it can form a complete circle.

Fig. 1A shows how the light from the sun enters at the top of the drop, is internally refracted and reflected then refracted again as it re-enters the atmosphere at a very specific angle to the incoming light ray. The refraction of the light breaks it into the full spectrum of the colours of the rainbow: red, orange, yellow, green, blue, indigo and violet.

In the primary rainbow, the paths of the red and violet cross over when reflected at the rear of the spherical drop, and the red comes from drops on the outside of the bow. Due to the geometry of the sphere, the emerging angle is very small between the red and violet rays. If it were spread over a large angle, the emerging light would be so weak that the rainbow would be difficult to see.

The secondary rainbow is formed by the light travelling around the spherical droplet along a different path, as seen in Fig. 1B, producing a rainbow at a higher angle in the sky, but with the violet on the outside of the bow. There is also a third rainbow, but this is not often seen due to the angle and weakness of the emerging light.

Rainbows do not form when the droplet is less than 0.3mm in diameter, so a very fine mist will not produce one. Raindrops range from 0.5 to 4mm in size.

So, by simple reflection within a small droplet of water, we have the delicate array of one or more rainbows every time it rains. They are yet another display of God's beauty and at the same time an important reminder of the terrible Flood that God brought upon the whole world because of its great sinfulness. The vast majority of people are unaware of what it symbolises.

Of those who are aware, most prefer to ignore it - at their peril.

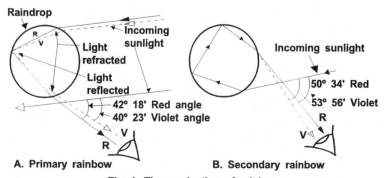

A. Primary rainbow   B. Secondary rainbow

Fig. 1. The production of rainbows

Section 3.4

NOAH'S DRUNKENNESS

One surprising incident recorded in the Bible is of Noah becoming drunk on the wine he had made from his grapes (Gen. 9:20-21). Here was a man who alone was righteous before God (Gen. 7:1), had been specifically chosen by God to continue the survival of the human race, and had received God's covenant regarding the symbolic importance of the rainbow that now appeared. What could have caused such a "fall from grace"?

Dillow has written about the Water Vapour Canopy (Dill:103) and assumes that there was the equivalent of 40 ft (12m) of water dispersed as water vapour suspended in equilibrium above the earth. He suggests that Noah had no intention of deliberately becoming drunk, but that this was a result of the change in atmospheric conditions after the Flood regarding which Noah appears to have been unaware. The atmospheric pressure would have been reduced by a half after the Flood, and this would have resulted in two factors that brought on his unexpected intoxication.

(i) The first is on the fermentation process. Alcohol is produced by the fermentation of grapes, and the reaction that takes place involves the escape of carbon dioxide. If the atmospheric pressure is higher, the carbon dioxide partial pressure will also be higher. This higher pressure level will reduce the escape of the carbon dioxide, and the whole reaction is slowed down.

Noah may have been well aware that stored grape juice would ferment, and before the Flood he would have known how long he could drink it before it began to ferment and produce alcohol. Not realising that the reduced pressure would speed up the fermentation process, he had drunk wine that he thought would be alcohol free, but was now, unexpectedly, sufficiently fermented to result in his intoxication.

There is the additional aspect that, presumably, he would have not drunk alcohol before, and this would have made him more susceptible to it than if he had taken it regularly and become acclimatised to it.

(ii) The second factor is that alcohol has a greater effect upon the metabolism when the pressure is lower; the lower the pressure the less alcohol is needed to become intoxicated. It is for this reason that people become more easily intoxicated in the lower air pressure used in aircraft cabins.

The Ukrainian creationist, Sergei Golovin, in a pamphlet on the same subject, recounts a game that the local inhabitants of the highlands of Southern Caucasia play upon unsuspecting lowland visitors. They invite them to drink with them and if they refuse to match the drinking of the locals, this is said to be a disrespect for local traditions. The result is that the locals, well adapted by use to the lower pressure, can remain sober while their guests gently subside under the table!

This reduction of the atmospheric pressure is the explanation presented by Dillow for Noah's drunkenness, but there may be a problem with it for he assumed that the 40 ft of water stored as vapour in the Water Vapour Canopy was the most reasonable assessment. This is the amount that has often been quoted in creationist writings but as we have seen in Section 3.1, the actual quantity may have been very much less due to various physical problems that this amount raises. The difference in pressure may therefore have been very much less than he assumed, greatly reducing the effects set out above.

In considering this, although the reduction in pressure may have been much less than the 50% Dillow assumed, there may still have been enough to have increased the speed of fermentation and heightened the effect of alcohol on the body. Alternatively, it is another possible indication that the pressure was much higher before the Flood than after.

Whatever the pressure difference might have been, it is an interesting explanation of how this "man of God" could have become drunk.

The Christian and alcohol

There is some misunderstanding about the use of wine in Biblical times. What is not appreciated is that in those days they could only allow the grape juice to ferment naturally. It could only reach a maximum of 14% alcohol, at which point the yeast would be killed. In practice, the wine would only be about 2 - 6% alcohol. Even then, the wine was watered down, making it extremely low in alcoholic content. Today, the content can be very much higher by various production methods. This renders the situation far different from that existing in those simple days, and the strictures on strong drink even more important.

The Bible gives various warnings about strong drink. It would seem that elders are to abstain from all wine (1 Tim. 3:3), but deacons must not be "given to much wine" (1 Tim. 3:8). This is presumably so that the church leaders set a good example.

What then of Paul advising Timothy to "take a little wine" for his stomach's sake (1 Tim. 5:23)?

Researchers have shown that the best natural protector against gastroenteritis is orange juice closely followed by grape juice. Grape juice contains a natural substance that combats stomach organisms, but it is gradually destroyed by increasing fermentation (Mast:68).

On this, it is interesting that grapes are used by some in treatments for cancer. Also, in the treatment for allergies, grapes and lamb chops are considered as having no allergic reactions. They are used as a starter diet to discover what a sufferer may be allergic to as other foods are gradually added.

Vines, grapes and wine are frequently mentioned in the Bible, for they are referred to in harvesting, drinking, grafting of the branches and the uselessness of the vine wood. The warnings against "strong drink", however, are frequent, even though it was far weaker than today's potent products. The present appalling level of alcohol abuse results in many unnecessary deaths from a variety of causes; an unheeded destroyer that swamps almost all other causes of misery in people's lives. With this in mind, although permitted in the Bible, many Christians abstain lest "weaker brethren" are not thereby led into a practice that has ruined an untold number of lives.

SECTION 3.5
FLOOD STORIES IN FOLK TALES

The study of the various races and tribes that inhabit the world has always been a fascinating subject. Anthropologists have lived with remote tribes for long periods and recorded for posterity all their strange customs, rituals, dances and language. Similarly, historians have studied ancient civilisations such as the Greeks, Romans, Egyptians, Incas, etc.

Having made their explorations and investigations, the anthropologists would return to their institutions, compare their notes and discuss the relationships between the differing tribes.

From all the vast amount of information collected, one very interesting common feature was found. In the folk tales of many of the tribes that had been visited, they had a story of a great flood which covered the earth, and from which only a few humans and animals survived to repopulate it. The story appears in cultures widely separated by distance across the earth, and it is also recorded in ancient civilisations, separated by hundreds of years in time. Yet many have a number of small, unusual features (such as the release of a bird, etc.) in common with each other, which indicates a common ancestry. How could such a story have arisen "spontaneously" in so many different tribes yet have such similar details?

As one reads these accounts the numerous similarities are obvious. That they are local or national versions of the same story is very evident. Some of the names are very similar to those of nearby nations with whom they may have had much in common, particularly having a similar language or whom they may have conquered. For example, the Assyrians and Babylonians (given the joint name of Akkadian) were close neighbours with similar languages, and the Sumerians were also nearby. Throughout the world, some of the incidents recorded are so similar to the Genesis account that the person corresponding to God, Noah and his descendants, etc. is easily recognisable.

Even some of the events unique to a particular version have echoes of the Bible record. What is fascinating is that there are occasional minor comments that exactly match those in Genesis. Some examples are as follows:

(a) There are two accounts of the Flood in the tablets found in the library of Asshur-bani-pal in Nineveh. One contains the phrase spoken by the god Ea: "The cattle of the field, the wild beast of the field...*I will send to thee that they all may wait at the door*" (Nel:171). This is paralleled by Genesis 6:20 that "two of every kind *will come to you* to keep them alive."

(b) Another record from Syria is recounted by Lucien who said that Deucalion Sisythes "put himself with his wives and his children in a great chest, and thereupon *there came to him* boars and horses and lions and serpents and all kinds of animals" (Nel:175).

We will be considering this subject of the animals coming to the Ark again when we deal with objections by critics of the Flood account in Section 3.6.

(c) Ovid, the Latin poet, gives an account of the Flood in his *Metamorphoses* and this mentions that Jupiter "disperses the clouds, and the showers *being moved by the north wind*, earth and heaven behold each other again" (Nel:179). In Genesis 8:1 we read, "And God made a wind to pass over the earth and the waters subsided."

(d) The people of Apamea in Phrygia, near Iconia that is mentioned in the New Testament, had a style or pillar to denote where they believed the Ark landed. They also struck a coin depicting Noah and his wife emerging from the Ark and the name of Noah can be seen on the side of the Ark

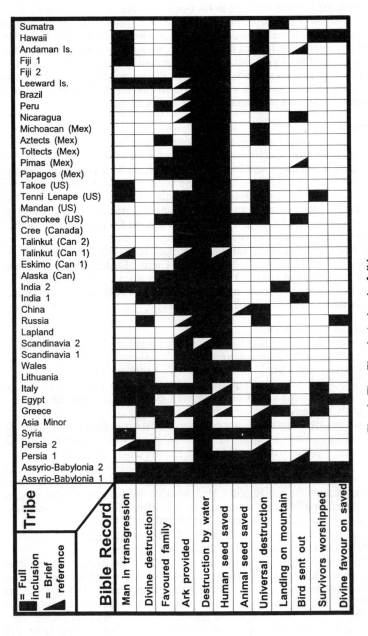

Fig. 1. The Flood stories in folklore

(Nel:176).

(e) The Hawaiian account has many close parallels to the Biblical record. Nu-u made a canoe and took in his family and the animals. After the Flood he emerged and, mistaking the Moon for Kane, the great god, he worshipped it. Kane came down on a rainbow and rebuked Nu-u. As Nu-u did this in mistake he was not punished, so Kane left the rainbow behind as a token of his forgiveness. In all the accounts I have read, I have never seen a reference to a rainbow in any of the pagan stories. It is interesting that this should, nevertheless, have been preserved by a tribe about as remote as you can be from Babel, the centre of the dispersion.

The Miao people

These once lived in a large area of south China but were later driven into the mountains of the south-west by the better armed Chinese. They recite their folk stories at weddings and funerals in verse form which has kept their folk stories very accurate. The similarity to the Genesis account is remarkable with references to making man from dirt, the rain for forty days, the Flood, the sending of a dove, etc. Even the beginning of creation is similar to the opening words of Genesis; "On the day God created the heavens and earth..."

Many names are easily recognised. Adam is called Patriarch Dirt, with descendants Se-teh (Seth), Lusu, Lama (Lamech), Nuah (Noah), Lo Han (Ham), Lo Shen (Shem), Jah-hu (Japhet), Cusah (Cush), Mesay (Mizraim), Elan (Elam), Ngashur (Asshur). They trace their ancestry from Japhet so they are of Indo-European stock and not from Ham from whom the Chinese probably descended (ICR Impact Article 214).

The spread of the stories

In an early creationist film it referred to the number of folk stories that had been recorded on the different continents. These were -

N. America - 59, Central S. America - 46, Europe - 31, Middle East - 17, Asia - 23, South Sea Islands and Australia - 37. This gives a total of 213. Many more have probably been discovered since the film was made, and no doubt many yet remain unrecorded.

An informative source of information is an early creationist book *The Deluge Story in Stone* by Byron C. Nelson (Nel) in which he gives several of these stories in some detail.

He also took the record of the Flood as given in the Bible and divided it up into 12 major components. He then analysed 41 folk tales taken from various locations around the world and noted whether they contained the incident, only referred briefly to it or omitted it altogether. The resulting interesting chart is given in Fig. 1. The nations are listed along the top very roughly in the order of their closeness to Babylon which was the centre from which all the nations dispersed after God confused their language.

From this chart it can be seen that, firstly, the main elements of the story (Ark provided, destruction by water, human seed saved) are present in almost all the stories. Secondly, as you move further away from Babylon, the stories lose some of the details, but others are kept, often in a corrupt form. This is precisely what one would expect as remote tribes wandered across the world. They would pass the story on by word of mouth, forgetting some parts of the story, and exaggerating others to conform to their culture or environment. It is interesting that unusual incidents are preserved at remote locations. Thus, the sending out of one or more birds to check the dryness of the land, and the act

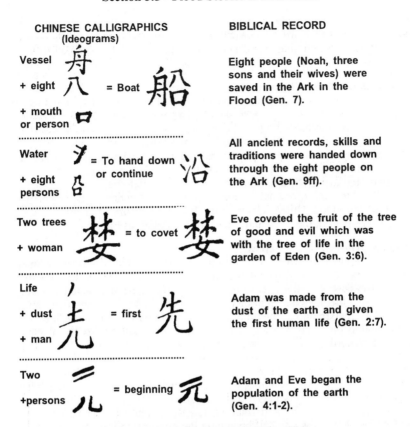

CHINESE CALLIGRAPHICS
(Ideograms)

BIBLICAL RECORD

Vessel

+ eight

+ mouth
or person

= Boat

Eight people (Noah, three
sons and their wives) were
saved in the Ark in the
Flood (Gen. 7).

Water

+ eight
persons

= To hand down
or continue

All ancient records, skills and
traditions were handed down
through the eight people on
the Ark (Gen. 9ff).

Two trees

+ woman

= to covet

Eve coveted the fruit of the tree
of good and evil which was
with the tree of life in the
garden of Eden (Gen. 3:6).

Life

+ dust

+ man

= first

Adam was made from the
dust of the earth and given
the first human life (Gen. 2:7).

Two

+persons

= beginning

Adam and Eve began the
population of the earth
(Gen. 4:1-2).

Fig. 2. Chinese pictograms and the Bible

of worship by the survivors of the Flood on their emergence, are recorded by
a few tribes, even as far away as Hawaii, but not many between there and
Babylon.

This suggests that there were many groups that kept reasonably intact as
they dispersed across the globe. Some groups managed to maintain certain
features in their folk tales of the Flood as they travelled. An alternative form
of migration might have been that generally a group might have established
themselves in one area, but then as population pressure increased, some of
their number would have moved on to colonise areas still unoccupied. With
this method, had the central group lost a part of the story, then it would have
been lost for all subsequent migrating generations. That specific incidents
were preserved by distant nations, but not by intermediate tribes, suggest that
migration may have been by large groups travelling reasonably directly to
fairly specific locations around the world and then settling there. We discuss
this in Section 3.6 - The Dispersal from Babel.

Here again, in this story recorded by tribes all over the world, we have
further independent evidence of the reality of Noah's Flood and the
dispersion after the Tower of Babel.

It is of interest that an examination of the *Encyclopaedia Britannica* gives very little information about these Flood stories, particularly how numerous and widespread they are. The writers may not have wished to give too much publicity to evidence that supports the Bible that had been obtained from so many sources.

The evidence from China

An interesting book has been written by C.H. Kang and E.R. Nelson (Kan) entitled *The Discovery of Genesis* which gives translations of Chinese words. Each word is a stylised drawing (ideogram) which is made up from simpler pictures (pictographs), usually to convey more abstract ideas. Certain words are made up from specific pictograms which reveal a great deal of the background of experience and ideas that are behind these words. For example, the ideogram for "boat" consists of the pictographs for "vessel" + "eight" + "mouths (persons)." This is surely a reference to the eight who survived the Flood. Other links with the Biblical account of creation and the Flood are given in the book and a few are illustrated in Fig. 2.

The Assyrio-Babylonian epics

C.W. Ceram has written a fascinating account of the discovery of many ancient civilisations and documents in his book *Gods, Graves and Scholars* (Cer). He describes the excavations of Layard as he uncovered the huge statues and the invaluable library at Nineveh. In this library were found stories of creation and a flood that closely paralleled those in the Bible.

Following these discoveries of the ancient Assyrio-Babylonian tablets of clay that recorded different versions of a story of creation and a great flood, they were used to cast doubts on the originality and veracity of the account of the Flood in Genesis. These stories, such as the *Gilgamesh Epic* and the *Enuma-Elish* (*Epic of Creation*), have a number of similarities to the Biblical record, but contain many pagan features, often quite gruesome. For example, in the *Enuma-Elish,* the god Marduk defeats Tiamat, the primeval mother, and divides her body, one half becoming the heavens and the other the earth. He also killed the demigod Kingu and from his blood man was formed. Many pagan stories have similar events that are obviously purely mythical.

As you read them, it becomes clear that such stories of the activities of gods, demigods and humans are a very corrupt and pagan account of the Creation and the Flood. In contrast to these, the account in Genesis, whilst miraculous, is perfectly acceptable as the activity of a good and loving God who could create this material world out of nothing, and for a purpose that He then reveals to the man He created. Yet it is the pagan stories that are hailed by anthropologists as the original folk story of the Flood, whilst the Biblical account is relegated to being just a later Jewish version of it!

Ceram, in his account of these archaeological discoveries, gives the story of the Flood in the *Gilgamesh Epic,* and then makes a comment, consistently echoed by all writers on the subject, when he says:

> Impossible to question the fact that *the earliest version of the Biblical legend of the deluge had been found* (Cer:191)

The truth is quite the opposite. It is the Bible which gives the correct account of what took place in that unforgettable event, the Babylonian clay tablets being only a grotesque pagan version.

In fact, it has been claimed that the epic does *not* describe a flood, and the story got its start from a mistranslation of the famous tablet XI! The reference to birds in the tablet cannot have any connection with the Flood account. The vessel is not an ark and the tablet is dated centuries later than even the latest dating of Genesis. "This gross error has been known for more than a century, but the story goes on and on as a monument to careless scholarship and it is routinely referred to today as solid evidence that Genesis is a late collection of myths." (Fange in Q23/3:97 referring to Rapaport, I. "The Flood Story in Bible and Cuneiform Literature" *Bible and Spade* 12(3-4):57-65)

This deliberate twisting of the evidence is just one of very many examples of the means by which secular historians and archaeologists consistently attack the events recorded in the Bible in their unceasing efforts to destroy its credibility. Surely the most rational explanation of these stories of the Flood appearing in the folk tales of tribes all over the world *is that it really did occur to their ancestors.* The Great Flood of Noah was such an awe-inspiring catastrophe that it would have been remembered for many generations as they dispersed from the Tower of Babel.

Attempts have been made to say that tribes might have learnt the story from travelling missionaries. But if this were so, then other Bible stories, such as the Exodus or New Testament stories of Jesus should also be recorded in their folk tales. None however are. Furthermore, the stories come from a far wider area of the globe than missionaries had covered at that time.

I was privileged to speak on creation in Moscow, and at the Academy for the History of Science a lecturer claimed that the reason there were so many stories of a Flood was that they were recounted by tribes who in primeval times lived in lowlands that were liable to local flooding. I pointed out that this could not be a correct interpretation because many of them had very specific incidents, such as the release of a bird, even the same bird - a dove - that occurred in too many of them to have been coincidental.

Creation accounts

The *Encyclopaedia Britannica* (17:368) notes that the famous scholar Sir James Frazer "took an *evolutionary* survey of human culture and religion [and] held that the notion of the creation of the world by a supreme Being occurred only in the highest stage of cultural development." We should note that the "survey" was specifically taken from an evolutionary standpoint: i.e., it was evolution that dictated how these stories were to be interpreted. There was no suggestion that the stories should be allowed to be their own witness.

The *E.B.* does continue by saying that this view was challenged by the Scotsman Lang and Shmidt of Austria. They proved that even in very primitive tribes there was a belief in a supreme Being or high God. That the evidence was there for Frazer and his evolutionary colleagues to use but chose to ignore illustrates the dominance of evolution in the writings of the vast majority of those who achieve public eminence.

The Ebla tablets

Wilson recounts (WilsonC) the discovery of the thousands of cuneiform tablets at Tell Mardik, the site of the ancient city of Ebla, situated near the north-east corner of the Mediterranean Sea. Amongst them was a record of creation that is very similar to that recorded in Genesis 1. It says: "There was a time when there was no heaven and Lugal (The Great One) formed it out of nothing, there was no earth, and he made it, no light, and he made it."

This translation was mentioned by Prof. Pettinato to a casual gathering of archaeology experts and he said that the nearest account to this was Genesis

1. This was greeted by those present with stunned silence. One of them then said: "A first millennium oral Hebrew tradition, in a third millennium written document."

The significance of these tablets and the datings is that according to Wilson, they were written 1,000 years before the time of Moses. Secular archaeologists have always claimed that Moses only wrote down what were "oral traditions" founded on the pagan versions such as the *Gilgamesh Epic*. In fact, some contend that they were actually not written until the time of Solomon. Yet here we have a written account with the same majestic story of creation as Moses was to write down many centuries later. It is therefore clear that he was not recording what had been up to then only a "Jewish oral tradition", but had access to ancient written records of these events; records that may have been retained since the time of Noah or even before. We have noted that some verses of Genesis (2:11-14) are written in the present tense as though the writer is describing the country as if it still existed.

One can understand why this should be greeted by the orthodox experts with "stunned silence", for one of their basic assumptions had been swept away.

We say they were written 1,000 years before Moses "according to Wilson" as he accepts the orthodox time scale, dating the Ebla tablets to 2,400 BC. As it is the contention of this writer that the Flood occurred about this date (see Section 3.9), these tablets would have to be written some time after that.

We would hope that, in contrast to the constant secular bias in interpretation, these world-wide accounts of a great Flood will stand as yet another testimony to the accuracy of the Bible.

THE DISPERSAL FROM BABEL

This is the key to history. Terrific energy is expended - civilisations built up - excellent institutions devised: but each time something goes wrong. Some fatal flaw always brings the selfish and cruel people to the top and it all slides back into misery and ruin. That is what Satan has done to us humans. (C.S. Lewis - *Miracles*)

....

In researching this section and the following two problems were encountered that were of a different nature to those met when a more scientific subject was investigated.

Documentary sources

In dealing with early history, there are certain problems and decisions that are peculiar to this field of study. Unlike a scientific field, where disputed experiments can be carried out again, we can only use the written evidence of earlier historians. This raises certain problems such as the following:

1. Is the document ascribed to an author a reliable record of events? If it contradicts other writings, this is against its reliability. The problem then arises that an error in one passage does not necessarily mean that all the rest of that author's works should be dismissed. He may only be repeating what others have recorded, with other incidents being accurately reported. Alternatively, his account may be accurate, with the others only copying each other.

2. Was the author nearer to the time of the event than later writers? Even this does not guarantee that his account is therefore more accurate, but it is a fairly important factor as he may have had reliable documents to hand that have since disappeared.

3. Are there contradictions or exaggerations that destroy credibility in the account? Again, this might not apply to other events recorded.

4. Is it possible that the events have been fabricated in order to "encourage the faith of the faithful"? There are a number of records in the annals of the medieval church involving pieces of the Cross, the nails, the bones of saints, etc. Many of these were produced during the Dark Ages and caused great superstitious "wondering" amongst the people. Nations and towns vied amongst themselves to have a more important relic or miraculous happening.

   In the historian's case, events may have been fabricated for a variety of reasons to prove that certain nations have roots in early Christianity to "stir up faith" or what are known as "pious frauds."

   Another possibility is that events may have been fabricated or inaccurately reported for some ulterior motive, i.e. political expediency of the times or flattery of a king.

5. The fact that many writers state the same incidents does not necessarily mean that this gives added confirmation. Particularly with later writers, they may be quoting each other as authoritative, but they may all be founded on one unreliable record of events.

6. What makes accurate research in this field particularly difficult is the lack of help that can be obtained from normal modern historical sources.

   The viewpoint consistently disseminated by historians, mass media and inevitably the education system regarding the first book of the Bible is that it is pure mythology, being only a Jewish version of earlier pagan myths. The result is that today few would give any credence to the stories of Adam and Eve, the Great Flood of Noah and the descent of all nations from the eight survivors.

There is additionally a consistent bias against anything that supports British achievements and early Christian conversions. Searching standard encyclopaedias or reference works by modern authors results in little information on the important early history of our nation. They are at times positively misleading and virtually useless as reliable sources. Early documents are denigrated as fables or unreliable and are rarely held by local libraries.

All surviving records of ancient tribes that supply any independent corroboration are also dismissed as being unreliable records and events fabricated by the author to support his particular and biased (i.e. pro-Christian) view of history. However, those who have seen the way in which evidence against evolution and for creation is disparaged and blocked from any publicity will have little difficulty in recognising the parallels between the treatment accorded to these two subjects.

In view of the dismissal of many ancient histories, tracing out the true sequence of events is far from easy. I would here acknowledge my debt to the research of Bill Cooper who has spent some 25 years tracking down these ancient documents and checking their reliability. He has set out all this evidence in his book *After the Flood* (Coo95), having been blocked by established historians from presenting his findings in a more formal and academic publication. Such opposition to his evidence is understandable, for it contradicts much that academics have been claiming as accurate accounts. What he has presented now gives a very different picture of the early history of a British nation that readily accepted the Apostolic Christian faith. As we shall see, this came via Rome around 50 AD, long before the coming of Augustine in 597 AD.

Some of what follows is based upon his book and several discussions with him on subjects not included in it. I am grateful for his leads in certain incidents that have been of specific interest to me. His book is highly recommended to those interested in the documentation of early British history and our descent from Japheth.

As well as Cooper, two other sources were the main ones examined.

A.C. Custance

Custance has written a most interesting book on this subject - *Noah's Three Sons* (Cus). We will be dealing with his views of the dispersal of man later, but he has written much about the way in which the nations moved across Europe after Babel. He differs from Cooper at various points and tends to trace the movements of tribes by saying they are the same group but there were local changes in the pronunciation of their name. At times this method seems strained and it was difficult to know how far this could be accepted as accurate.

The British Israelite Federation

These have a number of publications, some of which are very informative and provide interesting leads on various topics. However, some of their publications suffer from two great deficits:

(a) There are generally very inadequate references to many statements that they make. This greatly reduces any reliability that could be placed on them.

(b) They have several publications dealing with the movement of the various tribes across Europe after Babel. Their overriding concern is to prove that the British are descendants of the lost ten tribes of Northern Israel, in particular the tribe of Dan.

One problem with such a thesis is that this would have been after the Assyrians took them into captivity in 722 BC, some 1,300 years *after* the dispersal from Babel about 2000 BC. By this time, most of Europe would have become inhabited by earlier migrations who must have been far more numerous, yet these are hardly mentioned: All interest is focused on how these later "tribes of Israel" were the founders of many European nations.

The principal link they forge is between Omri, a king of one of the deported northern ten tribes, whose name they claim is written as "Humri or Khumri" (or "Ghomri") on the Black Obelisk of Shalamanesar. Fifteen years after their capture, the "Gimira" or "Gamira" or "Ghomri" are mentioned "in precisely the identical area into which Israel had been placed". These were later to be called the Cimmerians and their path is traced through Europe and to Britain. Thus the name of one northern king of Israel is used by what might be called "name bending" to force a very devious link with the Cimmerians. The names of the tribes that spread across Europe after Babel appear to be claimed as part of the much later spreading of the Ten Tribes of Israel. Both Cooper and Custance agree that the Cimmerians were the descendants of Gomer, the son of Japheth, whose descendants ranged across Europe, long before the captivity of the ten tribes of Israel.

Were the Ten Tribes dispersed?

An examination of the Bible shows that **(a)** all the Levites and the faithful of the Northern tribes removed to Judah at the time of the division (2 Chron. 11:13-17); **(b)** God then spoke "to all Israel in Judah and Benjamin"; **(c)** more came over at the time of Asa (2 Chron. 15:8-9); **(d)** the Assyrian Sargon only carried away 27,290 people, and they would hardly have been allowed to leave and travel across Europe. Furthermore, **(e)** those returning from the later Babylonian captivity are called "House of Jacob", "Israel" and "Judah" by Isaiah (48:1); **(f)** "Jew" and "Israelite" were interchangeable for the Jewish nation from this time. At the time of Christ, Anna was from Asher, Christ appealed, not to the Samaritans, but to "the lost sheep of the house of Israel" (Matt. 10:5-6) and Paul spoke to "the house of Israel" (Acts 2:36) (www7).

Thus, the core of the Israelites was in Judah still - not in the deportees.

THE DISPERSAL FROM BABEL

With all the problems in trying to trace their movements in mind, we will give an outline of the main features that seem to be reasonably supported of the migrations of mankind from the Tower of Babel.

When Noah eventually emerged from the Ark, he and his children were instructed to "fill the earth" (Gen. 9:1). Yet men ignored this command and in Genesis 11 we read how mankind began to build a huge tower or ziggurat "whose top is in the heavens" so that they could "make a name" for themselves - "lest we be scattered abroad over the whole face of the earth."

The self-centredness of sinful man is demonstrated once again. He is consistently opposed to God's directives and constantly seeks to run the world his own way.

It has been found that other ziggurats had temples at their peak dedicated to the tribal god. If this first of such constructions also housed a temple, as seems most likely, we can understand God's angry reaction. His punishment was to "confuse their tongues" and as a result, man migrated throughout the whole world. We have seen in Section 3.5 that many tribes took with them the terrible history of the Flood that their ancestors had lived through. As the tradition continued, these ancestors were elevated to the position of gods in the tribal folklore.

Folk stories of Babel

Although not as numerous as the stories of the Flood, there are some that refer to the confusion of languages and subsequent dispersal. They are mentioned in the Assyrio-Babylonian accounts, in the writings of Josephus the Jewish historian, and in the American Indian's tales (Q11/2:97). As far away as Indonesia they have a tale of "a tower, God's anger and the scattering of people over all the earth" (Q12/1:75).

The population growth

Peterson (Q19/2:87) has shown that from the eight people in the Ark, the population probably grew at the rate of 7.29% annually, that the dispersal took place about 100 years after the Flood (the date of Peleg's birth) when there would have been some 12,008 people at Babel. He calculates that if these were divided equally between each leader (218 each), then there would have been 3,056 Japhethites, 6,550 Hamethites and 2,402 Shemites. By 200 years after the Flood, the population would have reached some 245,000 and would have split up many times into local tribes around the world.

Languages

The subject of languages is interesting. Many can be traced back to an earlier language and a "tree of descent" can be drawn up. That for the Indo-Europeans given in Fig. 1 is mainly from Yule (the full lines) (Yu:168). He connects these to an unknown proto-Indo-European language, and there are several indications that there are links between these main groups, principally the similarity of many common words. However, he notes that there are "thirty such basic languages which have produced the more than 4,000 languages in the world." It is probable that these thirty "basic" languages are the original language groups formed at the time of Babel.

Taylor notes (E96/10(1):23) that one expert reduced the families to 16. Also, languages are divided into stress-timed, syllable-timed and tonal which might have some connection with the linguistic inclinations of the three sons of Noah.

Is dyslexia due to Babel?

One creationist, Johnson, has suggested that dyslexia may be due to the "confusion of tongues" at Babel (John). He suggests that each group at Babel were perfectly "programmed" by God for their new language, complete with the ability to read from left to right or *vice versa*, their word orders, etc. As time progressed, these groups have gradually intermarried and some of the children are learning one language but are genetically organised for using another language.

It had been noticed in some cases that eye movements sometimes drifted right to left. He was therefore amazed when one person with this tendency mentioned that she had found Hebrew very easy to learn - and she had Jewish ancestry!

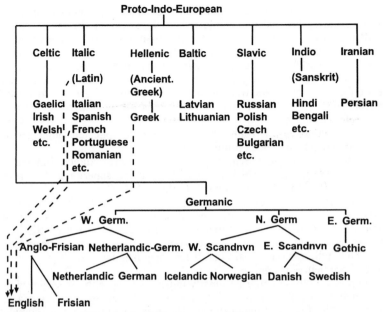

Fig. 1. The Indo-European language group

In another case the parents had noticed that their boy tended to use words in the order they are used in German. The family were of German stock. A Jewish boy's severe dyslexia disappeared while he was studying for his Barmitzvah ceremony which involves studying passages of Hebrew which is written right to left.

Yet another case is that of a boy, living in Japan with English-speaking parents, who had difficulty in reading his native English but could read Japanese easily. This has presented a problem to psychologists.

Babel and Pentecost

Johnson refers to the separation of people at Babel by confusing their languages. Many creationists point to the miracle at Pentecost when this process was temporarily reversed, for ordinary people were given the gift to speak languages that they had never spoken before.

Will there be a time when all men will be given the gift of speaking in one language again? There is no indication that this will occur before the return of Christ. It is likely, however, that following that event, all will be reunited in one "tongue" again.

The complexity of "primitive" languages

One aspect of these early languages that is little realised is that, far from being "simple" in cases or vocabulary, they were extremely complicated. Those who study Latin can testify how much more complex the grammar is than English. We give two examples.

During the Second World War, the Americans wanted to have rapid communication between commanders whilst the battle was raging. To have to encode every message into a virtually unbreakable code would have taken too long in urgent situations. They wanted to speak to each other urgently yet have these messages indecipherable by the Japanese. If they were able to decode them even a few hours later, the information would be out-of-date and therefore useless. Their solution was to select from the ranks all the members of the Navaho tribe of North American Indians because their grammar and pronunciation were extremely complex. The commander had only to speak to one of the tribe members who would then talk over the radio to another member (often a relative) to have the message safely relayed to the other commander (Kah:550).

This is given as an interesting use of the very complicated languages that still exist amongst so-called "primitive" tribes.

Yule quotes a British Indian official who, in 1786, studied Sanskrit, an unused Indian language, which he considered to be superior to Greek and Latin although it was obviously related to them (Yu:167).

By way of another example, some South Sea islanders have numerous names for "coconut" which precisely describe the many stages that this produce goes through, but no general name to describe the fruit. Similarly, Eskimos have many names for different types of snow but no ordinary name for it. This indicates once again that these early languages were very precise and far from being "primitive."

Examples like these could be greatly multiplied and only go to prove that man did not arise from a primitive cave-man who could only grunt a few noises in his first communications. He was created with a complete vocabulary and probably a complex grammar from the very first days of his existence, with new, equally complicated languages being given at the time of Babel.

The Fertile Crescent and the paths of migration

The paths that the many tribes travelled over the earth is indicated in Fig. 2 which is based on Custance. It will be seen that they all diverge from the Middle East where Babel is sited. For many years, anthropologists acknowledged that this was the area where civilisation was first established, and named the flat area of rich soil the Fertile Crescent. Other centres, however, are now being suggested by modern historians.

That the migrating tribes were able to cross vast stretches of seas has been demonstrated by the expeditions of Thor Heyerdahl. There is also the possibility of land bridges existing allowing man and animals to reach the furthest parts of the continents. One such bridge was probably the Bering Strait which is only 20 ft (6m) deep in some places. These may have been submerged in the days of Peleg "when the earth was divided", but this event would have had to have been *after* the dispersion from Babel. This would mean the "division" of Peleg was a geological event rather than the "division" of languages at the time of the Tower of Babel. There is still uncertainty on the precise meaning of this verse.

Custance's theories of the dispersion

Arthur C. Custance has written several books on this subject, and made a most interesting proposal on the areas to which the ancestors of Noah's three sons dispersed. This is found principally in his book *Noah's Three Sons* (Cus75) in which he provides good evidence in support of this view.

His interesting suggestion is that each of these three sons possessed a greater degree of one attributes than the other two.

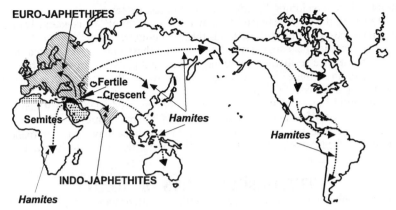

Fig. 2. The dispersal of the nations from Babel

SHEM emphasised the "religious" aspects of mankind - he was searching for RIGHTEOUSNESS. Even today, the Jews and the Arabs hold to their differing religious beliefs with great fervency.

JAPHET has a particular gift for a philosophical approach to life - he was searching for UNDERSTANDING. It was this that generated the scientific attitude that was to eventually bring such benefits to civilisation.

HAM was the very practical son who was very inventive and was therefore able to live off the land no matter where he roamed - he was interested in POWER. His use of whatever materials were to hand enabled him to survive in even the most difficult of conditions. Custance claimed that it was the Hamites who were the people who dispersed around the whole world, long before the (Japhethite) Europeans made their "voyages of discovery" in the 15th century.

In support of his thesis, he gives many examples of inventions of the Hamites, whilst the Japhethites are only accredited with the invention of the windmill. To give just two examples of their inventiveness:

The wolf is an annoyance to the Eskimo as he preys on the caribou the Eskimo needs for food, but he is too quick and keen-sighted to be caught. The Eskimo deals with him using a small piece of whalebone. This is sharpened at both ends, bent into a bow, tied with sinew, covered with fat and left to freeze. After cutting the sinew, the morsel is left out for the wolf who swallows it whole. The fat melts in his stomach, the whalebone springs open and kills the wolf.

When the Eskimo has to lift a ton weight walrus out of the water, he makes a U-shaped hole further away and uses this as a "pulley" anchor point for a rawhide line passing through slits in the walrus. The line is passed several times between the hole and the walrus exactly like a block and tackle. He pulls on one end and raises the huge walrus out of the water (Cus:163).

Custance contends that when the philosophical Japhethites became acquainted with the many inventions of the practical Hamites, we had the beginning of the scientific revolution. He quotes the expansion of printing in Europe when it had been brought from China, and their use of rockets which led to gunpowder. This last claim may not be correct as various Europeans were experimenting with gunpowder. Generally, Ham was inventive but had no interest in developing his ideas to their fullest extent.

However, the new "science" dehumanised civilisation - it needed Shem to give men the righteous attitude to all these accomplishments.

What Custance also suggests is that when all these abilities are united once again in one race so that the religious, mental and practical aspects of life are combined, then there will be a great outflow of the use of the world's materials for the benefit of mankind.

We would suggest that such a union can be achieved even now. When any man bases his life upon the culmination of Shem's search - Christ, who revealed the true nature of God - only then will he have the permanent foundation from which he can then rightly administer his God-given abilities in these other areas of life.

THE DESCENDANTS OF NOAH

Both Cooper and Custance give the settled locations and routes followed by the various descendants of Noah after Babel, but it must be realised that the whole of Europe at least became a swirling mass of people moving backwards and forwards, fighting, conquering, being enslaved and disappearing from history. Tracing their history is extremely difficult as reliable documents about this period are scarce. We will here only give a summary of the main Biblical characters and those events that seem to be the most likely. Fig. 3 gives the genealogy from Noah with the races that descended from him.

Japhet

His descendants split into two groups - one moving west into Europe, the other going east into the Indian plain (Fig. 2). Custance provides a number of cultural links between these two groups and secular anthropologists agree on the common ancestry of Europeans and Indians.

One of the most fascinating links is the retention of the patriarchal names in their folklore. Japheth was the founder figure of the Europeans, and the Greeks have modified this to "Japetos" as the name of their founder. He became "Jupiter" to the Romans.

In the Indian account of the Flood, their equivalent of Noah is "Satyaurata" whose sons were Iyapeti (Japhet), Sharma (Shem) and C'harma (Ham). They also recorded that Satyaurata cursed C'harma because he laughed at him when he was drunk, following closely the account in Genesis 9:20-27 (Cus75:81).

Gomer

He was the most notable descendant and his people eventually covered much of Europe. They were known as Cimmerians who became the Gauls of France and possibly the Goths of Germany. Custance also claims that they became the Celts of Britain, and their strong links with their European relatives seems to support this. Cooper, as we shall see, presents an alternative route by which Brutus first colonised this land.

Custance often traces the movements of these people and others by the similarity of names that are recorded. Thus Gomer becomes GMR - GWR - GUR - GUL = Gaul - Celtai = Celts. It is difficult to know just how far this "stretching" of the linguistic evidence can be taken as one feels that almost any name could be connected by such methods as we have seen with the British Israelites above. He does give other historical references, however, to support his views, and this approach is used by other creationists.

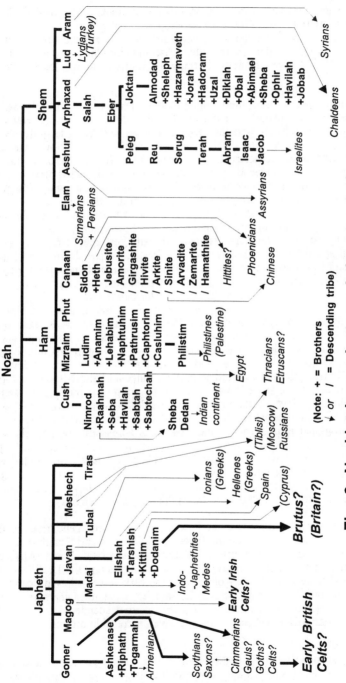

Fig. 3. Noah's descendants and the races of man

Ashkenase

The son of Gomer, Custance proposes that Ashkenase eventually joined with his relations, the Goths in covering Europe, giving their name to the Scythians, Sakasene, Saxons and Scandinavians. The name can be found in several locations, such as the Lake Ascania and the people once called Askaeni. Fig. 4 gives the possible routes of migration across Europe.

"The Thirteenth Tribe"

Regarding Ashkenase, there was a strange development in the area of the Caucasian mountains that was inhabited by the Khazars in the 8th century AD. They were a warlike group that became rich by collecting tolls from all the merchandise passing through their land. To clarify what follows, we should mention that after the destruction of Jerusalem in 70 AD, the Jews dispersed to many European countries, many settling in Spain and elsewhere in Europe, becoming known as Sephardic Jews. There is today a synagogue of Sephardic Jews in the City of London, and it is from them that Benjamin Disraeli came. Jews were not allowed to hold political office at that time but his family left Judaism and he later became Prime Minister of the country.

About 740 AD, the Khazars decided that they should have a national religion and invited the three principal faiths, Christian, Jewish and Muslim, to present their case. After much intrigue, they decided to become Jews. Their history has been most thoroughly investigated and documented by Arthur Koestler, himself a Jew, in his book, *The Thirteenth Tribe* (Koe76).

That there was a Jewish state in Asia came to the attention of Hasdai, a Sephardic Jew in Spain, and about 958 AD he sent to the Khazan ruler a questionnaire on their history and faith. They described how they adopted their religion by a decision as against the descent by birth that the Sephardic Jews possessed. They therefore had no blood relationship with OT Jewry.

The Khazars gradually dwindled in importance and all trace was lost, but at the same time there arose in Poland a Jewish group known as the Ashkenazim (and Hasidic) Jews. Although the available evidence was not decisive, Koestler was confident that these were the direct descendants of the Khazars. These migrated into Germany and westwards across Europe and elsewhere. The Sephardic Jews were well integrated into the culture of the nations, and their relationships with the expanding Ashkenazim Jews, who today vastly outnumber them, were not always cordial (*E.B.*1:626).

This interesting event is related to indicate just how complicated the histories of nations are. It demonstrates that they are often not quite the simple patterns that most people imagine.

A more recent claim is that the Khazars were the lost Ten Tribes of Israel whose blood descendants are the Picts, Anglo-Saxons and Scandinavians and that the Khazars also migrated to Europe, America, South Africa and Australia! From this, the present-day Jews of Judah and the Lost Ten Tribes are urged to recognize each other, and to work towards re-unification and reconciliation. Strangely, Britain is said to have the characteristics of Ephraim, whereas the British Israelites say we are descended from Dan! It will be interesting to see if these claims are given increasing prominence.

Togarmah

His descendants mainly settled around the area of Armenia. It is thought they might have given their name to Turkey, and by dropping the first syllable, to Germany.

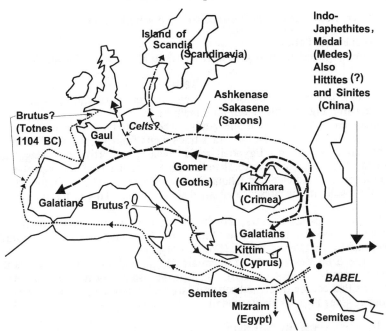

Fig. 4. Possible migrations in Europe after Babel

Magog

Custance points out that Ma-gog seems to mean only "the land of Gog" and says they were the founders of Russia. There is also the possibility that they gave their name to the Mongols, for there are pockets of people who still retain traces of an Indo-European form of language amidst the Hamitic Mongol people around them (Cus:90).

There was certainly much movement and dispersal even within one tribe, for Cooper says that the early Irish Celts traced their lineage back, not through Gomer, but through Magog to Japheth (Coo95:201).

Madai

These were the Medes who were the main Japhethite settlers of the Indian sub-continent.

Javan and Elisha

They became the Ionians and the Hellenes who were the two tribes that composed the Greek nation.

Dodanim

These settled in the area of western Turkey and gave their name to the Dardanelles. Cooper, differing from Custance, says that the early Britons traced their decent from Dardanus (Coo95:203).

Tarshish

Their locality is unsure but they may have given their name to Tartessos in Spain. The Septuagint renders Tarshish in Isaiah 23:1 as Karkedonos which is Carthage. The owners of the "ships of Tarshish" and the traders at these ports, however, would have been Phoenecians who were Hamites.

Meshech and Tubal
These migrated north to give their names to Moscow, Tiblisi and Tobolsk.

Shem
Shem's descendants - the Semites - remained principally in the Middle East as shown in Fig. 2. This is still their main location today. The Semites are, of course, both the Jews and the Arabs. The Jews trace their descent from Abraham and Isaac, whilst the Arabs trace theirs from Abraham and Ishmael - Abraham's son by his Egyptian maid Hagar (Gen. 16). Both Hagar and Ishmael were rejected by Abraham's wife Sarah, but God returned them to Abraham and predicted that Ishmael's descendants would be a multitude who would dwell "in the presence of all their brethren." This is the present-day situation.

Not all Arabs are Semites, though, for there are some who are of Hamitic descent. These are referred to as "Must'rabs" ("pretend" Arabs) and are much despised by the Semitic Arabs. (Coo95:174).

In Fig. 3 the descendants of Shem are set out with the various nations that settled mainly in the Near East. Most of the names given were founders of nations that can be discerned today or are well known from ancient records. Cooper gives these in greater detail.

Peleg - what was the "division"?
In his days, the "land (Hebrew = *eretz*) was divided" (Gen.10:25). There has been considerable debate amongst creationists as to whether this refers to the dispersal due to the confusion of languages or the splitting of the continents: i.e. plate tectonics. Cooper and Custance agree in a third view - that the evidence from the language and historical allusions shows it refers to the division of the land by canals and waterways. This might indicate the first establishment of private property between individuals by the marking out of boundaries.

Although the subject is still a matter for debate, it should be noted that the scattering from Babel was in the second or third generation after the Flood (Gen. 10:5, 20, 32). The division in the days of Peleg would have been in the fourth generation (Gen. 10:21-25). Furthermore "*eretz*" usually refers to the population of a land it refers to. The word for "divided" in Gen. 10:25 is "*peleg*" which usually refers to some form of physical division (often land), whereas the division of the people in verses 5 and 22 uses "*parad*". Thus, the weight of the textual evidence is that it was the physical land that was divided, which involved the divisions of the "people". Whether this was by canals (into properties) or the splitting of the continents is still not determined.

Abraham
He was the man, called by God, to separate himself from the pagan worship going on all around him. His family relationships are complicated and these are set out in Fig. 5 for clarification.

By a strange twist of reasoning, many fundamental Jews, contrary to their own *Torah* (Old Testament), contend that it is Abram who is to be praised for it was he who made the decision to lead a holy life and to worship God (MillA:para648). God had been waiting for someone to volunteer but no other man was prepared to, and the Jews "elected that role for themselves"

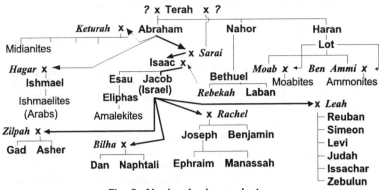

Fig. 5. Abraham's descendants

(para646).

In the OT, Gen. 18:19 says that God "knew" (KJV) Abraham but in the NIV this is rendered "chose", both of which are possible translations of the Hebrew "*yada.*" Ezekiel 20:5 says God "chose Israel" (Heb.=*bachar*) which is clearer. Deut. 7:6 and many other passages state the same. In the NT Paul stood up in the synagogue and said that God "chose our fathers." This is the only possible inference of the Greek "*eklegomai*" and his statement was not disputed by the Jews who were listening. It is abundantly clear that it is God who does the choosing of both nations and individual men.

Ham

Cooper quotes a most interesting passage (Coo95:186) recounting that the family of (C)Ham travelled into "diverse unknowne countries, searching, exploring and sitting downe in the same... and that no inhabited countryes cast forth greater multytudes, to raunge and stray into diverse remote Regions." This supports Custance's view that it was Ham's descendants who travelled across the whole world.

The quotation goes on to say that wherever they went "there beganne both the Ignoruance of true godliness...and (the) adoration of falce godes and the Devill." Certainly, the prime mover of this seems to have been Nimrod. Hislop, in his book *The Two Babylons* (His), claims that from him sprang the pagan practices of many religions, and his whole book is devoted to demonstrating that these pagan rituals form a large part of Roman Catholic symbolism, practices and ceremonies. This has been exposed by others also, but on historical subjects Hislop often draws sweeping conclusions on the basis of minor and inadequate quotations which tends to mar his case.

Nimrod

He was a "mighty man" of his day and his infamy still resounds. He is credited with the establishment of Babel and its tower. He is considered to have been the foremost pagan idolator who began the worship of idols. He is portrayed as the child at the breast of his mother and from him came the worship of the mother and child. This is a feature of many pagan religions where the mother and child have a variety of names - Rhea and Tammuz (Ezek 8:14) or Bacchus, Isis and Osiris in Egypt, Isi and Iswara in India. So deep-rooted is this concept that when Catholic missionaries reached Tibet, China and Japan, they found they also worshipped this image. They reported:

> "Shing Moo, the Holy Mother in China, being represented with a child in her arms, and a "glory" around her, exactly as if a Roman Catholic artist had been employed to set her up" (His:21).

We see, again, that those events that took place early in the life of the nations, like that of the Flood, have been retained in traditions over many centuries. Fig. 3 gives other descendants of Ham and the nations they founded.

EARLY SETTLEMENTS

After the Dispersion from Babel, the tribes migrated to different areas until they eventually penetrated to the far corners of the world. As we have previously commented, they would have used whatever natural materials were locally available as tools.

Cave Men?

If they were only passing through an area, then if caves were available they would have used these for shelter and would not have spent time making more permanent accommodation. As a result, the caves may have been inhabited by several groups passing through a locality.

The occupants have been given the classification of "cave-men" - with all the inference of low intelligence and primitive living that that implies. In fact, they would have been just as intelligent as present-day man - if not more so. The many cave paintings they made are an indication of the high level of their abilities and culture.

In addition, the resonance of some of these caves has been examined, and the sound often bears a close connection to the paintings - the sound of hooves with paintings of horses. They had a strong resonance at frequencies between 95-120 Hz (cycles per second) which is the range of a male voice chanting, suggesting their use for some form of ritual. Some stones appear to have been placed at specific points to enhance these particular resonant frequencies (Dever).

As a demonstration of the advanced level of their culture and skill, we will give two further examples.

A. Stonehenge and stone circles

A "Megalithic Yard" of 0.892m (2.93 ft) was used for the accurate setting out of these astronomical observation posts for the whole of England, Scotland and Brittany. Had this measure been copied from one tribe to another, it would have rapidly changed noticeably in length. This suggests there was a common culture covering all these areas that enabled this accurate measure to be used throughout. Probably a special group of men, perhaps priests who travelled around, were trained in this skilled craft . Yet this was during the late Neolithic and early Bronze ages - implying a higher social culture than is generally accepted for such "primitive" periods.

It is the opinion of this writer that this "priestly caste" entrusted with this knowledge would have been the Druids. They were admirably suited for this role as we will see in the next section.

The large megaliths of Stonehenge came from a site 18 miles (29 km) away, some weighing 50 tons. Certain 4-ton "bluestones" came from Pembrokeshire in Wales. The tops of the huge megaliths had a "peg and socket" joint to

"Orthodox Ages"

Age name		Parallel Ages	Approx. start dates BC
STONE	Eolithic	Villefranchian	>2M - 700,000??
	Early - Paleolithic	Abbevillian	2M - 100,000
		Acheulian (Chellean)	
	Middle - Mesolithic	Mousterian Levalloisian	16 - 10,000
		Aurignacian	
	Late - Neolithic	Solutrean	8,000
		Magdalenian	
COPPER	Chalcolithic		5 - 4,000
BRONZE	Early		3,300
	Middle		2,000
	Late		1,550
IRON	Early		1,200
	Middle		900
	Late		600

Fig. 6. The orthodox "Archaeological Ages" of civilisations

prevent the movement of the top stone bridging across the uprights. These supported stones were shaped on a curve and not left straight-sided. The accuracy and workmanship employed has astonished those who have investigated this amazing structure (Tyl79).

B. An orchestra

In 1978, the American Museum of Natural History mounted an exhibition of culture ascribed to the period 35,000 to 10,000 BC - say Late Palaeolithic-Mesolithic from Fig. 6. These included a bone flute with four holes above and two below requiring complex fingering, a percussion orchestra of painted mammoth bones which gave different timbres and tones, paintings of bearded and moustached men in cap and costume, women gowned and coiffed, some of them in prayer.

In Slovenia, a portion of a Neanderthal flute was found. It had four finger holes and was capable of producing pentatonic melodies - "true music" (*Independent on Sunday* 25/2/96 p15).

Considering such evidence of an advanced culture so early in the history of man, no longer should it ever be said that *any* culture was primitive - with the implication of low intelligence. They were intelligent people who only had access to natural materials. Simple - yes. Primitive - no.

Migration of tribes

The European/Caucasian race appear to have travelled much further abroad in ancient times than is usually appreciated. The Manchu dynasty in China (1644-1911) had many Caucasian features - white skins, etc. A number of skeletons with European characteristics have been found in the Far East. Similarly, Caucasian bodies and bones have been found in America, but these have been quickly removed from scientific examination by classifying them as ancient Indian bodies that Indians can bury in their tribal cemeteries (Bon). In Section 3.5 we referred to the Miao people of China who trace their ancestry through Japhet and not through Ham, the ancestor of the Chinese through the Sinites.

The Toltec Indians record that seven of their ancestors "came to these parts, having first passed great lands and seas, having lived in caves, and having endured great hardships *in order to reach this land*: they wandered 104 years through different parts of the world *before they reached the Hue Hue Tlapalan*, which was in Ce Tecpatl, 520 years after the Flood" (Q11/2:99).

Folk stories indicate this also. Josephus, in his *Antiquities* (Bk 1, Ch 5) says that they "took possession of that land... unto which God led them." We deal later with the migration of animals, but we see here that the differing groups *seemed to sense that they should reach a specific location in which they would finally settle*. It is suggested that this may have applied to many tribes, if not all.

On the settling of America, the Yucatans say they came from the Far East, passing through the sea which God made dry for them. The Olmec say they came by sea from the east and the Algonquins say they are of foreign origin and came by sea. This differs from a migration via the Bering Straits, and both routes may have been used to reach America.

When all these different people reached their appointed place, they would then build more permanent houses, but these would still be of local materials. Where timber was scarce, they would use clay bricks - either dried or burnt.

Archaeological dating methods

By classifying the expertise of early man in the fashioning of stones, bronze, iron and broken pottery (shards), archaeologists have labelled the various stages they consider marked man's progression from "cave-man" to historical times (about 330 BC - the time of Alexander the Great). Fig. 6 gives the orthodox period names with very approximate dates they spanned. The Mesolithic onwards are from Courville (1C:79), and the earlier ones are approximations from authorities that gave widely differing dates for the same ages.

This table is given as these names are often used in archaeological papers and it will enable each period to be related to others. However, we do not accept this classification and dating for the following reasons:

Firstly, it is often thought that each age existed for a considerable time and that it was fairly uniform throughout the whole of Europe and the Middle East at least. This would provide a means of dating and correlating settlements thousands of miles apart. Most archaeologists are aware, however, that there can be considerable overlap between widely differing ages, but this is usually confined to their specialist journals.

These classified ages imply an orderly sequence of events, but Fange gives many examples of artefacts found that completely contradict this impression (Q13/3:133). He reports a vase with contents that looked remarkably like a battery, and that there were electroplated articles nearby. Electroplated articles have been found elsewhere. A shield was found in Kentucky with a Welsh coat of arms, Roman coins found in several American states, and many more similarly unaccountable artefacts. The article following his (Q13/3:150) gives the considerable evidence that there was great migration from Europe (Celts, Vikings, Romans, etc.) to both North and South America prior to Columbus's voyage. This is a subject of considerable debate in America but little appears in the popular press.

We have earlier referred in the "Survey of Genesis" to Job's description of a "lower" race of men who were probably Neanderthals, and to the fact that there is evidence that there were farming communities at the same time as there were hunter-gatherers. Man did not progress from one method to the other but used the best means available to feed himself.

We consider that these early cultures were the primitive living conditions that a small tribe would have to adopt as it moved into virgin country. They would only have simple stone tools to construct shelters against the weather, but as they developed their tools and found local material, they would construct more permanent structures and develop more sophisticated utensils and ornaments. Therefore, we would suggest that the classified "ages" are only a guide to the stage of development that a local group had reached. To assume that such an age lasted for a considerable period and could be used as a means of determining a specific date for a particular site is unwarranted.

Courville contends that "age cannot be determined on the basis of the materials used in the making of tools and weapons" (Cou.v1:79). He quotes Kathleen Kenyon, a disciple of orthodox dating, who acknowledged that "several (ages) may have existed side by side" (Cou.v2:169). We will therefore make little reference to this method of dating.

Secondly, it will be obvious that the orthodox time scale is far longer than is acceptable to creationists. Did these stages of civilisations last for long periods of time? Courville shows how rapidly many layers of habitation could have been built up and how few in number the early occupants were.

The size of the early settlements

There are numerous mounds (called "tells" from an Arabic word) in the Middle East that are the remains of early towns and cities. They consist of many layers of habitations that have been built over one another for generations. Archaeologists excavate these tells and trace the different civilisations that have occupied the site over "thousands of years". By classifying their implements, shards of pottery and many other artefacts such as jewellery and metalwork, they have classified these civilisations into "ages" as discussed above.

There is little wood in the Middle East so the walls of their houses were made of mud shaped into a brick and often only sun-dried. There is evidence that the rainfall was very much higher in the period following the Flood, and it would quickly soften the mud and the walls would disintegrate. This mud could not be used to make replacement bricks and fresh mud would have to be collected. It is likely that such structures would have to be rebuilt at least once a year and possibly even more frequently. In this way a mound would be rapidly built up.

Over many years, the mound would grow in size and later occupants would use better materials. Sun-dried bricks can rapidly disintegrate under heavy rain, whilst fired bricks or stone walls may fall due to earthquakes or be destroyed and burnt by invaders, each level retaining relics that would enable modern archaeologists to classify each strata (Cou.v2:161). It might be thought strange that each series of occupants should elect to build upon the older levels to increasingly higher elevations, but this would provide an advantage as an additional barrier against invading forces, who would have to first climb the escarpment to reach the slope or wall around the city. As we will see, some actually plastered the slope to give a hard smooth surface (glissade) that would make access even more difficult.

It is interesting that these early sites often did not have any defences, but later ones did as the population pressure forced people to find fertile areas to live in and they invaded established settlements.

Courville also gives examples of just how small these early sites were. The second level at Troy was only 100 yds (90 m) in diameter and the first group to settle at Jericho after the Dispersion occupied an area of only 100 x 250 yds (90 x 230m). Excavations of many sites show that there are remarkably few cemeteries - there were only 60 for the whole of the Neolithic period at Mt. Carmel. At Alaja, there were only 13 graves that covered several occupation levels. It is evident that the groups who moved out during the Dispersion from Babel consisted initially of only a small number of people.

Jericho is one of the oldest cities in the world, and it is thought that it may have been inhabited just prior to the Dispersion from Babel. This first level had a stone building that appeared to have been a shelter from the elements. What was surprising was that two large stone blocks had holes drilled into them some 2.5 ft (0.8m) (Cou.v2:155). How they could have achieved this with presumably primitive equipment is a mystery but does indicate that they possessed a high level of intelligence to achieve such a feat. There are several books on the subject of extremely sophisticated artefacts found in early layers and at great depths in the geological strata (Hit. and Fang.).

In the upper layers, many levels of habitation were found - Courville only mentions 10, 19 and 26 levels and the total must have been very many more, indicating not that the periods of occupation were very long, but that each layer was frequently destroyed and needed rebuilding. These provided the huge mound on which eventually the famous walls of Jericho would be built against the invading Israelites, a subject we deal with in Section 3.8.

The Acheulian "hand axe"

As evidence of the advanced abilities of these migrating tribes, we give the discovery of the actual use of what have been known for many years as Acheulian "hand axes".

These are stone implements shaped from flint, or other hard stone, that were thought to be hand-held axes for chopping. As can be seen from Fig. 7, however, they are sharp on all edges and would have damaged the hand of the user. Their length ranges from a few inches to 13 ins. long.

O'Brien has demonstrated that they were far more likely to have been used as a missile for wounding or killing prey some distance away (O'BrienE). A resin replica, weighing 4 lb. 3 oz. (2kg), thrown flat and spinning like a discus, rose to its maximum height whereupon it unexpectedly turned on its side and descended on its edge, still rotating horizontally but more slowly. What was surprising was that it generally descended with the point towards the ground. Out of 45 throws, 42 landed on the edge, and, surprisingly, it landed on its point 31 times. Thus, 70% of all throws landed in its most lethal orientation. (Fig. 7 gives our understanding of the descending spin.) How did these early men know that this particular shape of stone would perform in this strange but useful way?

Its use for throwing at gatherings of feeding birds and animals some way off can be seen. This is confirmed by the discovery of many of these implements near to streams and water-holes, often found on their edge. The accuracy was also high, the "axe" hardly diverting from a straight line in its flight.

We have noted that the production of the first bolas stones for entangling the legs of running animals requires a extraordinary level of inventiveness, far beyond that of any "primitive man" (Bow88:104). The same would apply to the bow and arrow and to these carefully shaped stones that have been wrongly identified for so long. Although made from stone, they are the

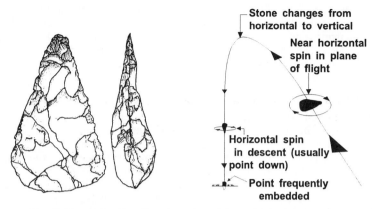

Fig. 7. The Acheulian "hand axe" and its spinning flight

product of a mind that is far more advanced than evolutionists like to admit. One expert, at least, has refused to accept that they were used for throwing.

These implements, which should no longer be called "hand axes" but "throwing stones", would have been an important weapon to men as they migrated across the world from Babel, shaping the local hard stones for this purpose. They are, in fact, found as far afield as India and Indonesia.

Skill, strength and accuracy of throw would have been of importance to the survival of a tribe, and O'Brien suggests that there is an echo of these abilities in the contest of throwing the discus in the Greek Olympiads: a link that is highly likely.

The boomerang

This is an extremely sophisticated instrument, designed with an aerofoil section to give lift to the two arms. It is considered that it was used to frighten birds into nets strung between trees (EB2:373), and as a pastime, but one might have thought that thrown into a flock of birds it would either bring down a catch or return to the thrower for another try. Its great advantage was the long time it could remain airborne. Although associated with Australian aborigines, it is actually a very early invention and has also been found in Palestine, Egypt, Europe, Africa and America but these were of the non-returning type that only curved in flight. These were heavier and used for hunting and warfare. It appears to have been carried to these lands from a single source, but many tribes had lost the art of making them.

The founding of Britain

There are two views on how these isles were first populated. Custance maintains that it was by migrations across Europe, whilst Cooper quotes the history of Brutus who came from Italy. We give the route Brutus followed in Fig. 4 and will examine this subject in the next section.

Troy

We would here mention the city of Troy, which fell in 788 BC (2Cou:274). Its history was recounted by Homer in his Odyssey but long regarded as purely mythical until the excavations of Shliemann in 1868 proved him accurate. Ceram graphically describes Shliemann sitting in the village square reading the 23rd book of the Odyssey to the local people. They still bore Trojan names and were the descendants of those who had been dead for 3,000 years. One can imagine the poignancy of the event as they heard of the exploits of their ancestors for - "Overcome by emotion, he wept, and the villagers wept with him" (Cer:24).

THE DEVELOPMENT OF THE VARIOUS HUMAN RACES

One question often asked is, "Are the different races an example of evolution?" The answer, of course, is, "No." Let us look at a parallel example.

Dogs have all been bred from a basic mongrel type, and by carefully selecting certain characteristics possessed by the young offspring that the breeder wants to emphasise, he will interbreed them and gradually, over not too many generations, a new breed of dog will emerge. The purity of the new breed has to be carefully preserved by only mating with other dogs of the same breed. To ensure this, the breeders maintain a strict record of the ancestors of all those dogs of a particular breed so that its purity can be maintained.

What is important to remember is that *all breeds are still dogs: they are not a new species.* They can all interbreed and have fertile offspring.

Genetically, the human race has developed and diverged on the same basis. As men began to disperse over the world, they would begin by being only a comparatively small group of people. This means that they would only have a part of the total "gene pool" that would have been originally possessed by the whole human race.

As they moved out as a small inter-marrying group, there would arise certain specific characteristics, just as in the interbreeding of dogs. As the numbers grew, they in turn would separate and form small inter-marrying groups. In this way would develop the very dark skin of the Africans, the pale skin of the Europeans, the straight black hair of the Chinese with his distinctive eye shape due to the epicanthic fold of the upper lid across the inner corner of the eye. A long list of specific characteristics of the various races could be drawn up.

It is also possible that the selective process may have been hastened by the choice of desirable features in a mate. One sex might find that a certain feature in the opposite sex becomes an attractive feature, and there would be a tendency for the possessors of these to find partners most easily, thus emphasising them in the development of the racial characteristics. This may have been a factor, but its effect might not have been great.

The "African Eve" theory - has it been discredited?

Certain features of the genetic information of cells is contained in their DNA - the genes and chromosomes. The DNA in a particular part of the cell - the mitochondria - is specific to it (mtDNA) and it is always inherited from the mother only. By examining the number of mutational changes in these mtDNA, geneticists concluded that there must have been a "bottleneck" at some time in man's past: i.e. that there was only one ancestor from whom all races have descended. Their results showed that the most likely centre for this was Africa and it was called the "African Eve" theory.

Creationists have taken this to indicate that all humans have sprung from one couple - usually Adam and Eve - but more correctly, this should be Noah and his sons with their wives who would have been the most recent "bottleneck".

The investigation began with the massive amount of information on the 147 DNA samples they had collected which the computer had to sort out to find the basic DNA arrangement from which all the others had diverged. Further investigations of the programming of the data that was used by the original investigators has revealed that it was sensitive to the order in which the basic data was fed into the programme. When the data was entered in a random manner, quite different results were obtained (Hed). The authors say that their results "suggest" an African source, but that it cannot be proven by this investigation.

It was proposed that this particular investigation should not be quoted by creationists due to the programming flaw. Further examination showed that although the place and date of the "bottleneck" was in doubt, that there *had* been a restriction, the main point of interest, was unaffected (Q31/1:10,31/4:2 02).

This was confirmed at a meeting actually held to disprove the "Eve" theory. One worker, who had found the flaw in the original programme, had investigated another human mitochondrial gene and declared: "all evolved from a common ancestor quite recently" (E93/7(2):201).

This only confirms the Biblical record. Noah had three sons who married three women from other families. The mtDNA bottleneck would therefore have been in this small number of people who may have been closely related in any case. There would be no bar to marrying a near relative in those days as discussed in Section 3.1, and the "godly" line of descendants of Seth preferred to marry near relatives (Gen.24:3-4). The (possibly related) women in the Ark would pass their mtDNA to their daughters, whose descendants dispersed after Babel to form local tribes that developed into nations. Many generations later, that a bottleneck once existed has now been detected by geneticists.

A very recent examination of the dating method using the mutation rate of the mtDNA (1/generation) and the number existing has yielded the surprising date of only 6,500 years since "mitochondrial Eve" lived (Plais). This has been "explained away" by assuming the elimination of earlier mutations.

THE MIGRATION OF ANIMALS

There are many puzzling features of how various specialised animals, when they left the Ark, could have reached the locations they now inhabit in such widely different areas of the world. Except for the dingo, which is placental but may have been brought in by man, there are only marsupials in Australia. There are some other specialised locations. Lemurs only exist in Madagascar and the nearby Comoro Islands. Elephants, of two different types, only live in Africa and India, and many similar examples could be quoted. How could they have reached these distinct locations, and why *only* these in particular?

Little is written about this, and creationists are generally silent on the subject: those models that have been suggested have not been convincing. Creationists usually point out that the evolutionists also have problems in explaining the present situation. There is no easy natural explanation, particularly how small creatures could have travelled long distances. Nevertheless, we would suggest that there is a possible explanation. Before we introduce this, let us examine two incidents in the Bible regarding the movement of animals.

The first is in Genesis 2:19 where God requires Adam to name all the beasts. To do this, God Himself "brought them to Adam to see what he would call them."

The second has been mentioned before and is in Genesis 6:20, where God says to Noah that two of each animal "will come to you" to be taken into the Ark. We would here note that if there was a uniform climate around the earth, then all the major pre-Flood species would be distributed fairly uniformly, and a suitable selection of them would not have been far from the Ark. There would be no need for two kangaroos to have to travel all the way from "Australia". It would not have existed at that time in any case!

There is the additional phenomenon of the instinct of seasonal migration, particularly in many birds. It is known that some young birds are able to travel huge distances along routes that they have never followed before as their parents had left some time earlier in the season. Similarly, pigeons, dogs and other creatures have an instinct to find their way back to their home having been transported many miles away.

We have two incidents in the Bible where God controlled the movement of animals and there are many examples of a deep-rooted instinct in some animals - perhaps all - to reach a very specific location. We have also shown that tribes appear to have migrated from Babel to specific locations appointed to them by God.

With all this in mind, there is surely no great difficulty in accepting that it was God who, having placed an instinct within a selected number that brought them to the Ark in the first place, then used the same means of dispersing them to specific locations around the world when they emerged from the Ark after the Flood. He would, of course, guide them to habitats suitable for their metabolism: polar bears would have difficulty surviving in the middle of a desert area!

Regarding specialised animals like polar bears that have obviously been designed for cold climates, the question has been asked, "How did they survive in the pre-Flood climate that, according to creationists, was uniformly warm under the Water Vapour Canopy"? This would only require the same change in features of animals and plants that took place after the Fall. All acts of creation ceased after the sixth day, and therefore all changes after that day would be modifications to the existing genetic material that resulted in a change in many animals and plants. After the Flood, further genetic changes could have taken place in the descendents from just the two of each kind in the Ark. Thus from the bear kind, all the different bears, adapted to various environments, could have developed over just a few generations. God would then have had them migrate to the locations most suitable for each animal by an instinct He planted within them.

This scenario seems to be the only reasonable conclusion that can be drawn, and it is presented as a proposal that solves a quite intractable problem and does have support from both the Bible and nature.

Some animals appear to inhabit land and exist in climates for which they are very specially adapted to. For instance, the polar bear is extremely well adapted to living in the very cold conditions around the North Pole. How could it have survived very much hotter climates on its journey to such remote and inhospitable places?

One possible explanation is that the original pair of bears, or perhaps a few that had the full gene pool between them, travelled to various areas, and during their migration gradually adapted to the climate in the area that was their allocated destination. This would be in a not dissimilar way in which humans have adapted, but by a much lesser degree, as they travelled to their respective locations after Babel.

It must be admitted that there is still the problem of how small creatures and insects that are designed to live in extremes of climate reached these locations. It is possible that they may have travelled long distances over many generations, but this is difficult to envisage this and there would have been many different climates they would have had to pass through. Whether there was a similar adaptation as they travelled would be difficult to prove.

We would here mention that in some books, fossils of certain species are used as evidence of their migratory passage to remote areas. We would suggest that such evidence is dubious, as it is based upon the assumption that their travels took many thousands of years at least, and some left their bones as a record of their passage through the area; i.e. it is based upon an evolutionary viewpoint. If it is assumed that all the strata were laid down a the time of the Flood, then the distribution of the fossils would have no connection with the final locations of the animals after their emergence from the Ark. If some of the upper strata were laid down subsequent to the Flood, then they would have to be carefully checked to ensure that any fossils they contained could have been on their way to a more remote location.

SECTION 3.7
EARLY BRITISH CHRISTIANITY

Whilst not strictly part of the thesis of this book, it is hoped that the reader will find this digression as fascinating as this author did when Bill Cooper casually mentioned in conversation the British lineage of Linus and Claudia in the Bible (2 Tim.4:21). It is his research that much of this section is based upon, and I am indebted to him for his permission to use it and to build upon his foundation with additional research.

We should first explain why it is necessary to examine ancient Welsh documents to learn about early British history. In the 7th century AD, 1,800 years after the early Britons had landed and colonised Britain, they were forced out into the remote area of Wales by invading Saxons. The earliest records of British history are therefore to be found in ancient Welsh records; records that have been almost completely ignored by modern scholars.

THE FOUNDING OF BRITAIN

As mentioned previously, Custance assumes that the first inhabitants were Celts from the European mainland. Cooper's view is that Brutus led a group of slaves to these isles, and it is this that we will examine in more detail.

Cooper quotes an address by Flinders Petrie entitled *Neglected British History* in which he drew on an ancient document, the *Tysilio Chronicle*. This was a translation into medieval Welsh in an early British record by Geoffrey of Monmouth (Coo95:54).

This tells of Brutus, illegitimate son of an Italian king, who was banished to Greece for accidentally slaying his father in a hunting accident. Here he found a group of slaves taken prisoner after the fall of Troy. He led them to victory in a battle against the Dorian (Greek) king, following which he took the king's daughter as his wife and sailed away with his men, initially towards Egypt. Flinders gives his precise route and he remarked on the accuracy of the record, for they referred to well known locations with the names that were only used at that time and which fell out of use soon after.

One particular location was the isle of Levkas which has the remains of many oak trees, and Cooper wonders whether this was the origin of the importance of the oak tree in the Druid religion (Coo95:64). In Spain, Brutus was joined by Corineus, who was to give his name to Cornwall. In France, they had a fierce battle with Picts, but eventually arrived at Totnes in Devon in 1104 BC. Their passage to Britain is set out in Fig. 3.6.4.

The works of Geoffrey of Monmouth, particularly his *History of the Kings of Britain* are dismissed by historians as fabricated romance. Certainly, some incidents in this latter book reads like medieval fables, but this does not mean that everything he records is to be dismissed; certainly not the *Tysilio Chronicle*. Indeed, it is one of the main complaints of Cooper that there are many reliable documents that have been ignored by historians simply because they contradict the picture of the early British as being little more than uncivilised pagans - until the advent of Augustine in 597 AD.

Is there any independent evidence that supports this story of Brutus's colonisation of the British Isles? There are some interesting pointers.

(i) There is a stone in Fore Street, Totnes, close to the East Gate known as the Brutus Stone (Fig. 1). Now why should this stone, after all these centuries, still refer to the existence of a Brutus if there was no one of such name? Even if so named as a tourist attraction, there must surely be a hint of truth about a long-standing fable that makes it still worth referring to.

(ii) Seaman quotes two authorities on jurisprudence who trace British laws back to Trojan law and another who refers specifically to Brutus writing his laws in Greek (Sea:53).

(iii) In a well researched and referenced book by Elder about the Druids, it was mentioned that:

> Only once before, in the war with Antiochus, 192 BC, [had] the Romans met with similar chariots, but never in any European country. The British chariot was built after the *eastern* pattern, adorned with carved figures and armed with hooks and scythes. British chariots were prized possessions of the Romans.

Fig. 1. The Brutus Stone at Totnes

> Diodorus Siculus, 60 BC, states: "The Britons live in the same manner that the ancients did: they fight in chariots, *as the ancient heroes of Greece are said to have done in the Trojan wars*".
>
> Britain, long before the Roman invasion, was famous for its breed of horses and the daring and accomplishment of its charioteers (Eld:24).

(iv) In the same book, it mentions:

> Canon Lysons says: "It is to be remembered that the earliest British coins are not imitations of the Roman coinage; *they much resemble the coinage of Philip of Macedon, Alexander the Great and the Greek and eastern mintage*'" (Eld:29).

(v) The *Encyclopaedia Britannica* mentions that the Druids studied for up to twenty years but they left no written records as "they thought it wrong to commit their learning to writing *but used the Greek alphabet for other purposes*" (EB18:895). This use of Greek letters is referred to in Ceasar's *Gallic Wars* (Cae:bVI s14).

Why should this highly learned religious order, of all the languages they could have used, specifically use Greek for the few writings they did make? They were separated from Greece by many miles and there is no obvious connection. They were established long before Greek became the language used for trading in the Middle East. Surely all this evidence suggests that there *was* a very strong link between the British and a Greek origin.

(vi) Possibly the first Christian church in London was St. Peter on Cornhill, founded by Lucius (crowned c 124 AD). It was destroyed in the Great Fire but the dedication stone is preserved in the vestry. This states that Lucius "reigned in this land after Brute 1245 yeares" (Jow:207). This would date Brutus's arrival about 1121 BC, very close to the 1104 BC given by Cooper. Lucius presumably traced his ancestry back to Brutus, and before the Christian era, British dating appears to begin from the year of Brutus's arrival.

One cannot say that these pieces of evidence are a definite proof that Britain was founded by Brutus, but we will leave the reader to decide what level of conviction they provide.

On the death of Brutus, the land was divided between his three sons.

LOCRINUS'S area was in the north and was known as Loegria. It is interesting that still today, the Welsh name for England is Loegr.

KAMBER took the area of Wales, which was known as Cambria. The Welsh call their land Cymru. It is this name that is given to the Cambrian rocks in geology.

ALBANACTUS settled in Scotland, known then as Albany. The present Gaelic for Scotland is "Albaiin".

That these names are still current in our language is a remarkable tribute to the longevity of place names in language and folk history. They are yet another witness to the true historicity of the people to whose existence they testify.

THE MOLMUTINE LAWS

There were a number of successive kings who ruled the central area of Britain. One of them deserves special mention for the laws that he enacted. Dunvallo Molmutine ruled for 40 years (420 - 380 BC), an extremely lengthy reign for those days, when the majority ruled for only 5-10 years. His reign was very peaceful, mainly due to the Molmutine Laws that he enacted, which are considered to be the foundation of British justice as they were clear, brief, just and humane. Alfred used them as a basis for his Anglo-Saxon code and Geoffrey of Monmouth, writing fifteen hundred years later, said that they were still famed and revered in his day. (See Coo95:215f and Eld:20).

These were very strict, and so severe was the punishment of criminals that crimes of violence were virtually unheard of. Other laws were the ownership of property which no one could take from an ancient Briton. They were not allowed to keep slaves. Prisoners of war could be used as employees, but after the third generation they were allowed to become full-fledged citizens. A foreigner could become a citizen after nine generations. The monarchy was an elected one.

Judges were to respect the local customs and, most surprisingly, after a court case the records were destroyed. This prevented the establishment of law by precedence - each case was judged on its merits and not what was judged before.

Billingsgate may be named after Belinus, the son of Dunvallo, who founded London (Eld:23), but Bile (Belenus, Beltaine) is also the name of one of the many Celtic gods and it may have been named after him.

THE DRUIDS

The major factor that united this country with the tribes of Europe was the Druid religion. Very little is said to be known about their beliefs and practices as they did not usually commit them to writing.

There are two views regarding the teachings and practices of the Druids. One is that they were teachers of a noble faith that paved the way for Christianity. The other is that they indulged in magic and human sacrifices.

Druid teaching

Morgan (Mor) and Elder (Eld) contend that the Druid beliefs were so very similar to that of Christianity that they adopted the new faith with ease. They were a highly trained body of men whose education lasted 20 years. They operated as far as France, Germany and southern Scandinavia, but they were centred in Britain at three "universities" - Caer Llyndain (London), Caer Evroc (York) and Caer Lleon (Carlisle). This is confirmed by Julius Caesar who said that the centre of European Druidism was Britain (Cae:bk VI s15).

There were many similarities between their highly moral faith and that of Christianity. One difference, however, seems to be that they had a form of belief in reincarnation. They had several gods but principally a triune godhead, with the names of Beli (or Teutates), Taran(is) and Esu (or Yesu). Morgan and Elder present them as an extremely noble and high-minded religious body who were formed as such, in the purposes of God, to readily accept Christianity, for their whole ethos was so very similar. Their motto was "Truth against the world", and its similarity to the Christian world view is obvious. When Claudius banned Druidism in Gaul in 54 AD he excluded Britain. The reason given for this ban was their practice of human sacrifices, but it has been suggested that the real aim was political (Ross).

Hislop does note (critically) that crosses were worshipped in many tribes, amongst them the Druids, long before the coming of Christ. He quotes one author who said that they selected the most beautiful tree, cut off the side branches and fixed two large branches near the top on each side so that they extended outwards like the outstretched arm of a man (His:199).

They trained their youth in academics and trade skills, and also had a form of social support for the sick and injured. Women were given high status and could become rulers over men and even warriors, as we see in Boadicea and Maeve. All this would have created a highly organised culture of great benefit to any nation in which it operated.

The darker side

All this puts the Druids in a very good light, and it is understandable that those presenting this view would want to ignore any darker side that contradicts their case. Initially, this viewpoint was accepted, but correspondence with Mr. Peter Kelly who researched this aspect of the Druids in depth, persuaded me that many Druid practices were the complete antithesis of NT Christianity. With all their noble teachings, they also engaged in the casting of spells, alchemy, magical ritual, the occult and almost certainly human sacrifices. Spells were often used to bring victory in battle.

Human sacrifices

Some writers deny that the Druids engaged in human sacrifice, but others quote Julius Caesar's writings in support. However, a careful reading of his comments suggests that on the continent, they appear to have officiated at pagan rituals that may not have been part of their Druidic training.

The highest centres of learning were actually in Ireland, which upsets the British Israelite view of Britain being the centre for pre-Christian Druidism. It has been suggested that the name of the god Esus was as a forerunner of Jesus, but this is only a coincidence. In fact, each of the three gods required sacrifices in different ways: Taranis - fire or blows from an axe; Esus (or Ileus or Isis) - stabbing or hanging; Teutates - drowning (Ross:46).

A clear example where these ritual slayings were used on one body is that of "Lindow Man". This body, found in a peat bog, had been ritually killed by two blows to the skull, one to the neck, garroting, cutting of the jugular vein in the neck and then thrown into water (Ross:25f). Ross suggested that this was a Druid who was sacrificed in view of the Roman invasion. It is thought that Druids, who were often noblemen, would have considered it an honour to have been the victim. There also appears to be some evidence for many Celtic tribes here, in Ireland and in Europe indulging in cannibalism.

Over 80 bodies that appear to have been sacrifices have been found in Britain, mainly centred in the north, whilst over 1,000 have been found in Denmark and Northern Germany. Ellis points out that these bodies were on the fringe of the Celtic world and may have been the result of *Scandinavian* influences (Ell:150). He also claims that there is no direct evidence that the Druids engaged in or taught human sacrifices. He contends that all these charges are made by their enemies and could be only "war propaganda".

However, sacrifices could not have taken place without the approval of the Druids in view of the powerful position they held in their society, but just what part it played in Druidic teaching is still debatable.

Was the Druid religion preparing the ground for Christianity? Kelly contends that gradually it became amalgamated with the early NT Christianity in this country, thereby destroying its real basis. When true Christianity is mixed with anything else, no matter how small, its foundation is removed (Gal. 1:8-9). However, it must be emphasised that *any* Christian influence, no matter how distorted it may be, upon a pagan society will have a great beneficial influence, and this is obviously the case with the Druidic form of Christianity that spread so far across Europe.

But just how far some features were from NT Christianity can be seen in the life of St Columba (Colmcille) (521-597). He was a converted Irish Druid, a Culdee, who angered his tutor when he secretly copied an important book and was put in prison. He escaped and raised an army in Ireland, fought in and won a battle with the King Dairmid. However, he was *banished* to the north and eventually he came to Iona which was already a sacred island to the Druids. Here he asked to found an abbey, but a sacrifice was required for this. In 1984 a body was found in the foundations of the abbey which may have been one of his companions (Ross:134). Here he founded his own colony of priests and sent missionaries throughout Europe. However, his form of Christianity included many Druidic practices, such as charms and spells for healing and foretelling the future. They may also have fought in wars, although they were exempt from military service (Ross:135).

The layout of Druid monasteries was extremely symbolic and their influence can be seen in many churches today. Ante temples (outer courts) for new converts, naves for lay members and the sanctuary only for priests, with the altar and seat of authority, are reminiscent of the hierarchical OT Jewish Temple and Druid temples. This is in contrast to the NT gatherings in the homes of the people in which the equality of believers is stressed.

Similarly, all the "well dressings", parades and other such practices have Celtic origins and act as subtle diversions from the true Christian faith.

One of the practices of Druidism was monasticism, which appears to have come from Egypt before the time of Christ. There are the examples of Christ and Paul spending time in the desert, but this was to specially equip them for a life of service within the community. There is no warrant in the Bible for a permanent monastic life and the influence of monasticism in diverting true Christianity has been profound. There is this constant human pressure to concentrate power into large institutions which can then be ruled by a few men in positions of authority. In contrast, true Christian faith comes as a direct gift from God to each individual (Eph. 2:8-9). God's influence is seen most clearly in the periods of revival - which are rarely referred to by liberal Christians.

Today, Druidism is not only very active but growing. It is playing an important part in the paganisation and amalgamation of the religions of all nations, and is one of the many "religious" (in the broadest sense of that word) organisations that are connected at a very high level. We find this occult thread not only connecting apparently independent organisations, but extending back into the dim past also. Thus, Babylonian, Egyptian and Greek schools influenced the Druids, which Hislop also points to as the sources of pagan influences on the Christian church (Hisl).

There are now many links between the major secret organisations. Indeed, to progress to the top of their organisation, Freemasons are required to become involved with other occult bodies. The masonically inspired World Council of Churches, the New Age Movement (with its many connections with other organisations), Druidism, Cabbalism, Rosicrucianism, Theosophy, Knight Templars, the Findhorn (Buddhist) community and other such secret societies are all interconnected at the very highest levels. Members of one are often members of others or have close connections with their leaders. This co-operation, which is little known, is set out by Alan Morrison in his book *The Serpent and the Cross* (MorrA). For example, both Nehru and Gandhi were theosophists (p88). W.B. Yeats was a member of "The Golden Dawn" organisation, as was Alistair Crowley, the self-confessed Satanist. Yeats and Eliphas Levi often visited the occultists Madame Blavatsky and Annie Besant (Kelly: priv. comm). These connections between well-known people seem to be endless. We are indeed surrounded by webs of intrigue that exert enormous influence that few realise.

A further development of this unholy alliance is the story now being put around that Christ did not die upon the Cross, but lived and fathered children. As a result, His descendant has been, or is expected to be, recognised as the new messiah who will be revealed in due time. This new appearance of a "saviour" is a central theme of Judaism, Zionism and other faiths and will no doubt be accepted by some "christians". One of several books propagating this blasphemous idea is *The Holy Blood and the Holy Grail* by Baigent (Corgi 1983). We can expect to see more "startling revelations" on this subject and other similar claims when the timing is deemed suitable.

We would therefore conclude that Druidism, whilst raising the culture of the land to a high level, nevertheless practised many occult rituals, and when many Druids converted to Christianity they eventually corrupted the purity of the Christian faith that first reached these isles. However, it would appear that much of the good influence of the new Christian faith and its teachings on the right conduct of one's life was retained and spread abroad, benefiting all who responded to it.

British culture and morals

Elder quotes a number of eye-witness accounts of the high level of morals and culture of the early Britons, the more impressive being those of foreigners. The Phoenician Himilcar, about the 6th century BC, records that the Britons were "a powerful race, proud spirited, effectively skilful in art, and constantly busy with the cares of trade". They were skilled in metalwork and the art of enamelling which few other nations could emulate.

We have quoted Diodorus Siculus, 60 BC, regarding the British accomplishments on chariots. He also commented:

They are plain and upright in their dealings, and far from the craft and subtlety of our countrymen.... The island is very populous.... the Celts never shut the doors of their houses; they invite strangers to their feasts, and when all is over ask who they are and what is their business (Eld:25).

Ross records that the Druids taught that "the gods must be worshipped, *and no evil done*, and manly behaviour maintained" (Ross:141).

Elder also notes that the so-called Roman roads were built by Molmutius. The Dover to Holyhead road was called Sarn Wydellin (Watling Street) and that to the north from London was Sarn Ikin (Icknield Street). These permitted the rapid passage of their chariots and were free for trading by all foreigners. They were under the King's protection, giving rise to the term "The King's Highway" (Eld:24).

Tacitus commented on the British showing spirit when in battle, and that although they were prepared to pay tribute, etc., they "bitterly resented" abuse by the occupying forces "for they are broken in to obedience, but not as yet to slavery" (TacAg:63). Caesar also commented on their bravery as we shall see.

A British woollen cloak was a treasured possession in Rome, and Strabo, a contemporary of Caesar, said that trade with the very commercialised British would be more profitable than conquering them and then having to keep an army in residence thereafter (Ellis:68). This differs from Caesar's description of them as half-savages.

Thus, far from being the woad-painted, half-civilised pagans, as our ancestors are so frequently described, contemporary records show that they were highly civilised, industrious, fair-dealing and courageous in battle.

THE COMING OF CHRISTIANITY TO BRITAIN

In examining this subject, we find that there are a number of tantalising pieces of information that throw a light on the way in which Christianity may have first come to these shores. The problem is to piece them together without forcing them to say more than the slim facts can bear. In view of this, we should first deal with the Glastonbury story published by the British-Israel Association (now called the British-Israel-World Federation - BIWFed). As we have said, this organisation also contends that Britain was founded by the northern Israelite tribe of Dan, but few Christians accept this.

Joseph of Arimathea and Glastonbury

It is claimed that Christianity was first brought to these islands by Joseph of Arimathea who arrived at what is now Glastonbury. He is said to have been cast adrift by the Jewish authorities in a boat containing Mary, the wife of Cleopas, Martha, Lazarus, Mary Magdalene and several others. They are supposed to have drifted to Marseille (in an open boat without oars!) and then travelled to Britain where they set up the very first Christian church at Glastonbury. They brought with them the Communion Cup that Christ used in the Upper Room which became known as "The Holy Grail".

A full account is given in Jowett's *The Drama of the Lost Disciples* (Jow) which is filled with dramatic detail but only a bibliography at the end and a sprinkling of specific references. Consequently, his work is difficult to check.

Accounts of events such as those surrounding Glastonbury initially suggested an element of medieval fabrication to stimulate the faith of the many illiterate peasants in those days. Indeed, one has the strong feeling in reading his book that Jowett has used the very slimmest of evidence to support his claim that all the main characters of the Biblical drama around the Cross had resided in or visited these isles.

For example, Jowett (p33), quotes the story that they were all cast adrift in an open boat without sails or oars, and eventually drifted to Marseille. How they could have survived such a journey of some 2,000 miles (3,200 km) he does not question, and its improbability does not seem to trouble him. It surely fails the very first test of whether any recorded event is reasonable.

Jowett's authority for this is Baronius, a Catholic writer in the 17th century. Baronius is criticised by Protestant historians, and one historian, quoted in the *Encyclopaedia Britannica*, called him a recorder of fanciful tales. However, Seaman, and others, consider him a most careful historian. What is interesting is that a Catholic should record an account in very ancient documents of the arrival of the Christian faith to a Protestant nation at such an early date! We will find this is repeated in other events.

This nation is portrayed as the centre of true Christian religion following the expulsion of Joseph and his boatload of saints and others later. Britain did become the first Christian nation, as we shall see, but Jowett indulges in a degree of fanciful extrapolation where there are no hard facts. At times he contradicts the Scriptural account and he should be read with caution.

A far more reliable writer on this subject is Rev. R.W. Morgan. He gives many more references and where he is not certain he leaves the reader to judge whether a record of particular events is accurate. Unfortunately, even he, on the basis of Paul sending greetings to Rufus and "his mother and mine" (Rom.16:13) proposes that Paul was Rufus's half-brother. There is good evidence that Christianity came to these isles at a very early date, and any unnecessary and exaggerated extrapolations, such as we have examined, only damage its credibility.

We would also particularly recommend Seaman's *The Dawn of Christianity in the West* (Sea) which carefully records much more evidence that we have had to omit due to limitations of space.

An unexpected confirmation?

It is thought that Joseph of Arimathea was a rich trader in tin who made many voyages to England. What was his relationship to the Holy Family?

Seaman refers to two manuscripts (in the British Museum and Jesus College) that state he was the younger brother of Mary's father - i.e. Jesus's great uncle. The Bible often gives the family relationships between people it refers to, yet despite all four gospels describing Joseph obtaining Jesus's body from Pilate there is not a single reference to what would have been an important relationship. On the other hand, it was the well-established rule that near-relatives were responsible for others related to them in many social situations and this included the burial of the dead. This would explain why Joseph could ask for Jesus's body from Pilate and was granted immediate permission.

To escape persecution, Joseph may have left Jerusalem with several other Christians whilst the apostles remained in Jerusalem (Acts 8:1). The party may have landed at Marseille and travelled through France. Eventually they sailed up to the present site of Glastonbury, and struggled up "Weary-all" hill. The British king granted them a site on which a simple church was built. This became a centre of religion which is still recognised today.

Surprisingly, support for at least the basic elements of this story can be gleaned from Ashe, a writer who is very critical of these early "fables" in his book *Mythology of the British Isle* (Ash). It is worth quoting him at length for the admissions that he is almost forced to make regarding the errors historians have made about early British history and the unusual degree of support that there is for some events;

> Despite the lack of evidence that this happened early, the legend has touches of plausibility and may reflect a long standing belief, even, as suggested, a belief known to Gildas: not necessarily about Joseph in person, but about someone or something. At the beginning of the Christian era the Glastonbury hill-cluster was almost an island in times of high tide and flooding. Vessels could reach it from the Bristol Channel. Two nearby lake-village, centres of the La Tene culture, had long had overseas trade connections. Voyagers from distant countries could thus have known the area and made their way to it. Again, the notion of a British king being able to make land grants in 63 (AD) would, until recently, have been rejected, because the Romans were assumed to have conquered south-west Britain by then and stamped out its independence. Yet excavations of the Cadbury hill-fort a few miles off has demonstrated a Roman assault in the 60's or even later. Boudicca's [Boadicea] rising may have had a western offshoot. A British chief may have been holding out, like Hereward the Wake, in a miniature realm among the hills, islands, lakes and marshes of central Somerset. Arviragus? In Geoffrey (of Monmouth) he is impossibly the king of all Britain. Yet it is curious that the one authentic allusion to him, Juvenal's, shows Romans recalling him as one who made trouble for them.
>
> On the face of it, the monks who composed the story of Joseph could scarcely have known any of this, because the data on the lake villages and Cadbury have emerged only from archaeology. They would not have contrived their tale as manifestly plausible. Apparently it was not. Perhaps they did draw on knowledge that has escaped documentation (Ash:147-8).

This is surely a most enlightening passage in many ways. Not only does Ashe clearly admit that historians have been wrong on several counts, but says that the monks did record the event with accuracy as shown by evidence that has only recently been discovered. The story could not have been fabricated after the area could no longer be reached directly by ship.

It is certain that these records are far more accurate than historians dare admit. The slighting reference to Arviragus (described as "semi-historical" by another historian) ignores the fact that the British tribes not under the Roman yoke were united under an elected Pendragon to lead them into battle. Arviragus is the main Pendragon in the annals of Geoffrey of Monmouth.

Other evidence he gives is that "the church which he was alleged to have built did exist. Fire destroyed it in 1184; the Lady Chapel today marks its site" (p147). He also seems to accept that between 174 and 189 what he calls papal missionaries - actually returning missionaries called by Lucius (see later) - journeyed to Glastonbury and found "Joseph's derelict church, with crosses and other signs of the former occupancy" (p146). Even more interesting is his reference to the "fable" of Joseph and his tired group climbing "Weary-all Hill" where he thrust his staff into the ground and it blossomed:

As for the Glastonbury Thorn, the parent tree grew upon the slope of Wearyall Hill, or correctly, Wirral. A Puritan cut it down in 1643, but many descendants are flourishing, including a fine specimen in front of St. John's Church in the High Street. The famous white blossoms do make their appearance round about Christmas, and a sample from St. John's is dispatched to the reigning sovereign. Allusions to the Thorn are found in the reign of Henry VIII, not certainly before, and even then it is not associated with Joseph. His miraculous staff is post-Reformation. The tree is a kind of hawthorn, Crataegus oxyacantha praecox, and is not quite like any other English tree, *but does resemble varieties in Syria and Palestine, whatever one cares to make of that* (Ash:149).

Although Ashe entitled his book *Mythology of the British Isle*, in this particular chapter, far from demolishing the "myth" of Glastonbury he has given a fair amount of evidence in its support.

Regarding the granting of "twelve hides of land" to Joseph at Glastonbury by Arviragus, it is surely significant that one thousand years later, the Domesday Book records that the Glastonbury Church had "in its villa XII hides of land which have never paid tax" (Sea:43).

Although this author was at first fairly sceptical of what appeared to be extravagant claims for early British Christianity, the combined evidence was somewhat better supported than expected. Early authorities who mentioned this were:

(i) The Augustinicio Mission (597 AD) notes "Britain officially proclaimed Christian by King Lucius at the national Council at Winchester, 156 AD"

(ii) Eusebius (early 4th century) "The Apostles passed beyond the ocean to the Isles called the Britannic Isles"

(iii) Tertullian (208 AD) "The Christian Church extended to all the boundaries of Gaul, and to parts of Britain inaccessible to the Romans but subject to Christ."

Many others could be quoted. Even the Catholic *Westminster Year Book* for 1997 notes that "It is certain that Christianity had penetrated eastern Britain under the Romans.... It is possible as well that Christianity penetrated the west of Britain at a very early period - hence the legends of Joseph of Arimathea, not altogether implausible."

There is the saying, "No smoke without a fire", and it is like finding a few ashes scattered around and a distinct smell of smoke that suggests there was a fire at some time in the past.

Jesus in England?

We would here mention the story of Jesus being taken on a visit to England by Joseph of Arimathea, said to be his great uncle and a trader to these isles. Whilst here he is purported to have built a small church at Glastonbury. It is this story that gave rise to William Blake's poem "And did those feet in ancient times...."

There is some evidence for this and we will simply set it out with little comment.

(i) In the library of Canterbury Cathedral there is a letter, purported to be a copy of one in the Vatican, written by Augustine shortly after his arrival on these shores. He says that they had found a church (at the site of Glastonbury) constructed "by the hands of Christ himself for the salvation of his people" (Sea:11). This news would not be welcome to the Roman

Catholic hierarchy of that day intent as it was on establishing its supremacy over this nation. The original is said to have been mislaid and not recorded in the archives. Did it ever exist, or was it "removed"?

(ii) In the area of Looe, south Cornwall, there is a tradition that Jesus and Joseph landed there. Britain supplied the world with tin and there is a tradition amongst tin metalworkers of Joseph being in the tin trade and bringing Jesus to these shores. The two rich veins of tin in Cornwall are known as Corpus Christie (the body of Christ) and Wheal (Cornish for mine) Jesus. Were these only "pious practices" initiated by the Roman Catholic church for the benefit of their superstitious believers, or do they contain a grain of truth?

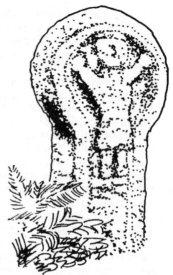

Fig. 2. The "Tunic" cross at Feoch, Truro

(iii) There are a number of stone "Tunic Crosses" in the west country in the tin mining area. They have a carving of the Celtic Cross on one side and on the other that of a boy in a knee-length tunic, holding his hands up as if in a blessing. Were these also Catholic institutions? Fig. 2 is from a photograph in Seaman's book in which he gives several other anecdotes (Sea:37).

What could be the source of the names for the tin mines and crosses? There are three possibilities.

(i) They may have been an invention of the later Catholic church. However, to propose that Jesus *did* visit these shores would give this nation such a prominent position in the direct interest of Our Lord that their claim that Peter was the founder of the church in Rome would pale into insignificance.

(ii) They may be fables and wishful thinking. But then arises the question of why Jesus should be referred to in two different subjects and both in the same area of the country? As we have seen, there is often a basis to these ancient tales.

(iii) There was a direct link with the young Jesus.

Further than this we will not go.

THE ROMAN INVASIONS OF BRITAIN

After the settlement of Brutus, there was a succession of kings of each area, banding together when threatened and placing themselves under one of the kings (the Pendragon) for coordinating their combined forces in battle. This is of importance when we come to the first Roman invasion of Julius Caesar in 55 BC. He used this to test the British methods of fighting and almost lost the battle before he could even get onto the land for the Britons waded into the sea to reach the invaders even before they had landed. In his records (Cae) he admires the skill of the charioteers who could fight by balancing on the poles and then leap back into the chariot. When it was advantageous they would dismount and fight like infantry showing "the mobility of cavalry and the stability of infantry" (Cae:bk4, para33-4) throwing the Romans into confusion.

The Britons resisted with extreme ferocity, using "guerilla" tactics to harass the enemy and Caesar only penetrated a few miles inland. The invasion the following year in 54 BC was not much more successful. He reached the Thames and some tribes submitted to Roman rule, but both visits were virtual defeats. For a general who had won so many great victories, his failure to overcome the British is particularly significant. What is interesting is that on both invasions, just after landing, his fleet was badly damaged by storms, and this may have induced him to return to the continent soon after his invasion rather than be faced with a winter of hostilities in Britain. The Channel has been our bulwark for centuries.

After Julius Caesar's effective defeat, Morgan (Morg) quotes several sources who note that the British were the only people in Europe who could walk the streets of Rome as freemen.

In 43 AD, it was more effectively invaded by Aulus Plautius under the orders of the Emperor Claudius. As before, the resistance of the Britons was fierce and many reverses were inflicted on the Romans. The invaders never conquered the whole of Britain but they gradually occupied much of the area of England by about 80 AD. It was then that they built Hadrian's Walls in the north to keep out the marauding bands of Picts and Scots. Tacitus noted that between 43 and 86 AD, no less than sixty pitched battles took place, indicating the ferocity with which the Roman invasion was resisted.

Caractacus

When Plautius invaded, the elected British War Leader (the Pendragon) was Arviragus who resisted the Romans for many years. The Claudian campaign against the British lasted nine years and it is noteworthy that Arviragus continued to fight the Romans and was never conquered. The British king of the area of Wales who fought with him against the Romans was Caractacus (Caratacus or Caradoc) who was later made the Pendragon.

There is some confusion on the identity of Caractacus. All the standard sources claim that his father was Cunobelinus and brother Togidumnus. However, their only authority for this is the Roman historian Dio Cassius (Cass) who lived 150 years after the events and relied entirely upon the Roman view of the battles as recorded in their archives. It is quite likely that they confused Caractacus as the brother of Togidumnus as they fought together against the Romans.

The Welsh Classical Dictionary quotes this authoritatively, but then notes that "realising that the Welsh form of Caractacus was Caradog it occurred to someone that Caractacus was none other than the legendary Caradoc ap [son of] Bran. This led to the 'Bran conversion fable'"! Their use of the word "fable" is indicative of the dismissive attitude of the authors to these ancient chronicles. The writings of Dion Cassius, compiled many years after the events, was preferred to the more accurate Welsh records.

Morgan, by contrast, gives the full ancestry of Caractacus and Bran which is in the *Pantliwydd Manuscripts of Llansannor* (Morgan:89). What does seem strange is that Geoffrey of Monmouth does not mention him but does deal with the exploits of Arviragus. It has been mooted that they may have been the same person.

The formidable opposition of the British, led mainly by Caractacus, meant that the Romans had no less than three famous generals (Vespasian, Titus and

Geta) in the field to try to defeat the British. They sent to the Roman Emperor Claudius for additional forces, and he came with more men and a number of elephants. He remained here only seventeen days, during which Cameludonum (Colchester) was captured and on his return to Rome he was given (or arranged?) a triumphal entry that was awarded to heroes.

Ostorius Scapula took over from Aulus Plautius in 47 AD and eventually defeated Caractacus in Wales in 50 AD. The site is said to be at the confluence of the Teme and the Clume in Shropshire but Jones places it at Llanymynech (JonB) as being the only site that complied with the description in the Annals of Tacitus Book XII, 33-5.

Arviragus managed to escape from the field, and Caractacus took refuge in the north with Queen Cartimandua - who promptly betrayed him to the Romans. He was led away in chains and with his wife, daughter and brothers, who had been captured after the battle, they were all taken to Rome. There is no mention that any sons went with him in these records at least. One son, Linus, is mentioned later as being in Rome, and the most likely explanation is that he joined them after the whole family had settled there peacefully.

The ferocious resistance of the Britons against the experienced Roman legions was well known in Rome. Huge numbers turned out to see this much feared warrior and his family in the triumphal procession of victors and vanquished that always followed successful campaigns. Caractacus, in chains, bore himself with great dignity and defiance before the crowd who seem to have admired his renowned courage and that of his warriors.

It was the inevitable fate of Roman prisoners-of-war to be kept starving in the infamous Tarpeian dungeons, humiliated, maltreated by the soldiers and finally killed by strangulation. Their bodies would then be dragged through the streets and cast into the river. It is a well known fact that the fate of Caractacus was quite the opposite, all being carefully recorded by the Roman historian Tacitus.

He was tried in the Senate which was packed to capacity. Caractacus entered accompanied by his daughter at his side. She is named Gladys in some records which means "princess". It is thought that her name was changed to Claudia in honour of the Emperor (a common practice) who had pardoned them all.

Caractacus's speech

On arriving at the tribunal, Caractacus made a passionate speech, recorded by Tacitus as follows.

> Had my government in Britain been directed solely with a view to the preservation of my hereditary domains, or the aggrandisement of my own family, I might long since have entered this city as an ally, not as a prisoner: nor would you have disdained for a friend a king descended from illustrious ancestors, and the dictator of many nations. My present condition, stripped of its former majesty is as adverse to myself as it is a triumph to you. What then? I was lord of men, horses, arms, wealth; what wonder if at your dictation I refused to resign them? Does it follow, that because the Romans aspire to universal domination, every nation is to accept the vassilage they would impose? I am now in your power - betrayed, not conquered. Had I, like others, yielded without resistance, where would have been the name of Caradoc? Where your glory? Oblivion would have buried both in the same tomb. Bid me live. I

shall survive for ever in history one example at least of Roman clemency. (Tacitus, Annals book 12 chapter 37 - see ref. Tacitus)

As a result of this speech, Claudius, to the acclaim of the whole meeting, released Caractacus and all his household. Tacitus said that this pardoning of a conquered king was the only known example. This, however, may be doubtful. On this, it was interesting to read in his *Gallic Wars* (Cae) how quickly Caesar, an ambitious and cruel man who took the family of the conquered rulers as hostages, would nevertheless quickly make peace with the leaders of tribes who had only just recently been trying to kill him and all his troops. This was probably as much to pacify them so as to reduce the threat to his army.

That Caractacus should not have been condemned but pardoned speaks volumes of the effect this British leader had upon the Romans - a civilisation noted for its cruelty to captives at least. In reviewing this turn of events, it does seem likely that such was the fame and nobility of Caractacus that the Romans had probably decided beforehand that he should be pardoned. In all ages, bravery in the field of battle has always been acknowledged even by one's foes.

There is an alternative explanation, suggested by Cooper, which is that Claudius, eager for honour from his people, carefully stage managed the whole procedure in conjunction with Caractacus. It is also possible that the failure of some Welsh historians to mention Caractacus was due to his fleeing from the battle and leaving behind his family. Was this the action of a coward, or did circumstances prevent him from rescuing them?

After the pardoning, it is appears that the family were given (or purchased from their tributes allowed from Britain) a very substantial residence that became known as the British Palace - "Palatium Britannicum". It is in this palace that the early Christian meetings are said to have taken place.

Caractacus was sent back in 51 AD to rule on behalf of the Romans. His father, Bran, remained behind as a hostage, returning to Britain in 58 AD. The British family remaining in Rome became very friendly with the Roman nobility and married into it.

THE BRITISH CHRISTIANS IN ROME

It is at this point that we will first try to establish what reasonable documentary evidence there is for what follows as it is crucial to this account. Much that Morgan claims in addition to that presented here may be correct, but we will limit ourselves to the more proven facts he presents.

Linus, the first Bishop of Rome

So far, it seems fairly certain, as recorded in the British Triads, that there were four generations of the Silurian tribe of British nobility taken captive to Rome - Llyr Llediaith (Shakespeare's "King Lear"), the father of Bran, who was the father of Caractacus (Caradoc), who was the father of Claudia. What is far less proven is that there were any other of Caractacus's children in Rome at any time. Morgan claims there were three others - Eurgain, St. Cyllinus, and Linus. Only for the latter does he give any documentary support which is from Clement I of Rome, the third "Pope" (88-97 AD?). Morgan (p171) quotes his statement - "Saintly Linus, brother of Claudia." As Clement lived at the same time as the British family in Rome, this seems an acceptable authentication.

Now Linus is named as the first Bishop of Rome - after Peter (?) - by the

Roman Catholic church. If he were the son of Caractacus, his name in Welsh would be Llyn - a name reflecting his grandfather's - a common practice even today. If we put these facts together, we can conclude that the very first appointed Bishop of Rome was of pure British noble birth and not of Roman origin.

We would, however, dispute that Peter was ever in Rome. The *New Bible Dictionary* claims he was, based mainly upon 1 Peter 5:13 where he sends greetings from "She who is in Babylon" as a code that he was writing from Rome (NBD:918). But Criswell provides good evidence that Peter was not in Rome (Cris:1772). Peter was to go to the Jews (he wrote from Babylon) and Paul to the Gentiles (he wrote from Rome) (Gal. 2:7). Linus was almost certainly appointed by Paul, who knew him personally, over the fledgling church in Rome. There is no record of Peter ever being in Rome.

Claudia and Pudens

The next matter is that of the marriage of Claudia to Rufus Pudens Pudentiana. Morgan quotes an ancient Gallic writer, Moncaeus Atrebas (1642);

> The cradle of the ancient British Church was a royal one, herein being distinguished from all other Churches: for it proceeded from the daughter of the British king, Caractacus, Claudia Rufina, a royal virgin, the same who was afterwards the wife of Aulus Rufus Pudens, the Roman senator, and the mother of a family of saints and martyrs (Morg:158).

There is further intriguing evidence in support of this statement. Living in Rome at that time was Martial, a writer of epigrams - short pithy verses - two of which refer to a "Claudia and Rufus." The first (book 4 verse 13) are verses to a relative of Rufus bearing the same name telling him of the forthcoming wedding. It begins;

> O Rufus, my friend Pudens, marries the foreigner Claudia.

Another of his epigrams (book 11 verse 4), written much later, praises the virtues of Claudia and her adoption of Roman culture (WillJ:12):

> Concerning Claudia Rufina -
>
> Seeing Claudia Rufina has sprung from the azure Britons, how come she has the feeling of a Latian maid?
>
> What grace and beauty! With the daughters of Italy she may pass,
> As a Roman, with those of Attica, as an Athenian Matron.
>
> Thanks to the Gods, she has borne many children to her holy husband,
> And still young, hopes to see sons and daughters-in-law,
> So may the Gods grant that in her one husband,
> And her three children, she may always find her happiness."

Martial had high regard for her literary abilities for there is another epigram complaining of her strong criticisms of verses he asked her to comment on. Martial was known for the bawdiness of some of his epigrams.

There is yet further evidence regarding the family of Pudentinus. A stone was found in Chichester, known as the Chichester Stone, on which was engraved a dedication of a Roman Temple to Neptune and Minerva (WillJ:21). The interesting fact is that it states the ground was donated by, "..ente Pudentini filio" (=(Pud)ente, son of Pudentinus), the first few letters being missing. This is possibly the same person that married Claudia, referring to land he gave whilst serving in Britain. Williams suggests that they

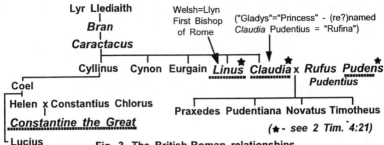

Fig. 3. The British-Roman relationships

met first at the famous Roman fortification at Chichester and that she was actually the daughter of Cogidumnus, a British king ruling under Roman authority on the south coast, but this is not well supported. That he gave land for a temple does indicate religious sensitivity - a characteristic that emerges later.

There is then very good evidence that Claudia married Rufus Pudens and had several children, all of whom became martyrs in the later Roman persecutions of the Christians.

It is when we examine Paul's second letter to Timothy, writing from Rome, that we find he sends greetings from "Pudens, Linus and Claudia" (2Tim.4:21). The fact that he mentions them all together suggests that they were the members of one household. So we have the independent witness of Martial that there was a British woman and her husband - Claudia and Pudens - living in Rome who were a cultured leading family of the times.

There are, then, three witnesses; the historical records, Martial's epigrams and Paul's letter to Timothy - all referring to the same names. It therefore seems fairly certain that these were one and the same people. The coincidence of there being two such families with identical names and two witnesses say the woman was British is remote.

From this, the Claudia and Linus that Paul knew were British nobility, being the children of Caractacus. With her important and affluent husband, Rufus, they all formed a large Christian household in the centre of Rome. In Acts 28:16,30 we read that Paul was allowed to rent a house whilst awaiting trial but presumably could not leave it. He would receive many visitors, amongst them would surely be the members of this Christian family.

It is interesting that Martial speaks of Rufus as a "holy husband" ("sancto..marito"), suggesting that Rufus had become a Christian with all the gentleness and sanctity that it can bring in its train.

The house that they occupied was known under various names over the years - Palatium Britannicum (British Palace), Titulus, Hospitium Apostolorum (Apostle's Hospice), and today - St. Pudentiana - for a church still stands on the site in Rome in the Via Urbana. It is interesting that the critic Ashe mentions that "Catholic archbishops of Westminster have sometimes been styled 'Cardinal of St. Pudentiana'" (Ash:151). This is yet another link between the Christian family house in Rome and British Christianity.

Rufus and Claudia had four children - Novatus, Praxedes, Pudentiana and Timotheus (WillJ:42). The latter was possibly named after the Timothy of the Bible who would have known them, for Paul sent Timothy greetings from the parents and Linus. The whole family, except Claudia, were to become martyrs in the ensuing persecution of Christians, and each of the children were canonised as saints. On the building of St. Pudentia there is an inscription relating that this was the house of "Sanctus Pudens" in which many martyrs were buried by Pudentiana and Praxedes themselves (Morg:107). Catholic tradition says that Peter stayed here, but it was almost certainly Paul. We suggest the identities have been switched.

Fig. 3 gives the genealogy of the British family in Rome, based upon the charts of Morgan. For a full study, Morgan's and Seaman's books are recommended.

Bran's conversion

The Welsh Triads state that Bran was converted whilst in Rome, and on return to this country he converted many in the royal court.

The commentaries generally seem to agree on the chronology of Paul's travels and writings. He appears to have been imprisoned in Rome twice. The first, from 60 to 63 AD, is described in Acts 28 v 28-31 when he had considerable freedom. The second was from 67 - 68 AD when he was incarcerated in a prison and from whence he may have been executed.

It is thought that Paul wrote to the Romans in about 57 AD. Reading Romans 1:8-14 it seems certain that Paul had never been to Rome when he wrote that letter. As Bran returned to Britain about 58 AD, then it is unlikely that he was converted by Paul himself.

What cannot be doubted is that there was a zealous group of true Christians in Rome when he wrote that letter about 57 AD. If it was not formed through Paul's direct ministry, then it was probably through travelling Jews converted at Pentecost for we read in Acts 2:10 - that there were, "visitors from Rome (both Jews and converts to Judaism)." There may also have been soldiers returning from the Palestinian occupation who had been converted. It was these Christians that met Paul at the Three Taverns when he arrived as a prisoner on his first visit to Rome (Acts 28:15).

Aristobulus

In Paul's letter to the Romans, he sends greetings to the "house of Aristobulus" (Rom 16:10). It has been inferred that Aristobulus himself was not present as he was away accompanying Bran to Britain. There are several ancient documents that specifically say that Bran returned with Aristobulus (Mor:132, WillJ:46). The Welsh version of his name was Arwystli Hen (=very old), which suggests that they knew him personally to give him the title "old". There is also a district in Montgomeryshire bearing his name and said to be the site of his martyrdom.

There are also "saints days" recorded for all the names in the Bible, but there is no entry for Aristobulus. Would this be due to his martyrdom being outside the area under Roman jurisdiction and therefore not recorded? There is the further small point that as the Bible notes he was the head of a household, he was not a young man, and the therefore the title "old" given to Arwystli would be in keeping with an older person as Aristobulus must have been.

A historical bias?

The events set out above are surely a most fascinating glimpse into early Christian history. Two names in the Bible are actually British, one of them becoming the first Bishop of Rome. There also seems to be evidence that Aristobulus came to these shores.

One must ask why this evidence is virtually unknown by the public in general and the Christian Church in particular? It has been publicised by the British-Israel Federation and the writings of David Gardner and a few others. Unfortunately they are usually dismissed as they have often been included with less credible (hi)stories that have been derived from facts that have been forced to fit predetermined theories.

Could the lack of publicity by scholars and the media of this evidence be due to the encouragement it gives to Protestant Christianity in this country?

Let us look at one example to show how the facts of history can be "rewritten" in such a way that, without lying, the reader is left with an impression that is quite the opposite to the truth.

The *Encyclopaedia Britannica's* reference to Caractacus gives his father as Cunobelinus, and having described his defeat and capture concludes with the sentence "He and his family were featured in a victory parade of Claudius, who granted them pardon and life" (EB 2:842). In the Everyman's Encyclopaedia it similarly concludes "He was sent in chains to Rome where Claudius spared his life."

Let us pause here and note what the reader of these important reference works, wishing to study the life of early British kings, would find. He would have the distinct impression that the whole life of Caractacus was one of defeat and disgrace. This would be written up by the average student and for which he would receive full marks.

But what would the reader *not* discover? There is no mention of Caractacus's bravery, or of the renowned fearlessness of the men he many times successfully led into battle against the Romans; no reference to the fear he inspired in the Roman armies that even Roman citizens knew about and therefore crowded the streets to see this warrior; no notice of the courageous speech he made which resulted in his pardon that was even acclaimed by his former enemies. The various British and continental documents that show his family were early Christians in Rome and their subsequent activities are all dismissed and ignored by modern historians.

To show how rapidly this bias has arisen, a book entitled *The Story of the British People* in Pictures (Odhams) has a picture of Caractacus and an extract of his speech. This was published as recently as 1949, but it is doubtful if it has been referred to since. Caractacus's speech was often memorised by public schoolboys as an inspiration to serve the nation bravely.

In such a way are those parts of our national history, in which we may have a justifiable sense of pride, taken away from us by those who seek to remove any reference to the early coming of true Christianity to this country and to undermine our basic British national identity.

Boadicea's uprising

After the capture of Caractacus, Arviragus continued the fighting with renewed ferocity. In 42 AD, Claudius had decreed the death penalty for Christians and Druids and sent a huge army to Britain to destroy our people and institutions. Their worst act was the slaughter of the monks, women and children of a large Druid community at Menai c 60 AD. During their terrible atrocities, Queen Boadicea (British = Vuddig (Victoria) = Boeddig = Boudicca) and her daughters were desecrated. These two events roused the whole nation and they rallied behind her and her tribe, the Iceni of East Anglia. She personally led her men into many battles and defeated the might of the Roman army, killing many thousands of the barbarous troops that she now so hated. In her last battle, it is said that she was briefly cut off from the main force and fearing she might be captured, took poison.

War with Rome continued but such was the attrition that the two sides agreed to live more at peace with each other. In 86 AD Agricola made a treaty with the Britons that allowed them to keep all their rights and privileges, and this peaceful coexistence lasted for 200 years. Although the Romans theoretically controlled the whole of England and Wales, they never completely subjugated the people as they did with many other nations the Romans conquered.

The appeal of Lucius and papal authority

The Christian King Lucius was the ruler of Britain from about 137 to 186 AD. His father was Coel (of "Old King Cole" fame) who was the son of Cyllinus, the son of Caractacus.

The religious state of Britain varied over the years and in 157 AD Lucius was said to have sent to Eleutherius the Bishop of Rome for teachers to spread the Christian faith further afield in this country. This is sometimes taken as showing the submission of the British monarchs to Papal authority. This is not necessarily the case, however, for he was possibly seeking the return of missionaries he had previously sent to the continent. In his reply letter, Eleutherius makes it abundantly clear that Lucius had full ecclesiastical and spiritual authority in Britain, calling him the "vicar" of this nation (Jow:205).

As this question of religious authority has a continuing influence upon British religion and politics it should therefore be considered at this point.

Despite frequent protestations to the contrary, there was never any automatic predominance of the Bishop of Rome at any ecclesiastical council for many centuries. In fact, for the first few Councils *priority was given to the British bishops as representatives from the first nation to declare itself Christian.* In 1517 a deciding document was published stating that three Councils confirmed that:

> the Churches of France and Spain must yield in points of antiquity
> and precedence to that of Britain as the latter church was founded
> *by Joseph of Arimathea immediately after the passion of Christ"*
> (Disp, Jow:80, Sea:69).

It was not until many centuries later that the Roman Bishops took control of all future councils, and it was in fact not until 1870 that Papal authority over the whole Catholic Church was eventually approved by the first Vatican Council. Roman precedence was also rejected by the Eastern Orthodox church and they broke away from the Roman Catholic church for good in 1054.

Another point is that the first councils were not called by the church but by Constantine, the first Christian emperor of Rome who, immediately on his accession, declared Christianity to be the national religion. His British roots we will consider later. The first was held at Arles in 314, the second at Nicea in 325 at which he presided personally. The third was at Constantinople in 337. At none of these was the Bishop of Rome given any particular precedence and what is more, all the expenses of the delegates were paid for by Constantine himself. No Roman Catholic church authority was involved at any point.

THE BRITISH ANCESTRY OF CONSTANTINE THE GREAT

In 265 a daughter was born to King Coel and named Elaine (Helen). She became a Christian and was not only highly educated and gifted but was also a very able political administrator. Constantius Chlorus was sent from Rome to subdue Coel which he did, but following this he married Helen. When Coel died, Constantius declared himself king.

The city of Rome was a hotbed of intrigue and assassination, and it is said that some Emperors preferred to rule their empire from the more peaceful city of York. Two are buried there - Septimus Severus (211 AD) and Constantius Chlorus (306 AD). The latter, after a battle with the Roman invader Allectus in 296 declared himself Emperor but remained in York. He overcame the Roman invasion ordered by Diocletian that tried to eliminate Christianity in Britain but not before they had succeeded in a terrible destruction of most of the Christian churches and thousands of people.

Unfortunately Constantius only ruled for two years as Emperor. On his death in 306 his troops declared his son Constantine Emperor, but he declined this for the lesser title of Caesar. It was he who was later to become the famous Constantine the Great, the first Christian Emperor of the vast Roman Empire, and under whom the Christian faith was to flourish. His British mother was an extremely important influence in his very successful rule over the Roman Empire during its golden period of greatest peace and affluence.

In reading secular accounts of the lives of these three people, one begins to wonder whether they are dealing with the same people, for there is absolutely no mention of the fact that Helen was a British Princess, that her husband spent many years in York or that she was the mother of the famous Constantine the Great. All reference to any connections with the British royal family are eliminated. Helen is described as "a native of Bythinia", that she only became a Christian "after the Edict of Milan (313)" and that she "made a pilgrimage to Palestine" (*Everyman's Encyclopaedia* and *EB*).

It can be seen that all trace of British ancestry of any of these people has been removed by the historians, a subject we have noted before.

THE CHRISTIANS OF IONA

As the military power of Rome gradually weakened in the face of huge bands of invading Goths, Huns, Visigoths,, etc., they retreated from the further posts of their empire, and the run-down of troops in Britain began in 410 AD. Life continued in these isles, but the administration and culture of the Romans was a great loss to the native inhabitants.

In 384 AD was born Succat, a young carefree boy of a Christian household, who was captured by Niall, a raider from Ireland (and great grandfather of Columba!) whilst still very young and taken to Ireland. There, far from any Christian influence, he experienced at the age of sixteen a true working of the Holy Spirit and poured out his prayers to God. He was eventually rescued but then set his heart on evangelising the Irish pagans he had known. He returned to them and the Gospel of Christ's free forgiveness gradually spread throughout the land. Succat became known as St. Patrick and founded many churches and centres of religion (d'Aub:27).

200 years later, Columba built an abbey on Iona in 563 AD and in the ensuing years they took their faith not just to Scotland and Bangor in Wales but went far afield - to the Netherlands, France, Switzerland, Germany and Italy. As we have discussed above, just how much of their Christianity was mixed with Druidic occult influences is difficult to determine. Their

Christianity predominated and it was this that had a great influence on the development of this nation and others. We shall see this when they met the Catholic delegates at the Council of Whitby in 664 AD.

THE SAXON INVASION

Between the evangelising of Ireland by St. Patrick around 400 AD and the establishing of Iona in 563, England become open to invasions from the Picts in Scotland. Vortigern, the British king at that time (449 AD), called upon their one-time allies on the continent for help to repel them. The Saxon adventurers, Hengist and Horsa, duly arrived but having defeated the Picts decided to stay on. Over many years they, and their relatives, the Angles and Jutes, gradually forced the Britons out of England and into the remote, inhospitable but more easily defended land of Wales, as well as Scotland and Cornwall. It is the Welsh people who are the purest representatives of the early Britons and they kept many of their records.

Contrary to what most believe, this invasion was far from being a historical case of "ethnic cleansing" of the original British Celts. An examination of the bones in Anglo-Saxon graveyards showed that 50% were Celtic. They could be recognised as they were buried without weapons and they were two inches shorter. Within a few hundred years the original Celtic genes had swamped the Anglo-Saxon arrivals by inter-marriage and their stature reduced by one inch. The culture was still mainly Anglo-Saxon, however (D. Tel. 16.12.95 p10).

Some of the Britons migrated to Brittany in France to escape the invading hordes of Anglo-Saxons, and this can be seen in the names of some of their towns and those of Cornwall, where they use the prefix of Tre- and Pol-. The Bretons still have their own distinct language and customs and there is a movement to declare their independence from France.

When the Britons retreated into Wales they took with them their Christian faith. Such was the cruelty of the conquering Saxons that the British Christians and those on Iona made few attempts to convert them.

The situation, then, in the middle of the sixth century, was that the pagan Saxons held almost all of England, the Christian Britons were in Wales, the Scots had been evangelised and the Isle of Iona was still a Christian centre of renown. It was then that a Christian faith from another continent entered into the picture.

THE COMING OF AUGUSTINE

It is well known that in late sixth century, Gregory (he refused to be called the first Pope) was passing through the slave market place in Rome when he saw some Saxon slave children with their fair hair and blue eyes. Hearing that they were Angles he said "Not Angles but Angels." He later authorised Augustine to go as a missionary to the shores of Britain.

Augustine, with a band of forty other missionaries, landed in Kent in 597. The Saxon king at that time who ruled SE England was Aethelbert, who received them at Canterbury. He would only meet them in the open air under an oak tree as he feared they might cast a spell over him. They began by staging an impressive parade, headed by a monk carrying a huge cross with a representation of Christ on it, and chanting in Latin. Such was the impression made upon this pagan king by such practices that he accepted the Catholic doctrines, including that of Papal authority, that they set before him and his court.

From this position of authority, other main centres of government submitted to Roman Catholic jurisdiction, but surprisingly, little was done for much of the outlying areas.

Gradually, more of the country controlled by the Saxons was converted to Rome. There were, however, the British (Welsh) in the west and the Ionian centre in the north that had to be taken in to the fold of Rome.

The Welsh still had a Christian centre at Bangor under Dinud, a gentle and pious leader. Augustine sent to Dinud to have a conference requiring their submission to the authority of the Pope of Rome. Dinud replied:

> We desire to love all men and what we do for you we do for him
> also whom you call the pope. But he is not entitled to call himself
> the "father of fathers", and the only submission we can render him
> is that which we owe to every Christian (d'Au:37).

After several meetings with the established churches who refused to submit to Rome, Augustine declared "If you will not unite with us in showing the Saxons the way of life, you shall receive from them the stroke of death" (d'Au:41).

The Saxon forces were marshalled against them, and a battle followed at Bangor, where the Saxons were defeated, but not before they had massacred 1,200 British monks assembled there to pray for the success of the British forces. Bede, the catholic, recorded that this massacre was a fulfilment of the prophecy "of the holy pontiff Augustine."

Thus, far from being the first to bring Christianity to these shores, Augustine was instrumental in destroying the existing Christian faith that could trace its ancestry back to the time of Paul, simply because it refused to submit to Papal authority.

The Welsh are still fiercely proud of their land, and their impressive Christian pedigree is till apparent in the number of chapels they have and the degree of religious interest they show. That it has unhappily in many instances become more liberal is but the natural man once again emerging from a more zealous era. It is not a coincidence that Wales was the scene of a number of striking revivals around the turn of the century. The strong independent spirit that prompted Dinud to refuse to bow the knee to the Pope in the sixth century was to reappear more clearly one thousand years later in a Welsh king of England.

THE COUNCIL OF WHITBY

The conversion of the Saxons to the Catholic faith was not deep, and many of the kings and their subjects reverted to their pagan beliefs. Such was the counter-reaction that all the Bishops but one fled the country back to the safer haven of the continent (d'A:40). Some returned to the fold of the Catholic church after various changes of heart. Thus did the religious beliefs of the rulers of the nation fluctuate.

The Christian outpost of Iona still had a considerable but varying influence in the north. The Saxon king Oswiu, in order to decide between the two forms of Christianity represented by the Catholics in the south and the followers of Columba in the north, called a conference in 664 AD at Whitby in the north. Each side presented their arguments, but the witness of the monks of Iona was weak and the final appeal of the Catholic contingent to the claim of Peter possessing the "keys to the kingdom" of heaven won over the king to their religion.

From that moment, the Catholic faith spread further over the whole of the land of England.

THE INDEPENDENCE OF THE BRITISH ISLES
Although the Saxons followed the Roman Catholic rites in their churches, the nation as a whole were reluctant to submit to total control by the Pope. This attitude rumbled on for generations, and when Pope Clement IV tried to impose French cardinals upon the British church, in 1350 Edward III passed the Statute of Provisors.

This made void any ecclesiastical appointments not approved of by the king, chapters or patrons. This naturally caused great consternation to the Papal authorities, a concern that turned to increasing horror as the even more stringent laws of Praemunire were passed in succeeding years.

These laws said that Papal bulls, laws, rulings or excommunications were invalid in the kingdom of England. Indeed, anyone bringing such documents into the country were to be deprived of the kings protection, to be considered outside the law, and therefore anyone committing such an act could be killed without any repercussions under the law. The king was held to be the supreme political and ecclesiastical authority above all others. No higher authority existed and anyone appealing to a foreign state was to be treated as worse than a traitor and lost all legal protection!

It was by using these laws that Richard Hunne angered the Catholic Church just before the time of Henry VIII. He was a devout Catholic who refused to pay an exorbitant mortuary fee and invoked these laws. He was imprisoned and tried but no hint of heresy could be found. Unable to convict him but fearing others might similarly refuse to be obedient to the Pope's authority, he presented a problem. This was "solved" by murdering him in his cell that same night in 1514, but the ensuing outcry paved the way for the rejection of Catholic supremacy in the land (d'Aub:133f, Coo96).

THE FINAL BREAK WITH ROME
The first Tudor monarch was Henry VII, who was of direct Welsh ancestry and from whom our present queen traces her lineage. By careful diplomacy he united the whole of Great Britain, and by destroying his opponents he established a strong centrally controlled government. He built up considerable trade with the continent such that, on his death, he handed over a rich and powerful nation to his son Henry VIII.

Henry VIII was a very gifted young man who turned into a despot. When his first wife failed to produce an heir to the throne, he badly wanted to marry Anne Bolyne. That the Pope would not permit this forced Henry to declare his independence from the Pope's religious control, and made himself the highest authority, both political and ecclesiastical, in the land.

Cooper, however, considers that this decision to break away from the authority of the Pope was not a sudden decision surrounding Henry's divorce. As we have said above, resistance to the control of this nation's affairs by a foreign power was considered treason of the worst order and punishable with the most extreme retributions. This feeling was particularly strong in the Welsh whose religious ancestors had been massacred at Bangor by the Saxons at the instigation of Augustine. It is therefore understandable that when the first Welsh king was established on the throne of Britain, this whole subject should come to a head. Cooper contends that the question of the divorce should be looked upon as happening to be the particular situation over which was decided the more important subject of where the final authority over the

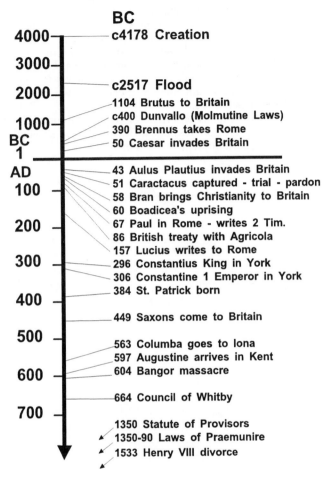

BC

4000	c4178 **Creation**
3000	
2000	c2517 **Flood**
1000	1104 **Brutus to Britain**
BC	c400 **Dunvallo (Molmutine Laws)**
1	390 **Brennus takes Rome**
	50 **Caesar invades Britain**
AD	43 **Aulus Plautius invades Britain**
100	51 **Caractacus captured - trial - pardon**
	58 **Bran brings Christianity to Britain**
	60 **Boadicea's uprising**
200	67 **Paul in Rome - writes 2 Tim.**
	86 **British treaty with Agricola**
	157 **Lucius writes to Rome**
300	296 **Constantius King in York**
	306 **Constantine 1 Emperor in York**
	384 **St. Patrick born**
400	449 **Saxons come to Britain**
500	563 **Columba goes to Iona**
	597 **Augustine arrives in Kent**
600	604 **Bangor massacre**
	664 **Council of Whitby**
700	1350 **Statute of Provisors**
	1350-90 **Laws of Praemunire**
	1533 **Henry VIII divorce**

Fig. 4. Early British chronology

nation should reside; whether it should be under the British Crown or the Roman Mitre.

To clarify this brief outline of British history, Fig. 4 gives the chronological order of the major events.

We would comment that the first introduction of the pure Christian faith with the return of Bran to these shores was eventually corrupted in some measure by the Druidic influence. This was followed by the incoming Catholic faith to these shores that was followed in turn by the "Dark Ages" of the medieval years. The nations of Europe had to await the translation of the Bible into the common tongue before the people awoke, threw of the cloak of superstition and return to the true Christian faith that they were now able to study for themselves in God's word to mankind.

A FINAL "THOUGHT FOR TODAY"

We have in this section shown the way in which the independence of this nation has been fiercely defended, usually successfully and certainly so since 1066. This refusal to allow any foreign power to have any control over the nation was eventually embodied in the Laws of Praemunire. What few realise is that *this ancient law was quietly repealed in order to allow EEC laws to rule our nation.* This bulwark against foreign influence has been removed and laws have been passed that allow the European Community to control all our major institutions. Edward Heath jubilantly claimed "We have done what Napoleon and Hitler failed to do."

We are now rendered virtually powerless to prevent the encroaching control of the unelected European Commission in Brussels. If we succumb, we will be dominated by European politicians - and their faith.

SECTION 3.8
ISRAEL AND EGYPT:
ARCHAEOLOGICAL CONFIRMATIONS

For about a century, archaeologists have generally held that there is no evidence of events in the Bible that can be correlated with any parallel record in the Egyptian chronicles. As a result, the Biblical record has been considered as fiction and therefore ignored by earlier archaeologists who rigidly held to the chronology they had constructed over many decades. This secular chronology has been increasingly criticised as being too long.

The main basis for the "long" chronology is the list of Kings recorded by Manetho, an Egyptian historian living about 250 BC. His list is taken as the reigns of consecutive pharaohs which results in a long period of time. This time scale was then said to be supported by several other "proofs', one being the identification of the Egyptian Sheshonk I with the Shishak who sacked the Temple of its treasures in the time of Rehoboam.

A number of researchers, amongst them Isaac Newton, have challenged the "long" Egyptian chronology, but Velikovsky was the first to claim that Egyptian documents corroborated the Exodus in his book *Ages in Chaos* (Vel73B). In this he showed that if the dates were shortened by about 600 years, there was a very good fit between Israel's and Egypt's records.

Those who use the shorter chronology contend that many of the "kings" in Manetho's list were local regents ruling at the same time, or co-regents of pharaohs, etc. and that the whole chronology should be very greatly reduced.

Another critic is Courville who, in his two volume work *The Exodus Problem and its Ramifications* (Cou), makes much the same claim, but assumes the Bible records are reliable and that the history of other nations should be examined in this light. He acknowledges Velikovsky's work and agrees with much that he says but makes drastic alterations to the sequence of the Egyptian dynasties and proposes even greater changes in Egyptian chronology.

The most recent work criticising the orthodox timescale is by Rohl, an Egyptologist, in his book *A Test of Time* (Roh) (*Pharaohs and Kings* in America). He uses the Bible as a basis for his research but he makes it clear that he is not using it as a Christian would, but as an ordinary document that is as reliable as any other archaeological record. Indeed, he tries at times to find a rational explanation for what Christians would accept as a miracle, such as the death of the first-born prior to the Exodus.

Of the three works, Courville's is the most detailed, wide ranging and the more interesting to the Christian as only he assumes the Bible is accurate and interprets history in its light. He wrote it to prove the accuracy of the Bible for those Christians who had doubts about its historical reliability - as this work tries to do over a wider area. He gives far more information regarding dates, etc. of the history of Israel and his evidence was sufficiently convincing for this work to initially use it as a basis for the chronology of the Bible related to the surrounding nations - with two important amendments of dates.

The first is that we would not accept his placing of the Flood between the Palaeolithic and Neolithic "stone age" cultures, but we would contend that the Flood removed all evidence of the pre-Flood world. The clear break between these cultures that he claims may be due to some other factor, but would not be due to the Flood of Noah as he claims. This seems to make little difference to the rest of his studies, but makes correlation with the pre-Flood patriarchs difficult, although this is a period he does not deal with in depth.

The second disagreement is the 215 year period of the "sojourn" of the Israelites in Egypt which we will show is 430 years - a subject we discuss in detail later.

Using the 215 year period for the Israelites stay in Egypt and Courville's books as a basis for a chronology of Egypt and Israel, a basic chronology for the whole of history from Creation was developed for this section and the following on chronology. Subsequently, email correspondence with Brad Sparks, an American archaeological researcher, convinced me that not only was Courville wrong on a number of his conclusions, but that the "sojourn" of the Israelites in Egypt was 430 years. This required a drastic revision of both sections, and what follows is an approximate chronology for the histories of Egypt and Israel. We have used some points from Courville, Velikovsky and Rohl, corrected where Sparks has made relevant comments. A detailed examination of this subject will have to await a book produced by Sparks on the subject. We would here record out grateful thanks to him for the many careful comments he has made on this section We would mention that Sparks does not provide exact dates for events as his very thorough researches have shown that many events, dated with certainty by respected authorities, are actually not known within a hundred or more years. There is a degree of repetition of assertions by earlier historians that are not always as well founded as we may imagine.

Only these four authorities, Sparks (Sp), Courville (1C and 2C), Rohl (R), and Velikovsky's *Ages in Chaos* (V) will generally be referred to as most other reference books on this subject are based upon the orthodox "long chronology" and give little support to the Biblical record.

Before examining the history of the Israelites, there are two subjects that should be discussed - Velikovsky's theories and the length of time spent by the Israelites in Egypt

VELIKOVSKY: AN ASSESSMENT.

There is some confusion amongst Christians regarding Velikovsky's views which he presents in his books *Worlds in Collision* (Vel72), *Earth in Upheaval* (Vel73A) and *Ages in Chaos* (Vel73B). He had studied psychoanalysis under a student of Freud, and it was his reading of Freud's *Moses and Monotheism* that began his interest in Egyptian history. Freud had claimed that the Pharaoh Akhenaton was the first monotheist and that Moses borrowed the concept from him! (Q22/1:35).

Although Velikovsky is a Jew and frequently quotes the Old Testament and Hebrew legends, in all his works there is no serious reference to accepting the early date of creation or the worldwide Flood of Noah.

It is quite clear that he is writing from an evolutionary standpoint, even though he contends that civilisations were affected by several major catastrophes. Despite having a lengthy discussion with a well known creationist, he remained unconvinced. One of the major features of his theory is that there were more than one "near misses" of the earth by Mars and Venus. This has been examined in detail and several important objections can be made (Q13/1:6, Q15/1:55). Bouw, an astronomer, says that Velikovsky's theories cannot work and there is no evidence of any "near miss" (Q13/4:224).

These planetary close approaches are said to have caused much upheaval of the earth's crust, with earthquakes and eruptions, and there were consequent effects upon the various civilisations around the world, creating mass migrations, etc.

For much of this information, Velikovsky turns to the folk stories of many tribes and produces considerable supporting information. This seems to make his case very firm, but despite this, this writer remains unconvinced. As is so often the case, it is not so much what he says, but what he does not say that raises questions.

Had there been a near miss by a planet, this would have affected the orbit of the earth. The climate would have been very much hotter when the earth was near the sun and much cooler when furthest away. These much hotter and colder periods would have occurred each year, the degree of variation depending upon the eccentricity of the earth's orbit, but there is no record of such a period of greatly intensified seasons.

He appears to have predicted the features of certain planets that were only confirmed later. However, one well publicised prediction said to have been fulfilled - that Venus was surrounded by hydrocarbons in quantity - has *not* been confirmed (Science 163:1191, Q6/2:107, Q10/3:143). "If his case is not substantiated at this point, then virtually all of his other postulates from the historical record must be held in question" (Q10/3:142).

Throughout the whole of his book, one is presented with a series of wide ranging snapshots, but whilst this appears to be convincing, the final effect upon this writer was eventually one of confusion, particularly when there is no full scenario presented. That there is not a single diagram or illustration in the whole of his books suggests that there is something lacking in his presentation of evidence. Some events are so cataclysmic that one would have expected them to be clearly recorded in the annals of very many nations so that the event would have been well known, but many of the quotes are to "darkness, noise", etc. and not to specifically recorded events or geological disasters. This lack of hard evidence forms a major objection to Velikovsky's theories.

Followers of Velikovsky have been effective in presenting catastrophic events to secular, uniformitarian researchers, and understandably have met with organised resistance (Bow81:244f). However, Gerardus Bouw commented that Velikovsky's ideas have become popular amongst those who seek "catastrophist" explanations, but wish to avoid the moral implications of the far more obvious Flood catastrophe recorded in the Bible. For all such events, they look for a "natural" explanation. The result is a form of "fundamentalist astrology" where the planets had a considerable significance on the lives of mankind. Bouw predicts that this form of catastrophism will enter into other areas of science that have been constrained by the "uniformitarian" view until now. Nevertheless, that they have broken away from the uniformitarian "straight jacket" is a major step. That they cannot take the next step of accepting Biblical Catastrophism is understandable in the light of 1 Cor. 2:14 - "But the natural man does not receive the things of the Spirit of God, for they are foolishness to him; neither can he know them, because they are spiritually discerned."

THE "SOJOURN" OF THE ISRAELITES IN EGYPT

We will first outline the evidence used for the period to be only 215 years.

The 215 year "sojourn" in Egypt

There are several verses indicate that the Israelites "sojourned" in Egypt for

430 years, 400 of them being years of "affliction" (Gen. 15:13. Acts 7:6). However, Galatians 3:16-17 says "To Abraham and his seed were the promises made... the covenant that was confirmed before of God in Christ, the law, which was 430 years after" This suggests the Law (the Ten Commandments), given just after the Exodus, was 430 years after the promise to Abraham when he was entering Canaan and not when the Israelites, with Jacob, entered Egypt, which was long afterwards. Can these be reconciled?

Expositors have suggested that the sojourn of the Israelites in Egypt was only 215 years with the previous 215 years sojourning starting with Abraham's entry into Canaan.

Dr. Charles Taylor has said (E92/6(1):72) that the correct translations support Galatians as the figure of 400 years in Gen. 15:13 and Acts 7:6 are not the period of their time in Egyptian, but is a summary of the total time of all the events in the earlier part of the speech or record.

Courville supports this view for he quotes both Josephus, the Jewish historian, who agreed with this understanding of the verse, and the Septuagint version of the OT which adds the words "..*in the land of Canaan* and in the land of Egypt, was 430 years."

Thus, the 430 years could be taken for the period from Abraham's entry into Canaan to the giving of the law on Sinai. By adding the ages of the patriarchs, this gives 215 years from Abraham to the descent into Egypt by Jacob during Joseph's time, leaving a further 215 years for their stay in Egypt. That the sojourning began at the time of Abraham has some support from Hebrews 11:9 which states that Abraham sojourned in the Promised Land by faith. This 215 year period has been adopted by many reputable authorities including Bullinger, Courville and van Lennep.

Using this sequence of events, a chronology was constructed giving the widely accepted date of creation about 4000 BC, the Flood at 2345 BC and the Exodus at 1445 BC. This worked well with the line-up of planets in 4001 BC (Section 2.3) and the date of the tilt of the earth's axis (Appendix 5) that coincided with the Flood date of 2345 BC. For the reader's interest, we give the chart of this chronology in Section 3.9 - Fig. 2. However, as we have said, Brad Sparks showed that there is good evidence for the sojourning of the Israelites in Egypt to be the full 430 years and not 215. He presented the following evidence.

The 430 year sojourn in Egypt
(i) Genesis 46:2-4 shows that Jacob received a confirmation that he would be the father of a great nation on the night before he entered Egypt. This confirmation to Jacob is also stated in Psalm 105:10-11. Thus, the *promise* was given to Abraham, but the *confirmation* of Gal. 3:16-17 was *not* to Abraham *but to Jacob*, and therefore the 430 years applies only to the stay in Egypt and did not include Abraham's period in Canaan.

(ii) Gen. 15:13 (and Acts 7:6) says Abraham's *seed* "shall be a stranger in a land (singular) that is not theirs, and shall serve them: and they shall afflict them 400 years." It is not Abraham but his seed, Jacob, who will be afflicted in a (one) strange land for 400 years. This eliminates Abraham's period in Canaan before Isaac at least was born. More important, there was no time of "affliction" whilst in Canaan. The "affliction" was in *one* country only - Egypt, and it was the only country from which they came out "with great wealth." This removes the whole period in Canaan from the sojourn.

(iii) Exodus 12:40 says that "the sojourning of the *children* of Israel (Jacob), who dwelt in Egypt, was 430 years." Thus it applied to the children of Jacob only, and *not* to the children of Abraham. Ex. 12:41 continues by saying that they came out 430 years after they entered "even the selfsame day." Such a specific event can only look back to God's confirmation to Jacob (Gen. 46:2-4) just before he entered Egypt.

(iv) Jewish scholars admit that the Israelites time in Egypt of 430 years and under bondage for 400 of them was so objectionable to the translators of the Septuagint that this passage was deliberately altered to include the period in Canaan, leaving only 215 years in Egypt. Wacholder (Wach) gives 8 citations on this. Furthermore, the translators of the Septuagint forgot to amend the text of Genesis 15:13-14 which still referred to 400 years of oppression and bondage in *one* land, out of which God would bring Abraham's descendants with great wealth! This could not possibly have referred to an additional period in Canaan.

Sparks engaged in lengthy correspondence with Courville on this very topic of the 215 years period in Egypt and proved to him that it was 430. He also pointed out that Josephus, in two other places, did *not* agree with the 215 year period and appears to merely record, without approval, the additional words in the Septuagint that included Abraham's period in Canaan.

We concluded that his evidence for the stay in Egypt being 430 years was better supported than that for the 215 years, even though the latter may be the more widely accepted. Accordingly, a revised chronology was drawn up and is given in Section 3.9 - Fig. 3 which gives the Creation in 4178 BC and the Flood 2517 BC. In that section we discuss how the revision affected the date of Abraham's birth and other considerations. We have also based the chronology of Egypt in Fig. 1 on this revised timescale.

EGYPTIAN CHRONOLOGY

In view of its great antiquity and the volume of its records, often carved in long-lasting stone, the chronology of Egypt has been used by secular archaeologists as the foundation for dating the rest of European history. Any alterations here would affect the datings of many other nations, and one can understand why any proposed changes have been strongly resisted. There has been a gradual reduction of the length of this chronology, however.

It should be explained that the periods of various reigns of rulers has been grouped into 30 dynasties where there has been a degree of continuity of ruling. These have then been grouped into larger "periods" of reigns - e.g. Middle Kingdom, etc. There are also three periods of comparative "disorganisation" called "Intermediate Periods" where no strong leadership was evident The shorter Egyptian chronology used in this work is obtained by having certain dynasties reigning at the same time as another in a different part of Egypt.

The Sothic list gives the founder of Egypt as Mizraim (Gen. 10:6,13) with the alternative names Mestraim and Menes (1C:120) and it is probable that he founded Egypt very shortly after Babel. The Sothic list, however, is a late document (c3rd. cent AD) and has undoubtedly had Judeo-Christian additions such as these names (Spark).

There are a number of confusing factors in dealing with Egyptian history. Many kings (pharaohs) ruled at the same time as others in different sections of the Nile. Rulers may be kings or just local controllers. Many rulers were known by several names - often quite different ones - their official name, throne name, shortened name, familiar name, etc. Pharaohs had a standard five names and some had many more. Thutmose and Rameses had 60 - 100 names each. This not only applied to Egypt but to other nations also. All these factors generate much confusion and allow historians to "pick and choose" the evidence to support their views.

In addition, the use of the terms "Bronze Age" and "Iron Age", etc. can be very misleading, for as we have explained, one civilisation may be in the "Iron" age whilst at the same time another, not necessarily too far distant, may still be in the "Bronze" age.

Bearing in mind the many controversial and confusing factors and assumptions involved in Egyptian chronology, we can only outline some of the more interesting points that various authorities have proposed that have a bearing on the Biblical record.

JOSEPH

Joseph was a slave in Egypt about 1865-8 BC at the time of Pharaoh Djoser of the 3rd dynasty, in whose reign was the only recorded famine to last seven years. Joseph would have been released from prison about that date and made the second highest authority in the land. He undertook extensive works to increase food production and store it during the years of plenty. Although the date is not known for certain, a canal was dug parallel to the Nile and during the flood period water could be directed to a natural depression, Lake Moeris (now Birket Karun). The impounded water could then be used later for irrigation via a shorter canal to the Nile. The name of the main canal to this day is "Bahr Yussef" - *Joseph's Canal!* (Fig. 2).

There was general destitution of the people in the seven years famine and they became slaves to Pharaoh. It is in this reign that the very first pyramid was built (The Stepped Pyramid) and this would have been constructed by the massive slave force that the famine produced.

A number of authorities suggest that Joseph may have been the Imhotep who is credited with holding sweeping powers in the land and amazing knowledge of architecture and medicine - such that he was deified in later dynasties. However, his Egyptian ancestry is partially known and it would appear that he was Djoser's architect. It is likely that he took, or was credited with, all Joseph's achievements as the Egyptians would hardly want to give any praise to a man whose descendents would cause the nation's downfall at the Exodus many generations later (Spark).

Every year, the Nile floods and deposits a layer of fertile soil over the adjacent land. Famines are rare in Egypt as they require a series of very low inundations. Rohl claims that the famine resulted from the Nile rising too high, swamping the land, devastating the crops and drying too slowly for the next sowing. However, this would not have caused famine "over all the face of the earth" such that Jacob with many others had to go to Egypt for food.

Rohl suggests that the name pharaoh gave to Joseph - "Zaphenat Pa'aneah" (Gen. 41:45) means "He who is called (Ish)piankhu." Ishpi could be the way Egyptians might spell "Joseph', and the whole name would then be "Joseph lives"; a fitting name for a once-lost son!

The problem of Joseph's age.

If the Israelites stay in Egypt was for 430 years after Jacob's entry, and the oppression was for 400 years, then assuming the persecution started immediately after Joseph's death this leaves only 30 years during which the

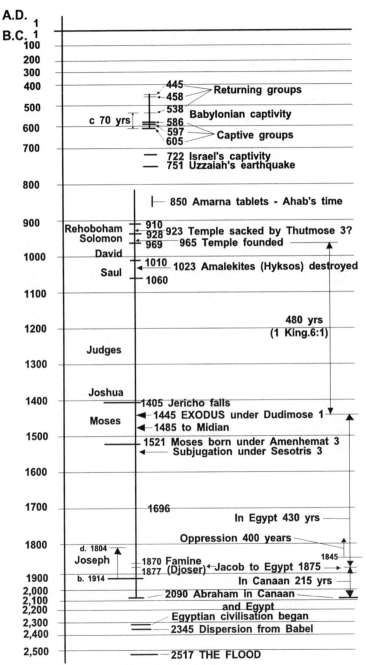

Fig. 1. The chronology of Israel

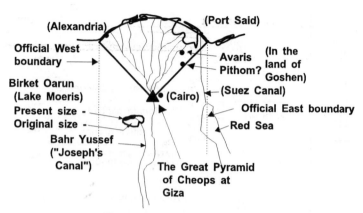

Fig. 2. The Nile delta

Israelites were protected by Joseph. Allowing 7 years of harvests and say 2 years of famine before Jacob came, this would make Joseph, who lived 110 years, take high office when he was about 71 years old. This does not agree with the reference of the chief butler to the "young Hebrew" who interpreted his dream. How can this be solved?

Brad Sparks has pointed out that Joseph's power seems to have begun to wane some time before he died. When he wanted to bury Jacob in Canaan, he does not address Pharaoh directly but pleads for permission through intermediaries (Gen. 50:4) and may have left the children as hostages (50:8). He was also accompanied by "chariots and horsemen" - as though he was under guard. As his fame was usurped by Imhotep, Pharaoh's architect, it is possible that Joseph generated such jealousy in the powerful Egyptian hierarchy that they conspired to undermine his authority, probably when a new Pharaoh ascended the throne.

Regarding the chronology, Sparks contends that historical dates are not known with any accuracy; i.e. +/- 100 years. However, we would suggest that it may be as follows - Joseph was born in 1914 BC, enters Egypt as a slave when about 18 (1896), comes to power aged 30 when 7 years of plenty begin (1884), famine starts (1877), after 2 years of famine Jacob enters Egypt when 130 (1875), Joseph's power decreases (1866), Jacob dies at 147 and is buried (1858), oppression begins (1845), Joseph dies aged 110 (1804). The Israelites did not become slaves until the last 100 years of their 400 years of oppression.

Joseph's city?

Rohl gives a very detailed account of recent excavations of the city of Avaris, the area of Goshen given to the Israelites when they came to Egypt at the time of the famine (Fig. 2).

Excavations show that long-haired sheep were introduced into the area, which accords with the introduction of sheep by the Israelites in Gen. 46:32 - 47:3. Although the Egyptians "abominated shepherds" (Gen. 46:34) it would appear that the Egyptians actually kept sheep for they had to sell Joseph their "flocks" (Gen. 47:17) for food. It was apparently the occupation of shepherd that they despised.

They have also found houses that were similar to those from the Levant

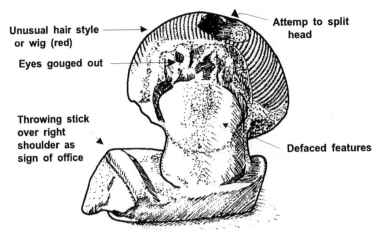

Unusual hair style or wig (red)

Attemp to split head

Eyes gouged out

Throwing stick over right shoulder as sign of office

Defaced features

Fig. 3. Is this the damaged head of Joseph's statue?

(Palestine) (R355). The name of Avaris is derived from Hawara meaning "The House of the Department." We know that Joseph lived near his family from Ex. 45:10 "for thou shalt dwell in the land of Goshen and thou shalt be near unto me." This "Department" would be the centre for Joseph's administration of the flood controls, food storage and disposal that he had already built, so he brought his family to this area.

Joseph's tomb?

Excavations in Avaris revealed the remains of a magnificent palace. In the garden were the foundations of a steep sided pyramid 8m square over an underground coffin together with an ante-room that once contained a large statue. Rohl claims that this was Joseph's house with his tomb and statue. The tomb was completely empty and the statue destroyed,

We know that Joseph's remains were taken into Palestine (Ex. 13:19) and this tomb seems to have been cleared of everything rather than robbed. The statue, however, had been smashed and much of it had been removed, but the head and shoulders were found.

The head had a large indentation in the crown as if an attempt had been made to split it, the inlaid eyes had been gouged out (one was found nearby) and the face desecrated (Fig. 3). Such vandalism suggests that this was more than just destroying a statue. It was more like the efforts to desecrate a monument of someone who was hated.

Was this a statue of Joseph? The statue had two interesting features.

Across the shoulder is a symbolic "throwing stick." Only the Pharaoh would have a crook and flail but the throwing stick was the hieroglyphic sign for a foreigner.

In addition, the figure was covered in a coat with many colours and edged with black and red. Clothes with a similar chevron shaped pattern like this are found in pictures of Midianite traders in some Egyptian tombs and records. It was Midianites who brought Joseph into Egypt, and this style of clothing was therefore not unusual at that time. Joseph's own blooded coat was returned to Jacob (Gen. 37:31), but it is possible that Joseph retained this style as an acknowledgement of his origins. Rohl gives a very impressive computer colour reconstruction of the original statue.

If this statue was of Joseph, as it seems it may well have been, we can understand the Egyptians venting their rage upon it after the Exodus of the Israelites. The impoverished Egyptians would have regarded it as a symbol of a race that had brought death and destruction upon their now ruined nation. Certainly, there is much that indicates that this may well have been the tomb and statue of Joseph, but the date of the palace may need examination as Rohl places it in the time of Sesostris I - 12th Dynasty, not Djoser - 3rd Dynasty.

The pharaoh "who knew not Joseph" and the enslavement.

For thirty years after their entrance into Egypt, the Israelites enjoyed the protection of Joseph. The huge numbers of the Egyptians impoverished into slavery to Pharaoh due to the famine were set to work building the stepped pyramid at Saqqara. Courville and Sparks contend that the pharaoh who enslaved the growing number of Israelites was the tyrant Sesostris III. Courville shows that during his reign regional lords were stripped of their power and all Egypt came under his direct rule. This would be when the Israelites lost their many privileges and became enslaved. In his reign and that of his son Ammenemes III, the Israelites used mud bricks instead of stone to build 2 pyramids covered in polished stone to resemble the classical pyramid. The Great Pyramid of Giza was the crowning achievement of pyramid building initiated by Joseph's skill and wisdom, although later the Egyptians would attribute his achievements to Imhotep. That this skill was achieved so early in the history of Egypt is a subject we examine later.

The Avaris excavations also demonstrated that the history of the area confirmed the Biblical account. As we have noted, sheep skeletons in the oldest layers indicate that Levantine long-haired sheep had been brought into the country, as we know Jacob did (Gen. 46:6) (R272).

At a later stage, there were far more adult women buried than men, whilst 65% of the burials were of children - far higher than normal (R271). One expert noted that about this period there was a large population of Asiatic slaves of whom a large proportion were females. All this would be in agreement with the period when the male children of the Jews were killed to keep the nation under subjection (Ex1:15-22). About the same date, mass graves were found indicating that the population had suffered a plague - also conforming to the Biblical record (R279).

MOSES

The name Moses is an abbreviation of a longer Egyptian name that means "bear or beget." This appears in such names as Thut*mose* and Ra*meses*. There are Egyptian names appearing in the Bible at this time such as Phinehas, Hophni and Pashur (1C20).

Moses was born about 1521 BC during the reign of Amenhemhet 3, according to Courville (1C223). His daughter was Sebeknefrure who would have been Moses's foster-mother who rescued him from the river. She ruled as an old lady for a few years and Courville speculates that Moses was groomed as co-regent for 9 years as Amenhemet 4 but fled to Midian when he killed the Egyptian. The reign of this king finishes at precisely this time and the tombs of all the kings of Dynasty 12 have been discovered except for this king (1C221).

The 24th name on the Turin king list gives the name Kenephres, and there is a tradition that the foster-father of Moses was one Chenephres. He may have been a prince at that time and by marrying Sebeknefrure he entered the royal household.

The Exodus

Moses was 80 when he led the Israelites out of Egypt, and the three "short chronology" experts, Courville, Rohl and Velikovsky, all date the Exodus within a year or two of 1445 BC.

The brick city Pi-Rameses that the Israelites built as slaves has been identified as Tanis, which is also the site of Avaris, on the east side of the Nile delta (Fig. 2). Almost all the pyramids of the 12th dynasty kings were built in brick at this time and not stone, and were located mainly in the east of the Nile delta, the precise location of the Israelites.

Sesostris 3 was succeeded by various kings who continued the subjugation of the Israelites until Tutimaios (Dudimose 1), under whom the nation suffered the plagues.

The ten plagues visited upon Egypt completely devastated the country, and the whole of the army was lost at the Red Sea crossing. The Israelites were able to walk out of the land which was left open for any invading tribes. The advancing Hyksos (= Shepherd Kings) took over the land without any battles and ruled it for the next 430 years. They were a barbarous nation and enslaved the native population. They had no culture of their own and left no monuments or records of achievements. Even their burial customs were distinct, the bodies lying on their left side, facing the west, the knees drawn up to the chin and the hands up to their faces.

The orthodox chronology claims that the period of the Israelites in Egypt is the period of the Hyksos as they were both of eastern origin. This is strongly refuted by the holders of the revised chronology who solve many anachronisms with the revised scheme. This shorter chronology is amply supported by the archaeological evidence of this period.

Both the Ipuwer papyrus and the el-Arish shrine describe a calamity overtaking Egypt very similar to that in Exodus. Darkness and plagues are vividly described, and the pharaoh dies in a whirlpool at Pi-Kharoti. This would be the Pi-ha-hiroth (Khiroth) of Exodus 14:9, the site of the crossing (V37).

Natural catastrophes

Velikovsky quotes evidence that the Hyksos were driven out from Arabia by plagues, a huge tidal wave and similar catastrophes (V61). These catastrophes and their results were at the same time and not dissimilar to those that befell the Egyptians at the time of the ten plagues. This does suggest that there was a significant cosmic catastrophe at that time that affected many nations. Velikovsky asserts that this was the only cause of the plagues. Whilst he may be right in pointing to such major upheavals causing devastation and these mass migrations, he cannot accept that this may have been all part of God's plan and that some of the plagues in Egypt were of a miraculous nature.

Courville refers to the quite separate Great Earthquake of Uzziah's time (Amos 1:1) that was so notable that it was referred to by Zechariah (Zech. 14:5) three centuries later who notes that they "fled" from the earthquake. He dates it at 750 BC and considers that it triggered mass migrations that involved the Dorian invasion of Greece from the north and the catastrophe at Crete. The "Sea People" were those displaced from Greece who overcame the Hittite nation and threatened to invade Egypt c700 BC but were defeated.

The cause was possibly a huge explosion on Thera just south of Greece. This left a crater 30 square miles, much larger than that left by the famous explosion of Krakatoa's which was only 8 sq. miles.

The Hyksos

The invading Hyksos appear to have come from the area of Syria and were Asiatic Arabs possibly of Hamitic stock. They were mercilessly cruel to the surrounding nations and blasphemed God by throwing the mutilated limbs of their victims towards the heavens (V86). They plundered the Israelites after the latter had settled in the Promised Land (Jud. 6:3-6) and were supporters of the Canaanites. We will see later that Garstang, who excavated Jericho, described the culture of City 4 that Joshua destroyed as "Hyksos".

Velikovsky contends that the reference to "evil angels" (malakhei-roim) mentioned in Ps. 78:49 that the Lord sent against the Egyptians as punishment is not only ungrammatical but should have been "shepherd kings" (malkhei-roim). He suggests that a copier, not understanding the meaning of the correct name, assumed it was a misspelling (V66).

It was these incoming Hyksos hordes that the Israelites met in battle shortly after crossing the Red Sea (Ex. 17:8-16), and perpetual enmity was sworn between them. It might be wondered where the Israelites, who had been slaves for generations, could have obtained the weapons that would enable them to fight the Amalekites so effectively. Josephus says that they had merely to collect the weapons of the Egyptian army that had been washed onto the banks of the Red Sea by the force of the returning water (1C94)!

About 420 years (c1023 BC) after this battle, Saul was told to go and exact revenge against them for their opposition to the Israelites as they came out of Egypt, and we have the account of his massacre of them in 1 Sam.15. God authorised Saul to carry out this total destruction of a wicked nation as he had previously instructed Joshua to do with the equally wicked Canaanites who appear to have been closely associated with the Hyksos and possibly of the same race.

The Egyptians of the south eventually rebelled and drove the Hyksos into their prepared fortification at Avaris. This was taken by the surrounding forces and they escaped to a nearby city of Sharuhen in southern Palestine (1C229). It is possibly here that Saul destroyed them.

Velikovsky gives an alternative version for he quotes an inscription on the tomb of an unnamed officer who fought against the Hyksos (V73). This refers to "One" who was the real conqueror in the battle at Avaris and Velikovsky suggests that had this person been an Egyptian king, this would have been stated clearly. The unusual silence indicates that it was a foreign king, possibly Saul, who was the principle conqueror of the Hyksos. It is possible that the southern remnant of the Egyptian rulers would have had difficulty in throwing off the Hyksos yoke and therefore would have taken advantage of the approaching Israelites as allies in their war with the Hyksos.

JOSHUA

It might be thought that God was unduly vindictive in ordering Joshua to completely annihilate the Canaanites - every man, woman and child. Why God should order this became more understandable when the religious practices of these tribes was discovered, for they performed hideous and degrading sexual rituals, including homosexuality and bestiality (EB24:64). This is recorded in the Bible which notes that "the men of Sodom were wicked and sinners before the Lord *exceedingly*." We will not describe their terrible practices at length, but give one example that should be sufficient to indicate their level of human degradation.

The Bible's condemnation of those who "passed their children through the fire" is actually referring to the hideous practice of child sacrifice to Moloch. This consisted of heating a statue till it all glowed, when the child was then placed in the outstretched hands. At that moment, loud drums were beaten to drown the screams of the infant.

With such perverted practices, it is understandable why God should decide to destroy them and give their land to a nation He would train in righteousness.

The walls of Jericho

The story of how Jericho was conquered by its walls falling down and then being burnt is well known (Jos. 6). Garstang (Gars) excavated Jericho in the 1930's and he claimed that he had found the walls that correlated with Joshua's conquest.

These walls had fallen outwards indicating a violent natural cause for their destruction (Fig. 4 - From Gars:Plate XVIII) and there was a very great depth of ash. These ruins of City 4 were dated by Garstang at 1400-1385 BC - Late Bronze Age by his reckoning. This would roughly agree with the period of Joshua's campaign if the Exodus was 1445, for the 40 years in the wilderness would give a date of 1405 BC. Ai was also conquered at the same time and completely destroyed by fire as described in the Bible.

This date of 1400 BC that supported the Bible was not acceptable to most archaeologists who dated the conquest of Canaan about 1250 BC.

To "check" Garstang's dating, Kathleen Kenyon investigated the site after the war. She dated Garstang's City 4 at 1550 BC based upon pottery shards. Although her excavations were carried out between 1952-56 and she wrote about her work in 1957 (KenyK), very surprisingly, the vital pottery data was not published until 1982! When examined by experts, it was realised that she had completely misdated the conquest of Garstang's City 4 which he had dated correctly at c1400 BC. She has been criticised for a number of errors, and Bryant Wood (WoodB) noted the following.

(i) She claimed there was no Late Bronze I pottery in Garstang's City 4, yet this was abundant.

(ii) She misdated two items, and used imported wares from Cyprus at another site to construct her pottery chronology instead of using local pottery of the period.

(iii) Although she dug several large trenches, her datings were mainly based on an excavated area of only 8m. x 8m.

(iv) She linked the date of 1550 BC for the destruction with the Hyksos being driven out of Egypt. This would have made them burn the city they would surely have wanted to live in after they had conquered it.

(v) She ignored the presence of Egyptian scarabs which supported Garstang's dating, classing them as ancient "heirlooms".

With such a list, one could be forgiven for wondering whether the whole purpose of Kenyon's excavations was to overthrow Garstang's identification of Joshua's outward fallen walls and the support it gave to the Biblical record. She has been criticised by one who worked under her at Jericho as gathering a mass of useless detail, never getting any real relationships and not seeing the "wood for the trees": i.e. she ignored the evidence that was staring her in the

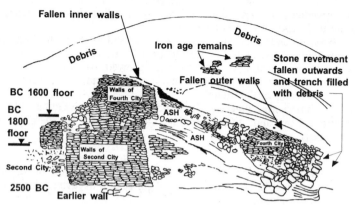

Fig. 4. Jericho - Garstang's trench section

face! (Q23/3:94). She was made a Dame as a reward for her work.

Kenyon excavated out to the defence ditch only on the western slope. She found it filled to the top with fallen red bricks which she claimed came from a Middle Bronze Age city at the top of the mound that had virtually disappeared due to erosion. Our simplified version of Kenyon's Trench 1 drawing is given in Fig. 5. Garstang, excavating on the northern end, showed a similar defence trench but filled from the fallen walls of City 4 (Fig. 4). Rohl, who used Kenyon's section of the site, admitted in a TV programme that there was only one set of fallen walls that Garstang could have attributed to Joshua's conquest, but that his dating error was "understandable". We would consider Garstang's walls *were* those of Joshua's conquest, and we discuss the datings of the walls below.

Rohl gives a section of the site which shows a sloping face of smooth plaster (glissade) to make approach to the walls more difficult for invaders (R304) (see Fig. 5). At the bottom, there was the large revetment ditch. When the walls fell outwards, the debris tumbled down the plaster face of the embankment and filled this ditch up, enabling the Israelites to walk over it, up the rubble covering the plaster face and directly into the city. This confirms the Bible which records that the encircling army was able to go "every man straight before him, and they took the city" (Jos.6:20).

The confused datings

We would comment on the confusion in identifying the actual walls that toppled outwards and the dates they are assigned. Garstang (Fig. 4) shows full height walls that have clearly fallen outwards and dates them as Late Bronze Age I. Rohl uses Kenyon's sections to show Middle Bronze Age walls long since eroded and the only evidence is the rubble filling the bottom revetment trench (Fig. 5). Thus, by "revising" the dating system and "misinterpreting" the pottery evidence, the walls Garstang found are dated to a time that does not agree with the Bible. These revisions of the dating methods were commented on by Garstang in which he noted even in his 1940 book reporting his 1930's dig that "MBAi (Middle Bronze) now becomes EBiii (Early Bronze)". Wood, writing as late as 1990, noted that the dating of Late and Middle Bronze was still an "ongoing debate". Wood (priv. comm.) said

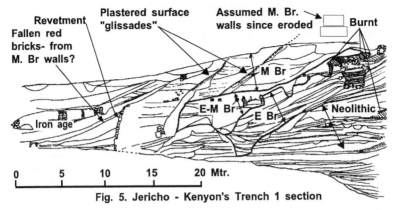

Fig. 5. Jericho - Kenyon's Trench 1 section

that the walls had fallen 17 times, mainly due to earthquakes, and that Garstang "misdated his walls to the Conquest" and that this was confirmed by later excavators. We would question how many walls fell outwards as Garstang's clearly had done. All this supports this writers distrust of the whole system of secular dating - even when accepted by Christian archaeologists. By "moving the goalposts", secular archaeologists can ensure that Biblical Chronology is at variance with "well established dating methods" - as Kenyon did.

The incoming invaders possessed many arms and cultural objects that were Egyptian, such that it was thought they proved the influence of the Hyksos in the area (1C94), but these were obviously the spoil that the Israelites brought out of Egypt and the weapons they collected from the dead Egyptian soldiers mentioned above.

Joshua's conquest of Palestine displaced several tribes and Courville considers that some of them were Hittites who moved to the north. They were then subjugated by Indo-Europeans (Japhethites as against Shemites) who took on their name and civilisation and eventually became the powerful nation mentioned in the Bible (2C296). The Phoenicians also called themselves Canaanites but were pushed out to the coast of the Mediterranean (1C98).

SAUL

In 1887 a hoard of over 380 cuneiform tablets were found at Tell el-Amarna that were the records of the official correspondence of Akhenaten (Amenhotep IV). There is difficulty in dating when they were written but both Courville and Velikovsky place them around 850 BC which is the time of Ahab in the Bible. Rohl dates them about 1020 BC, to the time of Saul's battles with David and other enemies, 170 years earlier.

Rohl's evidence is circumstantial, for he says that the situation the tablets describe fits those of the times of Saul. He notes some parallels with the Biblical record, but there are also serious differences.

The Amarna tablets make frequent mention of marauding bands of "Habiru" and Rohl says several scholars have noted the similarity they describe to that of David's early period (R201). For many years David lived the life of a wandering marauder fleeing from Saul or working as a mercenary for hire to local rulers.

Courville, however, claims that most scholars reject this equating of Habiru (Khabiru) with Hebrews. He provides evidence that it was the name given to any motley collection of foreign people (2C322).

DAVID

Rohl tries to show that the Amarna tablets refer to Saul and David, but he is extremely speculative. He notes that they once mention a "Dadua" which could have been David, but Courville's much later dating of these tablets is preferred which rules out any links with Saul or David.

Except for Velikovsky's mention of the Egyptian soldier's reference to "One" which might be Saul, there is no reference to Saul or David's exploits in Egyptian records. This is as might be expected in a nation that had only just thrown off the yoke of the Hyksos invaders that had subjugated them for 430 years.

SOLOMON

There are two interesting points made by Rohl. The first is the discovery of the Jerusalem Millo (1 Kings 9:15), a huge stone infilling made by Solomon that increased the area of the city by 6,500 sq. yds (6,000 sq m) (R180). Kenyon, misled (again?) by orthodox dating of pottery shards found in it, claimed this must have been formed 360 years before Solomon, and that he could have only "repaired" it!

The second was the discovery just north of Jerusalem of a site with many relics of Egyptian occupation. Rohl suggests that this would have been the residence that Solomon had specially built for his Egyptian wife whom he "brought up out of the city" (2 Chr. 8:11) to a position that overlooks the city from a small hilltop (R182). He identifies Solomon's wife as the daughter of Pharaoh Haremheb. There is difficulty in discerning which of the three Thutmose kings and Queen Hatshepsut ruled during this period. Courville says that it was Thutmose 1 who gave his daughter to Solomon although Queen Hatshepsut ruled for much of the time (2C212). Velikovsky has the same queen ruling but goes further by identifying her as the Queen of Sheba.

Who was the Queen of Sheba?

Velikovsky tries to demonstrate that Queen Hatshepsut was the Queen of Sheba who visited Solomon, but there are many problems with this view. Firstly, the record of her visit to the very wonderful country of "Punt" shows a voyage by boat and Velikovsky contends that this was around the triangular area of the Sinai peninsular landing at the north end of the Gulf of Aqaba. This seems an extremely long way round to cover a much shorter distance overland.

Secondly, the return journey must have been by boat in the Mediterranean as she landed at Thebes which can only be accessed from there, not from the Gulf. Velikovsky's explanation that she was "eager... to display both her fleets" (p119) is weak. She would surely have departed and returned in the same fleet. Wherever "Punt" was, it must have been accessible from the Mediterranean.

Finally, when Christ was recounting this event, He said that she was "the Queen of the South" and had come "from the ends of the earth" (Matt. 12:42). A land that is only some 300 miles (500 km) overland and to the west hardly conforms to this description. That she was from the south also conflicts with the sea passage of Queen Hatshepsut through the Mediterranean to Thebes mentioned above.

REHOBOAM

The Shishak who sacked the Temple in 925 BC during Rehoboham's reign was Thutmose III and not Sheshonk I (1C271). He portrays the many trophies of his conquest and the Temple basins, seven branched candlesticks, etc. can be easily recognised (1C271). Rohl identifies Shishak as Rameses II (R149f) but his evidence is less convincing than Courville's.

THE LATER YEARS

After this time, we move into the history of the northern and southern kingdoms and their separate captivities and transportation by the Assyrians and the Babylonians. There is little controversy amongst historians that these events in the Bible are well corroborated by secular records but Sparks contends that these dates are much less certain than is generally realised. We will not continue our historical investigation further as it is the early history of the Israelites that has been condemned as "fable" as it was claimed there was no confirmation from the orthodox chronology of Egypt. This we hope we have shown to be wrong. The true history of Egypt gives far more support to the Bible than is realised. As it is further clarified, the agreement will be even greater.

We would here note that for many years historians denied that the Hittites, who are frequently mentioned in the Bible, even existed as there was no archaeological evidence. It was only when excavations at Bogazkoy showed that at one time they ruled a huge area of the Middle East from the present-day land of Turkey was it realised that, yet again, the Bible had been right all the time. Accounts of Hittite history do not usually mention how wrong the archaeologists had been previously.

We will conclude this section by considering one of the strange mysteries that the sands of Egypt hold.

The Great Pyramid at Giza

The ancient Greeks made a list of the Seven Wonders of the World, all being huge constructions built by man. Of them, only one still stands - the Great Pyramid of Cheops at Giza.

Many readers will already be familiar with the excessive claims of those who have examined this structure and say it records (and predicts) the major features of the history of the world. By measuring the lengths of certain passages inside the pyramid, using the Pyramid inch (virtually identical to the British inch) as equivalent to one year, they correlated certain rooms, steps, etc. with important historical events. Such people have been labelled "pyramidiots", and it is their zealous propagation of their theories that have cast such a black cloud over the whole subject. Few who value their reputation would even read any such nonsense.

With this we would agree, but has rejection of the whole subject resulted in some astonishing features being ignored?

Courville made a passing comment that suggested that there may be more to this structure than generally realised. He had mentioned that some scholars were not so readily dissuaded by these extravagant "pyramidiot" claims, and then said:

> the investigations had been prompted by statements made by certain of the ancient Greeks testifying that the perimeter of the base of the pyramid was intended to measure half a minute of longitude (1Cou:84).

This encouraged further examination of the subject, and Tompkin's *Secrets of the Great Pyramid* (Tom) seemed to be a very fair survey of many interesting features of this structure. Regarding the ratios of the dimensions of the pyramid to the size of the earth, careful measurements by some experts indicated that the perimeter of the base was equal to half a minute of the equatorial longitude, that the distance up the slope of the centre of the faces was equal to a stadia - one tenth of a minute of latitude at Giza, and many other ratios were claimed. However, Sparks maintained that neither Herodotus nor Agatharchides mention any relationships between the dimensions of the pyramid and the earth. The major question is whether the builders actually intended to include any such ratios. There is no evidence that they did, and all the careful measurements then related to longitude, etc. are comparatively modern proposals that lack historic support. Those wishing to examine this subject can refer to Tomkin's book. We will not dwell upon them but consider a number of other features of this amazing structure.

1. The size of the structure

The size of this huge structure is awe inspiring. Each side is 757 ft. (230m) and the height was 480 ft. (146m.) but is now about 450 ft. (137m.). 2.5 million blocks were used and the weight is about 6 million tons. The blocks have been made with amazing accuracy, such that the joints between the faces are less than 1mm. The pyramid has several passages but there was no obvious entrance. This was only later discovered in 820 AD when some Arab diggers excavated through the blocks and came across one of the internal passages.

The whole edifice was clad in brilliant white polished limestone and must have been a truly awe-inspiring spectacle. Limestone is actually superior to marble as it becomes harder and more polished with time whilst marble becomes eroded. The top was capped with a metal clad "pyramidion" that would have shone brightly in the sun.

It has generated enormous interest over the years and several famous people have spent much time examining its dimensions to find relationships with natural features of the earth. Amongst such men are Sir Isaac Newton, Sir John Herschel, Sir Flinders Petrie, C.P. Smyth (the Astronomer Royal of Scotland), and others.

Fig. 5 gives some basic dimensions and internal structure.

2. Its position

The delta of the Nile is virtually a quarter of a circle, with the curve following the curve of the north edge of the delta. The Great Pyramid is positioned *exactly* at the point of the centre of the circle. Furthermore, the ancient boundaries of Egypt were on two meridians on either side of the Nile. These passed through the most easterly and most westerly points of the quadrant (Fig. 2) (Hit:65, Tom:181).

The four sides are aligned along the true N, S, E, and W with very great accuracy.

It was noticed that the Great Pyramid was visible for many miles, and that with the smaller pyramids around it, they acted as lines of sight for establishing the boundaries of land. Each year the flood would obliterate many boundaries with its deposit of mud, but these could be remade by aligning the edges of the distant pyramids with plumb bobs and noting their shadows and angles (Tom:117).

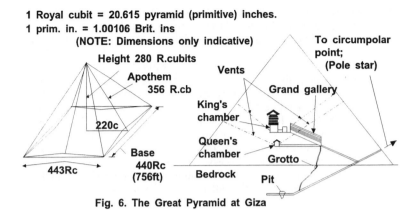

1 Royal cubit = 20.615 pyramid (primitive) inches.
1 prim. in. = 1.00106 Brit. ins
(NOTE: Dimensions only indicative)

Fig. 6. The Great Pyramid at Giza

The shadow would have been used as a sundial for measurement of time. A particular feature was the shadow on the faces of the pyramid. At noon precisely on the day of the spring equinox, the sun is just sufficiently high to shine down the north face of the pyramid, so that suddenly the shadow disappears. Thus the date and time could be accurately recorded. Tompkins mentions that "for some reason" it did not now occur on the precise date (p121). If the increase in the tilt of the earth's axis (See App. 5) in the period it was constructed were to be taken into account, this may explain the present discrepancy.

Even when the sun was too high to cast a shadow, the polished faces of the pyramid would reflect the sun to send a dazzling triangle of light on to the flat paved areas around. These were covered with slabs that were specially aligned for measuring purposes.

The above are just some of the many features that have been ascribed to this phenomenal structure, and one can begin to appreciate why it has created such interest in mankind ever since it was built.

3. The purpose of the pyramid

Ask people why pyramids were built and most will answer "as a tomb for a pharaoh." *Yet not a single body has ever been found in one in the 40 major pyramids!* Many contain a sarcophagus, some of them closed and sealed, yet still empty. It is possible that the body may have been placed elsewhere within the pyramid to escape tomb robbers, or taken to another location by the priests, but none have ever been discovered. Rohl does give details of many coffins discovered near Thebes that had been secretly stored (R63). These may or may not have been housed in a pyramid at one stage.

The Great Pyramid, however, had the way to the central sarcophagus blocked by huge stone "plugs" that may have been built into position rather than placed there afterwards. When eventually they were bypassed, the King's Chamber was found which had a sarcophagus with no lid and was empty. It was obvious that it had been left like this originally and that there was no way to or from the chamber. Why was it made like this?

What, indeed, was the whole purpose of such a costly edifice if it was not to house the body of a pharaoh? Why cripple the nation's economy for such seemingly useless structures? We will try to answer these questions later.

4. The dismissal of the pyramid evidence.

What is noticeable is the very little information that appears in standard books about this structure, the only one of the Seven Wonders of the World that still exists.

When orthodox authorities are silent on any subject, it can be taken that the evidence is highly embarrassing to them. This is the case with the Great Pyramid. The *Encyclopaedia Britannica*, apart from giving a few dimensions and weights, provides no details of its internal passages, its discovery or other interesting information that one might have expected in this large reference work of such a well known and outstanding structure. Petrie's work on it is virtually ignored and Smyth has no entry.

It is understandable that orthodox intellectuals would not want to be associated with the "pyramidiots" who claim it is a record of past and future events, but is there more to this silence than avoidance of this aspect? I suggest there is.

It might be thought that this huge structure was the culmination of many centuries of increasing skill of the Egyptians in the building of many earlier pyramids. This is not the case, however.

There are some 100 pyramids along the Nile, but the Great Pyramid, constructed in the Old Kingdom is only the sixth to have been built. Except for one other, it dwarfs all the rest (Hit:66).

The pyramid was built in the reign of Khufu (Cheops) which was at the beginning of Egyptian history and not at the end of a long period of experience in the building of pyramids. Later pyramids, in fact, were of a much poorer quality.

Tompkins notes that Erastothenes is credited with measuring the circumference of the earth, but Stecchini shows that he was only citing old Egyptian writings. He had been put in charge of the library at Alexander and this information was passed to other Greek geographers Hipparchus and Ptolemy who were "handling and mishandling traditional data of an advanced science that preceded them, and which they only understood in part" (Tom:215). Steccini made an extremely detailed investigation of ancient units of measurement and concluded that "there existed on this planet a people with an advanced mathematical and astronomical science several millennia before classic Greece" (Tom:216).

This pyramid demonstrates that even at the early stages of their emerging civilisation, the Egyptians possessed skills and knowledge of astronomy and many other subjects that were far higher than they "should" have had at that early date. It was in complete contradiction to the theory of evolution that said man gradually emerged from a very primitive "stone age" form of society to slowly gain an increasingly cultured civilisation around him.

Here was evidence of an extremely high level of intelligence and achievement at the very beginning of the long period of Egyptian history. We can, therefore, see why the whole subject is rarely referred to by secular writers and authorities.

5. Whence the knowledge?

Where did these early Egyptians get their skill and knowledge from that enabled them to build such an edifice?

More than one expert could only ascribe some superhuman agency providing them with such knowledge. Tompkins notes that the initiation ceremony used in Freemasonry claims to have been based on Egyptian rituals when initiates were accepted into the association of those possessing "higher wisdom" not revealed to ordinary people. This connection between Freemasonry and the Great Pyramid is demonstrated in the American Great Seal and one dollar note which depict a pyramid with the capstone above the top bearing the "evil eye" of Horus. Almost all those who signed the Declaration of Independence were Freemasons and one of their many symbols is now embedded in their political and financial system.

As Egypt was one of the first major civilisations, many occult organisations have claimed to be connected with its secrets and ceremonies. This is all part of the "secret knowledge" or "gnoses" (Greek = knowledge; the gnostic heresy) that the Bible warns against (1 Tim. 6:20). In complete contrast to this secret knowledge that was transmitted to only a selected and trained few, all Christians seek to spread the Good News and publicise what they know as widely as possible, so that "all may come in."

We have previously noted in Section 1.1 the giving of specialist skills for particular work. God gave Moses specific instructions about the tabernacle (Ex. 35f) and "filled" certain men with "wisdom and understanding" in all manner of workmanship" (Ex. 35:30-1). Similarly, God granted Solomon "exceeding great wisdom" (1 Kings 4:29) and the construction of the huge brassware for Solomon's Temple was by Hiram who was "filled with wisdom and cunning" for this work (1 Kings 7:14).

We read in Genesis 12:10-20 that Abraham went to Egypt during a famine which Courville dates from the Bible at 1875 BC, ten years into Khufu's reign. Courville refers to a stone with Khufu's symbol and the figure 17 which is thought to be the year of his reign. Thus, Abraham could have been in Egypt seven years before the building of the Great Pyramid.

Regarding Abraham's wisdom, Courville quotes Josephus (J. Ant. Bk1 Ch7 par 1) who says that Abraham "communicated to them (the Egyptians) arithmetic, and he delivered to them the science of astronomy; for before Abram came into Egypt, they were unacquainted with those parts of learning" (2C87).

This is all very intriguing, but the Bible gives it little support (Gen.12:10-2 0). When Abram first arrived, Pharaoh, having taken Sarah, gave him many gifts. Then at some unknown but surely short time afterwards, when Sarah was found to be his wife and not his sister, he was unceremoniously sent out of Egypt. If he had no influence on Egyptian culture or technology, this still leaves the question of where their high level of skill came from that enabled them to construct the Great Pyramid so early in their history?

Brad Sparks contends that the source was Joseph who was gifted with skills in architecture, administration, government, arts and science. The Bible notes that Joseph was the most "discreet and wise" in the land and had "the Spirit of God" within him (Gen. 41:38,39). He also had the power to enact all the improvements he wished to make upon the nation.

Arising from the slavery caused by the famine (Gen. 47:13f), the people were set to work building pyramids in order to keep them occupied. Such was the abundance of labour that Snofru (Sneferu), who reigned just before Cheops, built three pyramids. These skills were developed and culminated within fifty years in Cheop's Great Pyramid at Giza.

It is notable that the history of Egypt was generally not one of wanton cruelty or enslavement of nations such as was seen in the Assyrians, Babylonians and Hyksos. It rose to become a great nation at a very early date. Could this be ascribed to the early influence of the godly Joseph? Was it from him that much of the knowledge, attributed to the Greeks, actually came? Petrie, after his careful measuring of the Great Pyramid, said the accuracy "was limited to the skill of one man" (Tom:219). Joseph would have died before it was constructed but his skills could have been the foundation of the method, to be taken over by Imhotep - who then claimed all the credit.

There is much else that could be related about this structure. For example, Sir Willaim Siemens, the inventor, found that as he stood on the top of the pyramid, the atmosphere around could generate a voltage strong enough to concuss an Arab nearby.

At that point, we will leave the subject, trusting that some of the amazing features of this huge structure may have been of interest to the reader.

SECTION 3.9
A BIBLICAL CHRONOLOGY

In this section, we will try to provide the basis for a chronology from Creation to the date of the Exodus. After this period, although there is some discrepancy between Biblical dating and orthodox, it will be sufficient to draw a line at that point.

THE OLD TESTAMENT TEXTS

As we noted in Section 1, there are very many copies of both the Old and New Testaments. There are few differences in OT copies, but for the NT many of them differ slightly from each other. Biblical scholars spend their lives trying to discover by cross comparisons what the original authors actually wrote. This is known as Textual (or Lower) Criticism.

This is not to be confused with "Higher Criticism" which tries to discover who wrote certain parts of the Bible and when, etc. This approach, however, gradually undermined the authority and accuracy of the Bible, culminating in the JEPD (Jahwistic, Elohistic, Priestly and Deuteronomist) multiple authorship theory of the Pentateuch. This theory completely contradicts Christ's statement that Moses was its sole author. However, the theory has been thoroughly disproved by Archer and many others (Arch).

These "reinterpretations" are a fertile source for those who wish to destroy the faith of those who believe in the accuracy of the Bible. The first attack of modernists is upon the seminaries and Bible colleges. Liberal views of the Bible are gradually brought in over several years until the whole college loses its evangelical witness and espouses the "findings of present day scholarship." More than one keen student has entered a liberal theological college, only to be shattered to find that the first lessons are specifically aimed at completely destroying any trust he had in the reliability of the book that he had come to study.

The early versions of the Old Testament

It will surprise many Christians to know that the Massoretic text, which is the basis of our present Old Testament translations, was not the version that was used by the ordinary people at the time of Christ. They appear to have used a precursor of the Massoretic text - a proto-Massoretic text. Our OT is translated from the Massoretic text, which reached its present final form long after the time of Christ. This is why some OT verses quoted in the NT differ from the (Massoretic) OT wording in our Bibles. The Massoretic text itself, however, was formed shortly after the time of Christ.

Surprisingly, several quotations of the OT by Christ and the NT writers *did not correspond with the Septuagint or the Massoretic.* Either they were quoting from some other text, or were quoting "freely" with a particular point in view. Similarly, an analysis of the Dead Sea Scrolls showed that they also were "mixed". There is evidence of a proto-Massoretic text within the D.S. Scrolls. Support for this is the closeness of the Dead Sea copy of Isaiah which is virtually identical to the Massoretic text.

It is, therefore, suggested that there was one Ancient text that became the proto-Massoretic text that culminated in the Massoretic text from which our OT is translated (Sparks). Each book would have had its own history of finalisation, however.

The Aramaic speaking Jews in Israel would not have quoted from a Greek version produced in Egypt. In view of this, we would contend that Christ and the NT writers were not quoting from the Septuagint but "freely" quoting from this proto-Massoretic text.

Septuagint is the Latin for "seventy", named after the 70 scholars said to have translated the OT in Alexandria in about 260 BC. It is often referred to by the Roman numeral for "seventy" which is LXX. However, this story is based upon a letter by Aristeas now considered to be legendary. The Septuagint appears to have been translated by Jews of varying ability about that time (Wurth:52) but the period over which the translations were made may be as much as 200 years. It is generally thought that Christ and the writers of the New Testament quoted from the Septuagint, but this is very unlikely - a subject discussed later.

The *Samaritan Pentateuch* is another version of the OT which the northern Ten Tribes of Israel retained when they separated from Judah after the death of Solomon. What is a little surprising is that the Samaritan Pentateuch differs from the Massoretic text in 6,000 cases and agrees with the Septuagint in 1,900 of them (Wurth:43).

The Massoretic Text

The Massoretes, centred in Tiberias, were active from 500 to 1000 AD and it has been suggested that they "amended" the text to reduce the support that the OT prophecies gave to the newly emerging Christian faith and then destroyed all the old copies. This is hardly likely. Had the Jews wanted to produce a version that removed *all* such support, they would have had to have made far more drastic revisions to the Massoretic text we have today which still gives massive support to the NT; little of it would have been left. Furthermore, it is difficult to imagine the Jews either altering or systematically destroying the sacred text they had treasured for generations. Only one copy had to survive to proved they had vandalised their own scriptures.

In 70 AD at the fall of Jerusalem the Jews lost the whole of the written records of their genealogies and many OT records. This meant that they were no longer able to check the ancestry of anyone claiming to be a true Jew by referring to their records. To this day there is controversy over how a Jew can be defined. The loss of important OT copies appears to have been used by the Massoretes as an opportunity to produce a "final" copy of the OT.

The NT quotations

The fact that the OT quotations in the NT do not correspond with the wording of the (Massoretic) OT we have may seem to present Christians with a dilemma. Did not Christ say that "one jot or one tittle shall in no wise pass from the law, till all be fulfilled" (Matt. 5:18)? Can this be reconciled? Let us first show that the Massoretic text should be accepted as reliable.

(i) We know that "salvation is of the Jews" (John.4:22) and "unto them were committed the oracles of God" (Rom. 3:2). Therefore we should go to the Massoretic Text as this is the only one that has always been under their control and is not a translation to another language. The Septuagint and the Samaritan Pentateuch cannot claim such a pedigree.

(ii) Christ and the people of his time spoke Aramaic *and would not have used any Greek translation.* The Septuagint was produced only for Jews whose basic language was Greek.

(iii) To reject the Massoretic text is tantamount to saying that Christians have been following a false version of the OT chronology. This surely reflects upon the trustworthiness of the Holy Spirit's guidance of the composers of our present Bible (2 Tim. 3:16).

(iv) The ancient texts were copied with care by the Scribes and this was carried forward with even greater standards of care in the forming and copying of the Massoretic text. No other text has this tradition of such care in the copying of worn out manuscripts into new replacements. This suggests that the proto-Massoretic and the Massoretic text were part of the Holy Spirit's plan for the preservation of an accurate account for the use of the new Christian church.

The editors of the New Bible Dictionary note that in 1815 Gesenius "brought this barren controversy [regarding the LXX text] to an end and demonstrated the superiority of the Massoretic text. We are witnessing today an attempt to reinstate the Samaritan Pentateuch" (p1180).

(v) The only major differences that affect this work are the ages of the patriarchs which vary between all three versions.

Regarding this, it has been suggested that as the Septuagint was written about the same time as Manetho was compiling his "king list" which greatly extended the reigns of the Pharaohs, this may have influenced the writers of the Septuagint to do likewise with the ages of the Jewish Patriarchs.

The OT - NT text differences considered

Returning to the OT-NT discrepancies and Christ's claim, we have suggested that the Massoretic text is the most reliable one, but this does not entirely solve the problem that Christ and the disciples quoted from a slightly different version (the proto-Massoretic text). This has puzzled scholars for generations, so we are unlikely to provide provide a full explanation. We can only note the following points.

The original Semitic alphabet divided into several styles from which the rounded Old Hebrew and the square Aramaic script resulted. The more beautiful and neat-looking square script was eventually used in the sacred books. Kenyon (KenyF:41) suggests that the use of the square script must have been started some time before Christ's birth for he referred to the "jot" ("*yod*") as the smallest of the letters and this was certainly not the smallest letter in the earlier alphabet Williams (WillP) has pointed out that Matthew used "*iota*" - the smallest letter in the Greek alphabet - as a correct equivalent of "*yod*" and this could have applied to both types of script.

Later the square script was adopted for the final Hebrew version that was probably based upon the "proto-Massoretic" text already existing at the time of Christ.

Christ and the NT writers were, therefore, probably quoting from the proto-Massoretic text with which the common people would have been familiar. However, when Christ said not a "jot" would be changed, He was obviously referring to the square-charactered sacred Scriptures used in the synagogues - and the crowd would have known exactly what he meant. It is therefore possible that He was claiming that *these particular synagogue scriptures* were inspired. He knew that they would eventually form the Christian OT and provide the inspired record for all time for millions of His followers to come.

There is the additional complication that we do not have the actual words that Christ said. He and the disciples would have spoken to each other and to the crowds in Aramaic. When the Gospels and letters were written, they were all in Greek, and furthermore it was a basic version of Greek used for communication and trade known as "*Koine*" Greek.

Where there are differences it must be reiterated that they are small and have no effect whatsoever upon the Christian faith. On this, the differing texts of both the Old and New Testaments speak with a united voice. We will, however, review this problem in Section 6.7 - God's Hidden Presence.

The Date of Creation

Ussher's date

Archbishop Ussher (1581-1656) calculated that the universe was created in 4004 BC. This date has received much ridicule, but he was a very learned man and his date is probably very near the correct one. He was not alone in giving this date as several other experts arrived at a very similar date. It is also a little known fact that in his personal translation of his 1650/1656 Latin book (published posthumously in 1658) he clearly states that Day 1 of Creation began at 9 am on the morning of October 23, 4004 BC. Surprisingly, he also said that Creation began 15 hours earlier, at 6 pm 45th meridian local time, October 22, 4004 BC (Spark). Presumably, this was so that it started at 6 pm in the evening which is the start of the Jewish day.

Other dates of creation

As well as the Hebrews, various nations have chronologies from which a date for creation can be derived. Young's Analytical Concordance notes that Hale reported 120 dates and that there could be as many as 300. There are 37 dates in this work from various authorities and these are plotted in Fig. 1. It will be seen that there are different dates for the same text. This is due to the calculations and assumptions that the various experts make. It is interesting to see that there are concentrations around 6200 BC for the pagan dates, around 5500 BC for some Jewish and other texts and many at 4000 BC for those based upon the Massoretic text.

Watson shows (Q18/1:30) that many Roman writers were well aware that the earth was not very old and clearly stated this in their accounts, often quoting earlier authorities. Shakespeare's Rosalinde, in *As You Like It* (Act IV, scene 1), says "The poor world is almost six thousand years old", showing it was an accepted fact in the sixteenth century.

We have discussed above the various versions of the Old Testament, the Massoretic, the Septuagint, and the Samaritan Pentateuch. The last two of these give different dates for the ages of the patriarchs which affects the chronology of the Bible. If we assume the date of creation was 4000 BC based upon the Massoretic text, this would lengthen to 4299 BC using the Samaritan Pentateuch and to 5364 BC for the Septuagint. We will only refer to the Massoretic text

Fig. 2 plots the life-spans of the patriarchs and age at birth of their descendant the Massoretic text gives. As we noted in the previous section, we originally assumed a date for creation of 4000 BC and that the "sojourn" of

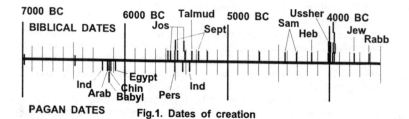

Fig.1. Dates of creation

the Israelites in Egypt was only 215 years, and Fig. 2 is the result. We discuss later this time being 430 years and the revision this requires in the dates.

Are there there "gaps" in the chronologies?

This has been proposed by a number of experts, but the evidence they produced did not fully convince this author. Their arguments are mainly "circumstantial" and can be answered, as Ozanne has done (Oz:213f). Sparks has also pointed out that the statements are categorical - B was born when A was X years old. It does not say that they were father and son and they may not even have been related, but a strict chronology can be drawn up from these statements.

If it is possible to allow gaps in these genealogies, then this renders the carefully recorded ages at birth totally pointless. We are presented with an unbroken series of ages which do not permit any extensions to be inserted if the Scriptures are to be accepted as inerrant (Spark and Q19/1:60)).

Watson has pointed out (Q18/1:37) that where there is a direct father-son relationship, the Hebrew "*yalad*" is *always* used; it is translated "begotten" in the King James Version. There are 450 other places outside these early chapters of Genesis where it is used with this meaning - with only four exceptions; Gen.46:18,20, Deut. 4:25 and 23:8. In all of these passages it is abundantly clear that later generations are included in the group.

Where a non-direct ancestry is indicated, Moses used "*ab*". This is seen in Gen. 4:20, 21 and 17:5 where the KJV translates it as "father" in the obviously wider sense of the word.

The use of the specific Hebrew "*yalad*" surely proves that there are no gaps in these genealogies. It is therefore certain that Moses intended the ages to be added and a chronology constructed from them. There can be no other reason for his recording of such details. Josephus, who was well versed in the Jewish lore of his day and nearer to the time of Moses, also added up the ages from Adam to the Flood. It was this that enabled Ussher and others to obtain dates near 4000 BC for creation.

These long life-spans result in some patriarchs living for many years at the same time as their famous descendants who were several generations later, but this is no major objection. There is nothing in the Bible that contradicts this situation.

The "insertion" of Cainan in the patriarchal list.

In the Septuagint (and in Luke 3:36) we find that Cainan is inserted into the post-Flood list of the patriarchs where he does not appear in the Massoretic text. Rosevear also suggests that Cainan should be excluded; "Many of the church fathers regarded Cainan as superfluous" (Rose).

Prof. Kulling (Kul) has written a more detailed booklet on the whole subject in which he agrees with Rosevear's views but gives additional pieces of interesting evidence that show not only that there are no gaps but that Cainan should be omitted.

(A) The NT inclusion of "Cainan"

Cainan appears in the OT of the Septuagint, but Kulling lists several other OT texts that do not include Cainan, and points out that there is no tribe or ancestry that can be ascribed to him in the Bible. There are also two NT manuscripts that omit him (WillP).

The most reasonable explanation is that the writers of the Septuagint included Cainan as a post-Flood patriarch to lengthen the ages of the patriarchs to match what Manetho was doing with the list of the Pharaohs. Luke wrote his inspired gospel omitting Cainan, and from this, several copies were made. However, the inclusion of his name in the Septuagint was noted and possibly Luke was "corrected" to agree with it. From that point on, many other copies were made.

(B) The numerical total

Kulling refers to the discovery of a German worker, Bodenstein, who added the "numeric values" of the names of all the 22 patriarchs from Adam to Israel, omitting Cainan. This subject of the "numeric values" is discussed more fully in Appendix 7, but it is sufficient here to say that Hebrew uses letters of the alphabet as symbols for numbers, and therefore, by the reverse process of numbering the letters in a word, any word can be given a numerical value. When this is done for all the names from Adam to Israel, the *total of all the numeric values of the names comes to exactly 7000!*

Obviously, if there were any generations that should be added, or if Cainan should be included, this precise value of 7000 would be completely lost. In addition, this figure of 7000 signifies "wholeness and completeness." To those who accept that there are numerical patterns in the Bible, this would be interpreted as an unexpected confirmation that not only are there are no gaps in the genealogies but that the Massoretic text, which excluded Cainan, bears the stamp of the Holy Spirit's endorsement! Others, more sceptical, may consider this as somewhat contrived.

(C) The name changes

Bodenstein also points out that in the original Hebrew, the names of God "*El Shaddai*" and "*Elohim*" have 5 consonants. He then examined the number of syllables in the names of the 22 patriarchs and found that they were all of 2, 3, 4 and 6 consonants - not one of them was 5! This is more than coincidence as nearly every fourth name elsewhere in the Bible has 5 consonants. We will see in Appendix 7 that the figure 5 has the spiritual significance of "Divine Grace."

This list would have the original four consonant names of Abram and Jacob before they were renamed to Abraham and Israel. When God specifically changed the names of these two particular people, he gave them 5 syllables as a sign of his special grace to one who would be the progenitor and the other the namegiver of the chosen race.

Summarising, the list of 22 Patriarchs is complete and warrants no additions or subtractions, and there appear to be confirmations of this within the text itself.

A BIBLICAL CHRONOLOGY

Having demonstrated the reliability of the Massoretic text, we will, with considerable trepidation, use this to try to provide the major dates for a complete Biblical chronology. As we have said, it was based on the "sojourn" of the Israelites in Egypt being only 215 years. Having formed a chronology that fitted two astronomical "external dates", Brad Sparks provided good evidence that the Israelites were in Egypt the full 430 years. We will briefly outline the original chronology and then present the second.

What was surprising was that, although there were some chronologies in creationist periodicals, there were not many who were prepared to give a complete chronology from creation onwards to say about 300 BC. After that date, although there are still disagreements about many historic ages, it will be sufficient for our purposes.

THE ORIGINAL CHRONOLOGY

Fig. 2 presents our original proposed time scale. The Anno Mundi (Year of the World - since creation) scale follows the OT text. We had assumed that creation was about 4000 BC, although it will be seen that this could be modified.

The date of the Flood would have been 1656 AM and with Creation about 4000 BC, this gave the date of the Flood as 2344 BC. Now this is almost the exact date calculated by Dodwell - 2345 BC - when the earth was tilted by an asteroid impact (See Appendix 5). The coincidence of these two dates was striking and suggested that the Flood was initiated by an asteroid impact in that year. In order for these dates to agree with scripture, Abraham had to leave Haran and enter Canaan some 42 years after the death of Terah. With the revised chronology below, he leaves only 5 years after the death of Terah. The 430 years "sojourn" was divided between 215 years in Canaan and 215 years in Egypt in this first chronology.

THE REVISED CHRONOLOGY

This chronology is longer than the original by an extra 178 years (215-42+5). This does not affect the AM datings of the early patriarchs but changes all the correlations with the BC dates. Several experts, Courville included, place the date of the Exodus at about 1445 AD and we will use this as a basis for preliminary calculations. When other factors are included, which are discussed later, we obtain a date of 4178 BC for creation.

Abraham's entry into Canaan

Assuming the period from Abraham's entry into Canaan to the Exodus was 645 years (430+215), then this dates his entry as 1445 + 645 = 2090 BC. These are dates arrived at by working from the "BC" end of history.

We will now obtain Abraham's entry into Canaan by working from the "AM" end - the date of creation.

Abraham's birth

The genealogies in Genesis are set out very clearly, A begat B when he was X years old., etc. However, when we come to Abraham's birth, we read "Terah lived seventy years and begat Abram, Nahor and Haran" (Gen.11:26). Gen.11:32 records that Terah was 205 years old when he died. Now it might be assumed that Abraham was the first born of these three, when Terah was 70.

However, in Gen. 12:4 it says that "Abram was seventy five years old when he departed out of Haran" and in Acts 7:4, Stephen says that Abraham left Haran after Terah's death. If we assume that Abraham left Haran the year Terah died, this would mean that he was born when Terah was 130 (205 when Terah died less 75 years before that). So Abraham was *not* born when Terah was 70, but when he was 130 years old - *or more.*

If Terah was born in 1878 AM (2300 BC), then Abraham would have been born 130 years later in 2008 AM (2170 BC). Terah died in 2083 AM (2095 BC) and if we assume for the moment that Abraham left Haran and entered Canaan the same year, then there is a 5 year difference to the date of 2090 BC from the "BC end" as shown above. The reason for this additional 5 years is given by Ozanne.

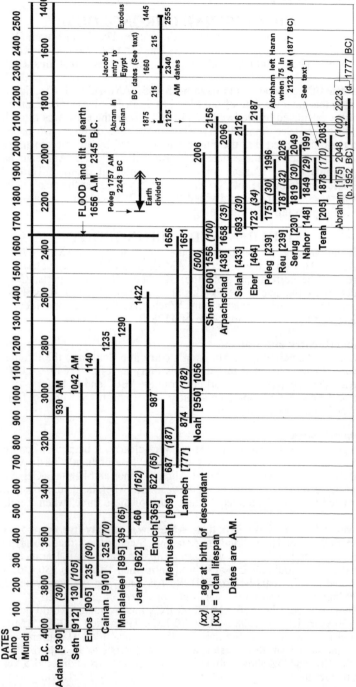

Fig. 2. The original biblical chronology (Israelites 215 yrs. in Egypt).

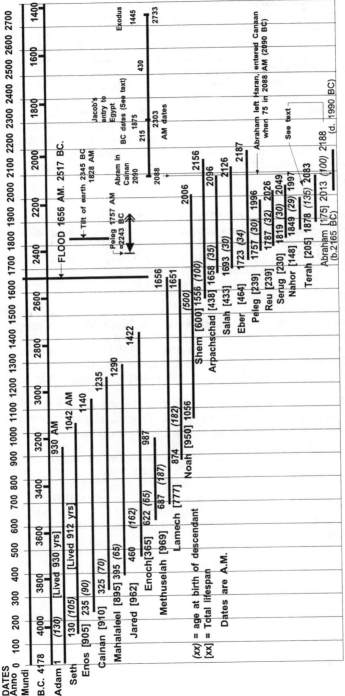

Fig. 3. A revised biblical chronology. (Israelites 430 yrs in Egypt)

Ozanne's observation

Ozanne suggested Abraham's call came at least five years after Terah's death (Oz:19). He noted that the rulers of God's people are in groups of seven. 7 pre-diluvial (Enoch was "translated" and Lamech died before his father, leaving "Noah the eighth" (2Pet.2:5), seven post-diluvial, 14 Judges and 21 kings of Israel and Judah.

Regarding the seven post-diluvial rulers, the rule (on their death) passed from Noah to Shem to Eber (to Abraham) to Isaac to Jacob to Joseph. Ozanne contends that Abraham could only be included in this list if he lived (say) *at least* one year after Eber's death in 2187 AM. If Abraham died in 2188 AM then he would have received the call in 2088 AM, 5 years after the death of Terah. This delay in leaving Canaan does not contradict scripture. Gen. 12:4 only says that Abraham left Haran when he was 75: it does *not* say that this was when Terah died.

The chronology

If we accept Ozanne's extra five years so that Abraham, by not dying until 2188 AM would have at least one year as the oldest surviving patriarch, then he would have entered Canaan when he was 75 in 2088 AM. Maintaining the Exodus at 1445 BC, this would then be 2733 AM, giving a date for creation at 4178 BC. Fig. 3 gives a chart of these revised dates.

This revised chronology conflicts with two dates in the first chronology that have been calculated independently of Scripture.

(i) Dodwell's "tilt" date of 2345 BC could be amended to 2517 BC to coincide with the Flood. However, he based his dates upon secular systems and these are generally too long, and this would have made his dating even longer. Retaining his date of 2345 BC places it in the days of Peleg and it may have been the impact of the asteroid that caused the continental masses to separate (plate tectonics) when "the earth was divided."

(ii) In Section 2.3 we examined the possible alignment of the planets in 4001 BC. If the date of creation is 4175 BC, then this alignment would have no connection with the starting of the "signs, seasons, days and years" for Adam's timekeeping.

All these problems can be resolved by dating the Exodus at 1267 BC, but this is probably far too late for most Bible historians.

We would hope that others may be able to provide a correlation between accurate scientific and historical evidence and Scripture. If nothing else, we have set out just a few of the many problems facing those who, like this author, are foolhardy enough to attempt to navigate the stormy seas of Biblical Chronology.

SECTION 3.10
JONAH AND THE "WHALE"

There are certain accounts in the Bible that are constantly ridiculed as unbelievable. The most frequent are - (1) creation in six days, (2) Eve made from Adam's rib, (3) the long life spans of the patriarchs, (4) Noah's Flood, and of course (5) Jonah and the "whale". We have examined the first four, but what of the "story" of Jonah?

1. Christ's authentication

Christ referred to Jonah being in the "great fish" (not a whale it should be noted) for three days and nights as a parallel to His time in the tomb after His crucifixion. Such a statement should be an adequate assurance to the Christian that this is an accurate record of what took place. Christ is hardly likely to have pointed to this if it had been only a "myth that pointed a moral" as it is usually assumed.

Some might hold that He may have known it was a "myth" but because His listeners believed it, He "accommodated" what He said to their beliefs at that time. Now, however, as we are "an educated and civilised people" we do not need such "tales" to prop up our faith. They do not seem to realise that they are accusing Christ of lying to his hearers. In addition, to even think along these lines is to enter onto the very slippery slope of doubting the reliability of the Scriptures that are inspired by the Holy Spirit. We discuss this later

2. Could it have occurred?

We should first point out that "whale" originally covered any large marine animal, and only later was it used to describe the specific type we know today. It should also be noted that God frequently made special provisions throughout this book. He "sent out a great wind" and more interestingly, "The Lord had prepared a great fish to swallow Jonah" (1:17). Did he just provide one at the right time or was it prepared beforehand (when created?) with the ability to swallow a man?

The "James Bartley" account

The most frequently related account of a man surviving being swallowed by a whale is that of James Bartley which is as follows:

Whilst harpooning a large sperm whale off the Falkland Islands in February 1891, he was knocked out of the whaling boat and disappeared. The next morning, when cutting open the whale's stomach he was found inside. He was unconscious, but was revived with a bucket of sea water. He was raving for two weeks but then recovered and went about his duties. His face, neck and hands had been attacked by the whale's gastric juices and turned white permanently.

He remembered the event and said that he had air to breathe, but that the heat (estimated about 105°F, 41°C) was overpowering. It was when he realised where he was that he passed out from shock. He contended that he could have stayed there until he starved.

This was related by Wilson (WilsA) who showed that a Sperm whale's stomach could easily have accommodated a man. His source for this story is the autobiography of Sir Francis Fox, an engineer. Wilson also claims it was investigated and accepted by two French scientists, one being the science editor of a journal. There is another 1771 newspaper account of a sailor being swallowed by a whale but soon after being spewed out on the surface, with little harm done.

With no contrary evidence then available, it seemed to be reasonable to accept its veracity. However, not long before publication, I was forwarded by my friend Paul Garner a copy of Edward E. Davis's article entitled *A Whale of a Tale: Fundamentalist Fish Stories* that appeared in *Science and Christian Faith;* the Journal of the American Scientific Affiliation (v43 n4 Dec. 1991). This article was the result of original research he had carried out in England and America.

To summarise his article, Davis found that the account appeared in the *New York Times* (22 Nov. 1896), which incorrectly attributed it to *The South Yarmouth Mercury*, England, in October 1891. It also appeared in the *New York World* (12 April 1896). He tracked down the original account which was in the *Yarmouth Mercury* dated 22 August 1891 on page 3 (not Davis's reference to page 8). He also discovered that there was a ship named *Star of the East* that was registered in London, and was sailing from Auckland in New Zealand, arriving in New York on 17 April 1891. This would have placed it near the Falkland Isles in February where and when the incident is said to have occurred. All this seems to confirm the account, but Davis found good evidence against it.

This evidence was:

(a) The ship was not a whaler but a normal cargo vessel;

(b) The crew list of 13 officers and men for the whole journey *had no name of James Bartley or anything like it*;

(c) The two French scientists never checked the story for themselves;

(d) The captain came from Yarmouth in Nova Scotia, not Great Yarmouth in East Anglia;

(e) A 1907 article copied a letter from the captain's wife which said:

> There is not one word of truth in the whale story. I was with my husband all the years he was in the Star of the East. There was never a man lost overboard while my husband was in her. The sailor has told a great sea yarn.

This is certainly damning evidence against the story, and we can only conclude that it is a fabrication. This will no doubt come as a shock to many creationists and writers that have reported the story in good faith. Certainly, this writer was also prepared to endorse it but Davis's article is thorough and I could detect no bias in his reporting as far as the crucial evidence was concerned.

What could have given rise to the story? Examining the original report, the journalist appears to have interviewed Bartley himself, but there is no indication of where he lived or other details. There is some mystery about the account. If a "James Bartley", with his distinctly yellowed skin, did make such a report, why was nothing ever heard of him later? Did the newspaper realise they had been fooled and kept quiet about it? Did they, in fact, fabricate the story? If they did, that would have been dangerous for their reputation, and in any case, it only appeared as an ordinary item on page 3.

Only two months before the Bartley story, there was an account in the Yarmouth Mercury in June of a whale that had been killed on the beach and exhibited locally. Subsequent comments noted that the event had inspired a number of exaggerated tales. Davis speculates, not unreasonably, that on reading this, a James Bartley spun his tale to the paper. He would have become a celebrity as a "modern day Jonah". Yet, strangely, there were no other details about him.

Davis spends much of the article castigating Ellis, a prominent American evangelical who had frequently repeated the story in the early years of this century, accusing him of fabricating evidence about it. He claimed that those who repeat unverified stories to support their Biblical position were engaging in "folk science" - a phrase we will meet again when examining the shrinking of the sun.

Davis's criticisms are understandable, particularly if Ellis did embellish the story. But the Bartley story was generally well supported, appearing in three newspapers and until Davis's article, no one had any evidence that contradicted it and some that supported it. It is understandable for evangelicals who are under attack to use what is considered to be reliable evidence to defend their trust in the Bible. That some may not be as well supported as others or were fabricated by fraudsters for gain should not worry them unduly and panic them into a sea of doubt, for the vast majority of evidence supporting creation is very well founded. I must comment that this is the *only* reasonably major subject where I have found a critic has adequately proven creationist evidence to be in error.

As we have maintained before, those evangelicals who hold to evolution have no irrefutable evidence whatsoever to support their case. This criticism of some creationist evidence is very relevant today, but with a difference, for some of it is stemming from creationists themselves. We consider that it is almost all unjustified and discuss this further at the end of Section 5.

3. Did Jonah exist?

In an interesting and full article on which much of this section is based, Cooper (Coo86) examined the history of the Assyrians who ruled most of the Middle East from their capital Nineveh. This was about the time of Jonah who was born approximately 800 BC. The Assyrians were a merciless people and on their monuments boasted of the number of hideous atrocities they had inflicted upon their captives; mass impalings, flayed alive, eyes and tongues torn out, etc. Their leaders were often effeminates who loved to dress and adorn themselves as women.

However, like all Godless nations, they eventually degenerated into civil war and its eventual collapse was clear to not only all their subject nations but to the citizens themselves. Tiglath-pileser III ("Pul" in the Bible) had just ascended the throne and knew that he would have little chance of averting the increasing chaos.

It was then, about 745 BC, that Jonah appeared on the scene and preached to the desperate city of Nineveh. With the record of barbaric cruelty this nation had, one begins to understand Jonah's reluctance to tell them of God's concern for them. Even when he had completed his task, instead of rejoicing at their change of heart, he appears to be almost annoyed with God that He should have blessed them in this way.

The Assyrian's god "Oannes"

The Assyrians worshipped a god called "Oannes" and the similarity to Jonah is obvious, for John, Jonah, Johannes, Yohannes, Oannes all have a related origin. What is particularly intriguing is that this god was a *fish*-god, and Jonah was vomited up on a sea shore by a "great fish" and proceeded to preach to the Ninevites and save the nation from ruin.

Hislop refers to "Oannes" in his *Two Babylons* (His), but his derivation of the name is extremely intricate and unconvincing. As we will see later, this tendency damages his reliability. He says that Oannes was a Babylonian god but Cooper shows that he was already a god to the Assyrians who preceded the Babylonians.

Cooper quotes the account by the Babylonian historian Berosus of the founding of the worship of Dagon. This was a god of many nations in the Middle East and his origin was a beast called Oannes who emerged from the sea.

He relates how the people were lawless, but a fish-man, named Oannes, emerged from the Erythraean Sea who taught them about the arts and sciences and how to live civilised lives.

It can be seen that there are differences with the record of Jonah in the Bible;

(i) The "Erythraean Sea" is the Red Sea, but Jonah embarked at Joppa which is on the Mediterranean Sea. However, Josephus says he was disgorged on the shores of the Euxine Sea which is the Black Sea and is accessible from Joppa.

(ii) He would have had no need to teach them how to build cities, collect fruits, etc. They were a great nation in size and organisation when Jonah came.

It appears that, before the time of Jonah, the Assyrians had a fish-god named Oannes who was their principle deity. It was probably all part of God's plan to use Jonah's disobedience to have him delivered from the mouth of a fish. The Assyrians may then be more prepared to accept him as their returning Oannes who would save them from the dire situation facing them. Jonah, however, would call them to repentance with the authority of the Living God Himself.

Allowing for the corruption of history, particularly about the "miraculous" abilities of the ancient gods, the record of a fish-god who taught the Assyrians how to behave decently is remarkably similar to that of Jonah in the Bible. Berosus may have understandably mixed the two accounts of their original founding fish-deity "Oannes" and the later advent of "Yohannes" from a fish's mouth. Fig. 1 gives two pictures of the Assyrian fish-god "Oannes".

The changed nation

Historically, there is no doubt that there was a distinct change in the fortunes of this great nation precisely at the time the Bible records Jonah preached to them.

Historians credit Tiglath-pileser with the amazing change in the fortunes of Assyria, for, within that same king's lifetime, they recommenced their conquering of adjacent nations. Cooper, however, contends that they were rescued from anarchy by Jonah's preaching to them. As a result, we know from the Bible that the king repented and the whole nation with him.

This did not last long, however for they soon resumed their wars with neighbouring states. It would seem that God's plan was to use them later to punish the Northern Ten tribes of Israel for their adoption of the cruel religious practices of their pagan neighbours. The Canaanites worshipped Moloch and we have described in the previous section their hideous practice of "passing their children through the fire".

When the Ten Tribes, who had known the One True God, adopted these practices, we can understand God's fierce wrath against them that He should use the Assyrian hordes as punishment.

Facing the ridicule

As we have said, Christians who accept the reliability of the Bible will have

Fig. 1. Two pictures of the Fish-god "Oannes"

the "story" of Jonah's three days in the whale thrown at them in ridicule. What should be the correct response - to adopt and air of vagueness about the incident to retain credibility with our listeners, or hold to it firmly?

This ridicule is not new. Every generation has a particular "stigma" to deal with. In the past it has been Christ's deity, justification by faith, etc. Paul was mocked at the Areopagus as soon as he mentioned that Jesus had been raised from the dead (Acts 17:31-2). In every case, the minority view is ridiculed and opposed.

If we try to circumvent the subject and offer spiritualised "interpretations" to explain why the book was written, we are being less than faithful to it than Christ Himself. It is suggested that this is yet one more test of the faith of the True Christian. Once we "give way" on the truth of this event, there will be no stopping elsewhere when other "hard" passages are encountered. Eventually, compromise on one small item renders the rest vulnerable and destroys trust in the Scriptures.

The Christian must bear such Godless reactions with quiet confidence in the rightness of his case, not before men, but before God Himself. He can take comfort in the fact that he is in good company; Noah was undoubtedly subjected to the same treatment.

This question of the ultimate reliability of the Bible is large and important, and we will leave the reader to consider it further. We will end by saying that in meditating on this point, two "sayings" came to mind.

One was "He who laughs last, laughs longest"; i.e. it is the despised

Christian who will finally be justified. Unfortunately, this common quip trivialises the crucial importance of the subject. No Christian should ever minimise the seriousness of what faces the unbeliever - even in joke.

The other saying, rather more appropriate, was:

I'm a fool for Christ:
Whose fool are you?

SECTION 3.11
DINOSAURS

Job describes the huge strength of the Behemoth with its tail like a "cedar tree", yet its food is grass (Job 40:15-24). Those who try to "explain away" Job's accounts sometime suggest that this was only a hippopotamus. Any resemblance of the minute tail of the latter to a "cedar tree" is a trifle fanciful. Job's "*Behemoth*" is probably referring to Diplodicus or an Apatosaurus - previously named the Brontosaurus (Fig. 1) and his "*Leviathan*" is possibly a Hadrosaur.

The great size of dinosaurs is well known, but some fossils of a huge specimen were found in 1972. It was similar to a Brachiosaurus but three times the size of the largest dinosaur known at that time for it was estimated to be 50 ft (31m) tall, 100 ft (62m) long and weighed 80 tons. This is about the size of a Blue Whale, the largest creature in the world. How it could function on land with this weight is a mystery. The largest pterosaur discovered had a wingspan of 51 ft (32m) which is much longer than some fighter planes (Q17/3:158).

There are many depictions of dragons breathing fire through their nostrils, and in Job 41:18-21 we read of the Leviathan:

> By his (s)neezings a light doth shine...Out of his mouth go burning
> lamps and sparks of fire leap out. Out of his nostrils goeth smoke...
> his breath kindles coals and a flame goeth out of his mouth.

The dinosaur Parasurolophus has channels in its crest that are linked to its breathing passages. It may have used these as sound resonators or for blowing heated gasses using a chemical reaction, as does the Bombardier Beetle (Bow91:81), but much hotter.

Job describes the Leviathan (41:1-34) that lives in the water, whose tough skin (scales?) cannot be penetrated by javelins, and all men fear him. We can begin to appreciate the high esteem that would be given to any man who could rid an area of such terrifying beasts. The Norse sagas recount Beowulf's fame for clearing the seas of these monsters that made shipping hazardous. Cooper gives the saga's vivid account of how Beowulf attacked the monster Grendel at its weakest point by engaging it closely to avoid its jaws and wrenching off one of its small arms from which it bled to death (Coop95:146f and Coop92). Hislop (His) contends that Nimrod, the "mighty hunter" (Gen 10:8-9), performed a similar service and was elevated to a God-like importance. From this position, he became the founder of all pagan religions and the pagan features that branches of Christianity took into its rituals.

The name "*Grendel*" simply means "dragon" and is retained in such names as "*Grindelwald*" - Dragon's wood - in Switzerland. Many other place names similarly testify to their existence. There are numerous accounts in old records of sightings of huge or unusual monsters. These are often couched in very matter-of-fact terms as though the event was unusual but not unknown.

Man and dinosaurs together?

There are many dinosaur footprints in the Paluxy river in Texas. There are also several tracks of human-like footprints, some giant in size, in the same beds, often crossing over the dinosaur prints. These were

Fig. 1. Apatosaurus/Brontosaurus - Job's "Behemoth"?

so clearly human that the film "Footprints in Stone" was made about them and widely distributed. This showed that the prints had every feature that would be expected of humans walking through soft mud. One trial of prints led towards a bank of earth. The bank was excavated and the prints continued in the same line, showing that they could not have been fabricated by humans who would have only done this on the exposed ground. The whole film was very convincing and the evidence seemed irrefutable. This conjunction of human and dinosaur footprints demonstrated that the so-called gap of some 65 million years between the death of the dinosaurs at the end of the Cretaceous and the emergence of man only a few million years ago was nonexistent.

In 1982, the American Humanist Association financed a team to investigate these tracks. In that same year, stains were noticed that gave the front of the tracks claw-like marks. The whole situation was re-investigated by the makers of the film. The ICR Impact article - No. 151 Jan. 1986 - that surveyed the situation, noted that the stains were on the surface and that the rock could easily have been stained using "certain readily available chemical agents". However, faint traces of staining were found in photos taken many years before, no fraudulent staining was detected and some dinosaur tracks has also developed some stains. Possibly oversensitive to the charge that creationists were using faulty evidence, the film was withdrawn. In the opinion of this writer, this was an unfortunate decision. The problem is still unsolved. and research on the site is continuing.

Daly reports that in 1924 a drawing of a dinosaur was found on the walls of a canyon in Arizona (Dal:72. His ref; Evolutionary Geology p133). In 1929, in the same canyon, the Curator of a Californian Museum found a carving of a dinosaur "some fifteen feet high by seventy to eighty feet long... reared on its hind legs". A carving of an Imperial Elephant shows it attacking a man whose arm is raised as if throwing a spear. More information on these reports would have been invaluable.

Fig. 2 shows the "Sirrush", a creature carved on the Babylonian Ishtar gate which was with other animals that are easily recognised.

The Chinese calendar has animals for each year in a cycle. All of these are ordinary animals such as dog, rat, pig etc., but it also has a dragon. This suggests that far from being a mythical animal, it was one that the Chinese were familiar with, for they still use it in many of their festivals. It is possible that large dinosaurs died out much later in that part of the world and were incorporated with all the other known animals into their calendar when it was originally formed.

Dinosaurs still living?

There were persistent rumours of a large unusual animal that was reported by natives in the depths of the inhospitable Congo jungle. An expedition had been mounted to this area about 1981 (Q19/1:72) but there has been no confirmation of any finds or photographs.

The BBC *Wildlife* magazine for December 1984 reported on another expedition to be mounted to this area. The article gave an artists impression of the animal, called Mokele-Mbembe, drawn from the native's description. There are still no reports of any sightings.

In 1980, sightings by several people of up to three plesiosaur-type animals at one time in the sea is recorded near Darwin, north Australia (Q17/1:74). This is, at least, in the same part of the globe where the plesiosaur-like carcase was dredged up which we discuss below. Marine dinosaurs are more likely to survive longer than terrestial ones as sea conditions are far more stable.

Shuker, an evolutionist, discussed nine reports of sea creatures but dismissed most of them as not providing any strong evidence of being "sea monsters", usually saying they were the decomposed bodies of basking sharks (Shuk). Two he mentions are particularly noteworthy.

In 1922 a huge 47 ft. (14.3m) beast covered in what looked like an 8 in.

Fig. 2. The Babylonian "Sirrush"

(200mm) long snow-white "fur" was seen by many people fighting a three hour battle with two whales off the coast of Natal. It was killed and its body was washed up on the shore later that day. It had a 10 ft. (3m) tail and "Instead of possessing a distinct head, it bore a long trunk-like appendage, roughly 5ft. (1.5m) long". It lay on the beach for ten days, and the fact that no zoologist examined it during that period we discuss below.

A whaling ship battled with a huge creature longer than the 100 ft. length (30m) of the ship and just under 50ft (15m) diameter. It had a 10 ft. (3m) long alligator-like head that possessed 94 teeth 3 in. (75mm) long. The account appeared in the London Times on March 10th 1852.

There are many other records that could be provided, showing that these large and very strange sea creatures were living until recently - or still are.

The Loch Ness Monster

There are many accounts of strange sightings. A number appear to be authentic and inexplicable but there is little that is conclusive. One picture that is now accepted as a deliberate hoax is the famous "surgeon's photograph" taken in 1934 showing a curved neck surrounded by ripples. In 1993 it was admitted that it was made from a toy submarine and plasticine (*D. Tel.* 1.1.98:p17). Whilst there may be creatures present, we await further and more convincing evidence before accepting they still exists there.

The 1977 Japanese carcase

The most recent surprising discovery is that of the 32 ft (10m) carcase dredged up by Japanese fishermen on the *Zuiyo Maru* in 1977. To avoid it ruining the catch it was thrown back but not before it had been photographed, measured and some fibres taken by Michihiko Yano, a qualified marine biologist, who was on board. Figs. 3-5 are from Yano's colour photographs and drawing of the carcase. It appears to have been very similar to a plesiosaur (Fig. 6) and was possibly a young one that had died only about a month before. The story was front page news for weeks in Japan but it received scant coverage elsewhere.

Five months after the event, the Japanese issued a series of stamps to mark the 100th anniversary of their Science Museum and one stamp pictured the skeleton of a Plesiosaur. The stamp was, therefore, not to commemorate the catch and the decision to portray a plesiosaur may have been taken before the catch became known. However, it is a strange coincidence that of all the animals they could have chosen, they used the one animal that had caused such great excitement throughout Japan for several weeks.

The criticisms - and replies

As one might expect, the secular experts were only too keen to dismiss this find as an ordinary sea creature. The most frequent claim was that it was only a basking shark that had rotted in a particular way to look like a plesiosaur.

As if to pre-empt future claims of "monster" discoveries, the *Encyclopaedia Britannica*, in its description of the basking shark, notes at the end "When found decaying on beaches, it is sometimes reported as a sea serpent."

One creationist article made two lists of the evidence for and against it being a shark (Q33/4:292). The evidence suggesting that it was a shark was very tentative, whilst that against it was far more concrete. This evidence was; **(A)** The four very large fins (paddles), **(B)** The odour of decay was mammalian, not ammonia which rotting sharks emit, **(C)** Red flesh along the back **(D)** No dorsal fin, **(E)** It had decaying blubber which sharks do not possess.

Considering these features, the most obvious conclusion is that the creature could not possibly be a shark of any sort. Possession of just one of the contrary features given above is sufficient to dismiss it as a shark.

We have drawn Figures 5-7 to the same length so that the proportions of the creature can be compared with that of a plesiosaur and a basking shark. It is obvious that it could not be a shark and is far more likely to be a plesiosaur or plesiosaur-type animal that still exists below the waves.

Eventually, the carcase was dismissed by an oft-used means. Fig. 8 is from Yano's photo of the carcase as it lay on the deck and the horny fibres on the end of a front "paddle" can be seen. An analysis of some of these fibres that Yano had clipped off showed they they contained 40 units of tyrosine per 1,000 amino acids which was close to the 44 units for elastoidin found only in sharks and not mammals (Koster). It was therefore dismissed as only the carcase of a basking shark. We noted that for some unknown reason the shark fibres were first soaked in sodium hypochlorite but not the carcase fibres. Koster reports that reptiles have not been tested for elastoidin - and plesiosaurs are classified as reptiles! We would ask (a) how could they be so certain that plesiosaurs never had this particular component, and (b) were other, unquoted, tests carried out that showed is was far from being a shark? This one *near* correlation was sufficient to dismiss the carcase.

In the account of a creature washed up on a beach in Natal described above, Shuker said it was "unbelievable" that "not a single zoologist took the trouble to examine it" (Shuk). This should not have been a surprise for such a response is only to be expected. No zoologist who valued his reputation would want to have it linked to a carcase of a prehistoric creature, only to have it later officially dismissed as a "gross misidentification". He would be the butt of ridicule from his fellow biologists for the rest of his professional career.

Those creationists who have repeated the evolutionist's claim that it is only a basking shark have been all too ready to quote the opinions of evolutionist experts as if they were reliable. They have forgotten that anyone whose work has the slightest connection with evolution, *without exception*, will not be allowed any great publicity to present evidence against the theory. The leaders

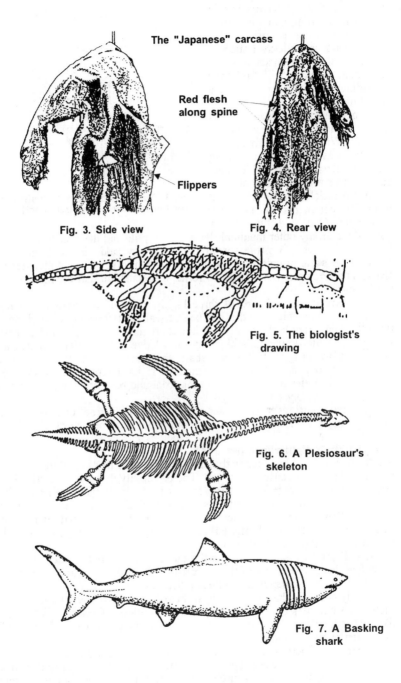

The "Japanese" carcass

Red flesh
along spine

Flippers

Fig. 3. Side view   Fig. 4. Rear view

Fig. 5. The biologist's
drawing

Fig. 6. A Plesiosaur's
skeleton

Fig. 7. A Basking
shark

of such professions have a vested interest in ensuring that when such unwelcome evidence arises, "official" reports are quickly issued to contradict it. Creationists who repeat their *opinions* will find they are riding a paper tiger - to use a mixed metaphor.

In this case the "official" report was by a panel of Japanese experts (Sasaki). What received much less publicity was a far more revealing article by Koster (Kost) which also gave Yano's four colour photos.

Fig. 8. The carcase on the deck showing the horny fibres on the front paddle.

In the article, Koster gives the following comments by Japanese professors. One said "It's not a fish, whale or any other mammal. It's a reptile and the sketch looks very like a plesiosaur". A professor of palaeontology said "Even if the tissue contains the same protein as the shark's, it is rash to say that the monster is a shark. The finding is not enough to refute a speculation that the monster is a plesiosaur."

Yano went before a board of three highly qualified professors in marine studies who commented: "If this had been a seal, the tail would be too long...If this had been a reptile the number of bones around the neck should be greater according to the drawing...Within my knowledge it looks like a plesiosaur. But I can't say for sure...If it were a shark, the spine would be smaller, and the neck is too long as shown in the picture. If its a reptile, it looks like a plesiosaur. The plesiosaur has fins in the front and back and the neck and tail were not too terribly long [Kost].

The person who repeated Koster's article on the internet commented "we hope you enjoy the article which evolutionists policed from your review."

Why are these sightings important?

The comment has been made that the identifying of these creatures does not help the creationist cause very much. The possibility that some are still living does not form crucial evidence for creationists. After all, there are such fish as the Coelacanth still alive and this has not changed people to accepting creation. This, however, is a small fish living at great depth with many other strange fish and can be dismissed. It is the large dinosaur-type animals that pose a greater threat to evolution.

The real problem they present is the question of the time scale. The rocks show that there were many of these creatures in the past, but according to the evolutionary time scale, all should have died out some sixty million years ago. It is surely arguable that if some are still existing, then it is very unlikely that such small numbers could have survived for millions of years. It is far more likely that they may have existed a few thousand years ago with gradually dwindling numbers since then.

Cooper (and others) has listed many sightings of dinosaur-like creatures and the various names of the sea-dragons that infested the ancient sea routes which we refer to below. As we go further back into time, these sightings are more numerous. This is compounded by the fact that there would have been a much smaller human population and fewer sea-going vessels in the early days, yet they described many dinosaurs and sea creatures. Today, with a far larger population and much more traffic on the high seas, there are fewer reports. If we imagine a graph of the these sightings as a falling curve, this sharp decrease in their number within a comparatively short time suggests that we are on the tail-end of the rapid decline of these large animals, and that not long ago they were far more plentiful.

If, then, they were more numerous in the fairly recent past, then there would have been many more still further back in time. This is in complete accord with the creationist time scale. There would have been large numbers in the sea that survived the Flood, whilst on land there could have been a rapid increase in population on the uninhabited land after the Flood, but a gradual decrease due to a changing environment or more probably being hunted by the rapidly increasing population of men.

This comparatively recent decrease in numbers totally contradicts the evolutionary time scale that insists they all died out millions of years ago. It is for this reason that any evidence of large, dinosaur-type creatures, whether on land or sea, is so vigorously disparaged by evolutionists.

What happened to the dinosaurs?

This question is often asked and the most likely answer is that when they emerged from the Ark the climatic conditions were so different to what they had been used to when they entered it that they had increasing difficulty in surviving. Although they may have flourished under suitable local climatic conditions for a while, there was probably some particular event or a stage in the changing conditions that these large animals could not overcome and gradually many species died out.

One contributory factor could have been the reduction of air pressure after the Flood due to the collapse of the Water vapour canopy. Many dinosaurs have large bodies and muscles but comparatively small chest cavities. The reduction of the air pressure after the Flood would reduce the oxygen intake and make life far more difficult for these large dinosaurs.

There was a mass extinction of dinosaurs at the end of the Cretaceous period, but this is probably the particular stage during the Flood when their bones were eventually deposited in the strata. The possibility of the Cretaceous being a post-Flood strata is considered in Appendix 4 - Geology.

In an article dealing with this subject, Cooper lists 81 locations in Britain where dinosaur activity is recorded or remembered, and says the list could be extended to 200 places (Coo92). He also lists 71 names the Anglo-Saxons used to describe a variety of dragons and beasts. For example, "ythgewinnes" was a "wave-thrasher"; "saedracan" was a sea-drake or dragon; "lyftfloga" was the general name for air-fliers of which the "widfloga" (wide-flyer) was probably a pteranadon. With such a large and detailed vocabulary, this surely indicates that these animals played an important part in the lives of these people in those early days.

SECTION 4
THE AGE OF THE EARTH
AND UNIVERSE

The age of the earth is a crucial cornerstone of the theory of evolution. Without millions of years available for its slow development it could not survive. It is for this reason that Charles Lyell made it the aim of his two volume work *Principles of Geology* written in the early 1830's to provide these great periods of time. He wrote that he had deliberately set out to "free the science from Moses"; i.e. Genesis and its record of creation in 6 days (Bow82:94).

Within days of the return of the young Charles Darwin from his Beagle voyage, Lyell visited him. It is this writer's conviction that it was Lyell who suggested to Darwin that he should write about evolution which would make him famous - a proposition that he could not resist. That Darwin did not think about evolution whilst on the Beagle voyage but only on his return can be demonstrated from his notebooks he kept on the journey and this has been acknowledged even by those who sought to prove otherwise (Bow82:42). Thus had Lyell paved the way for evolution by undermining the timescale of Genesis with his books on geology.

When the subject of a young earth (i.e. less than 10,000 years old) is discussed with members of the public, there is usually a reaction of incredulity, and one can sometimes sense that they are wondering whether you are quite balanced in your views. So frequently is the age of the earth or universe quoted in "billions of years" that the public are well and truly indoctrinated to think any other possibility as ludicrous. One can only continue to present the evidence in the hope that the young age of the earth will finally break through into the public consciousness.

What follows is a brief survey of some of the more impressive evidence. Some subjects have been covered in other books by this author, but for completeness a short outline of them is given below. It is hoped that the cumulative effect will be adequate to convince the more sceptical reader.

1. RADIOMETRIC DATING

In many rocks there are small amounts of radioactive materials, the ones most used for dating being Uranium, Thorium and Potassium. As the material decays, usually taking millions of years to do so, it produces a "daughter" element. By measuring the ratio between the original quantity and the daughter element, a measure of the time over which it has decayed can be obtained.

The major criticisms of the method has been discussed in my other two works (Bow81:64 and Bow91:114), but I summarise the main points as follows.

(a) Assumptions.
(i) It is assumed that when the rock rose from the depths of the earth it contained only pure radioactive material. This is a huge assumption, for only a minute quantity of the daughter element with it would give the rock an appearance of great age even at that time.
(ii) None of the daughter element is assumed to migrate from the rock or into it from another source. Yet simply running water over a sample has shown

that elements can easily be washed out. This excuse of either "loss" or "contamination" is used when tests are "discordant" to the dates "expected".

(iii) It is a basic assumption of science that the rate of radioactive decay is constant, and has been for all time. This is firstly unprovable and secondly, it has been shown that heat, magnetism and other influences can affect the rate of decay a measurable amount. For example, heating radioactive tritium with titanium from 115 to 160°C reduced the radioactivity by a very surprising 28% (New.Sc. 8.1.94 p16). In addition, we will see that there is very good evidence that radioactive decay has been very much faster in the past.

(b) All dates must conform.

All dating methods, of whatever type, *must* conform to the evolutionary time scale. Field workers submitting samples for dating have to give the range of dates "expected". Where the results are considerably different, they are ignored and the material is classed as "unsuitable" for the method due to "inclusions", etc.

For example, in the dating of Richard Leakey's "1470 Man", an initial dating of 220 million years was about 100 times too high to fit the evolutionary time scale. Subsequent dating of the same strata by the same method gave the more acceptable figure of 2.6 million years which was the date that was publicised (Bow81:205). Many other examples could be quoted.

(c) The only acceptable method.

There are a number of methods of obtaining an approximate age of the earth and some of these will be examined later. Although there are great differences in the datings given by the various methods, almost every one of them gives a date that is very much less than those resulting from radiometric dating. These lower dates are therefore completely ignored, and only radiometric dates are used as this is the *only* method that can give the vast time spans needed for evolution to take place.

(d) The shortening of radiometric dates.

We will see that there is very good evidence that the speed of light has been very much higher in the past. This is a fundamental physical "constant" and it directly affects the rate of radioactive decay. There is evidence that the speed of light was up to 10^{11} times faster than it is at present. This would produce a much more rapid decay of radioactive elements, making the rock look very old in a short time.

Just how much it would reduce the existing dates that are given to the rocks would depend upon the shape of the curve the speed of light followed as it fell to its present level. Certainly, the factor would be in the order of millions, reducing the dates to orders of thousands or tens of thousands of years. Such a reduction cannot be contemplated by evolutionists, and therefore this is an added reason for rejecting the whole proposition that the speed of light has decreased.

(e) The apparent correlation of dates.

The popular concept of radiometric dating is that it is very accurate and enables strata to be precisely dated. This is far from the case as we have considered above. Morton (Mor82) produced a graph of actual measurements against the accepted date, based upon Woodmorappe (Q16/2:113). We give this in Fig. 1. Although they were selected if they were approaching 20% too high or too low to demonstrate their scatter, Morton surprisingly claimed that they did at least show a trend. He blamed the scatter on the variability of "natural conditions" - leakage, etc. But if these "conditions" produce such a wide range of results, then this alone makes the method unacceptable, even if the basic theory may be correct.

The important question is "How do scientists know that unsuitable conditions are present?" The answer is that they do not - *it is only used when the dates to not conform to the accepted age - **never** if they do*. Escape or ingress of constituents are only blamed to discredit a "wrong" date, but they have no proof that this is so. If the date conforms, no question of any loss or gain is mentioned!

Examination of the spread in Fig. 1 shows that rocks with an expected date of 300 MY could give results ranging from 100 (A1) to 400 (A2) MY, and a radioactive dating of 300 MY could have come from rocks whose accepted ages ranged from 80 (B1) to 540 (B2) MY. With variations this large, the method is useless, and it can be seen why measured dates have to be within the "accepted range" before they are published.

Radiometric dating - the false simile

Creationists have long pointed out these wide discrepancies, but Morton quotes a jibe from *Time* magazine (Mor82:229) that said:

> The creationist argument is a bit like claiming that because some trains are cancelled or run way off schedule, the basic timetable is totally inaccurate.

But this (as ever) is yet another false illustration. (1) It is known beforehand when a train ought to arrive - there is a timetable previously provided. Late arrivals can be accurately recorded and the reason investigated. In geology, the "timetable" is the (evolutionary) geological column and reasons for radioactive dating errors have to be assumed. (2) Supposing almost all trains were late by varying and unpredictable amounts; the timetable would then be useless. Radiometric dating is likewise useless as a final authority for determining the age of a strata.

This highlights the overriding importance of the fossils in the geological column and their accompanying dates. Where a radiometric date differs badly from the fossil dating, the latter is always the superior authority. Thus radio dates are only ever used when there are no other indicators of age such as fossils. When fossils are present where expected in a strata, radio dates are only used to *confirm* an age. Some experts, keen to make a name for themselves, will seize upon an errant radiometric date that gives their fossil discovery precedence over others - as Richard Leakey did with 1470 man.

The reader will remember that in the introduction I contended that there is no evidence that supports evolution that cannot be heavily criticised. I would add to this that there are no illustrations or similes that evolutionists use to "explain" their theory - and they use them frequently - that cannot also be shown to be completely inappropriate after careful examination.

That there is a very rough correlation radiometric dating and expected dates might suggest that there is some basis for its acceptance. There are two possible explanations for this - source level and zone melting.

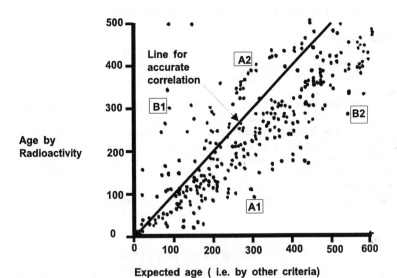

Fig. 1. The poor correlation of radiometric dates

Source level

Setterfield has suggested that it can be explained by the sequence in which the molten rock reached the surface of the earth at different stages. Towards the centre of the earth, the rocks may have been increasingly richer in the heavy elements - which would include the radioactive elements. When the speed of light was very much faster, they would have been very active, and the centre of the earth would have become very hot. The molten rock would have risen and poured out onto the surface. The rock nearer to the surface, with its lower level of radioactive material, would have reached the surface first. Later the deeper, richer strata would have surfaced on top of the earlier strata.

In this way, rock with a larger percentage of radioactive elements would be overlying rocks with a lower amount. Such a distribution would provide the younger ages for the higher rocks richer in radioactive material, and lower ages for the less rich strata below.

Zone melting

Cook mentions another process, zone melting, by which the radiometric elements could have been redistributed (Cook66:31). If a rod with impurities is heated to partially melt it along its length, the impurities, in this case the radioactive elements, will be the last to resolidify, will flow with the melt zone and redistribute themselves in an exponential concentration along the length. The principle is used by metallurgists to purify metals.

He suggests that solidification of the earth, due to its pressure-depth characteristics, began at the base of the mantle and progressed towards the surface as the rocks cooled. This would result in the radioactive elements mainly at the top and decreasing with depth, giving an apparent gradation of age.

This would not explain Flood strata that had many layers of sediments with igneous intrusions, but a combination of both these factors may go a long way to explaining the present apparent broad gradation of age with depth.

Isochron dating

We would here briefly mention the method of Isochron dating which uses *ratios* of radioactive elements in rocks. This is claimed to provide a dating method free of some of the assumptions listed above. But this method also is flawed.

Some results have given obviously incorrect dates and some even negative dates, so the method *cannot* be accurate. The main explanation is that the materials have become mixed during the geological history of the rocks giving these apparently concordant dates. This mixing conforms to the way in which the strata were brought from the earth's interior as solutions in supercritically heated water (hydrothermal water), a subject considered more fully in the geological section.

The technical explanation of the method used is complex and not suited to a work such as this, but criticisms of the method can be found in Aust88 and Brow94.

2. CARBON 14 DATING

This relies on the decay of radioactive carbon 14 (C14) which is generated in the upper atmosphere by cosmic radiation. The carbon becomes a known fraction of all living organisms along with the normal carbon 12 (C12). When an organism dies, the C14 is no longer replenished and the quantity decreases by radioactive decay. The amount of C14 is measured and this gives an indication of the age since the animal died.

The subject is more fully covered in Bow91:123f which examines the many problems associated with this dating method. It is only suitable for dating up to about 3,000 years. Even in this period, the graph by Suess by which the dates are usually correlated with the C14 measurements is far from being a smooth curve. At many points, the variation is such that one C14 level will give three different corrected dates. It is difficult to accept that they are able to ascribe a date based on C14 activity with such precision, and the degree of accuracy they are claiming is quite spurious.

One Nobel prizewinner said:

> If a C14 date supports our theories, we put it in the main text. If it does not entirely contradict them, we put it in a footnote. And if it is completely "out of date" we just drop it (Q10/1:20).

This was written in 1973, and shows the attitude even in those days. We would contend that this is still the current approach and that it would apply to radiometric dating also.

PROBLEMS WITH THE METHOD

(i) The high rate of generation

The method of dating assumes that the present level of C14 has been reasonably constant for many thousands of years at least. However, the rate of generation in the upper atmosphere is over 30% higher than this. Creationists therefore contend that the present level will continue to rise to this higher level until the system stabilises. This makes the level of C14 with which the organism is assumed to have had when it died very much lower. When this correction is applied, it greatly reduces the calculated time since it died because the level at which the C14 actually started (See Fig. 2. point A) is less

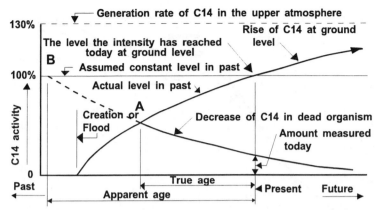

Fig. 2. The non-stablised rise of C14 activity at ground level

than the present level (point B) which it is assumed has been constant for thousands of years.

The actual point at which it began to rise is probably the Flood; rarely is C14 found in coal which suggests that there was none or very little in the biosphere in which the trees were growing before the Flood.

ii) The earth's magnetic field

We deal with this subject later as it is an excellent proof that the earth is young. Here we will only refer to it in connection with its effect upon the generation of C14. The first measurement (8.57 "units") was made in 1835 and it has consistently decreased since then, with a "half-life" of 1,400 years, and there is no reason why this situation should have changed since the date of creation. The magnetic field bends the cosmic radiation away from the earth (see Fig. 3.1.3) thus reducing the amount of C14 being generated in the upper atmosphere. This would naturally affect the total amount of C14 that reaches the biosphere on the surface of the earth. As shown above, this would reduce the calculated time since death of an organism.

The effect of the magnetic field in reducing the generation of C14 is considerable. Brown reports that reducing the magnetic field to zero would double the amount of C14 produced (Q5:68). As a working approximation it could be assumed that doubling the field would roughly halve the production rate. If we take creation as 6,000 years ago, this would allow for about 4 doublings (6000/1,400) of its strength to reach a value of 137 "units" (2^4 x 8.57) - resulting in only 1/16th of the present production rate.

With the combination of this low initial starting rate and nil C14 at Creation, it is easy to see how the ground level C14 has risen slowly to it present level, falsifying all those extrapolations that assume a near constant, stabilised rate of production.

iii) Tree ring calibrations

There are various calibration curves, such as the Suess curve, another using Irish Oak wood and yet another based on an Egyptian calibration curve, but they all differ from each other, which illustrates the inaccuracy of the method (Q15/1:70). Generally, when claims are made that tree rings correlate between different logs, invariably allowances are made for "missing rings"

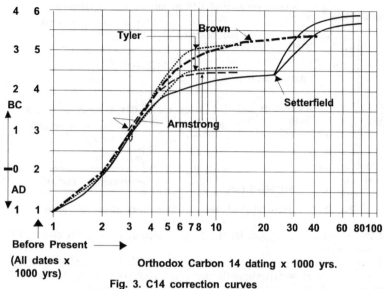

Fig. 3. C14 correction curves

and extra "false rings" before a reasonable match can be made. This is not always detailed in the reports, and requests for justification data have been angrily refused (Q15/1:25). Tree rings are used to calibrate C14 checks, and C14 is used to check on tree ring dates - a circular system! Those who have investigated tree ring dating in depth have recorded their disenchantment with the method (Q15/1:24), and therefore its use for calibrating C14 dates is equally suspect.

iv) The carbon reservoirs

The total amount of carbon actually in circulation is distributed throughout the earth system, the vast majority of it being in the deep ocean. This makes calculation of the amount in the biosphere difficult, particularly when trying to estimate how much might have been present in past years. It would only take 100 years to build up the level to its present value, but these reservoirs considerably extend this period.

v) The Water Vapour Canopy and the Flood

All attempts to estimate the conditions in the distant past involve a considerable amount of supposition. At the time of the Flood we have the sudden precipitation of the Water Vapour Canopy and the effect of the Flood waters themselves pouring from the interior of the earth. This makes correction of the official C14 datings difficult. However, creationists have produced various correction curves to obtain more accurate dates from C14 datings and Fig. 3 gives curves by Brown (CRSQ29/1:46), Tyler (Q15/1:16), Armstrong (Q2/4:28) and Setterfield (Sett86). Setterfield's paper is a major work and allows for a higher generation of C14 due to the higher rate of radioactivity when the speed of light was faster. His two curves after the Flood are for uniform C14 or a build up from zero from Creation.

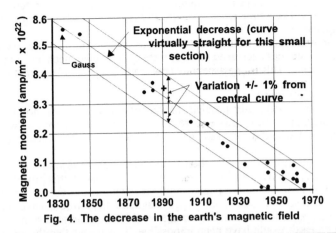

Fig. 4. The decrease in the earth's magnetic field

3. THE DECREASE IN THE EARTH'S MAGNETIC FIELD.

This evidence of the comparatively rapid decrease in the earth's magnetic field is amongst the strongest that demonstrates that the age of the earth is young. The subject has been studied by Barnes and reported by him in various works - see the references under his name.

In 1835, the scientist Gauss carried out a world wide survey of the strength of the magnetic field. From these measurements he worked out that the power of the magnetic force at the centre of the earth that would produce such a strength was 8.56 Amps/m2 x 10^22. This was checked a few years later by other experts and found to be 8.45. This has continued to be measured over many years and there has been a consistent fall in the value. A plot of the measurements is given in Fig. 4.

What is the source of this magnetic field? It cannot be due to the iron core acting like a permanent magnet, as molten rock cannot retain any magnetism. By far the most likely cause is an electric current circulating around the interior of the earth almost parallel to the equator. This was proposed by Lamb in 1883, who easily explained the decrease in the field as due to the electrical resistance of the earth slowly reducing the circulating current.

In any circuit where this happens, the decrease follows the well known mathematical exponential curve. As the current decreases, this causes the magnetic field to reduce, but as it collapses towards the earth it is in a direction that tends to increase the current. Thus, the stored energy in the magnetic field tries to keep the decreasing current flowing. The result of this exchange of energy is to slow down the rate of decrease of both the current and the magnetic field to give the well-known flattening exponential curve. Only a small section of this curve is given in Fig. 4 over which it is almost straight. In time, the curve will reach zero.

This exponential curve is of the same shape as the one given by the decay of radioactive elements. Both phenomena have the same property of a constant half life - i.e. the time taken for the value to reach half its original value is the same for it to then reach a quarter of its original value, then one eighth, etc.

By examining the measured values mathematically, Barnes found the half life of the magnetic field to be about 1,400 years. From this feature of the curve, there will be a time when virtually all (say 99.9%) of the magnetic field has disappeared.

An important point of this most obvious explanation is that once the electrical current has decreased to zero, there is no known mechanism that can increase it again. This is one aspect that ensured its rejection by evolutionists.

The original strength

There is an even greater problem facing orthodox scientists, not so much because the value will decrease to zero, but for the implications of what the magnetic field would have been in the past, which can be calculated quite accurately.

With a value of 8.56 in 1835, then 1,400 years earlier the value would have been 17.12, 2,800 years earlier - 34.24, etc. By continuing this process it can be shown that for ages more than 10,000 years ago, the circulating electrical currents necessary to obtain this large magnetic field would have had the power of a magnetic star and the currents would have generated so much heat that life on earth would have been impossible. This means that the age of the earth must be much less than this value - say 6-8,000 years?

The short section of the curve shown in Fig. 4 is only a small portion of the well known exponential curve *which a decreasing electrical current will follow*. Hayward, a strong critic of young-earth creationists, tries to ridicule Barnes's use of this curve by saying he "carried out one of the most daring extrapolations in all history... with breathtaking courage he extrapolated his short curve all the way back to 20,000 BC (Hay:137). He discounts this method, pointing out that the earth has reversed its magnetic field many times. In reply, this writer does not accept these reversals have taken place. Also, there is still no known mechanism that can adequately cause such reversals. We examine these two aspects in Appendix 4 - Geology.

Hayward claims that the reasons for the earth's magnetism "are not fully understood". What he fails to tell his readers is that a circulating current is a perfectly adequate explanation of all the measured phenomena, but as with all "long agers", whether creationist, as Hayward claims to be, or evolutionist, they flatly reject this for it does not provide the long ages they must have.

The "dynamo" theory - criticised

The electrical decay theory was the most obvious explanation of the decreasing magnetism, but this was quite unacceptable to evolutionists and a counterproposal, called the "dynamo effect" was soon made. This claims that the magnetic field is caused by molten rock circulating around the interior core of the earth. As the core is still molten, then it is assumed that changes in these swirling currents are the cause of the variations in the earth's magnetic field - even to the extent of causing complete reversals many times over. The experts have no explanation of what causes this.

This alternative explanation was shown to be very inadequate by Cowling in 1934 (Cow) in which he considered the way in which sunspots were thought to create the magnetic field that flows vertically through their centre. After a mathematical analysis he proved that movements of matter cannot sustain a magnetic field that it has generated itself. He also points out that in dynamos, the current is used in a different place to that in which it is generated - i.e. it is generated at one place but is then conducted to another place to produce the magnetic field. The field generated directly by the flow movement itself is not self sustaining. He concludes:

> The theory proposed by Sir Joseph Larmor, that magnetic field of a sunspot is maintained by the currents it induces in moving matter, is examined and shown to be faulty; *the same result also applies for the similar theory of the maintenance of the general field of earth and sun* (Cow:47).

Thus the claim that it is the moving magma that generates the magnetic field is disproven mathematically.

The Faraday disc has been used to explain the reversals, but Akridge showed that this only allows one reversal of the disc's motion and even then the magnetic field remains in the same direction (Q17/2:118).

The sun is said to reverse its polarity, but Barnes has pointed out that no one has been able to detect a dipole moment. It would appear that in the boiling surface of the sun there are many small intense local magnetic fields, and these migrate to produce a field at one pole and about 11 years later at the other pole. *There appears to be no concentration of field at the opposite pole where it would be expected* (*New Scientist* Sept. 24 1994 p11). Thus, the sun's magnetic field is due to a completely different cause to that of the earth's.

The problem has been made more acute by the discovery that the half life of the earth's magnetic field is not 1,400 years but only 830 years (Mag). This would make the age of the earth very much shorter still.

Opposition to Barnes" evidence was spearheaded by the American Civil Liberties Union who were behind a 1983 article by Dalrymple in the *Education Journal* (Dalrym. in Barn83). In this article, Dalrymple insisted that "there is near universal agreement that a dynamo exists in the earth's core" but then has to admit that "the exact mechanism is not known." Where the energy for these liquid currents comes from is also a problem about which Dalrymple comments: "At present, scientists do not know which of the several sources actually drives the dynamo; in fact, it may be some combination of sources." He suggests that the most likely force is gravity, which Barnes, in his reply, dismisses as "nonsense" (Bar83).

Dalrymple's main contention is that there is so much variation in the measured values around the earth that a circulating electrical current cannot explain. Barnes's reply is that these are variations due to local effects or changes due to electrical storms, etc. These variations are the "noise" that has to be averaged out in order to get the remaining "signal" of what the underlying magnetic field is. It is these variations that required Gauss (and subsequent workers) to use stations around the world to achieve his remarkable results.

It is noticeable that Dalrymple could write to a wide audience by courtesy of the Education Journal in which his article appeared. Barnes's reply in an Impact article (Bar83) would have had a much smaller circulation in comparison.

The *Scientific American* article

Dalrymple's suggestion that the energy for the field might come from gravity had been put forward earlier by Carrington and Gubbins in an article in *Scientific American* in 1979 (Car). This paper is interesting in watching how secular scientists try to overcome major problems with their theories.

They admit that electrical currents do not give a long enough time for the geologists (and thereby evolutionists). In their article, details of a most elaborate experiment are described involving a fast spinning sphere inside another to represent the solid inner core and the liquid outer core. After much deliberation, this approach seems to be discarded because the effects of the magnetic field itself cannot be reproduced in the model. Other ideas are considered, but for each one, the problems become insurmountable.

In searching for the necessary energy to drive these liquid currents, they briefly discuss the possibility that it may be due to radioactive heating in the core. They then suggest that 3/4 of the present loss of heat from the surface of the earth (4×10^{13} watts) comes from radioactivity in the crust. We will see later when discussing the cooling of the earth that this would be too high and that furthermore the radioactivity seems to be concentrated in the crust. If this is so, there is no radioactivity in the core to provide the deep heat source they need over millions of years.

It is only in their last three paragraphs that gravitational forces are considered due to the "poor performance of thermal dynamos", and the whole article weakly concludes with the rather pious hope that "It seems likely that gravitationally powered dynamos will play a significant role in future models of the core."

We have spent some time in examining the dynamo theory in order to demonstrate its inability to explain even the basic facts of the magnetic field and the "reversals" geophysicists insist have taken place. It is felt that this is necessary as the decrease in the earth's magnetic field is one of the clearest evidences that the earth is young, and it is therefore only right that counterproposals should receive an adequate rebuttal.

The *Scientific American* is written for lay readers, and no references are ever given. Yet this article contains several extremely complex theories, none of which are found to be satisfactory, and one can only conclude that their readers have been "blinded by science" in order to cover their ignorance. (See No. 21 in the "List of Deceptive Stratagems" in Bow91:221)

In reading this paper, one is once more intrigued by the various ways in which secular scientists will go to such desperate lengths to avoid the most obvious solution. Not unlike being entertained by clowns at a circus, we can similarly appreciate the mental gymnastics of secular experts in their efforts to produce an acceptable theory that can explain the decrease in the earth's magnetic field.

Magnetic decay in rocks

One feature that has received little attention is the natural decrease of the magnetism in the rocks. Freshly molten lava that has cooled has the maximum magnetic strength - The Thermal Remnant Magnetisation (TRM) - but it gradually decreases over time. Its Natural Remnant Magnetisation (NRM) decreases exponentially.

Cook (Cook66:280) examined this and showed that Pleistocene rocks at the top of the geological column had already lost 32% of their strength. From this, there should be no magnetism left in any rocks older than about the Pliocene rocks just below them.

He notes the magnetic strength of rocks "is generally regarded as extremely stable only because scientists have supposed the age of rocks to be around 10^5 times greater than they may actually be." (p283). Using this as a guide, if the Cambrian is assumed to be 600 M.yrs. old, dividing this age by his factor of 10^5, would give an age of about 6,000 years.

We would suggest that this is yet another indication of the young age of the earth that warrants further investigation and publicity.

4. THE SHRINKAGE OF THE SUN

For much of the 18th. century, there was considerable debate on the age of the earth. One of the subjects discussed was where the enormous energy of the sun could come from. Before radioactivity was discovered it was calculated by Helmholtz (Hel) that the simple collapse under its own gravity of a large gaseous body like the sun would be more than able to supply the energy required. The kinetic energy of the collapse would be transformed into heat. It is the same principle operating, but in a very small way, when an object becomes slightly heated on hitting the ground after falling from a height.

The problem this presented to evolutionists is that if this contraction is taken backwards in time, it can be shown that in only a short period of a few hundred years the sun would have been so large that life on earth could not have existed (Akr80).

Such an explanation of the origin of the sun's heat was unacceptable and the subject was rarely referred to. When radioactivity was discovered, it was immediately seized upon as able to provide all the energy coming from the sun for the millions of years necessary for evolution to take place.

More recently, doubts have been cast upon even this theory. The type of radioactivity presumed to be active in the sun should be emitting a number of particles called neutrinos. Experiments, carried out deep underground to filter out other particles, has shown that there are only 1/3 of the neutrinos that would be expected (Stei80). Furthermore, the amount peaks every 21.3 days and can vary from 30% to 100%, with generally more at night! (*Science* 273:1663 1996 and *Science News* 151:279 1997). Thus, the neutrino "problem" - and its implications - are greater than most scientists realise.

For the sun to generate radioactive energy it is expected to have a very dense core. This means it would have a natural radial pulsation of one hour. To their astonishment, it has been found to be 2 hours 40 minutes which indicates that it is almost homogenous; i.e. the same throughout its interior (Q17/3:144).

Two articles in *Nature* also contend that nuclear reactions do not heat the sun (259:92-95 and 259:87-89), the latter saying: "Nuclear... reactions are not responsible for energy generation in the Sun."

If the heat is not coming from radioactivity, this leaves gravitational collapse as the only reasonable source.

In 1979, two astronomers, Eddy and Boornazian (Edd79) startled the scientific community when they presented a paper at a conference that showed that the sun was shrinking by 0.1% of its diameter (2.25 seconds of arc) per century. They had examined the records of the Greenwich Observatory from 1836 to 1953 and found the sun's diameter was decreasing. They then checked their findings by using the similar records of the Naval Observatory in Washington D.C. since 1846 which confirmed their claim.

These observatory measurements had been made to accurately determine the position of the centre of the sun relative to the earth (and stars). The time is noted when the leading edge of the sun crosses the vertical hairline in the telescope pointing due south, and then the time for the trailing edge. From these, they can determine when the centre of the sun crossed the meridian. This is important for the exact position of the sun must be accurately known by astronomers and is also used by mariners and others who "shoot" the sun with a sextant to determine their position on the earth.

This general decrease of 0.1% of its diameter per century was "secular" i.e. with no apparent periodic cycle, and was more than enough to provide the immense heat of the sun without any nuclear reactions required to maintain it. We give a graph of its decreasing diameter in Fig. 5.2.1 where it is discussed in detail, to which the reader might like to refer at this point.

If this rate of decrease is taken backwards in time, in the space of only 100,000 years it would be twice the present size, and life could not exist under such heat. To illustrate this high rate, the sun's diameter would be equal to the earth's orbit in only 21 million years. This rate of collapse was 170 - 250 times more than that necessary to generate the present heat of the sun according to Helmholtz's theory. As one can imagine, as far as the orthodox scientific community was concerned, this had to be dealt with and "explained away".

There followed a spate of papers, each of them showing that Eddy's paper was flawed in various ways. This barrage of criticism has resulted in the evidence now being ignored by the secular scientific community, as it has now been "dealt with" by competent scientist in this field. As a result, creationists who continue to cite the evidence are criticised by Christian scientists for adhering to "disproven theories" and ignoring the "latest accepted views".

This hostility to young earth creationists by Christians in science is most strongly represented by Van Till and his co-authors in their book *Portraits of Creation* (Van Til). In this, creationists views are strongly criticised, principally in two subjects, geology and the sun's shrinkage. Henry Morris, George Barnes and others are accused of using "folk science" and of exhibiting a lack of scientific integrity in continuing to present a one-sided view of the evidence of the sun's shrinkage and ignoring the later papers. In Section 5.2 we examine this accusation and what the published articles actually say in some detail. From it we might be able to see which of the two sides has the greater claim to the "high moral ground" that has been seized by Van Till and his colleagues.

Suffice it to say at this point that this evidence by Eddy and Boornazian has not been overthrown by any subsequent paper. Indeed, read carefully, these critical papers either do not deal with the long period covered by the observatory measurements, or actually confirm them in varying degrees. Therefore, the fact that the sun is shrinking comparatively rapidly has not yet been disproven, and presents another sound piece of evidence for a young earth.

To conclude, although Eddy believes the earth is about 4.5 billion years old, he has been quoted as saying:

> However, ... I suspect that we could live with Bishop Ussher's value for the age of the earth and sun. I don't think we have much in the way of observational evidence in astronomy to conflict with that (Q17/3:143).

5. THE EARTH'S ROTATION

Evolutionists constantly quote the age of the earth as 4,500 million years (4.5 billion years). However, an examination of the rate of rotation of the earth by their own mathematicians show that its age must be much less than this figure.

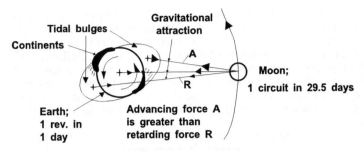

Fig. 5. The tidal bulges due to the moon

As the earth rotates once each day under the slower rotation of the moon (29.5 days per circuit) around it, the gravity of the moon pulls the sea on the earth nearest to the moon towards it. The next nearest object is the mass of the earth itself, and the furthest object, which gets the least pull, is the sea on the far side from the moon. Thus, the sea is (slightly) elongated into two bulges on the near side and far side of the earth to the moon (Fig. 5). It is this attraction of the moon for different parts of the earth that gives us two tides each day rather than the one tide that might be expected from a simple attraction of the sea nearest the moon.

The sun also has a similar effect but it is much less. When the earth, sun and moon are in line and act together we have the large "spring" tides, and when the moon and sun are at right angles as seen from the earth we have "neap" tides.

This reaction between the earth and the moon has a number of consequences, all of which indicate that the system cannot have been in existence for 4.5 billion years. There are three main aspects - the moon's distance, the earth's bulge and the tidal drag - but all are interconnected.

A) The moon's distance

The gravitational attraction between the moon and the earth creates tension in the rocks of both of them, and if the moon came sufficiently close, this tension could be high enough to pull the rocks of the moon apart. This distance, which can be calculated for all astronomical objects, is known as Roche's Limit and is the nearest distance that a circulating object can approach another body without being shattered by the tensile stresses generated by gravity pull between them. From this, the moon could never have been closer than 11,500 miles (18,500 Km).

As the tidal bulge sweeps around the earth it meets the eastern shores of the continents and islands that prevent it progressing further. These ocean tides, of course, are very slow and comparatively small and the breaking waves we see are entirely due to winds and storms at sea.

This reaction of the tides on the eastern shores slows the rotation of the earth. In addition there is an unknown amount of energy lost due to the friction of the tides on the shores which slightly heats the earth. The slowing of the earth means it loses energy which is transferred to the moon, and Fig. 5 shows how this happens.

The moon creates two bulges in the sea but the earth's spin pulls the one nearest to the moon in front of the moon's position which makes the moon speed up. The rear bulge is behind the moon's position which slows it down but as it is further away it has less effect than the nearer bulge. The moon, therefore, goes faster, but this makes it move to a larger orbit away from the earth. Thus the energy is transferred from the earth, which slows down, to the moon, which speeds up. As it is going faster, it moves out to a slightly wider orbit, and this increasing distance has now been measured. Reflecting mirrors have been placed on the moon and accurate laser measurements show that it is receding from the earth at a rate of 1.6 in. (40 mm) per year. Eventually the earth will slow down and the moon speed up so that they will be locked into synchronous rotation with a day 50 times longer than at present (*EB* v11 p759).

The moon is circling at a distance of 239,000 miles (385,000 km) and is receding at 1.6 in. (4cm.) per year. This rate would not be an average as it increases as the sixth power related to its closeness to the earth. We examine later how long ago the moon may have separated from the earth.

B) The moon's effect upon the earth's equatorial bulge

William Thomson, who became Lord Kelvin, was one of the most brilliant scientists of his day whose work in many fields has never received the credit it deserves. For many years he contradicted those who said that the earth was millions of years old.

If the moon were much closer to the earth than it is today, this would have made the tidal forces very much stronger. The attraction would have produced a large bulge around the equator of the molten earth when it was said to have been first formed 4,500 million years ago. When it cooled down it would have solidified and "frozen" the bulge existing at some early date. This bulge would have been very much greater than the small amount that exists at present. This shows that the earth-moon system cannot have existed for a great length of time.

Lord Kelvin showed that even if the earth was only 1 billion (one thousand million) years old and still molten, its rotation then would have been fast enough to produce an equatorial bulge in the land mass that should still be present. As the rotation slowed, the seas would have flowed more to the poles, leaving a land mass around the equator. Yet this is not the case today for the land areas are not on an equatorial belt.

The main problem facing evolutionists, however, is the slowing of the earth's rotation due to the effect of the tidal drag upon it.

C) The tidal drag on the earth's rotation.

As we have said, the tides meeting the eastern shores slow down the rotation of the earth. The mathematical investigation of this is not easy, mainly due to uncertainty about how much force the tides exert, the flexing of the earth's interior, the loss of energy due to friction, etc. However, scientists have made certain assumptions and have found that at an age much less than the 4.5 billion years they ascribe to the age of the earth the spin must have been very much faster. The reason for this is that at higher rates of rotation, the drag effect is very greatly increased. So to arrive at today's rate of 24 hrs. per revolution, its rate would have had to have been very much faster, for as you go back in time, the rate rises very rapidly indeed. There is then a limit to the age of the earth.

The problem it presents to evolutionists can be seen in a paper by Slichter (Sli). He gives the results of his mathematical analysis in a graph in which the rotation of the earth rises dramatically as you go into the past (Fig. 6). A range of three different coefficients for the indeterminate retarding forces are

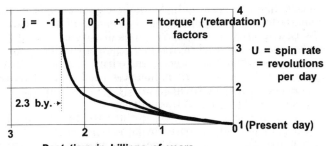

Past time in billions of years
(Note: Earth's age = 4.5 billion years)

Fig. 6. The earth's theoretical rate of rotation in the past

given and even the most generous one produces a rapid rise only 2.3 billion years ago. With a very high rate of spin at that time, it would by now have just slowed down to the present 24 hour rate of rotation. The worst coefficient gives an age of only 1.4 billion years. Schlichter has no explanation for these results. Kearst notes that if the moon is accelerating at 40 arc sec/cent, the moon would be touching the earth within 0.9 Billion years (Kear). A measured value of 50 arc sec/cent would greatly reduce this and a further reduction would result if it could not be nearer than Roche's limit. Creationists have calculated similar periods. Ian Taylor (TayI:330) quotes a value of less than 1 billion years since the moon could have separated from the earth whilst Brown (BrownW-Special edition:177-181) gives 1.2 Byrs.

From this it can be seen that the slowing action of the moon on the earth's spin gives from a half to a quarter of the 4.5 billion years that evolutionists ascribe to the age of the earth. Creationists, on the other hand, can easily accommodate a very minute increase in rotation 6-10,000 years ago.

The only explanation that evolutionists have for the short time their calculations give, is that the disposition of land and sea was much different to what it is today, giving much less drag on the tidal bulge. This is possible, but it should be noted that they are resorting to ad hoc explanations. When it suits them, they insist on uniformity; past conditions are like the present. In this case, they plead that they were different. Once again, the goal posts have been moved!

Atomic clocks indicate that the day is lengthening 1 second every 50,000 years. However, the rotation of the earth can vary comparatively widely, and this is imposed on the general slowing,. It is this variation that is the main reason for "leap seconds" being added roughly every 18 months. As can be seen, the subject is far from simple and the figures quoted could be misleading if wrongly interpreted.

6. THE COOLING OF THE EARTH

As you go deeper into the earth, it is found that the temperature rises about 1°C for every 100 ft. (30m.). We are therefore living on a planet that has an extremely hot interior, and the earth must have been hotter in the past.

Lord Kelvin made various calculations on the rate of cooling of the earth and showed that even if the earth had been molten at the time of creation, it would have cooled to its present temperature gradient within 100 million years, but allowing for uncertainties he suggested 20-400 My. He later amended this to 20-40 MY (Ing:100). All of these ages were far too short for the evolutionists and they struggled in vain to overcome his evidence.

When the heating effect of radioactivity was discovered, this was quickly used to explain the present level of heat in the earth's interior. However, this subject has been re-examined by Ingersoll and others. Without any radioactivity, the age of the earth would be 22 million years, and with radioactivity this would be extended to only 46 million years (Ing:107). However, there is a complicating assumption with these calculations.

There is only a minute amount radioactive material in the upper layers of the earth but if this were to be consistent for the full depth of the earth the amount of heat it would generate would be many times that needed to provide the present amount of heat within the earth. In view of this, it is assumed that only the top crust has radioactive elements within it, supplying a quarter of the total heat lost. This gives the figures quoted above.

The problem is that there is more radioactivity in the continental crust than in the ocean crusts and no one knows what the radioactive content of the earth is. Kelvin's calculations demonstrated it would only take a comparatively short period of time to establish the present temperature gradient with depth. Slusher has shown that this is still viable, and subsequent experiments have supported this claim. (Chaf87).

Cook points to several additional sources of heat and concludes that "one cannot be sure whether the earth is heating, cooling, or in a perfect steady state from heat balance data alone" (Cook66:81). He also discusses the effect that the pressure at great depths has upon the melting points of the various geological materials.

The present situation is that heat calculations indicate a young age for the earth, but they involve the assumption that radioactive material is limited to the crust alone. This is a very specific and limiting assumption without any evidence in its support. If this is accepted, then a supplementary theory needs to be advanced to explain why it should be only in the crust and not in the depths of the earth if the earth was completely molten when first formed.

There is yet another complicating factor; CDK. When the speed of light was much higher, the heat from radioactivity may have been higher but, as we will see in Appendix 1, not significantly so. However, it may have has other effects upon certain atomic properties.

In summary, heat calculations indicate a young age for the earth, but there are some problems that have yet to be satisfactorily explained - by evolutionists.

There is a similar problem with the moon. The path of the lunar satellite Clementine indicates that the moon is not as rigid as it was thought, and that part of it may still be molten. (Science 264:1666 1994).

On this subject, it is noted that Mars is 20 degrees cooler than it was now that its dust storms have abated. (Science 267:1912-1995). This is yet another rapid change that the evolutionists have to produce an ad hoc explanation for.

7. POLONIUM HALOES

In this topic we will consider an unusual feature discovered in igneous rocks. Whilst not directly dealing with the age of the earth, it does raise many problems about the way in which the early rocks were laid down.

As is well known, there is a small amount of radioactive material in most igneous rocks. As these active elements decay into a "daughter" element there

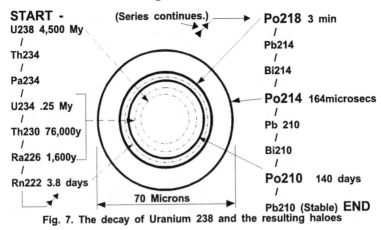

Fig. 7. The decay of Uranium 238 and the resulting haloes

is a loss of energy which is radiated outwards. The heavy element Uranium 238 is one of three elements that are at the beginning of a chain of decay stages. The figure 238 is the atomic weight of the element, and at each stage of decay it loses an alpha or beta particle, but only the alpha particle damages the surrounding rock which is the main interest of this study. Each stage has a different "half life" period (the time taken for half the initial quantity to decay) and the full sequence is given in Fig 7.

Particular interest is focussed upon the Polonium sequence for these have very short half-lives.

Each alpha ray has a characteristic energy related to the particular element it is ejected from, and, depending on the amount of energy, each damages the local crystalline structure of the rock at a specific radius as it is slowed down, the maximum distance being just under 40 thousandths of a millimetre (40 microns). As a result, decaying U238 becomes surrounded by a minute series of haloes. Where these occur in biotite, a crystalline mineral usually found in granites, they are visible under a microscope and the haloes for each stage can be identified. These haloes were discovered about 1885 and their cause was unknown until the discovery of radioactive elements. They have been studied and experimented upon by Robert V. Gentry who has made some startling claims.

Normally, with their very short half-life, polonium haloes should only be found as part of the decay series. The series of haloes is given in Fig. 7. Those produced prior to the polonium haloes that are sometimes missing are shown dotted.

The important discovery Gentry has made is that many polonium haloes have been found where there is no evidence of haloes from the preceding elements whatsoever. The absence of these earlier haloes indicates that the polonium was created without any preceding ancestral radioactive elements! What is more, the rock must have been created in a crystalline form at the same time in order to retain these haloes, as molten rock cannot do so.

It might be thought that the rock may have crystallised just at the very point when the polonium stage had been reached. But assuming that many of the preceding elements, having much longer half-lives, were present in the nodule in the molten rock, there should be still a large number not yet decayed that will continue to produce their distinctive haloes in the now crystalline rock.

These haloes of earlier long period elements should still appear with those of the polonium haloes. None, however, have been found.

It should be remembered that it is not a case of each stage being completed before the next one starts. As the first U238 decays to U234, some of the U234 will already be starting to decay to U230. There is therefore very considerable overlap, and at times there will be decay of many of the various elements going on at the same time.

Gentry has been most meticulous in checking alternative explanations. He has bombarded the nodules with other atomic energies to check if there are any earlier elements still in the nodules, but none have been detected. The quality of his work had received high praise even from scientists who cannot accept the implications that his results present.

The scientific community, both evolutionists and creationists, are therefore faced with the existence of polonium being suddenly created in solid rock without any preceding radioactive elements that should have been part of the normal series of decay.

This presents insurmountable difficulties for evolutionists, and it also presents some problems for creationists, for it implies that the Precambrian strata in which they have been found, must have been created as a solid to begin with. There could have been no fluid period, whether molten or as a hydrothermal solution, that would have allowed the strata to flow into the obviously layered Precambrian formations now visible.

Garner (CRSQ 26:152) points out that polonium haloes have been found in granites that have inclusions of other rocks, have diffuse contacts with other rocks and finer grain size indicating it has been chilled by the cooler rock. These all suggest that the granite must have been in a hot fluid state before its emplacement.

In his reply, Gentry suggests that too much of the interpretation is based upon conventional geology and that the rocks could have been created in the form they are found. He makes the important point that molten granite cools to form rhyolite, not granite and that from this the granite must have been created as otherwise it would appear as rhyolite. However, there are examples of thin granite veins penetrating fossilised strata, indicating that, in some way, granite can be deposited in a fluid state and not form rhyolite (Garner, personal communication).

Wise also tries to make a case against Gentry (CRSQ 25:171) but a careful reading shows that he does not provide convincing evidence.

In order to disprove Gentry's claim, what is needed is to find a deposit of granite that not only contains Polonium haloes but also has obviously flowed into a fossil bearing deposit, preferably as a thin vein. This would prove that it was deposited after the Flood and therefore long after creation. As far as this writer is aware, this combination has not yet been discovered at the time of writing.

Even if such evidence were to be discovered, whilst it would render Gentry's view that the granite was created in place untenable, it would still not answer the problem of how these Polonium haloes could have come into being on their own - although we present a possible explanation below. Neither would it answer the question of what was created ready for Adam's presence in a mere few days.

Were the Precambrian granites created in the stratified layers found today? Initially, this seems difficult to accept, but if rejected, how can we obtain a rock foundation on which humus must have been created to support plant life all within six days and perfect for Adam to occupy?

Ultimately, this leaves the question; "Can Gentry's critics provide a better scenario that fits both the Bible and the geological evidence?"

A proposed (partial) solution to the problem of the Polonium haloes

In my first draft of this section, I left the solution of this problem to other, more knowledgeable, creationists in the future. However, in pondering many aspects of the creationist model, particularly the importance of the Fall, I would suggest that there is one consideration that may go some way to solving this problem.

We must return to the fact that when God had finished His creation of the universe on the sixth day, he declared it to be "very good" i.e. perfect. This means that there was nothing harmful to man in the whole universe - *including radioactivity.*

When Adam fell, he brought the whole of creation with him, and it is still "groaning" to this day (Rom. 8:22).

It is therefore proposed that radioactivity only commenced at the Fall.

All God needed to do was to reduce the binding forces in the nucleus of the atom to a lower level, and the heavier atoms above a particular atomic weight would begin their process of disintegration.

This proposal would be able to explain how the Polonium haloes could exist without other decay haloes being present. The Polonium atoms, created by God as part of the whole spectrum of elements, could have been in the (hydrothermal) outflowing of rock material in the early period of creation, forming the Precambrian strata, and later flows also bearing nodules of Polonium atoms would penetrate these same (pre-Flood) rocks. When the Fall took place, the Polonium would then begin to decay radioactively, producing the haloes now examined by scientists.

This proposal does at least allow a period of fluid flow for the granite and the polonium only decaying some time later at the Fall. It is more in accord with the declared perfection of the Genesis creation and there appear to be no reasons from any evidence in physics that should result in its rejection.

There is one additional piece of evidence that has come to light. A diamond has been discovered with over 75 haloes in it, with the initiating halo of U238 missing but the other radioactive inclusions appear to be present in many of the haloes (ArmM). Where the diamond came from is not known. Now diamonds are found in minerals that have come from a very great depth within the earth, and are therefore assumed to have been formed under conditions of great pressure and heat. But just brief periods of high temperatures will erase these haloes, so diamonds could not have been formed in the assumed conditions of high temperatures at least.

A possible explanation is that the diamonds now bearing haloes were formed complete with their radioactive inclusions and solidified. With the Fall, the radioactive elements began to decay and the haloes were produced. Any subsequent transport of the diamonds would not necessarily involved high heat. This is where the formation of strata by "hydrothermal" (supercritical) water solutions may play an important part as discussed under geology in Appendix 4. The temperatures involved in this method of strata formation would be very much lower than if intrusive rocks were in a molten state.

This may provide an adequate solution to the whole problem of Polonium haloes. We have already noted that granite cannot as yet be produced in the

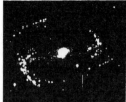

Fig. 8. Typical spiral galaxies

laboratory which indicates that its origin is different to what mineralogists believe. It is therefore suggested that the crystalline biotite, complete with its haloes, could have been transported as a "mush" in the hot water that was at a low enough temperature not to erase the haloes. This "mush" would then suddenly "set" at a specific temperature as it cooled to give the present granite formations. In this way, biotite crystals, with their haloes already formed, could penetrate thin veins in rocks - *even those that were fossil bearing and therefore formed much later than the decay of the polonium.*

The sequence would then be as follows;

1. Creation of biotite (and diamonds) with inclusions of Polonium.
2. The biotite flows into various levels and places within the pre-Flood strata.
3. At the Fall, the Polonium and other radioactive elements begin to decay making haloes in the biotite.
4. At the Flood, the strata are mainly formed by hydrothermal water at a comparatively low temperature bringing chemical solutions to the surface which engulf many fossils.
5. Later flows of hydrothermal water bring halo-bearing biotite crystals in a "mush" that penetrates pre-Flood and Flood strata, solidifying to form thin veins within these strata.
6. Similarly, diamonds are brought up from great depths in a low temperature "mush" to be discovered by man in the huge "pipes" such as at Kimberley.

If radioactivity did commence at the time of the Fall, this would also have a bearing on cosmic radiation and its effect upon life on earth. If God pronounced His creation "very good", then it would be difficult to imagine that it included high-energy rays that were lethal to life and man's only protection was the earth's magnetic field and probably the Water Vapour Canopy. It is therefore suggested that these cosmic rays and other harmful radioactive phenomena did not exist for the (possibly short) period between Creation and the Fall.

The scenario described above is presented as being a possible explanation for the presence of Polonium haloes in strata, even where they may be in veins that penetrate post-Flood fossil-bearing strata. It is left to others to check with actual conditions in the field regarding geological strata, heating conditions, crystal-bearing properties and temperatures of hydrothermal water, etc. to see if the theory is viable.

8. THE SPIRAL ARMS OF GALAXIES

As astronomers look into distant space, they have found that there are other massive collections of stars like our own galaxy. Many of them have a circular pattern as though they consisted of a flat disc of stars with arms extending from them. These arms are curled like the arms of a rotating catherine wheel as seen in Fig. 8.

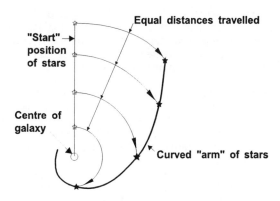

Fig. 9. How galaxies "wind up"

These curling arms of the galaxies present at least three problems to astronomers.

a) The speeds of the stars

It has been assumed by astronomers that there is a large mass of stars at the centre of these galaxies, and that the stars rotate around the centre at the right speed to maintain their present orbit. This is similar to the way in which the planets rotate around the sun - i.e. those nearest the centre travel at higher speeds than those further out - which is known as Keplerian rotation. This would maintain the stability of the system much as the planets are stable in their orbits.

It is possible to measure the speed with which these arms are rotating and surprisingly, Comins and Marschall report that the stars near the centre are travelling at the same speed as those near the ends of the arms (Com). This is due to the mass of the galaxy being distributed and not concentrated near the centre as it is with the sun at our centre.

The result of this is that if we imagine the stars arranged in straight "spokes" when they were first formed, then as the inner was moving as fast as the outer edges, the galaxy would begin to "wind itself up", as indicated in Fig. 9. For any period of time, each of the distances travelled is the same for each section of the galaxy's arms, resulting in the "winding up" of the arms. This gives a slower "winding action" than Keplerian rotation but the effect is still the same. What is certain is that the arms are not rigid forms that rotate without changing their shape.

One surprise is the recent discovery that up to one half of the stars in many galaxies are rotating in the opposite direction to the rest! (Roy. Ast. Soc. Month. Not. 283:543 1996).

b) The time for a complete winding.

Paul Steidl, in his excellent book "The Earth, the Stars and the Bible" has pointed out that from the measurements of the speed with which the stars are moving, it has been calculated that for the centre of the galaxy to complete one turn more than the furthest stars would take about 100 million years. As astronomers believe that galaxies have existed for about 10 billion years, then they should have about 100 "turns". Yet none have more than about 1 or 2 turns at the most, which would give them an age of 100-200 million years. This is far less even than that given on the geological time scale since the Cambrian era is said to have started about 600 million years ago.

If, of course, they were created with some degree of spiral already, then they would be very much younger than even these ages.

c) All galaxies are wound up about the same amount.

Astronomers use the red shift of galaxies to measure their distance from us. The most distant is at least 10,000 million light-years away (MooP:155), so as we look at these distant galaxies, the light left them many millions of years ago. This means that the further a galaxy is from us, we should be seeing them when they were much younger than the nearer ones. From this, astronomers would expect to see the galaxies with much less "spiral" in their arms - but to their surprise they do not. The amount of only one or two turns of spiral in the arms is independent of their distance from us. This suggests that these spirals have always been present. Yet, they have measured the speed of the stars in the arms and they are clearly circling around the centre and "winding up"!

Recent results from the Hubble telescope has shown that there are many "young" galaxies in deep space, but with them are a number of "old" galaxies also with tightly wound arms, so the problem still remains (Nature 381:555 1996).

In order to avoid the inference that these spirals were there at the time the galaxies were formed, and that they could not have been created very long ago, alternative theories of how these spiral arms could be formed have been sought for several years.

The article by Comins and Marschall (Com) reveals their puzzlement with many aspects of galaxy spirals which becomes almost a cry of anguish when they say:

> What's wrong here? How can stars have different orbital periods - as we observe - and also trace out spiral patterns - as we also observe - yet still not wind up over periods of billions of years?

They suggest that there may be two explanations, but they are both very abstruse and they admit that they have problems of their own.

One suggestion is that the stars "bunch up" at certain points around the galaxy's surrounding star population, and this bunching effect passes around the galaxy. Thus the stars do not rotate, it is only this bunching that is noticeable. However, they admit that calculations have shown that this effect would die out in a billion years, and furthermore the position of observed stars do not match those predicted by the theory.

The second suggestion proposes that exploding stars (nova) trigger the formation of stars from the surrounding material as the compressed front of the gas moves outwards. This also is recognised to have "several shortcomings" due to factors that the computer programme used to check the theory does not take into account.

In summary, as is frequently found in other subjects, efforts to "explain away" the most obvious "young earth" interpretations of these spiral arms look increasingly like "theories of desperation". All this is brought about by the unbending demands for "millions of years" by their evolutionist geological peers.

There is one interpretation that at least solves the problem of why distant galaxies have no less a degree of spiral than near ones. This is the (also observed) fact that the speed of light has been faster in the past. If this increase was of the order of 10^11 proposed by Setterfield and Troitskii (see Appendix 1), then the light from these distant galaxies would have reached us very much more quickly than the "millions of years" the orthodox scientists accept. However, to accept such a solution would open a veritable Pandora's Box of problems for them. Consequently, such a proposition is both shunned and ridiculed.

9. THE AGE OF STARS AND PLANETS

Large stars burn up their matter much faster than smaller stars and cannot last as long. Hot stars (O and B types) should have burnt out long ago, yet they still exist together with smaller stars in the same cluster which suggests they were all formed at the same time.

Even if the 10 billion years age of our galaxy as proposed by astronomers is taken as a basis, there has not been enough time for a star one half the size of the sun to have evolved to the white dwarf stage, yet many do exist.

In addition, some stars are grouped into globular clusters and are considered to be amongst the oldest astronomical objects. They are rapidly flying away from each other against their mutual gravitational force. From their measured speed, it can be calculated that they would have all been close together only a few thousand years ago (Slu). Furthermore, all stars emit a solar wind that should build up into a considerable amount of gas when there are many stars together as in a globular cluster (Hess:143). This gas should be easily detectable, yet there is no evidence that it exists.

This suggests that the stars and galaxies were created much as they are seen today in the comparatively recent past.

Supernova Remnants (SNR)

Supernova are stars that explode with huge amounts of energy released, sometimes sufficient for them to be observed in the daytime. The results can be seen in a telescope as an expanding cloud of stellar debris. These can be seen in galaxies also and they remain visible for about 1 million years.

Records show that for the average galaxy there would be one supernova about every 25 years, and with this frequency, thousands of SNRs should be visible. Totalling the three stages they pass through, 7,291 should be visible if the universe is millions of years old, but only 270 if it is only 7,000 years old. The actual number observed is 205, which supports the young-earth view (Davies). Davies reports the puzzlement of astronomers who ask "Where have all the remnants gone?"

The planetary system is unstable!

Newton considered that the orbits of the planets were unstable and that God had to make occasional minor adjustments. Laplace tried to show they were stable but his proof was not rigorous. It has now been found that the orbit of Pluto is unpredictable within 20 MY and that its wild orbit would affect other planets making them all unstable in time (Science 241:433-7). As well as showing that the planetary system must be quite young, it also reminds us that we are surely living in a much more precarious universe than we think - give or take a few million years!

The 3K background radiation

In an important article, Akridge, Barnes and Slusher (Akr81) examined the standard theories that proposed this was an "echo" of the Big bang, and demonstrated that the photons would have left the universe and would not register today. To obtain a result, the mathematics (implicitly) assume that the energy is constant; i.e. there is a reflective layer around the universe - which is nonsense. Akridge's (et al) explanation is that the radiation is due to the energy emitted by the stars gradually warming the intergalactic dust. Making approximate assumptions, they calculate that if the universe is billions of years old, the temperature should be about 100°K. The present level of 3°K gives an age of about 6,800 years!

10. THE MICROMETEORIC DUST ON THE EARTH AND MOON

There is a continual "rain" of micro-meteoric dust falling on to the surface of the earth and moon. The figure quoted by many creationists is that given by Petterson (Pett) as 5-14 million tons per year. The actual amount is difficult to estimate and values down to 10,000 tons have been suggested (Taylor, P. p70).

Certainly, when the first journey to the moon was being organised, there was very great concern that the satellite would disappear in a huge depth of dust, and it was provided with large feet to guard against this possibility. When it was found that the depth was very much less than the uniformitarian assumptions had predicted, there was considerable downward revising of the rate of fall of dust on the moon.

In a very long article, Snelling and Rush surveyed the latest information and concluded that the amount falling on the earth is 10,000 - 20,000 tons/yr (Snel93) from satellite records but 100,000 - 400,000 t/y based upon chemical analyses. The amount falling on the moon is about 10,000 t/y. These are well below the original assessments and the authors conclude that moon dust thickness should not be used as evidence of a young moon by creationists.

We would question such conclusions. There are so many indications that the universe is young that hidden within the secular data must be evidence in its support. A careful examination of the assumptions of the authors might allow an alternative conclusion. Adopting the results of such papers could be misleading. Others have examined the subject in considerable depth also and have come to different conclusions.

Bouw reports (BA68:5) that the amount of dust landing on the moon over 4.5 billion years is sufficient to result in a minimum of 500 lbs. on each square inch - about 50 ft. depth (15m.). The actual amount is roughly one ounce per sq. inch. Furthermore, of the 1 inch (25 mm) thickness, most of it is powdered lunar material mainly thrown up by meteorite impacts but also from the pulverising of the sun's radiation. Only 1.6% of it is meteoric material (BA80:18 - Ref: Science 170:533).

Bouw, who is an astronomer, has watched the "moon dust" controversy over the years and contends that it was only after the small amount had been found on the moon that estimates were revised downwards. Recent measurements support the earlier high values of dust in space. Instruments left on the moon also show that the quantity of micrometeorites arriving is in line with the high level assumed originally.

Brown calculates that for a life of 4.6 B.yrs., the dust should be 50 times thicker than it is (BrownW:215). An abandoned spacecraft showed many more impacts than expected and confirmed the original higher infall rate (Science 22.10.1993). This would produce 35Kg./cm^2 in 5 B.yrs. but only

0.04 grms./cm^2 in 6,000 years.

Thus, with the the amount of descending dust comparatively high and the amount of it on the moon so small, this gives an age for the moon much less than required by evolutionists. In addition, these calculations always assume that the present rate has been maintained some 4.5 B.yrs., but it was probably very much higher in the past. This is indicated by the huge impact craters on the moon which are not occurring now but suggest that there was much more interplanetary material circulating in the past. This would rapidly produce considerable dust and give an appearance of greater age. Whether this was so cannot now be checked, but if this possibility is accepted, then the present thickness would easily be achieved in 6,000 years.

The dust should not be there!

The fact that this dust exists at all is additional evidence of a young solar system. There is a band of dust that circles the sun on the equatorial (planetary) plane. It is the reflection off this dust that gives what is known as zodaical light visible just before sunrise and just after sunset.

As the dust spirals around, it experiences two opposite forces. One is the radiation pressure of the sun which tends to flush it out of the planetary system, the other is that the radiation coming from the sun that strikes the dust is re-radiated by the dust in all directions. This radiation "bunches" in the direction of travel and the ultimate effect is to slow it down which makes it spiral into the sun. This is known as the Poynting-Robertson effect, and the forces balance for a critical size of particle. Larger particles spiral towards the sun and smaller ones are flushed outwards.

Samec (Sam) has shown that the first force should have cleared the very fine dust out of the whole planetary system within 2.5 million years. The second force, acting on the average size of particles the earth meets on its orbit, would have spiralled into the sun within about 1,600 years. This means that the dust that started 6,000 years ago between Mars and the earth has by now fallen to the orbit of the earth.

That we still have this dust around us argues for a recent date for creation. Perhaps this explains why the Poynting-Robertson effect is not referred to in the *Encyclopaedia Britannica*.

11. SHORT TERM COMETS

Comets are considered to be "dirty snowballs" regularly circling the sun and each time they pass by it, the sun's heat burns off some of its material, leaving a smaller comet for the next pass. Those returning in less than about 200 years are called "short return comets", and they should have been completely burnt away within 10,000 years. One such is Halley's comet with its 77 year return period.

That about 100 short return comets still exist indicates that the universe is young. To overcome this, the astronomer, Oort, proposed (more accurately *invented*) the "existence" of a cloud of long-term comets in outer space that circled the sun at distances too far to be seen. They would occasionally be deflected by a star towards the solar system, be perturbed by Jupiter's gravitation to circle the sun closely and thereby made into a short-term comet.

Almost all criticisms of Oort's theory has come from creationists, but Lyttleton published a strong critique of Oort's original paper with the striking title of "The Non-existence of the Oort Cometary Shell" (Lytt). He points out that Oort manipulated his analysis of the cometary data to give a false result.

In fact the very high peak on one crucial graph had no evidence in its support - all the data being on one side of it! He is unsparing in his descriptions of the methodology of Oort and those who have published the numerous papers on this fallacious theory. His paper is peppered with phrases such as "an elementary mistake of general principle... preposterous absurdity... the outright improbability of the whole shell-theory.... in breach of the most elementary scientific principles." He points out the accuracy with which the comets would have to be deflected towards the sun from such large distances from it, and other highly improbable circumstances that are required to make the system "work". The interested reader is referred to this paper for his full critique.

When Oort proposed these circling comets he estimated that they were just reaching the position where stars could deflect their orbit towards the planetary system, but further investigation showed that they only reached one fifth of the distance to the nearest star Alpha Centauri; "Comets must therefore come down from the Oort cloud in several steps." (*EB* 27:583).

To overcome the many difficulties in explaining how comets could still exist after millions of years, it has been conjectured that there are no less than three levels of cometary "belts", each one "feeding" the next in the series. Van Flandern, a critic of the theory, sets one version out as follows (Fla:183);

1. A "Kuiper belt" of comets "in nearly circular orbits near the plane of the other planets, beginning just outside the orbit of Neptune... there is no observational evidence for this region..." This "belt" feeds an "inner core" of comets.

2. An "inner core" between the planetary region and the Oort cloud. "There is no observational evidence for such a region - it is simply a theoretical construct".

3. The Oort cloud, thought to consist of more than a trillion comets orbiting the sun at distances 1,000 times that of Pluto - so remote that passing stars would frequently pass through it (p217). There is no observational evidence for this "cloud" either. Passing stars are thought to "disturb" these comets, sending them on their journey towards the sun.

It was found that various articles gave conflicting values for distances, number of clouds, numbers of objects, etc. This is as might be expected if speculation is the whole basis of the theory; each expert can make his own formulation.

There are many other problems with Oort's theory.

(1) Steidl (Ste79:59), a creationist critic, points out that it is just possible that Jupiter could have affected the orbits of these comets to make them into short term ones but this effect is so slow that it cannot explain the number that exist today. Also, there are two comets that have circular orbits that do not intersect with any other planet (Ste79:115).

(2) One of the major problems is that comets paths are intrinsically unstable. It requires only a perturbation as they pass near a planet and they would be ejected from the planetary system. Many comets go 1000 times further out than Pluto and are travelling over 40,000 m/s. If they were only 0.5 m/s faster they would never return and Flandern says "Mechanisms that can pump up comet velocities so close to the critical velocity in such great numbers have been difficult to imagine" (Fla:183).

(3) Most short term comets orbit the sun in a prograde direction and are near the ecliptic - the direction and plane of the planets around the sun. In

contrast, long term comets (about 500) were thought to have random orbits, but they had been carefully "selected". In fact they come principally from five directions, one direction in particular, which is much less easily explained. Such are the differences between them that one expert has said that long term comets do not turn into short term ones.

Van Flandern's noted that 84% of comets come from one half of the hemisphere of the sky and the remaining 16% from the other hemisphere (Flan:218). What explanation can astronomers give for this extreme imbalance of orbits?

Steidl (Stei:87) examined several theories of how the Oort cloud could have been produced as well as long and short term comets, and showed that none of them stood up to a critical examination; the mechanics of the planetary system cannot provide the numbers even with millions of years available.

(4) Over a long period of time, cosmic rays would have polymerised the surface chemicals on all comets so that they would not be vaporised when they came near the sun. The present large bright tails show that they are quite young. High energy cosmic rays would also change many of the atoms in Carbon, Oxygen and Nitrogen to Lithium, but there is no Lithium present in their spectrum (Stei87).

Recently, it has been claimed that 30 (later increased to 50) small objects have been detected in the "Kuiper disk", "the fossilised remnant of the dusty disk from which the planets formed", and they are said to be the source of short-term comets (*Astronomy*). Their presence was only detected after the team used "sophisticated image processing and statistical techniques to eliminate unwanted stars, galaxies, and cosmic ray strikes on Hubble's CCD detectors". None of these objects could be found in a later search (Science News 1996 149:395).

Incidentally, it is interesting to see how dissident scientists, such as Arp, Alfven and van Flandern, whilst not being creationists, often provide some interesting but little-known information (rather like giving away "trade secrets") that supports the creationist's position.

It should be mentioned that van Flandern has presented considerable evidence that asteroids, comets and other planetary system objects are the result of the "missing planet" (named Phaeton) exploding not very long ago (Fla). He points out that comets dim rapidly after their first few passes but then remain at a low level thereafter. This would extend the life of the short-term comets, but it is doubtful if the time could be extended to millions of years. Steidl agrees that there is some evidence for the theory, but that there is no known process that could cause a planet to explode, although a collision might account for it (Stei87).

Summarising this subject, it is clear that orthodox astronomers have had to produce a theory, no matter how unfounded and speculative it may be, for the public's acceptance in order to explain why short-term comets still exist after millions of years of planetary evolution.

12. HELIUM IN THE ATMOSPHERE

In the decay of uranium and thorium, the alpha particles emitted become helium 4, an isotope of helium. Calculations show that there is only 1/2,000ths part of the amount of helium in the atmosphere to what should have accumulated if the earth was created 4.5 billion years ago.

It might be thought that the helium may have escaped from the earth into space, but despite considerable investigation this does not appear to have taken place (Mal94). In fact it is possible that helium may have been added to the atmosphere. The ratio of isotopes of helium 3 and 4 in the earth is only one tenth of the ratio in the atmosphere, indicating the addition of helium, reducing the age further. With all this in mind, an age of about 12,000 years is indicated (Cook57).

Vardiman has also examined the subject (Va86r and TayP:65) and has proposed it would only take 1.8 MY for the amount of He4 and 370 thousand years for He3 to have accumulated.

In order to check if there was any new evidence that might contradict the "young-earth" view, we looked at some internet web sites where creation is hotly debated. One site, (www2) was a 46 point rebuttal of young-earth evidence, but the level of reply was extremely poor. There was only one point I had not heard of before dealing with the possible ways that Helium could be dispersed. Quoting Dalrymple, it referred to "photoionisation by the polar wind" and that "good estimates [!] show that these processes roughly balance the rate of production." This was stated with great confidence and readers would be left with the impression that the problem was solved.

Vardiman, however, has said that "Mechanisms other than thermal escape, are considered, *even by the long age scientific community*, to be speculative and of undetermined significance" (TayP:66). Some explanations seem very convincing until you try to find if they are at all realistic by putting figures to them.

In fact helium should be accumulating in the atmosphere as it is an important component of the solar wind. One scientists admitted that the escape problem "will not go away and it is unsolved" (TayP:66).

13. CONTINENTAL EROSION

In the evolutionary timescale, the earth was formed 4.5 billion years (BY) ago and the first cell would have evolved not later than 1 BY ago. The depth of sediment in the oceans is surprisingly thin, being only 0.4 miles thick and weighing about 820 million billion tons (MBT). The amount of rock standing above the sea level is about 383 MBT. Thus the continents would only have to be eroded twice to provide all the sediments in the oceans.

It is estimated that the amount of material entering the oceans, mainly by the rivers, is about 27.5 BT/yr. Using these basic quantities, Nevins draws some surprising conclusions (Nev).

a) Erosion of the continents

If there is 383 MBT in the land mass then *it would only take 383/27.5 = 14 million years to erode all the continents into the sea* (Nev).

b) Deposition of the present depth of sediments

Similarly, the time it would take to deposit the present sediments in the seas is 820/27.5 = 30 million years only.

These periods of time are far too short in the evolutionary time scale. All the present strata are supposed to contain fossils that go back to the Cambrian that is said to have been laid down 600 MY ago. If that age is correct, it should have been eroded many times over and not a trace should remain.

c) Depth of ocean sediments

If the oceans have existed for 1BY, then we would expect to see a depth of sediment *nearly 19 miles thick* (27.5 BT/yr x 1 BY = 27.5 bill. bill tons / ocean area = 97,500 ft. depth).

The quantities given above are not really disputed by evolutionists, and it requires only simple calculations to show that there is something seriously wrong with the time scale they apply to the geological column.

Regarding the thinness of the ocean sediments, there are two possible explanations that might be offered to overcome this problem;

(i) The sediments might be uplifted to (re)form the continents.

However, there is about the same amount of sedimentary material on the continents as there are in the oceans. Adding all the continental sediments to those in the ocean still does not provide the 100,000 ft. depth they should have if they have existed for a billion years.

(ii) The "sea floor spreading" might remove them by subduction under the continents.

However, the rate of spreading is estimated to destroy about 2.75 BT/yr which is only 1/10th of the amount of sediments added to the oceans each year.

From all this, as the title to Nevins's pamphlet declares, *The Oceans say "NO" to Evolution.* We will return to this subject of the erosion of the continents when we deal with geology in Appendix 4.

14. THE POPULATION INCREASE

Statistics indicate that the population of the world is increasing about 2% each year. So concerned are the governments that some have tried to bring in strict measures to reduce this trend. Yet studies have shown that there is ample food for all many times over.

This was confirmed by Clark, an acknowledged world expert on the subject. He made some very perceptive remarks which we summarise (Clar).

(i) If the land is well farmed, a population of 50 billion could have a rich "American style" diet compared with the 5.5 billion population today, many of whom are starving. If the more frugal and healthy diet of the Japanese were to be adopted, this figure could become 150 billion.

(ii) When faced with this, the "experts" change their ground and refer to the exhaustion of the mineral resources. Clark checked this and found that from data in 1949 we should have run out of copper, lead and zinc several years ago!

The explanation is that because exploration is expensive, mining companies only explore a few years ahead of their current requirements, hence the low "reserves" they appear to have. The known resources are hundreds of thousands times more than what has been explored.

(iii) He makes a most important correction regarding "zero population growth". It is thought that this is still not achieved because the number of births exceeds the number of deaths. He points out that the present number of deaths represents a much smaller population some 60 - 70 years ago. "If current births do no more than replace current deaths, it means that they will be quite incapable of replacing the present younger and middle-aged generations which are far more numerous".

He had calculated that New Zealand was 10% below the replacement requirements, and the worst case was Germany, "miserable in the midst of its riches", that is 30% short. Urban areas are well above the replacement level, particularly the Muslim population of Central Asia.

As one sees world events, it seems that what is causing the shortages and starvation in many areas is not the lack of land but man's greed that produces wars and unfair distribution of what food there is. Sometimes food is abundant but artificial shortages are deliberately created to force up prices (Bow93).

One of the factors that generates a high rise in populations is that poor people in impoverished nations tend to have large families as a protection against old age; the more children you have the more relatives there will be to look after when you are unable to work. In contrast, where the standard of living is high, this aspect is much less significant and the size of families falls - as we see in our prosperous western society.

With the present rate of increase in population fairly well documented, some have calculated what the total world population might have been in the past. This is easy to carry out mathematically.

With a growth rate of 2% per annum, the present population could have sprung from two people only 1,075 ago. To reach the present population over 4,000 years, the growth rate would have needed to have been only 0.5% per annum.

The population in 1650 is estimated to have been 600 million and in 1800 to be 1 billion. The rate of increase between these dates is 0.33% If this rate is applied, it would take only 6,000 years to reach the present level of population (Morris - CRI Impact No. 21)

It might be thought that the growth of population would be severely retarded by wars, pestilence and famines, but these have negligible effect on the long term trends. In Europe, the Black Death of 1438-80 killed 150 million and Taylor shows with a graph that this was made up for within 200 years (TayI:339). In even the bloodiest of wars, not every soldier is killed, and the whole army is only a small portion of the total population of a nation.

These statistics, approximate though they may be, all indicate that the population reached the present level in a very short period of time. Two main reasons are the improvement of living standards and transport, the latter enabling food to be brought from areas of plenty to those of famine or dense population.

Fig. 10 gives a graph of different population rates to reach the present number over various periods. Assuming the Flood was in 2345 BC and the population was only the eight people on the Ark, we can see that the increase would only need to be about 0.5% per year to reach today's value. As the population is increasing at a much higher rate of 2% each year, the starting rate would have been lower - about 0.4%. The present rate of 2% arose only in the late 1700's (EB). The suggested changing rate of increase is given on the graph.

A possible explanation for the initial slow rate is that the early inhabitants reached maturity at a much later age than today. This is indicated by the late ages that the pre-Flood patriarchs had their first child (assuming the genealogies of Genesis giving the spiritual descendants were their first-born).

A degree of confirmation of this is provided by two articles in the same issue of the Ex Nihilo Technical Journal v8(2). The first was by Cuozzo (Cuo) in which he showed that the teeth of Neanderthal children erupted later than present day children. He concluded:

> Many of the "archaic" features of some strains of "early man" are *very likely due to delayed maturation in early post-flood people* who still had (as the bible record indicates) significantly longer

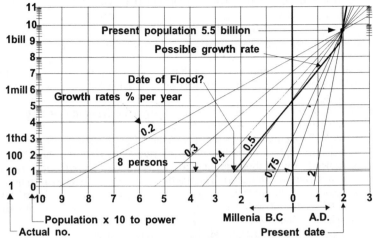

Fig. 10. Graph of population increase

lifespans than today [emphasis his] (Cuo178).

Beasley's article on the Tyrolean Ice-Man notes that the amount of wear on his teeth indicated an age of about 35-40 years, but from his teeth and the still visible sutures (joining lines) in his skull, that he was about 25-30. He similarly concluded:

> the Tyrolean Ice Man was *maturing skeletally in many respects at a much slower rate than today* [emphasis his] (Bea:187).

Another factor is that it might have been customary for a man to marry late and father children only when he was established and mature.

15. TRAPPED GAS, OIL AND WATER

One other piece of evidence for a young age of the earth is the existence of high pressure oil and gas in the earth. Cook discusses the problem of "old reservoirs" and a "young trap" and of water pressures within the earth. He records several pressures in wells that are well above the normal pressure increase due to the weight of the water alone and that one pressure even higher than the total weight of the rock above it had been recorded (Cook66:254f).

Cook points out that in a study of eight wells, all still had very high pressures even though seven of them had seepages at the surface, indicating that they must have formed recently. The measured permeability of the strata containing these pressures are "hundreds and thousands of times greater than those required by a uniformitarian model" (p260) and therefore they should have lost their pressure comparatively quickly.

He concludes that the present pressures and trapping of the oil and water in the rocks requires that they were formed not only fairly recently but rapidly also. This would, of course, be in complete agreement with them being formed during the Flood or shortly after.

Other studies have shown that methane could percolate through a 250 ft (400m.) shale cap to give a half-life of 4.5 million years. Within only 45 million years (ten half-lives) there would be none left. There are also liquids under higher pressure than the overburden, and these would have been dissipated to normal pressure within 3 million years (Q20/4:230).

16. OTHER EVIDENCE

There are many other ways in which the age of the earth can be measured and Cook summarised 20 (Cook66:2). About 1974 Henry Morris gave a list of 76 of them (CRI Impact No. 17) that has appeared in various pamphlets and books. It is not necessary to present the whole list but an analysis of them is interesting.

Some, using certain radioactive changes, say that the calculated age of the earth from the data is "too small to measure."

There are 33 calculated ages that are obtained by measurements of various elements that are carried into the oceans by rivers. By dividing the amount in the oceans today by the total amount entering via the rivers, the *maximum* age of the oceans can be calculated. This method obviously assumes that initially there was none of the element present in the sea, that none has been lost or gained apart from that transported by the rivers, and that the amount carried by them has been constant.

The longest age of all the 33 calculated, 560 million years, is obtained from the amount of gold entering the sea, and is in fact the longest for the whole 76. The shortest age using this method is for iron which is only 140 years. The average age of all 33 given by this method is 17.6 million years.

With all these measurements, it is obvious that none of them give an age for the earth anything like the thousands of millions of years claimed by evolutionists.

The variation between these values is understandable. Where the age is very short, there must be some means by which the element is removed from the sea. For example, the iron might be absorbed by sea creatures and become part of the food chain, or there may be a degree of chemical precipitation.

It might be thought that this reasoning could explain why all 33 ocean/river ages in this list are so much shorter than the evolutionary dates. But this explanation would require every listed element to be removed from the oceans by some means or other. There are few ways by which elements can be removed, for they are at extremely low concentrations, and hardly any of the elements are anywhere near saturation level in the sea (Q11/1:41).

There are too many such examples for some general extraction from the sea to be appealed to as each chemical would have to have a specific method by which it could be removed. Collectively they stand as a body of evidence of a young age for the earth. We discuss this subject further when we deal with criticisms of creationists in the next section.

Where the age is very long, i.e. over 10,000 years, this would indicate that there was a considerable quantity in the oceans when they were formed. As we will see, hydrothermal water with huge amounts of chemicals dissolved in it, poured out over the earth, depositing its load which became the various strata. Many chemicals would have remained in the water, giving an apparent great age when the small amount carried by the rivers is assumed to be the sole source for the purposes of the calculation.

SUMMARY OF "AGE OF EARTH" SECTION

We have seen how there are a very large number of ways of obtaining at least a rough estimate of the ages of the earth and universe, and not one is able to provide the vast periods ascribed by evolutionists. We would repeat that *only* radiometric dating gives vast ages, and even this method can be shown to be not just unreliable, but, using CDK, correctable to a very much shorter period.

We would suggest that the evidence set out above is brought to the attention of school teachers and university lecturers in order to "put the record straight". This should help to counterbalance the evolutionary propaganda to which pupils are incessantly and insidiously subjected to without realising it every time the words "millions of years" are casually dropped into TV programmes and elsewhere in the mass media.

SECTION 5
REPLIES TO CRITICS

There are many books critical of the creationist viewpoint, and an unwarranted amount of space could be devoted to refuting them. We will therefore limit our examination to only three works; an anti-creationist publication, a group of Christian evolutionists and a Christadelphian scientist.

It might be wondered why these critics should be answered, particularly the Christians, so publicly. If one reads these three works, the most striking common feature is their superior attitude. Their writings have greatly damaged the faith of many sound Christians in the reliability of the Bible and therefore need to be corrected. They have made their criticisms in public and therefore need to be answered in public. Paul deliberately rebuked Peter openly (Gal.2:14) because the error he was committing (withdrawing from the Gentiles) was visible to all.

SECTION 5.1
A SECULAR CRITIC: MOORE'S ARTICLE

In this section, we will reply to the objections raised in a special issue of the American periodical *Evolution/Creation*, No. XI Winter 1983. Despite the seeming balance one might have expected from its title, it is strongly anti-creationist in its stand. The particular issue consisted of only one long 39 page article by Robert A. Moore entitled *The Impossible Voyage of Noah's Ark* which was devoted to ridiculing that event.

The introduction to the article is interesting as it portrays the thinking of the editor and thereby of the periodical in general:

> To many, it will seem bizarre that, in this age of scientific advancement and sophisticated biblical criticism, it would be necessary to provide a point-by-point scientific refutation of the story of Noah's Ark. Knowledgeable people are well aware that Genesis 1 through 11 is not scientific or historical but largely mythical, metaphorical, poetic, theological and moral. All people are not knowledgeable, however. Recent Gallup surveys reveal that 50% of adult Americans believe that Adam and Eve existed, 44% believe the earth was created directly by God only ten thousand years ago, and 40% believe that the Bible is inerrant. No doubt an equally large percentage believe in Noah's Ark.

Thus, he dismisses 50% of his fellow countrymen and women as being without "knowledge". That many of this ignorant group would have degrees and doctorates yet still believe the Genesis record is accurate is not even considered. He insists that they are all "not knowledgeable" - i.e. "ignorant and uneducated"!

Within the article there are many objections, some trivial and simply mud-slinging against creationists which will be ignored. Some, however, should be replied to as they are valid objections that some creationists may have difficulty in answering. I give a summary of these criticisms and each will be examined.

I would here mention that Woodmorappe has also refuted Moore's criticisms in his "Noah's Ark: A feasibility study" (WoodJ96). He shows that the conditions in the Ark were perfectly practical.

1. "Would the true and confirmed discovery of Noah's Ark prove that the earliest chapters of the Bible were true?"

The surprising answer given is "NO". Note then the devious reasoning from that point onwards. First the materialist philosopher Hume is quoted; "the knavery and folly of men are such common phenomena that I should rather believe the most extraordinary events to arise from their concurrence than to admit of so signal a violation of the laws of nature."

To present this quotation is both irrelevant and misleading. Although it would not prove that every event recorded in Genesis did take place, the undisputed finding of Noah's Ark would blow such a hole in the evolutionist's case that it would have great difficulty in recovering its present day prominence. The editor seeks to pre-empt such a discovery by blandly asking, "So what? - it proves nothing."

We come back to the fundamental point that in the eyes of all materialists God does not exist and therefore miracles are impossible. This is an "a priori" assumption - which no amount of evidence will change. Evidence for it will always be dismissed as the "knavery and folly of men".

2. "At a time when man was still using hollowed out logs and reed rafts as boats, Noah would need a thorough education in physics, calculus, mechanics, structural analysis and naval architecture to construct such a massive vessel that would not be exceeded for thousands of years."

Note firstly the evolutionary assumption that man arose from a primitive beginning and over thousands of years gradually acquired the necessary skills he needed for this undertaking. He repeatedly assumes that knowledge was acquired at the slow rate demanded by the process of evolution.

What Moore has failed to note is that God gave clear and detailed instructions for its construction, of which we only have an outline in the Bible (Gen. 6:14-16). Thus the Ark was designed by The Master Designer, who had no need to study differential calculus, etc. And "Noah did everything just as God commanded him" (v22). Moore contends "Obviously, the astronomical leap in size, safety and skill required by Noah is far too vast for any naturalistic explanation". *With this we fully agree.*

He briefly mentions that as the descendants of the survivors were "fanning out and 'replenishing the earth'" they carried with them "reminiscences of the deluge that would someday excite American missionaries from Sumatra to Spitzbergen." The more thoughtful reader will notice that he does not examine this issue in any detail. In his desire to pour as much ridicule as he can on the creationist evidence, he rather unwisely draws attention to one of the major evidences (the Flood stories) against his case which might otherwise have gone unnoticed by some readers. His article, however, is mainly for consumption by ardent evolutionists who are only too willing to uncritically accept anything that ridicules creationists.

3. "Pitch and bitumen come from decayed organisms and vegetable matter buried during the Flood. They were therefore not available for sealing the Ark before the Flood."

The existence of *chemically* produced oils, etc. has been shown in the explorations of Prof. Gold (GoldT). The possibility of the *chemical* production of the subterranean oils and gasses is receiving increasing attention these days.

4. "The boat would have been too long for the high stresses the timber would have been subjected to."

This criticism is based upon modern wave measurements and efficient boat design for transport. The bulky Ark was not designed for travelling at speed and had merely to survive whatever sea conditions prevailed during the Flood. We have no knowledge of what the wave dimensions were. Very short waves would have negligible effect upon the hull length whilst very long ones of even huge size would simply lift the Ark gently over a period of several seconds.

Noah would also have had the use of iron, for Tubal-Cain was "an instructor of every artificer in brass and iron" (Gen 4:22). This may have been used to provide strong joints in the timber structure, or even the main strength of the structure itself.

The very high level of its general seaworthiness has been checked by computers as we have referred to in Section 1, page 26.

It might be thought that the Ark would have difficulty in surviving huge breakers that might have developed. But waves normally only break under high wind conditions or when they approach the coasts. There is no mention of high winds during the Flood, except at the end when there was a "wind over the earth and the waters receded" (Gen. 8:1). There were also no coasts for the waves to break against when the earth was fully covered by water.

Moore contends the Ark would have been smashed to pieces. However, it would have been gently lifted by the incoming water, and the biblical record states the grounding of the Ark was quite tranquil.

5. "The problems of housing, feeding and cleaning out so many different animals for a year would have been insuperable for only eight people to have dealt with."

This is one of the most common, and understandable, objections that is made. We will divide the question into two parts - (A) the number of animals in the Ark and (B) the attendance they would need.

(A) The number of animals in the Ark.

This subject has been discussed in "The Genesis Flood" (Whitc69) where the average size of a mammal has been estimated to be about the size of a sheep and about 35,000 animals had to be accommodated. The volume of the Ark was sufficient to take some seven times this number, giving each animal plenty of room.

Dr. Arthur Jones (JonA) has examined the scriptural references to "kinds" of clean and unclean animals. His main contention is that probably each "kind" was what we call a "family" in animal classifications. He quotes a secular source for there being 793 families, both existing and extinct. There are many arguments amongst classifiers about what is a species, but little disagreement regarding which family each should be placed in.

By eliminating amphibia and water-dwelling groups he estimates that there may be from 628 to 800 family pairs that would be needed to go in the Ark. Jones shows that the Hebrew "seven seven" means "seven of each" for the number of clean animals. He concludes that there would be about 2,000 animals in the Ark. The rest of the very large volume would be taken up as living quarters for the human survivors and food for the whole shipload of humans and animals.

It is possible that much of the food taken on board (Gen. 6:21) might be needed in the period between the landing of the Ark and the collecting of the first harvest and to allow the growth of the wide ranging and abundant flora necessary for the habitation of the animals emerging from the Ark.

(B) The feeding and cleaning of the animals.

This is always seen as a major objection, but if Jones's figure of 2,000 animals is correct, the problem of feeding and cleaning is greatly reduced. Even if the number were greater, there is a very simple solution to this. Many animals have a period of deep sleep in winter (when it is known as hibernation) or in summer (aestivation). Studies have shown that the pulse rate falls to a very low value, body temperature falls, brain activity is greatly reduced and food reserves are only used slowly.

God had only to submit all the creatures in the Ark to such a process and what is considered an "insuperable objection" is easily solved. This is one possible, and very simple, solution to the problem. What actually took place in the Ark He has not seen fit to explain in His record.

6. "The animals in the Ark could not have contained all the genetic information that resulted in the phenomenal range of animals that exist now".

The genetic information is not contained only in the chromosomes of the cells. There is much information in the cortex and indeed, the information appears to be within the whole cell material. We have examined this subject in detail in Section 1 and in reference Bow82:124.

Geneticists have found that some 99% of the genetic material in the chromosomes are classed as "redundant" as no known use for them has (yet!) been discovered. It is possible that they may have contained the information needed to give the range of present day types and are no longer needed. However, this assumed "redundancy" has recently been called into question.

Regarding the wide range of species seen today, most of them belong to recognised types such as dog types (dingoes, wolves, jackals, coyotes, foxes, etc.), cat types (tiger, panther, etc.) and many others. By simple varieties of these basic types these various forms could be achieved. Dr. Arthur Jones has studied the wide range of cyclid fish that exist and that are classified as differing species. He found that they were all varieties of the same basic pattern that had been varied over a range of shapes and characteristics.

This, of course, also applies to the varieties within the human race. The various characteristics that have appeared since the time of the dispersion from the Tower of Babel are only specific features already within the genetic pool. This information would have been contained within the genes of the five people who were in the Ark - Noah, his wife and the three wives of their sons, all of whom may have been related as we discussed in Section 1.

If there were only a few thousand animals in the Ark then Moore's case, based upon millions, completely collapses - together with his ridicule. We will now examine some of the more extravagant claims he makes and the "straw men" he erects.

7. "Fresh water fish would die in salt seas of the Flood (and vice versa)."

In dealing with many subjects, it must be emphasised that we do not know what the conditions were before the Flood. It is a common mistake of evolutionists (and some creationists) to assume that they were much the same as they are today and then, on this assumption, to claim that the cataclysmic sequence of the Flood was an impossibility. There are several solutions to this question of salt and fresh water fish and I set them out below.

(a) **Tolerance.** If the original sea was all fresh, it is possible that the fish could adapt over generations to tolerate salt water as it gradually mixed in. There is a much wider degree of tolerance in fish than we may realise. Salmon and eels migrate between salt and fresh water and sharks are known to swim well upriver in some areas. Nelson neatly turns the tables on the evolutionists for he points out that there are a number of identical species of fresh water fish in widely different lakes around the world. He asks "if they originated in one spot, how, we may ask, did they become distributed in lakes and streams of almost the whole world?" (Nel:160).

(b) **Slow mixing.** As fresh water from the rain is less dense than salt sea water, it could have existed for some time mainly in a layer on top. This would allow each type to survive the Flood period (Q21/1:33).

With the eruption of the hydrothermal water from the "fountains of the deep" we propose in the geological sequence, when it had deposited its mineral load, the remaining water may have been fresh in some areas and salt in others. Thus both types of fish could have survived. The fresh water fish may then have been trapped in inland lakes later as the water drained from the earth.

Even though a storm may have been raging with huge waves and large and fast movements of water in the sea taking place, to get two huge masses of water to mix uniformly would take considerable time as it would require a specific mixing (stirring) action to have taken place to make this intermingling rapid. Waves only act for a very shallow depth and only a few metres below the surface they can hardly be felt. Wave action can of course be transmitted between the two masses with no mixing effect whatsoever. Similarly, large bodily movements of water have little mixing effect.

8. "The small sea creatures such as crabs and fixed crustaceans such as barnacles would be unable to escape and would be completely engulfed by the great depths of material deposited over them."

Moore does not propose this directly as a serious objection but asks how coral, which requires clear shallow water, could have survived. One answer could be that there were a few suitable areas where some may have survived. But there is another means of survival.

Many of these creatures produce a whole cloud of eggs which are fertilised by the male sperm released at the same time. These eggs are minute and would drift freely in the sea water, no matter how turbulent, and would have no difficulty in surviving. On hatching at the appropriate time and temperature, they would be able to feed off of the plentiful organic material from the dead pre-Flood creatures. The almost indestructible nature of the eggs of the many types of fish, crustaceans and sea plants that could explain how many different species survived the Flood.

9. "With the presumed huge population of human beings on the earth, why have there been no discoveries of them in very early strata?"

We discuss this in Appendix 4 dealing with various geological "models" and the fossil record. One possible cause of the lack of fossils is that there may have been comparatively few humans existing at the time of the Flood.

(i) The human population of the world may not have been large, and may have been concentrated in one area, in defiance of God's command to "fill the earth".

The animal and plant populations appear to have been created in huge numbers, but the human population began with only two. Due to the depravity of the antediluvian population, a large proportion would have probably engaged in homosexual and similar practices, thus lowering the birth rate. In the heterosexual population, sexual diseases may have been rampant. Murder and general disease would also have taken their toll.

(ii) The bodies of those who died would have floated and their remains eaten by scavengers.

(iii) The few relics left would have been difficult to find. There are some 700 million cubic kilometres of fossil-bearing (Phanerozoic) rocks. Taking Woodmorappe's approximation of a population of 10 million, there would be on average one human fossil for every 70 cubic kilometres of rock. With such a dispersal, they are hardly likely to be found in any numbers. In addition, the remains of those who died before the Flood, if not fossilised, would have completely disappeared within a fairly short time due to bacterial activity.

The conditions that govern fossilisation are even now not fully known. Organic acids and positive pH (oxidising conditions) both help to weather bone, and these conditions can occur in deep deposits. Thus the relatively few bones of antediluvian man that might have been eventually deposited in a stratum may have not become fossilised due to the environment it was in.

MOORE'S "STRAW MEN"

In order to show how easily he can ridicule the creationists case Moore sets up straw men for his subsequent demolition act. They are, however, easily answered and the arguments he uses do him little credit. The following are just some of the worst examples.

A. "For many species, the vast majority of their young do not survive into maturity but are taken by predators or succumb to their environment."

Here, Moore is using the present situation where there are many animals populating the earth. He has clearly overlooked the simple fact that the early conditions after the Ark landed were totally different to those today. During the early days there were no predators around to prey upon the small number of animals emerging from the Ark. Those who were predators may have lived off food stored in the Ark for a while (or extended their hibernation period) until the population of their prey was sufficiently large for them to be released into the area around.

B. "The journeys of the animals to the Ark would have been far too arduous for many of them from distant countries."

Again, Moore assumes that present conditions existed in the past. If there was a fairly uniform climate around the earth in Prediluvian days, then there would be much the same selection of animals in any given area and the journey to the Ark would not have been difficult. The wide range of varieties which have adapted to the range of present climates would have developed from the basic types taken into the Ark.

....

In his summary, he says "No doubt in days to come some erstwhile arkeologist will concoct "solutions" to some of the difficulties we have raised, but no intellectually honest person can any longer pretend that the legend of Noah can possibly represent a historical occurrence."

According to the surveys that he quotes, this would make some 50% of his own countrymen intellectually dishonest.

There are some additional problems that need to be addressed. It is only right that these should be set out, so that having discussed them, better evidence may be provided by others.

1. Seeds and pollination.

There is a difficulty in the germination of seeds that have been in either salt or fresh water for about a year. Those that could germinate, would have done so in a matter of a few months, and therefore would have died before they could have got to fertile soil. Did some finish up on the top of the drying land and sprout? If they did, where were the numerous birds and insects that could pollinate them? A rapid growth would be essential to feed the rising population of animals, and we show in Appendix 1 that this may have occurred due to the high speed of light. All the occupants may have lived off food stored in the Ark for a short time.

There is the paper by Howe (Q5/3:105) in which he carried out some experiments on the germination of seeds soaked in sea water for 20 weeks. A slight problem is that the seeds had to be scarified in order to germinate. They might have been scarified in the tumult of the Flood, but then they would have germinated too early, before the soil was prepared. He later noted that "Beggar Tick" seeds found in a 350 year old Spanish wreck had still sprouted (Q24/3:144).

2. The heat of the new earth.

It is reasonable to assume that the interior of the earth is very hot. The water and the chemical mixtures that were to form the sea and land surfaces would have risen up from the depths and it might be thought that they would have been at a very high temperature. As a result, the water coming to the surface would have been boiling, which would have made life a little difficult for all the occupants of the Ark!

What has been overlooked, both in this case and in many others, is that we do not know the formations of the earth's strata before the Flood. If the earth was heated at the very centre, either by the impact of material coming together, or by a high level of radioactivity at the centre due to the high speed of light, then it would take some time for this heat to gradually migrate towards the surface. This means that the surface could have been at a moderate temperature, and the upper layers similarly.

We will be showing that most, if not all, the Flood strata came from chemicals brought to the surface by water that was at only a moderately high temperature and under very great pressure which enabled it to dissolve a huge quantity of chemicals. As this rising critical (hydrothermal) water reached the cooler layers nearer to the surface, they would have cooled and their chemicals would be precipitated out in a specific sequence, depending upon the characteristics of the materials they contained.

There would then be no great heat left in the rising material still dissolved in the water. The last of the material would be precipitated and the much cooler water would then reach the surface and become the sea we have today.

There is the additional factor that if heated gases (as hydrothermal water is) under pressure are cooled whilst still under pressure, then their release and expansion results in considerable cooling of the mass. In the same way, the air released from a tyre can be quite cold on exit.

Furthermore, the increasing temperature as you go deeper into the earth may have been less than it is now, only reaching its present value in more recent times as the heat works out to the surface since creation.

SECTION 5.2
A CRITIQUE OF *"PORTRAITS OF CREATION"*

This is a book (Van Till) by four Christian authors - Van Till, Snow, Stek and Young - in which they defend their theistic evolutionary views and attempt to rebut those of the "scientific creationists" - i.e. the "young earth" exponents such as Morris and Gish. Much of the book is taken up with the historical account of how the present day interpretation by the experts eventually overtook the catastrophist view. Regarding the evidence for this they state:

> We hold that these reconstructions are firmly grounded in a wealth
> of carefully gathered data and have been repeatedly tested by the
> respected canons of science (p11).

Those who have ventured to examine ideas and evidence outside these "respected canons of science" will know that there is far superior artillery and ammunition available that has little problem disposing of their outdated armament - if you will forgive the pun!

They do not set out their specific Christian position but it is certain that they do not take Genesis literally. They set up the usual "straw man" of saying that as no one interprets the pictorial descriptions literally, then other parts of the Bible (which they then choose) are also not to be taken literally - in their case, specifically Genesis. Their liberal view of the Bible is clear from their appeal to the Higher Criticism of Wellhausen and others.

They note that in a 1988 poll of 749 readers of *Christianity Today*, 401 replied, of which 74% indicated that they favoured the teaching of creationism alongside evolution in public schools (p10 footnote). One might have thought that with evolution being taught with official approval, then those who want creationism to have a fair chance will have studied the subject adequately and arrived at a reasonable decision. This is not the attitude of our authors, for they say "it does suggest an alarming ignorance of science, of what evolution is, and of the shortcomings of scientific creationism." Like Moore's assessment of the "ignorance" of his American compatriots quoted above, they also have a low opinion of their fellow Christian's abilities to make reasonable judgments. More important, this poor level of logic should warn the perceptive reader of what to expect in the rest of the book.

Even at the outset they say that "many issues are thorny and varied" and that they are deliberately omitting any consideration of "organic evolution and the origin of mankind". This is a blatant avoidance of the strong evidence against evolution that these subjects provide. How they expect any informed reader to be convinced by the very few subjects they *are* prepared to discuss is difficult to imagine.

There is a section by Snow in which creationist publications are derided, whilst Morris and Gish are singled out for special criticism and patronisingly said to indulge not in true science but in "folk science" (in which he includes Einstein and Asimov! (p188)). He observes,

> At its core the contemporary creation science movement is an
> attempt to provide a scientific foundation for a folk science that for
> years had been floating free of any support within the professional
> scientific community (p195).

The two main scientific subjects they confine themselves to are geology and astronomy and, even then, only specific items. We will not analyse the criticisms they make against creationists in the field of geology (p66f) except to say that they are illogical, confused and misleading in what creationists claim about the fossil order. Neither will we deal with some astronomical points but will concentrate on their claim that the sun is not shrinking, as this has been accepted by many creationists.

THE SHRINKAGE OF THE SUN.

In discussing the possible sources of heat for the sun, van Till mentions Helmholtz's proof that the sun's heat could be entirely supplied by the energy generated as it contracts, but then says this is "unable to supply energy for the multibillion-year duration of the Sun's history" (p90 footnote). Thus, the dogma of the "millions of years" that geology (and evolution) demands forces van Till to sweep aside all evidence to the contrary.

The main examination of this subject, by R.E. Snow, has the emotive title "The shrinking sun: problems with the exercise of professional integrity." We would agreed that there is a problem of integrity; but on which side?

We have already discussed the subject raised by Eddy and Boornazian's lecture in Section 4.4 above. Here we will examine the resulting response by the orthodox scientists, and the way in which this is uncritically quoted by Snow against "young earth" creationists.

Snow first deals with the way in which orthodox professionals examined the subject and the resultant change in opinions that eventually took place. He then examines the "head-in-the-sand" attitude of creationists, particularly Morris and Barnes, who continued to say that the sun was shrinking and ignored all the "latest results" that contradicted the original paper.

The two papers Snow refers to as setting the record straight are by Parkinson (Par83) and Frohlich (Fro). He comments:

> While the original claims of Eddy and Boornazian were not sustained, the solar physics community emerged from the exchanges generated by their initial paper with a better understanding of the strengths and limitations of important data sets gathered over long periods at major observatories.... Eddy and his collaborators, because they continued to participate in the process of public criticism and analysis, maintained their status as valued members of the professional community. The episode provides a good illustration of the healthy operation of a professional community (p173).

Snow then pours contempt on the scientific integrity of Morris and Barnes for failing to heed these "revised views" of the professional community when they continue to quote Eddy's original conclusion as this is the only one which supports their young-earth creationist views. He refers to Steidl's "warning" in the March 1981 issue of the *Creation Research Society Quarterly* that the Eddy and Boornazian claim "had met with much scepticism, and the timing of transits of Mercury over the centuries seems to indicate that no shrinkage is taking place" (p174). For Steidl's and others acknowledgement of these criticisms, Snow seems to metaphorically award them several "Brownie points" for integrity.

At the end of this section, the reader is in no doubt that young-earth creationists at least, are pure propagandists for their views, with no scientific integrity and deliberately out of touch with "responsible professional scientists". But let us now carefully examine these documents upon which he based his dismissive comments.

My first very major surprise came some time after I had read several articles commenting on Eddy and Boornazian's paper together with a number of other papers critical of their conclusions. I eventually applied for a copy of their original 1979 paper (Edd79) which these other papers referred to. I was astonished to receive a one paragraph note outlining the main points of their paper that was to be given between 1400-1600 hrs. in room 377; i.e. it was only the notification of their forthcoming lecture! Thus, *Eddy and Boornazian's paper has never been published!* Yet a full article critical of their results was published in *Nature* and other articles have also appeared. In order to set before the reader some of the evidence they produced in their lecture, recourse had to be made to one supportive paper by Gilliland (Gil) and interpolated from an article by Lubkin, a journalists writing in *Physics Today* (Lub). Another article in *Science News* (115:420) added little. A letter direct to Eddy asking for a copy of his paper produced no response.

This needs to be remembered in the criticisms that have been made by Snow in his contribution to this book. No full record of their evidence has ever been published which is indicative of how revolutionary their paper was.

In preparing their paper, Eddy and Boornazian would have been fully aware of the effect it would have. They would therefore have been careful to have cross checked it for all reasonable (and unreasonable) criticisms that were bound to be fired at them. The main points are as follows:

(i) They first examined the records of Greenwich Observatory, and when this steady trend was noticed, they then checked with the American Naval Observatory and found virtually the same amount of change in diameter. These are two independent sources giving the same results.

(ii) The readings were taken by over one hundred different observers, and therefore there could not be any consistent "observer bias" that would give these results. One could comment that even if there had been only one observer, this would have been one variable eliminated. It is the consistent decrease that is the main feature.

(iii) Today, in a total eclipse the sun is completely blocked by the moon for about 8 seconds. If the decrease of 2 seconds of arc per century had taken place, then several hundred years ago, there would have been a very thin edge of the sun never blocked, and the difference would have been clearly noticed. This in fact was observed by a Jesuit astronomer, Christopher Clavius in Rome in 1560, who specifically referred to: "a certain narrow circle was left on the Sun, surrounding the whole of the moon on all sides." (Lub:18). This is a very simple and direct observation that corroborates that the shrinkage has been taking place over centuries, for it takes the evidence back nearly 400 years, not just the 117 years covered by the Greenwich data. This is surely a very convincing argument in favour of the shrinkage being very long term.

(On this aspect, "annular eclipses" with a thin ring of the sun always visible (Q22/1:7) still occur. However, not having Eddy's paper, we can only presume that he had checked that this particular eclipse in 1560 should have been a total eclipse and not an annular one.)

Eddy apparently concluded that the shrinkage is probably only a reflection of some slow oscillation of the envelope of the sun. There is really no mystery why Eddy and Boornazian should claim the decrease is "secular" i.e. continuing, and yet say in their paper that it may only be part of a long term oscillation. Had they not referred to this and said outright that it is a steady decrease with no increase and had been thus for at least 400 years, it is doubtful whether they would have been allowed to have presented their paper in view of its implications.

CRITICAL ARTICLES

Sofia's paper

One paper quoted by Snow against Eddy is that by Sofia et al (Sof). This paper is quoted by both sides as demonstrating that the actual shrinkage is only 1/10 of that claimed by Eddy. This is not correct. The paper does not itself directly *prove* any decrease in the sun's diameter but uses data from another scientist.

The whole aim of Sofia's paper is not to investigate the sun's diameter but to correlate changes of the "solar constant" (its heat output, which is difficult to measure) with changes in its diameter. They make a number of assumptions about the sun's interior and derive formulae then used in a computer programme. From this they provide a ratio between changes in the diameter and the solar constant. The only reason they refer to the changing diameter is as a check on the maximum change in the heat output. They searched for measurements of the diameter changes and eventually used those of Giannuzzi who examined Greenwich observatory readings over an 87 year period from 1850-1937. In referring to her paper they note:

> There is evidence in both the horizontal and vertical directions for a slow systematic decrease of the observed radius by about 0.2 arc seconds over this time; *although Giannuzzi removed this trend*, we have not done so in forming the above standard deviations, nor have we used her biennial running mean. It seems probable that the data do not indicate variations in the radius greater than about 0.25 arc second over this period...

What do we glean from these comments?

(i) There was a "slow systematic decrease" detectable in the data provided by Giannuzzi *which she then "removed"*. This decrease of the *radius* of 0.2 arc second "over this time" (of 87 years) would give a decrease of about 0.023% per century - compared with Eddy's 0.1%.

(ii) Sofia et al ignored all her calculations and carried out their own statistical investigation. However, they give no data or calculations.

Elsewhere in their paper they refer to "variations" of radius, but it is not clear whether these are a steady decrease or only fluctuations about a mean. There seems to be no clear statement by the authors of any consistent decrease in this paper but give "variations" in the radius not greater than "0.25 arc secs over this period" (= 0.03% per century). It is Parkinson's 1980 paper, that we examine later, that gives a decrease of almost 0.01% per century - 1/10 of Eddy's value. Considering these points, it is surely unwarranted to quote this paper as *proof* of a reduced rate for the shrinkage of the sun. We would contend that Eddy and Boornazian's value of 0.1% (=2.25 arc sec. of the diameter) per century still stands.

There are two other points worth examining.

(a) The dates of the articles

Giannuzzi published her paper in 1955
Sofia et al revised their paper in April 1979 and it was published in June 1979
Eddy and Boornazian presented their paper in June 1979

It is a reasonable assumption (but not necessarily correct) that Sofia et al had no knowledge of Eddy's paper when they wrote theirs. Their paper gave no data regarding their much lower rate of decrease. Yet commentators on both sides quote Sofia's paper as if it authoritatively reduced Eddy's value.

One has the impression that Sofia et al examined Eddy's data and derived a lower rate. In fact, they used data in a much earlier paper, ignored its statistical analysis and calculated a rate without showing how they derived its value.

(b) The "hidden" evidence
We have noted that Giannuzzi "removed" the secular decrease in the Greenwich data from her statistical calculations in 1955. Regarding this, it was revealing to read in the Bulletin that summarised Eddy's forthcoming lecture (Edd79):

> The same secular effect has been noted before by others who examined all or part of the Greenwich data set, and has generally been attributed to atmospheric effects or personal equation.

From this, Eddy and Boornazian were only the latest of several other astronomers who have noted this secular decrease in the Greenwich data! Obviously, this evidence has been known for many years yet how many papers have been written setting this out? In view of the repercussions that this information would have upon the scientific world and the fierce opposition that publication of it would receive (as has been meted out to Eddy and Boornazian), one can understand why astronomers have bypassed the subject. Eddy and Boornazian are to be congratulated on taking this bold step. That they have been forced to keep silent and virtually retract their findings to retain their professional credibility only conforms to expectations.

Parkinson's 1983 article
Another paper referred to by Snow as rebutting Eddy is by Parkinson (Par83). This paper does not examine the method of measurement by meridian timings used by Eddy, but deals only with timing the period taken by the shadow of the full eclipse to cross a site in its path, and by the time taken by Mercury to cross the face of the sun. It is interesting that in his introductory statement, Parkinson mentions that if the present view of the energy of the sun comes from radioactivity is correct, this should actually result in a very small *increase* in diameter over the centuries. Yet it is found in many of the papers critical of Eddy's, there is still a residual small *decrease* even after their statistical juggling of the data.

He adjusts the method of "weighting" the results of these two methods and concludes that the shrinkage is .004 arc sec/century - still a positive result it should be noted. He mentions that:

> The magnitude and sign of the trend obtained depend on the choice of weighting function used and cannot be inferred to result from a variation of the Sun. Thus there appears to be no evidence to support any secular trend in the solar diameter between 1715 and 1981 (Par83:519).

What exactly is Parkinson saying here? Having carefully analysed the measurements covering several years to give a small but still positive result, he points out that these statistical methods can be manipulated to give any sort of answer you require. He then says that this means no reliability can be placed upon these measurements, and therefore there is no support for the claim that the sun is shrinking! This is hardly sound logic and leaves him with little scientific credibility.

What he has done is that, in order to undermine Eddy's paper, he has confused the situation by claiming that statistics can be manipulated. But a *right* use of statistics would show that there *was* a decrease - as Eddy has shown. The rest of this short paper suggests there is an 80 year cycle in the size of the sun.

Frolich and Eddy's paper

Snow refers to the paper by Frolich and Eddy (Fro) as being a refutation of Eddy's original position. As we can see from Snow's quote above, it is implied that Eddy has back-tracked from his earlier claims which has gone unnoticed by creationists. This is refuted even within his own reference to this article for it is obvious that the authors have compiled measurements of the sun's heat output *only for the 17 year period of 1967-1983*. Such a short period can have no relevance to a secular decrease over 400 years. If the paper is examined, it is obvious that this period was chosen in order to obtain a relationship between diameter and heat output - as was Sofia's. It has nothing to do with a general long-term decrease in diameter.

Parkinson's 1980 article

Although Snow does not refer to it in his book, the paper that was to provide stronger criticisms of Eddy and Boornazian's paper was an earlier one by Parkinson and others (Par80), and it is revealing to study this longer paper published in *Nature* to see if their detailed criticisms are warranted.

In the first paragraph it notes that there are only one third of the neutrinos coming from the sun if all its heat is due to radioactivity. They then patronisingly observe that Eddy's paper is one of many "ingenious suggestions" to "resolve this apparent discrepancy". Thus, Eddy's carefully researched and important paper providing convincing evidence of a decrease is relegated to just an "ingenious suggestion". One can guess from this opening comment just how biassed the writers are going to be on this subject.

They contend that the original results are due to a "misinterpretation" of the observations, and that they will be using two other methods (timing the eclipse shadow and Mercury's transits) to support their claims. They are obviously searching for reasons to dismiss the reliability of Eddy's measurements and they make three criticisms.

(i) There was a change of instrument in 1851 and they claim:

> There is a clear discontinuity in the vertical measurements of the vertical semi-diameter coinciding with the change of telescope showing that the measured diameter depends crucially on the instrument used.

Now, firstly, the vertical measurement is the less important and not measured by timing the transits. Secondly, bearing in mind the wide variation over short periods of time, there seems to be no more sudden change at this point than for the general variation of the measurements - as examination of Fig. 1 shows. There is a similar change in the horizontal readings but this is not mentioned.

From this, their claim that the instrument used is "crucial" is nonsense, and demonstrates that they are seeking to dismiss these readings for the weakest of reasons.

(ii) They investigate which assistants set up the instrument at Greenwich between 1915 and 1940. They found that some operators had a regular bias. Of the seven regular observers, two were found to be more erratic and differed from the others. It was considered that as they made more observations in the 1920's they would have given a spurious result. These two observers, however, cannot have had so much effect that the

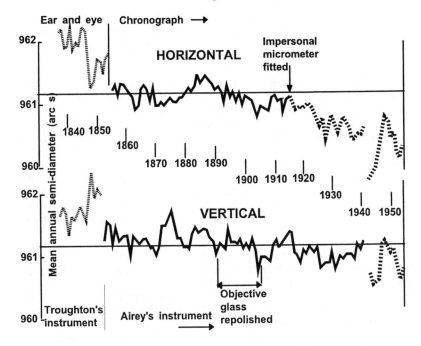

Fig. 1. The decrease of the sun's diameter

results should be dismissed. The maximum number of readings they made were only 25% of the total observations. As early as 1854 a chronograph was used to measure the transit times automatically, so observer bias would have been greatly reduced. They do not state just how these operator "biases" could enter into the setting up of the telescope.

(iii) In the Greenwich records the weather and seeing conditions are often described as "through cloud", "unsteady", "ill defined", etc. and the inference is that they are thereby unreliable.

But these are one of the many variations that such observations have to deal with. In no way does day-to-day variation affect the general trend of the decrease. Even if, say, only one day in five gave good conditions, this would still be more than enough readings to show the trend over one hundred years. To dismiss the results using this very poor criticism again indicates the underlying motive of this paper.

They conclude this section with the general comment that:

"These grave difficulties show that meridian circle observations are unsuitable for investigating possible changes in the solar diameter. We now discuss other, more accurate methods which have the advantage of covering a longer time span and are not so dependent upon the defects of the instrument used." (p850)

These variations are certainly not "grave" and do not make the method "unsuitable". It is, in fact, a very direct and accurate measurement of the diameter.

They then turn to two indirect and *less* accurate methods (transits of Mercury and solar eclipses) that are subject to as many, if not more, variables than the meridian measurements. There is no discussion of observer bias, weather conditions, statistical "weightings", etc. in the use of these methods. Although the resulting scatter and error bars are very wide, they still give a decrease. The transits method gives -0.014 +/-0.008% per century and the eclipse method "-0.008 +/-0.007% per century, well over an order of magnitude smaller than the rate claimed by Eddy and Boornazian". Yet, even with these results showing a decrease, Parkinson's introduction claims "there has been no detectable secular change in the solar diameter during the past 250 yr." - which he repeats within the paper.

Let us pause here and remember that we are here reading the conclusions of intelligent scientists. They produce results that are inaccurate, with very wide error bars, yet even these show a decrease. They then claim that there has been no decrease. But inaccurate methods *cannot* determine whether a value is rising, falling or constant. This can only be shown by an *accurate* system. They have no right to dismiss Eddy's conclusions, and these less accurate methods have only been used as a smoke screen to confuse the whole issue.

Gilliland's article

It should not be thought that the counter-criticisms set out above are only to be expected from a young-earth creationist attempting to defend his case. In Parkinson's later paper (Par83), he mentioned one by Gilliland (Gil) that was critical of this earlier paper (Par80). Reading this, Gilliland says:

> While the large (0.1% per century) secular decrease in radius tentatively suggested by Eddy and Boornazian (1979) is not supported by other investigations... the preponderance of evidence still supports a *negative* [emphasis his] secular trend over the last few centuries. It should be emphasised that stellar evolution theory predicts a *positive* [emphasis his], albeit indetectably small, secular trend of the solar radius.
>
> We have not thrown out portions of the Greenwich data as suggested by Parkinson.... It is probable that certain epochs of the Greenwich data have been biased by observer and instrumental changes. However, the removal of certain sections of the data set which show discontinuities correlated with instrument changes tend to introduce further biases into the data set.... subjective removal of certain sections resulting in support of the Parkinson et al premise that the solar diameter has been constant over the past 250 years should also be viewed with caution. (Gil:1146).

As well as criticising this paper for "subjective" removal of Eddy's data, he also says "the Mercury transit timing data must also be considered uncertain due to the discrepancies between the independently compiled data sets - e.g. the Mercury transit data may contain unrecognised systematic errors." (Gil:1146). He also notes that Parkinson's Mercury data "further muddle the issue" (Gil:1150).

In summarising all the measurements made by the various researchers using the three different methods, he finds that they *all* support a significant decrease. He concluded that the rate was about 0.1 arc secs/cent (0.01%/cent) and in a convoluted sentence says:

> Given the many problems with the data sets, one is not inexorably led to the conclusion that a negative secular solar radius trend has existed since AD 1700, *but the preponderance of current evidence indicates that such is likely to be the case.* (Gil:1150)

The eclipse method

As the eclipse shadow passes across the earth, observers can time how long they have total darkness, and this will vary depending upon how far they are from the centre of the shadow. Dunham took the records of such timings made in 1715 and concluded that the sun's radius had shrunk 0.34 arc seconds which is only 14% of the amount based on Eddy's rate of shrinkage (Dun). We would suggest that this one measurement, where the locations of the observers and their timings was not always known accurately, cannot compare with the records used by Eddy taken over many years.

The dates of publication

Eddy presented his paper in June 1979, but Parkinson's paper, severely critical of his findings, was received by *Nature* on 30 June 1980 and accepted in October 1980. It was therefore completed only 12 months after Eddy had presented his paper. Dunham's paper was submitted even earlier - on 14 November 1979. In these two cases, there may have been some forewarning of Eddy's paper long before it was presented, or much "burning of the midnight oil" to produce them as quickly as possible after Eddy's presentation. Whatever took place, the "Establishment scientists" made sure that these papers were presented in prestigious journals whilst Eddy and Boornazian's revolutionary paper remains unpublished to this day.

SECTION 5.3. A CRITIQUE OF HAYWARD'S *"CREATION AND EVOLUTION"*

Alan Hayward has written several books on creation, but is extremely critical of the "young earth" viewpoint. This is the main subject of his book *Creation and Evolution: The Facts and the Fallacies* (Hay) in which he presents his viewpoint in a very authoritative and convincing style.

His important omission

He contends that those who claim the earth is young "have given the whole class a bad name. So it seemed best to disregard all arguments emanating from creationist sources" (p8). He therefore limits himself to simply repeating the evidence from uniformitarian evolutionists.

As we shall see, *this means that he totally ignores any supporting evidence provided by creationists as replies or rebuttals, and he therefore presents an extremely biased case.* How many of his readers failed to realise the significance of this brief sentence early in his book?

We should be clear that the time scale of Genesis is *very* important, for either the creation took place over 6 days, as the plain understanding demands, or it did not; it is the reliability of the Bible which is at stake. He provides the usual "re-interpretations" of "days", etc. and many of his contentions have been answered elsewhere in this work.

His authoritative style and appearance of scientific integrity has caused more than one creationists to begin to wonder whether he has been misled by creationist propaganda and to question his position on the age of the earth. In view of this we will briefly examine just a few of the subjects he presents to see how he handles the evidence for the consumption of his less discerning or knowledgeable readers.

1. The speed of light

He is scathing in his dismissal of Setterfield's CDK evidence, saying:

> The full Setterfield paper is dressed with a great deal of theoretical analysis. Lest any reader should be overly impressed by this analysis, perhaps I should mention that I asked two professors of modern physics to look at it. One said it was unsound, self-contradictory, and based on an antiquated and incorrect concept of the atom. The other used even stronger language (p140).

He references the first professor as Prof. John Billelo of State University of New York.

In November 1984 I debated the age of the earth with Alan Hayward at Westminster Chapel. In the exchanged of letters on the subjects we would be raising, he sent me a copy of the letter from Billelo who said (amongst other things) that the Bohr model of the atom was 50 years out of date, that Setterfield's theory "leads to inconsistencies relating to the permittivity and permeability in Maxwell's equations" and called Setterfield's ideas "sillinesses".

These criticisms were forwarded to Setterfield and in his full reply to all the points Billelo raised, he noted that:

(a) All theories of the atom have the Bohr model as their first approximation. The Bohr model has been used for the sake of simplicity for the reader. (i.e. the simple model he used was adequate to demonstrate his point.)

(b) "This 'inconsistency' is in John's own grasp of the situation and reflects his hasty summation of the subject;...However, he has failed to notice that in the formulation there is the permeability term mu which is proportional to $1/c^2$. Accordingly, from the formula that he has given we find that ..(here followed some atomic formulae) .. and the whole thing balances perfectly."

From this it is clear that *Setterfield's grasp of atomic formulae is better than Professor Billelo's whom Hayward consulted.*

Now the whole of Setterfield's reply was sent to Hayward before the debate, and with such a rebuttal, I assumed that these particular criticisms would not be used by Hayward as part of his case. One can imagine my surprise when he read out the same extract from Billelo's letter during the debate. I hastily found Setterfield's reply and read out the relevant extracts rebutting his criticisms. We continue this point later.

2. Coral reefs

He fully accepts the case presented by Wonderly (Wond) that great depths of coral reefs have been found in the Eniwetok atoll, and dividing this by the very slow rate of their growth, they must have been in existence for "hundreds of thousands of years" (p85). During this same debate I read from Wonderly's book that, on his own admission, "practically all of it is limestone, with many fossils - especially corals, foraminifera and algae - embedded in it" (Wond:35). Dividing the depth of a limestone mass by the rate of growth of some coral embedded within it is totally unscientific. One would have thought that both Hayward and Wonderly would have realised this.

3. Coral and shellfish growth rings

The spin of the earth is slowing down making the days longer. This means the year had more days in the past. Some coral and shellfish exhibit daily growth rings, and fossils of these were obtained from the Devonian period. They are said to show a pattern of 400 days in each yearly cycle (Scr, Mazz) which agrees with the calculations of astronomers.

Examination of these papers does not inspire much confidence in their conclusions for the patterns are very confused. One could make anything one wished from them and the difference they were looking for is only 9%. Hayward, in fact, notes that these bands are "picked out" by researchers "with experience". But why should it take "experience"? Surely the spacings of the bands should be independent of the researcher and accurate measurements of the spacings of the rings subjected to statistical analysis so that there was no personal element involved. One cannot help wondering if the "experience" necessary was that of finding the "right" answer!

Furthermore, a later paper (KahnP1978) using similar banding in fossil Nautilus, dismisses the use of corals. However, even in this paper, four results that were widely different to the others were ignored and the line was drawn through those results that gave the required trend. They were puzzled why their results did not fully agree with calculations of the slowing of the earth by the lunar tides - as discussed in Section 4 - The Age of the Earth.

4. Relativity

We examine relativity later, but here note that Hayward accepts this theory as correct. Some creationists, dealing with the question of how light from distant galaxies could reach us within a few thousand years, quote a paper that referred to "Riemannian space" as a possible way in which light could take a "short cut" to reach us in a short time. Hayward dismisses this theory as "a curious mathematical abstraction". He appears to be unaware that it is one of the mathematical theories on which Einstein based his General Theory of Relativity.

5. Ocean chemicals

We have shown in Section 4 - The Age of the Earth - that the amounts of many chemical elements in the oceans, when divided by the small quantity flowing into them, indicate a much shorter age for the earth than that stated by geologists. Hayward dismisses this evidence by noting that they are "residence times" of the elements in the oceans and are not indicative of age. If you have a 60 gallon storage tank with water running in and out regularly at a rate of 30 gallons a day, then the "residence time" is 60/30 = 2 days.

Hayward refers to a standard text book on the subject (Ril), but examination of this work gives him little real support. The quantity in the oceans is divided by the entry rate for many elements, and the result is labelled "Residence time". These range from 260 million years (Sodium) to 100 years (Aluminium), and in general, the lower the concentration the shorter the "residence time" which is the *opposite* to what might be expected. The work was pioneered by Barth who "*assumed* a steady state system" whilst the "Residence times" in Table VI (p173) were said to be corroborated by "sedimentation" calculations, but the text mentions that these values were obtained by "*presumed*" rates of sedimentation. Hayward's case therefore relies on unproven and speculative assumptions.

The subject is dealt with over 34 pages, with discussions about high concentrations in shells, ferromanganese nodules, etc. We would acknowledge the difficulties of obtaining data and there is much admission of values being "rough estimates", "uncertainties", etc. However, the significant question is "Do these means of removal equal the amounts entering so that stable conditions lasting millions of years can be established?" This basic question is never addressed.

Bearing in mind the enormous quantity of sea water above every square metre of sea floor, if there had been ongoing removal for vast periods of time we would expect to see much richer deposits of elements than the few mentioned.

Having examined the evidence on which Hayward has based his claims, we would conclude that in practice, very few elements have been removed in any significant quantity. This makes the "residence time" equal to the maximum time the system could have existed. As we have explained in dealing with the age of the earth, many elements would have been already present at creation (or the Flood), so if the quantity in the oceans is divided by the input rate, the resulting time span would be longer than the date since creation. In the few cases where the time is shorter, then either the quantity of an element flowing into the oceans is greater than before or there is a mechanism by which the element is being removed from the oceans. Aluminium, for example, is a common element in eroded rock compounds, and the authors say that its low concentration is due either to it settling out rapidly as a solid or its high reactivy in sea water (Ril:174).

No corrections?

Billelo's criticisms were rebutted twice (by letter and at the debate). It was therefore surprising to find them still being presented in this latest edition of his book. It was written in 1985 but a third impression "with revisions" was published in 1994. In view of his claim of superior scientific integrity over creationists, one might have thought that this opportunity would have been used to delete Billelo's criticisms and to correct Wonderly's unacceptable dating method, but this was not done. As we have pointed out, Hayward specifically decided to ignore the evidence provided by creationists.

Much more could be criticised in this book that has caused some creationists to express doubts about the young age of the earth, but let us review the whole of this section and deal with some fundamental factors in all such debates with "long-agers" and anti-creationists.

AN EXAMINATION OF PRINCIPLES

Those that have been affected by *any* book critical of the creationist case have generally forgotten a basic principle of seeking the truth in *any* subject.

This is that they should *never, ever* be persuaded by a convincing-sounding argument *until they have heard the opposite case presented by a competent authority in the subject.* They have failed to heed Proverbs 18:17 - "He that is first in his own cause seemeth just; but his neighbour cometh and searcheth him" (See Bow91:153).

When this is adhered to, it will be found that in virtually every case the young-earth creationists have by far the better evidence. Whether the enquirer is prepared to be persuaded by it is a quite different matter.

"Professional credibility"

One aspect that greatly concerned Hayward was that "recent creationists have lost their credibility and antagonised the whole scientific world" (p157) and that "their unsound arguments for a young universe has stirred up a hornet's nest, and turned many scientists into bitter opponents of evangelical Christianity" (p205). This does raise the very important issue of whether creationists should strive for "credibility" in the eyes of the secular scientific community.

The answer of this author (which will surprise some readers and annoy others) is "*no*". In defence of such a striking conclusion we would make the following points.

There has been more than one creationist organisation whose principle aim was to present their evidence in a scholarly manner in the hope of convincing secular scientists of the rationality of their case. All such aims are doomed to failure. People at all levels of society, are well aware that if the creationist is correct, then an all-powerful creator exists, and they will one day have to answer to Him. This major "conceptual change" has first to be adopted, before *any* creationist evidence can be accepted as correct. Those who attempt to change a person at such a deep level of his "view of life" by purely rational arguments are displaying their lack of understanding of the way in which human nature works.

On this subject of the irrationality of mankind, there was an amusing letter in the *Daily Telegraph* pointing out that politicians were well aware that "man is not primarily a 'thinking animal' but a feeling, anxious, worrying, passionate and panicky being". The writer advised; "A politician who thinks he is in a rational business ought to consider a new career in accountancy"

This applies just as much to the fundamentally irrational way in which people treat the scientific evidence about creation. They will, indeed must, reject it to avoid a most painful reassessment of the whole basis of their life.

Those creation organisations that have maintained an uncompromising stance on a young earth and creation in six days have gradually grown in strength. Those that have embraced "long ages" or tried to appeal to the secular scientific community have had many problems.

Of course, critics will no doubt gleefully distort this dismissal of the opinions of the scientific community as "deliberately rejecting the findings of science" or some such, but this is not correct. The present scientific world is geared to distort or discredit *any* evidence that supports creation.

Repetitive questions

A creationist often finds that he has to answer the same few questions that frequently arise - Cain's wife; dinosaurs on the Ark, etc. This is understandable as we need to clear the ground for more positive enquiries.

What is less satisfactory is that for every question that creationists answer competently, three more will be posed by a sceptic. In this country at least, there are many more evolutionists than there are creationists. As nothing will convince those whose minds are made up, ultimately one concentrates on those who are willing to examine the evidence fairly, and these are invariably Christians or "earnest enquirers".

Far from being "unscientific", it will be found that the creationist case will ultimately be shown to be the only True Science, for it will be in complete accord with the One who created the scientific laws to begin with and this universe; hence the title of this book.

The search for truth

In all discussions, there are many who hold firm opinions on certain topics which is good and acceptable. When faced with criticisms, ad hoc explanations will be presented by defenders - which is also perfectly reasonable. However, as the contrary evidence gradually mounts up against a particular viewpoint, the explanations become less and less acceptable until the point is reached where the position becomes indefensible. Those who continue to hold to their original views usually go silent - but rarely will they admit that they have been wrong and accept the conclusions of their opponents. To do so would result in "losing face" in the presence of one's peers or critics, and this is a fearful prospect for us all. It is surely reasonable to conclude that *those who maintain this position are not really interested in searching for truth* for they have elevated their prestige above it.

We would suggest this would apply to the majority of evolutionists who try to defend their position. Regrettably, the creationist movement is not free from such attitudes. To publicly change one's viewpoint on any important topic in creation is almost as rare as it is for evolutionists. There are also an increasing number of articles, often ill-founded, that are critical of some long-standing creationist evidence. More seriously, there is always the shadow of ambition and a desire for prestige hovering in the background - as with all large movements. The pride of the human heart doth surely go very deep.

Summary

We have spent a very great deal of time and space on answering our critics, and it might be thought that some of the issues raised are little more than a technical "storm in a teacup" and hardly warrant such a lengthy examination. The reason for studying them so thoroughly goes a little deeper, however. We have tried to show that when *all* the evidence of the opposition is carefully examined, it will consistently be found to be baseless. It is for this reason that we have taken the trouble to pursue a few of them to the end of the line in order to demonstrate this.

Many more books could be criticised and more space has been devoted to this subject than some may think it warrants. One common factor amongst most critics of creationism is their condemnation of "young earth" creationists whilst claiming the "high moral ground" of "true scientific principles". Such works are riddled with evasions, have an air of superiority and use some of the 28 misleading stratagems or "tricks of the advocates trade" that I have listed in another work (Bow91:213f). These criticisms would equally apply to similar works by Christians who defend evolution such as Wonderley in his *God's Time Records in Ancient Sediments* (Wond. - see Bow91:8f) and Forster and Marsden in their *Reason and Faith* (For89A).

SECTION 6
INTERLUDE:
A MISCELLANY OF ITEMS

SECTION 6.1
POOR BILL'S ALMANAC

It is a serious contention that those who lack a sense of humour can often be found to have some degree of imbalance in their lives somewhere. To take oneself too seriously could imply an undue sense of self importance that betokens a degree of pride.

Fearful lest we be accused of any such tendency, we reproduce a an article that appeared in the CRSQ v8:89 June 1971. It was by William Rusch Snr. and consisted of a number of sayings he had collected.

We suggest that they should adorn the walls of all laboratories (and other establishments), and it is hoped that the reader will find them as uproarious as this author did.

He headed them as;

"Handbuch fur Uplausen das Laboratorie Werke und Ubercovern das Grosse Goofups".

Compendium of Ground Rules for Laboratory Workers and Cover-up of Large Goofups

(a) When you don't know what you are doing, do it *neatly.*
(b) Experiments should always be reproducible. They should all fail the same way.
(c) First draw your curves, then plot your data.
(e) A record of data is essential. It indicates you have been working.
(f) To study a subject best, understand it thoroughly before you start.
(g) In case of doubt, make it convincing.
(h) Do not believe in miracles, rely on them.
(i) Teamwork is essential in a laboratory; it allows you to blame someone else.

Handy guide to Modern Science:
If it is green and it wriggles, it is *biology.*
If it stinks, its *chemistry.*
If it doesn't work, its *physics.*

The Wisdom of Finagle.
Finagle's Creed: Science is truth; don't be misled by facts.
Finagle's Motto: Smile! Tomorrow will be worse.
Finagle's Constant: That quantity which, when added to, subtracted from, multiplied by or divided into the answer you got, gives you the answer you should have gotton.

Finagle's Laws:
First Law: If anything can go wrong, it will.
Second Law: No matter what result is anticipated, there is always someone

willing to fake it.

Third Law: No matter what occurs, there is always someone who believes it happened according to his pet theory.

Fourth Law: No matter what the result, there is always someone eager to misinterpret it.

The Wisdom of Giants Distilled for Your Improvement

Patrick's Theorem: If an experiment works, you must be using the wrong equipment.

Allen's Axiom: When all else fails, read the instructions.

The Compensation Corollary: An experiment may be considered successful if no more than half the data must be discarded to obtain concordance with your theory.

Carson's Consolation: No experiment is ever a complete failure; it can always be used as a bad example.

The Peter Principle: In every hierarchy, each employee tends to rise to his level of incompetence.

Parkinson's First Law: Work expands to fill the time available.

Weiler's Law: Nothing is impossible for the man who doesn't have to do it himself.

Rudin's Law: In a crisis that forces a choice to be made among alternative courses of action, most people choose the worst one possible.

Unknown Variant: If there is a wrong way to do something, most people will do it every time.

Albrecht's Law: Social innovations tend towards the level of minimum tolerable well-being.

Murphy's Law: Once a job is fouled up, anything done to improve it makes it worse.

Anonymous Law: If it happens, it must be possible.

Kneitel's Law: If the blasted thing works, leave it alone.

Clarke's Third Law: Any sufficiently advanced technology is indistinguishable from magic.

Gumperson's Law: The outcome of a given desired probability will be inverse to the degree of desirability.

The above is also known as the *Law of Perverse Opposites*. This law was the result of several years of reflection on the fact that the forecasting record of the Weather Bureau, in spite of the possession of the most sophisticated and expensive equipment as well as personnel has always been inferior to that of the "Farmer's Almanac".

Some spin-offs of Gumperson's Law have been noted as follows:

(a) After a salary rise, you will have less money at the end of the month than you had before.

(b) Children have more energy after a hard day's play just before bedtime than they do after a good nights sleep.

(c) Good parking places are always on the other side of the street.

(d) *Clarke's Law:* The junk you have will always expand to fill the available space (Of all the laws given, my wife, after a survey of our garage and basement, considers this the mostest).

The above might help to dispel the canard that Christian creationist scientists have no sense of humour.

SECTION 6.2
MENDEL'S RESULTS "TOO GOOD TO BE TRUE"

Whilst in a humorous mood, the following might be of interest also.

It is a little known fact that the results Gregor Mendel achieved in his experiments with breeding varieties of peas to prove his law of genetic inheritance were actually far too accurate to be true (Annals of Science v1 p115). They should have been much more wide of the ideal 1:4 ratio than that which he reported in his paper. By way of light relief, the following article entitled "Peas on Earth" appeared in a professional journal and was repeated in *Betrayers of the Truth* (Broad:33)

> In the beginning there was Mendel, thinking his lonely thoughts alone. And he said: "Let there be peas", and there was peas and it was good. And he put the peas in the garden and saying unto them "Increase and multiply, segregate and assort yourselves independently", and they did and it was good. And now it came to pass that when Mendel gathered up his peas, he divided them into round and wrinkled, and called the round dominant and the wrinkled recessive, and it was good. But now Mendel saw that there were 450 round peas and 102 wrinkled ones; and this was not good. For the law stateth that there should be only 3 round for every wrinkled. And Mendel said unto himself "Gott in Himmel. An enemy has done this. He has sown bad peas in my garden under the cover of night." And Mendel smote the table in righteous wrath saying "Depart from me, you cursed and evil peas, into the outer darkness where thou shalt be devoured by the rats and mice." And lo it was done and there remained 300 round peas and 100 wrinkled peas, and it was good. It was very, very good. And Mendel published.

SECTION 6.3
"ALICE IN WONDERLAND" AND EVOLUTION

Lewis Carroll's books *Alice in Wonderland* and *Through the Looking Glass* have delighted children and adults for many generations all over the world. Characters and sayings in his strange world of topsy-turvey logic have been used to express many facets of life - Tweedledum and Tweedledee; the Mad Hatter; "Jam yesterday and jam tomorrow, but no jam today," - to mention just a few.

However, few realise that almost every character in his books was a (not so gentle) lampoon of many of the famous people he knew. This has been researched by Jones and Gladstone in their interesting book *The Red King's Dream* (JoneJ95).

Lewis Carroll was the pen-name of Charles Lutwidge Dodgson, a mathematics don at Oxford who loved word-plays, puzzles and puns etc. His derived his pen-name from Charles = Carollus and Lutwidge became Lewis. Because of a stammer he would announce his name as Do-Do-Do-Dodgson, and so became "Dodo" to his friends - and one of the many characters he used in *Alice*.

The Red King's Dream is somewhat rambling in style but we would recommend it to the reader interested in tracking down who and what in the

Victorian society of his day Carroll was poking fun at. That it was not just a simple story for children is indicated by his choice of Tenniel for the illustrations - a *political* cartoonist for Punch!

All we will briefly refer to in this work are those passages about characters involved in the debate on evolution at that time - Darwin, Huxley, Owen etc. We will only refer to certain incidents in the book and indicate who he is referring to in note form.

Alice's neck grows in length (Lamarck's explanation of the giraffe's neck) and she is chased by a big puppy (A "Beagle" puppy - referring to Darwin's ship. Darwin was hurt by this caricature.)

Carroll almost certainly went to the famous Oxford debate between Wilberforce and Huxley (which, incidentally, is grossly misreported and was *not* won by Huxley - (Bow82:66)). Carroll represents this event and much of the ensuing controversy in the kitchen scene (his chapter 6) where the cook (Sir Richard Owen) is stirring a pot with too much pepper (producing a lot of "hot air") and everybody sneezes except the cook and the Cheshire cat (Dean Stanley who came from Cheshire and had much influence with Queen Victoria and others - he could afford to smile!).

Owen had "cooked up" the case for Wilberforce to present to Huxley and in *Alice* the cook starts throwing plates and dishes (debating arguments) at the Duchess (Thomas Huxley) who takes no notice of them.

The Duchess speaks brusquely to Alice saying "You don't know much, and that's a fact" - reflecting Huxley's overbearing debating method against Wilberforce who might have been out of his depth in discussing technicalities with Huxley. Eventually the Duchess throws the baby to Alice, but gradually the baby evolves *backwards* and returns to being a pig! Alice comments "If it had grown up it would have made a dreadfully ugly child: but it makes a rather handsome pig, I think". Carroll saw what a monster the theory of evolution could become and seemed to assume it would fade away. How wrong he was.

Many other parallels are suggested in the book (Lion and the Unicorn = Disraeli and Gladstone. The Gryphon = Ruskin. The Mad Hatter = Charles Kingsley). We leave the reader to follow the detective work of the authors as they gradually track down who the characters are in a book that has opened up the secrets that Carroll had buried in these seemingly innocent children's stories.

SECTION 6.4
HOW THE "SCOPES TRIAL" WAS "FIXED"

It might be of interest to reveal some of the background to this famous "trial".

In 1925 John T. Scopes was accused of teaching the theory of evolution to his class as a scientific fact which was against State laws. Scopes was defended by Lawrence Darrow whilst William Jennings Bryan, a great Christian lawyer, led the case against him. The impression today is that the evolutionists won the case, triumphing over the creationists, but the result was a victory for Bryan; unfortunately a hollow one. After the trial, evolution was gradually accepted and taught as "fact" in American schools.

A internet web site (www1) and two articles in the CRSQ (6/4:171 and 10/1:46) reveal some of the background to this case. A further website (www5) exposed the oft-shown 1960's film *Inherit the Wind* as blatant propaganda in which the transcripts of the trial were ignored and incidents and legal discussions fabricated. Henry Morris noted that when he spoke in several cities in New Zealand, the film would be repeatedly shown on TV in each area. Regarding the enormous publicity given to this case ever since it was held, it was noticed that original films of the trial show the front of the courtroom completely packed with reporters and newsreel cameramen.

Just after the First World War, many American states passed laws forbidding the teaching of evolution in the schools. Tennessee passed the "Butler" Bill forbidding the teaching of evolution and the American Civil Liberties Union decided to test the case and advertised that they would offer legal support to any teacher who would challenge the law. The advert was seen by George Rappelyea in Dayton and he met with a number of local leaders in a drugstore. He disliked "fundamentalists" and whilst he wanted to get rid of creation teaching in the schools he was even more keen to get as much publicity as possible out of the occasion to boost the declining trade of the town. Business would rocket with the notoriety it would bring. They needed a teacher and found John Scopes but he was initially reluctant to comply. He eventually agreed and they wired the ACLU. In such a way was the stage set (www1).

Scopes admitted he did not know enough about evolution to teach the subject, and on the very day he was said to have given the lesson, he was actually absent from the school. In fact he was persuaded "by George Rappelyea, a member of the ACLU, to say that he had taught evolution, although he did not remember having done so." (CRSQ 10/1:46)

Scope's main interest was sport and sometimes the biology period was used by the class for planning their tactics. He said "I reckon likely we never did get around to that old evolution lesson. But the kids were good sports and wouldn't squeal on me in court."

He admitted this in response to a question from a lady. Asked why she suspected he was away on that day, she replied;

> Oh, I began suspecting something several days ago when Mrs. Rapp [Rappelyea?] told me she overheard Darrow coaching the schoolboys what to say and what not to say on the witness stand. It took him a whole evening to get them letter-perfect. (CRSQ 6/4:203).

Scopes mentioned to a journalist that he was worried that the boys would say he was not at the school on the day. When the journalist suggested it "would make a good story", he replied "My God no... my lawyers would kill me." (www5)

The trial lasted twelve days. Darrow was known for his defence of "radicals" and had just finished defending two admitted murderers on pleas of insanity. Darrow was so obnoxious during the trial that he was nearly thrown off the case by the ACLU who had first employed him. His hostile attitude to Christianity and Bryan turned many moderate theologians away from evolution.

Darrow would not allow Bryan to cross-examine his expert witnesses so they never took the stand. He knew that just one technical objection could get the case thrown out and the law would remain untested. He also ensured that Scopes never took the stand lest it came out that he had not been at the school on the day mentioned in the indictment (www1).

Darrow also refused to call expert witnesses about evolution as they were likely to be demolished by Bryan. Eventually, Bryan agreed to be questioned on his Christian beliefs on the understanding that Darrow would also be questioned on his agnostic beliefs. Bryan was aggressively questioned by Darrow, but when it was his turn to be questioned, he surprisingly asked the jury *to find his client guilty!* Within eight minutes the jury found Scopes guilty and he was fined $100.

There were several reasons why Darrow used this tactic.

Firstly, it saved him from being grilled by Bryan. Secondly, it prevented Bryan from giving his closing speech. He had been working on it for seven weeks and it was to be "a speech consummating his lifetime of preaching". It would have badly damaged the case for evolution and would have been on legal record for all time thereafter. Thirdly, the main reason for bringing the case was to test the law in a higher court where there would be more sympathy for evolution than in this Bible-belt city. "On appeal, the state supreme court upheld the constitutionality of the 1925 law but acquitted Scopes on the technicality that he had been fined excessively. The law was repealed in 1967" (*EB* 10:558).

Five days after the trial Bryan died in his sleep from diabetes.

That the whole affair was planned by the ACLU is confirmed by the *Encyclopaedia Britannica* which notes that;

> The ACLU has not always succeeded in these trials, but the public airing of the issues has often led to success on appeal or the legislative reconsideration later (EB 1:326).

All this is surely an indictment against the machinations of those who would force evolutionary views upon the public. It is obvious that the whole case was carefully planned by powerful groups behind the scenes to blow the whole affair up out of all proportion, aided and abetted by the national press. They were prepared to "coach" the boys to lie about the lesson and then use this to ridicule the creationists.

Techniques of manipulating public opinion

It should not be thought that this case, so long ago, is only an example of nefarious practices of the past. Those heavily involved in promoting creation can tell of many devious activities by their opponents who take delight in such tactics.

Often, Christians are very naive about just how subversive their opponents can be. Let me give an example that deals with a much wider field than that of the creation/evolution debate.

There are many programmes that anti-Christian forces would like to see implanted in our society, but they realise that they will be strongly opposed by ordinary people who are keen to see only good changes introduced into their locality. Knowing this, specific steps are taken well in advance, to make their introduction less stormy.

One method is to set up a protest movement which draws many sincere people into its ranks. Much talking is done and effort is expended but little effective action takes place. When the members realise they have been fooled, the opposition has had time to become well entrenched. This tactic appears to have been adopted regarding fluoridation in more than one country. On a larger and more ominous scale, after the Russian revolution, the NKVD set up a "secret anti-communist group". When the time was right, the genuine members were duly arrested when "contacted" by Sidney Reilly - the so-called "Ace of Spies".

Another method is known as the "Delphi Technique", described by B.

Eakman in her *Educating for the New World Order* (Eak).

This technique is set out in some Rand research documents, funded by the American taxpayer, that show how to bring about changes in education. The method consists of inviting the help of a "technical assistant" or "facilitator" usually drawn from the ranks of those in the behavioural sciences and colleges. He first gathers around him people interested in the particular change proposed, making himself a friend of both those for and those against the idea. The purpose is to get to know their attitudes and reactions, strengths and weaknesses.

When the time is right, he then sets the "pro" group against the "con" group and uses the resulting "escalation of tension" for his own purposes. The "pro" group are promoted in importance, whilst the "con" group are made to seem "ridiculous, unknowledgable, dogmatic or inarticulate" and they are shut out of any publicity given to the subject. Eakman comments:

And the targets rarely, if ever, know they are being manipulated.

Or, if they suspect, they don't know how (Eak:128).

This technique may not strictly apply to the creation movement, but we can expect to be infiltrated by those professing to be creationists. They may be on committees and have inside knowledge of what creationists intend to do. They will have much media attention and act as spokesmen, but when there is a need for speaking out clearly on behalf of creationism, they will be found to suddenly fail. For example, an important court case may be led by them but at the crucial point they will present the issues so incompetently that the case will be lost.

Claims such as these may be thought exaggerated, but those who have had to deal with strong opposition to the creationist cause can tell of the underhand activities that they have been subjected to. The Christian should always be "as gentle as doves", but we have been warned that with it we should also be "as wise as serpents" (Matt. 10:16).

SECTION 6.5
THE BARRIERS TO MASS PUBLICITY

It is evident that the true Christian faith gets not just no publicity but considerable ridicule on TV and in many major papers and magazines. In plays, the vicar is often portrayed as either weak and timid or bold and bombastic. The only Christian services that are presented are either very highly emotionally charged or the very orderly high ritual of the older denominations. How many times has the real gospel been presented in any section of the British mass media?

I have been speaking and writing on the subject of the scientific evidence against evolution and for creation since 1969, and occasionally, after giving a lecture, an enthusiastic young person might come up and say that he had never heard this evidence before, and that this should be on the TV - "as they have special programmes for people like you with unusual ideas.", etc.

My reply is to encourage them to write to the TV company, but I warn them of the response that they will get. They will receive a polite letter explaining why they do not think that the subject is "appropriate" or they have taken the advice of experts (evolutionists of course!) who do not consider the case has any support from "senior members of the profession" - or some such excuse. If the recipient is not satisfied with the reasons given he might write again, but this time, if he is fortunate enough to receive a reply, it will be only a few lines in a fairly abrupt tone. It can be guaranteed that anyone who writes to the TV companies will *not* be able to persuade the controllers to transmit any programmes that would support creation. This barrier also applies to all the major publishing houses.

The whole of the mass media is controlled by people who are not open to a reasonable case on this subject and some others. They are there to ensure that only carefully edited programmes with the subtle intention of leading the public on the path that they have already decided in their "hidden agenda" are allowed to be broadcast by the mass media.

I have set out seven examples of how the creationist's evidence is stifled in another work (Bow82:127-132) but give here two other incidents.

The 1986 Oxford Union Debate - that disappeared!

David C.C. Watson suggested to the president of the Oxford Union Debating Society that the Huxley Memorial Debate should be on creation vs. evolution. "That the doctrine of creation is more valid than the theory of evolution" was debated on February 14th. 1986 and was principally between Dr Richard Dawkins and Prof John Maynard-Smith against Prof Wilder-Smith and Prof Edgar Andrews. The real surprise was that 37% of the undergraduates voted for the creationists - 115 for, 198 against!

This result no doubt shocked the University *so all references to the debate having ever taken place was expunged from the records!* No newspaper or periodical ever referred to it either (Wild87:v) Now the undergraduate organisers are under no obligation to keep any records of events, but it is doubtful if they would have taken such a drastic step without first consulting their tutors. To suggest that the academics may have been the prime movers is, of course, pure speculation. For whatever reason, that all records of the event were completely removed is a severe indictment of those who decided to take this action. It is also an indication of how fearful they are of any evidence against evolution (and by inference for creation) that they treat it as if it never existed. The society, wanting to completely wash its hands of the debate, even sold the copyright on the tapes of the meeting to David Watson who circulated a number of copies.

The second incident also involved Dr Wilder-Smith. He was speaking at a media conference during which he stated that the BBC presented the biggest barrier of all broadcasting corporations to creationist topics. In the audience were two high executives of the BBC who were annoyed that he should have publicly denigrated the integrity of the BBC. They offered to make a programme on the subject of evolution and creation which he promptly accepted, but the programme was never transmitted - due to "technical problems"!

This incident demonstrates very clearly that there are considerations far above getting good audience ratings. Even the ability to increase revenue is subordinate to not transmitting any views that will upset those who really control the mass media behind the scenes. Too much proof that God exists might start people asking awkward questions!

One of the barriers behind which evolutionists like Richard Dawkins and others hide is that their critics cannot ask awkward questions of the books and TV programmes that they make. If they lecture, rarely do they have questions at the end for, should there be a knowledgeable creationist in the audience, the weakness of their case would be exposed in public. Creationists, however, often lecture and invite questions.

On one occasion, a well known Christian evangelical who is a scientist and an author on theistic evolution attended a lecture I gave. During the question time he had ample opportunity to ask any question he liked that would have demolished my case, but nevertheless chose to remain silent. One might ask why, as a fellow Christian, he never raised a single question or even discussed points with me afterwards.

Editors of papers or book publishers might express some interest in a creationist's viewpoint, but nothing will appear in print. What are appearing now in the secular press are books that are critical of evolution. What is *still* barred are any positive facts that support creation as this would imply the existence of a great Creator God.

Some criticism of evolution is now permitted, but the new views that are receiving increasing publicity are those of the New Age Movement. The whole earth is now considered to be one huge organism that it slowly maturing, and we have the "Gaia hypothesis" in which "Mother Earth" is considered as an organic whole. In this, we are considered to be approaching the final "Omega Point" which is the end product in the false philosophy of the Jesuit priest Teilhard de Chardin. This is examined more fully in Appendix 2. Developments in this direction can be expected over the years.

Meanwhile, all that creationists can do is to give as much publicity as they can to the mass of evidence they have against evolution and for creation. The Creation Science Movement (originally the Evolution Protest Movement, founded in 1932) is the oldest creation organisation in the world and the largest in Great Britain. Ably led by Dr. David Rosevear and his wife Joan, it is providing the first permanent centre and exhibition of creation subjects in this country at 17 The Hard, Portsmouth. Those who would like to know more of the creationist cause are urged to join them by writing to the Creation Science Movement, P.O. Box 888, Portsmouth PO6 2YD. Only by spreading this "good news" as far as possible will people be able to hear the evidence that they have been denied by the mass media for over one hundred years.

SECTION 6.6
THE LADY HOPE "STORY"
- A RE-EXAMINATION

Many creationists are familiar with the account that a "Lady Hope" gave of her visit to Darwin a few months before he died. Although it has appeared in various books, we present it below for those to whom it is new.

....

It was one of those glorious autumn afternoons, that we sometimes enjoy in England, when I was asked to go in and sit with the well known professor, Charles Darwin. He was almost bedridden for some months before he died. I used to feel when I saw him that his fine presence would make a grand picture for our Royal Academy; but never did I think so more strongly than on this particular occasion.

He was sitting up in bed, wearing a soft embroidered dressing gown, of rather a rich purple shade.

Propped up by pillows, he was gazing out on a far-stretching scene of woods and cornfields, which glowed in the light of one of those marvellous sunsets which are the beauty of Kent and Surrey. His noble forehead and fine features seem to be lit up with pleasure as I entered the room.

He waved his hand toward the window as he pointed out the scene beyond, while in the other hand he held an open Bible, which he was always studying.

"What are you reading now?" I asked as I seated myself beside his bedside. "Hebrews!" he answered - "still Hebrews. 'The Royal Book' I call it. Isn't it grand?"

Then, placing his finger on certain passages, he commented on them.

I made some allusions to the strong opinions expressed by many persons on the history of the Creation, its grandeur, and then their treatment of the earlier chapters of the Book of Genesis.

He seemed greatly distressed, his fingers twitched nervously, and a look of agony came over his face as he said: "I was a young man with unformed ideas. I threw out queries, suggestions, wondering all the time over everything, and to my astonishment, the ideas took like wildfire. People made a religion of them."

Then he paused, and after a few more sentences on "the holiness of God" and the "grandeur of this book," looking at the Bible which he was holding tenderly all the time, he suddenly said: "I have a summer house in the garden which holds about thirty people. It is over there," pointing through the open window. "I want you very much to speak there. I know you read the Bible in the villages. To-morrow afternoon I should like the servants on the place, some tenants and a few of the neighbours to gather there. Will you speak to them?"

"What shall I speak about?" I asked.

"Christ Jesus!" he replied in a clear, emphatic voice, adding in a lower tone, "and his salvation. Is not that the best theme? And then I want you to sing some hymns with them. You lead on your small instrument, do you not?" The wonderful look of brightness and animation on his face as he said this I shall never forget, for he added: "If you take the meeting at three o'clock this window will be open, and you will know that I am joining in with the singing."

How I wished I could have made a picture of the fine old man and his beautiful surroundings on that memorable day!

....

This is the account that appeared on the 19th August 1915 in the Baptist "Watchman-Examiner" in Washington D.C. (Q29/2:70). In 1922, friends in Los Angeles who knew her wrote an affidavit (**L.A. affidavit**) (MooreJ:79). In 1940, Prof. Bole released a letter he had received from her in the early 1920's (**Bole letter**) (MooreJ:86). These repeated most of the above account with some minor variations and additions, and we will refer to these later.

An initial overview

Several writers have examined the evidence, including this author (Bow88:188). It has been interesting to see how critics of the story have had to retreat step by step. Firstly it was claimed that Lady Hope did not even exist. When she was identified, it was doubted if she ever had any connection with Darwin. Past issues of the Watchman Examiner were scanned and her account was not found in those available. It was later discovered and reproduced in the CRSQ (29/2:70). Eventually, it was not only admitted that she was in the area of Downe but that she did visit Darwin. She is then accused of "embroidering" her account of what Darwin said.

In view of the early lack of evidence, some creationists have advised that the story should not be used, mainly in view of the strong denial of the whole Darwin family, and the absence of any reference in Darwin's writings to a return to Christian beliefs.

Gradually, the details of her life became clearer and her presence at Downe at the time she claimed was fully established. She was an evangelical Anglican, very well connected in Brethren circles, and had held evangelistic home meetings in the Downe area about 1881. J.W.C. Fegan, an evangelist, was holding "tent meetings" in Downe at that same time.

By far the most thorough investigation is by Moore who set his evidence out in *The Darwin Legend* (MooreJ). He concludes that whilst she certainly seems to have visited Darwin, her account is untrustworthy on a number of points. On a brief examination, his evidence initially appeared reasonably convincing, but a discussion with my friend Dr. David Rosevear, Chairman of the Creation Science Movement, prompted a very careful re-reading of Moore's book. This re-examination of his evidence resulted in a much more careful examination of his evidence.

Another very interesting book is *The Life and Death of Charles Darwin* by L.R. Croft (Croft) in which he concludes that Lady Hope's account is accurate.

Lady Hope was a fervent evangelist, particularly involved in the Temperance Movement against drunkenness. Born Elizabeth Reid Stapleton-Cotton in 1842, she married Admiral Sir James Hope in 1877 and after his death in June 1881 eventually married Mr. Thomas Denny in 1893 - 11 years after Darwin's death on the 19th April 1882. She would, therefore, have been recently widowed when she said she met Darwin in the Autumn of 1881. She emigrated to America in 1913 and died in 1922 in Australia on her way back to England.

THE EVIDENCE SUPPORTING THE ACCOUNT

Moore provides a mass of detail, and the following is mainly based upon evidence he provides, for he agrees that Lady Hope *did* visit Darwin.

1. She certainly must have visited the house and seen Darwin in his upstairs bedroom.

She describes Darwin's dressing gown exactly, his nervous twitching of fingers, his animated countenance when speaking, the view from his window and the existence of a "summer house"; all known to be perfectly accurate descriptions. How could she have known the precise colour of Darwin's dressing gown and several other personal details if she had never seen him in his home? In the Watchman account, written in 1915, she says he was "sitting up in bed". In the Bole letter, written in the 1920's, she describes him "lying on a sofa". It was a sofa and not a bed as testified by his son (M:131). Here we see her later recollection correcting her first writing even in this small detail. In the Bole letter she also remembers that "It was a large room with a high ceiling" - a further testimony that she had entered his house.

It has been objected that Darwin would not have used such flowery descriptions, such as "grand(eur)", when referring to the Bible, but they were Lady Hope's phraseology. Yet this word is found in a flattering letter he wrote in 1859 about a book and in another letter in 1873 referring to "this grand and wonderous universe." This does at least show Darwin used this word to express his high esteem of any matter under discussion. Also, Parslow, his personal servant cum nurse, was converted by Fegan and may have used such phrases as "salvation", etc. in discussions with Darwin.

2. She told others of Darwin's conversation *shortly after it took place.*

One of the most obvious questions is, "Why did she wait until 1915 - 34 years after the event - and in America - before she told her 'story'?". This does seem as though she may have fabricated it or embroidered a visit to Darwin to impress her American friends.

One answer is that there were several reports of Darwin's "recantation" (if we can loosely call it that) circulating here shortly after his death.

(A) Moore's assertion

Moore, in fact, notes that *"There is no doubt that Lady Hope was making comments about Darwin to her religious friends long before the story was published"* (M:48). From this, it would appear that she *did* tell others long before going to America, but Moore reported only one - Sir Robert Anderson (see below). Were there many other instances that he does not record in his book? We discuss this later.

(B) Nicholls' account.

Nicholls, the village postman, was converted through Fegan in 1881, the year Lady Hope is said to have visited Darwin. His friend, Mr. Fawkes, reported his account in the Bromley and Kentish Times (7 Nov. 1958 p2) a year after Nicholls' death aged 97 - when his memory was still very clear. We feel that this account is little recognised and we therefore give the main part of Fawkes's report:

> During one of my [Fawkes] visits to him [Nicholls], he told me that this lady who had been in attendance on Darwin prior to his death had informed him that he requested her to read the New Testament to him and asked her to arrange for the Sunday School children to sing "There is a green hill far away". This was done and Darwin, who was greatly moved said: "How I wish I had not expressed my theory of evolution as I have done".

In his introduction to this, Fawkes describes the person as "the lady who had nursed Darwin", but then describes her as one who "had been in attendance". Moore contends this is Lady Hope, but Croft says it is probably a Mrs. Evans who "had been with the Darwin household as a nurse for many years". (Another writer says she was the cook. Actually she was the old housekeeper). Which is correct - was it Lady Hope or a lady in the house?

In her account Lady Hope was not asked to read to him and she does not mention a specific hymn he requested. Croft notes that Mrs. Evans was a member of the Gospel Room congregation and could easily arrange for the children to sing. However, there is no record of this taking place.

The crucial point is not who this lady was, but that Nicholls heard of Darwin's change. If it was Lady Hope, then he must have heard of this soon after the event as probably she was not in the area for long. If it was another lady, then this would be a totally independent witness from Lady Hope. Nicholls' account is so close to Darwin's home that it gives support to the story, no matter by what route it came to him.

(C) Sir Robert Anderson

One of the most interesting references Moore mentions involves Sir Robert Anderson who was the head of the C.I.D. at Scotland Yard during the time of the investigation of the "Jack the Ripper Murders". He was a well known evangelical, and a very close friend of Lady Hope. Obviously referring to Lady Hope, he wrote *as early as 1907*:

> ..a friend of mine who was much with Darwin during his last illness assures me that he expressed the greatest reverence for the scriptures and bore testimony to their value (M:48).

This is an important comment which we discuss later.

3. There were accounts circulating unconnected with her

Moore gives several of these incidents.

(A) May 1882 - only eight months after her visit and one month after Darwin's death in April. A preacher, Mr. Huntingdon, at Tenby refers to Darwin "in his last utterances confessed his true faith." Tenby "had been the home of Emma Darwin's (Charles's wife) Allen aunts; the Darwin's first cousin, the Rev. John Allen Wedgewood, still lived there."

Moore (p71) speculates that "perhaps clerical chit-chat got worked into the sermon". This is an interesting account, for, chit-chat or not, here we have a direct connection between the Darwin family and a report of a "recantation", *and Lady Hope is not involved*. If Huntingdon had fabricated his anecdote, his close neighbour would surely have heard of it and sharply corrected the record. This is surely of some value as independent evidence that there *had been* a "recantation" of some sort!

(B) September 1882. Robert Eadie F.R.G.S. is said to have sent to the Darwin family, who were collecting his letters for publication, a note he had received from Darwin in which he said that "he [Darwin] can with confidence look to Calvary". No letter from Eadie ever appeared in the published letters of Darwin (M:73) - which is not surprising in view of its explosive content.

(C) 1928. Ivor Panin (See Appendix 7) received information by a circuitous route that an Oxford professor had received a letter from Darwin, whom he claimed was a close friend, saying he had become a firm Christian. The professor had commented that, "The position is odd as both his son and grandson deny his Christianity" (M:85). His acknowledgement that the letter contradicted the family's claims only adds to the authenticity of the report.

Moore gives a few other accounts but they are mostly repeats of conversations with Lady Hope or poorly supported.

SOME FURTHER POINTS

It was whilst reading Moore's book that some other aspects arose.

4. The "Summer House"

There are several denials recorded, even by members of Darwin's family, that any "summer house" even existed "in the garden". This is often stated to demonstrate her story was pure imagination. What Moore points out is that there *was* a summer house, some 400 yds. away at the end of The Sandwalk, from which singing might have been heard on a calm day. It would not have accommodated thirty people, but this may have been a minor error of Darwin's memory who may not have visited it for some time.

Now this summer house could not be seen from the house, and this is probably why Darwin pointed to it as being "over there", i.e. not in the near garden below the window.

If we consider this for a moment, it will be apparent that Lady Hope would have been foolish to have fabricated such a comment that could so easily be refuted simply by looking out of any window. It therefore proves that she was accurately recording the words of Darwin who knew of this summer house some distance away. She would certainly not have known of its existence.

In addition, he wrote of sitting in the summer-house watching thunderstorms (M:33). Was this the distant summer-house or another one in the garden in earlier days?

5. The Book of Hebrews

Lady Hope said that Darwin was reading Hebrews when she entered the room, and that he said it was his favourite book in the Bible. When she was in America, she mentioned this which resulted in her account in the Watchman-Examiner given above.

Whatever else, Lady Hope was consistent in saying that Darwin liked reading Hebrews. There is the old saying: "liars must have good memories" so that their accounts of a fabricated incident are consistent. Lady Hope would surely have had that particular meeting etched upon her mind and no false memory would have been needed. Is there any independent support? Surprisingly there is.

Moore records in one of the notes at the rear (Note 4 to chapter 5 - Lady Hope's story, page 131):

> The Darwin Family Bible preserved in the Darwin Museum is unmarked *except for an unattributable small, backwards pencil tick opposite the first few verses of Hebrews 6.*

Now no one can say that this tick was placed by Darwin (unless he used it elsewhere!), but surely it is a surprising coincidence that the *only* mark in the Bible is in the very book that Lady Hope said was his favourite. It was possibly the same family Bible he was reading when she entered his room.

But that is not all. If we examine these early verses of Hebrews 6, we find that they speak of those who had "tasted the heavenly gift" but fell away and could not be renewed. We give the relevant verses:

> (v4) For it is impossible for those who were once enlightened, and have tasted of the heavenly gift and were made partakers of the

Holy Ghost, (5) and have tasted the good word of God, and the powers of the world to come, (6) if they shall fall away, to renew them again unto repentance; seeing they crucify to themselves the Son of God afresh, and put him to an open shame. (7) For the earth which drinketh in the rain that cometh oft upon it, and bringing forth herbs meet for them by whom it is dressed, receiveth blessing from God: (8) But, that which beareth thorns and briers is rejected and is nigh unto cursing: whose end is to be burned.

These verses may have spoken loudly to Darwin. He failed to become a doctor as his father had wanted, so he was entered for the Church, intending to become a country parson. He took theology at Cambridge, where he was so impressed by the logical arguments in support of creation in Paley's *Natural Theology* that he memorised them by heart. Following this he embarked on the *Beagle* and gradually he drew away from religion until, due to his writings on evolution and possibly the loss of a favourite daughter, he eventually became an agnostic.

He knew that fundamentally his theory of evolution was an attack upon Christianity, and therefore he had "fallen away" and his life's work had produced only "thorns and briers". Was the "tick" in Hebrews his, as an acknowledgement that these passages were an accurate description of his situation?

We will never know, but we would suggest that in fact they would *not* have applied to him. His hesitancy about becoming a parson hardly indicated a deep commitment to the true Christian faith or any zeal to spread the Gospel. It is therefore unlikely that he had "partaken of the Holy Spirit" or had been "enlightened", and therefore he had never "fallen away" in the first place. If Lady Hope account is at all accurate, then it would indicate that he may have now realised, in a personal way and at a late stage, the real basis of the Christian faith.

6. Did Lady Hope make more than one visit?

There is no direct reference to this in her account. However, not long before she died, several supportive friends in Los Angeles wrote a more full record of events (LA affidavit - M:81) that she had given in which up to four visits were mentioned. It was on the fourth visit that the reference was made to Hebrews and the "summer house meeting".

Her memory was said to be fully intact even in her last years, and the five signatories of the letter attested (again) to her "sincerity and reliability."

This was the first time that this writer had realised that there might have been more than one visit, and with this in mind, her account was carefully re-examined. On doing so, several phrases almost leapt from the page.

(a) The first point is what was *not* said. In those very formal days, if this had been the very first time that they had met, one would have expected them to have exchanged polite greetings and to obtain "background information" such as asking obvious questions about her work in Downe or his health etc. No such exchange seems to have taken place but *a degree of considerable familiarity is immediately adopted.*

Now let us read her words carefully, for an intriguing pattern begins to emerge.

(b) She says "*I used to feel when I saw him..(*he would make a fine picture*)..but never did I think so more strongly than on this particular occasion.*" These words clearly imply that she had seen him more than once before, but that she was struck by his appearance on this particular occasion on a glorious sunny day.

(c) "in the other hand he held an open Bible, *which he was always studying.*" How could she have known this unless she had seen him several times before?

(d) "What are you reading *now.*" She had obviously seen him reading the Bible before on previous visits, but wanted to know what particular passage he was reading this time.

(e) "Still Hebrews?" He must have been reading this when she came on a previous visit.

(f) "He was almost bedridden for some months before he died." In fact he was not bedridden, but if Lady Hope saw him *several times* but only in the afternoons when he was lying down having his regular rest in his dressing gown, it is only natural that she might come to this conclusion.

(g) In a later account, written in the early 1920's, she was not sure if he referred to the summer house "on this occasion or *another about the same time.*" (M:89)

As far as I know, the significance of her casual comments, written without any apparent subterfuge, has not been noted before. They fully support the LA affidavit in which possibly four visits were mentioned. It was the last of them that was the most memorable one, and it was this she recorded for the *Watchman-Examiner.* But within this first written account she had unwittingly provided the evidence that she had visited him several times before. That she may have confused on which specific visit certain subjects were discussed is understandable.

It was not until the LA affidavit, written in 1922, that earlier visits are referred to. Yet it is in complete conformity with what she had said seven years before in the Watchman-Examiner of a visit made 41 years before. These artless comments all add an unexpected confirmation of her accuracy.

Apart from recording the LA affidavit, Moore makes no other reference to more than one visit, except on page 118 where he says Francis "may have been absent on the day *or days* that she allegedly called."

(h) There is one final, and to my mind fairly convincing, piece of evidence. In Sir Robert Anderson's footnote given above, he specifically says that his "friend" was "*much* with Darwin"; i.e. she saw him on many occasions. This is a comment by Lady Hope direct to him some time before 1907, so the links in the chain are very short - adding considerable authenticity. It strongly suggests she was virtually Darwin's Christian friend as he neared death, a possibility as we shall consider later. *However, this raises the problem of why he never spoke to Fegan or his wife Emma of any new Christian faith.*

THE FEGAN LETTERS

Near the end of his book, Moore quotes two similar letters from Fegan to Mr. Kensit (The founder of the Protestant Truth Society) and Mr. Pratt, in which he, Fegan, is critical of Lady Hope's character (M:107f). Fegan dictated these to his secretary, Tiffin, in 1925 and the latter took copies with him when he emigrated to Australia in 1957. He did not make them public until 1977 when he read Lady Hope's account in a periodical.

Fegan was an evangelist who lived with his mother in Downe but worked in Deptford running an orphanage for destitute boys. He brought them to Downe for summer holidays in tents, held tent evangelistic meetings and services in the Downe Reading Room at the time Lady Hope was in the area.

Summarising these letters, they claim that; Lady Hope's visit and the service in the summer house never took place - they were "a fabrication on the part of poor Lady Hope"; she incorrectly held to the title of Lady Hope due to her vanity; she was a terrible trial to her second husband, Denny, and when he discovered that she was running a "Riverside Club" for the poor, he was shocked, and died from an illness he caught there; she was made bankrupt and when she left for America, Fegan refused to give her a letter of commendation.

These letters are certainly an indictment against Lady Hope, but is should be noted that they are the *only personal* criticisms of her character. All other available testimonies spoke most strongly of her honesty and sincerity.

Initially, there seemed to be some strange features. For example, why should Tiffin take copies of these letters all the way to Australia in 1957, and keep them for a further twenty years? Fegan had been "appealed to over and over again" about Lady Hope but we have only two of his letters. Why did Denny know nothing about his wife's activities and extravagance? He also was giving generously to charities for Moore notes that Denny, "having made his fortune in pork, larded the coffers of many evangelical enterprises" (p43).

In view of this we tried to check the complex route of the letters, but the outcome was unsatisfactory and unwarrantably tended to deepen the mystery. The authenticity of the letters was proven by a more direct line, for at a late stage in the investigation, this writer had been contacted about the Fegan letters by a correspondent who knew Tiffin's son. We discussed the letters, and the reason why Tiffin should have had Fegan's correspondence in Australia was explained in a note later received from Tiffin's son. Tiffin had been asked to write a history of the Fegan Homes but the war intervened. When he emigrated to Australia in 1957 to be with his daughter, he took the files with him. He eventually wrote, not about the Homes, but a tribute to Fegan's excellent work with the destitute boys of London. This appeared in a book entitled *Loving and Serving* (Tiff).

Fegan and Lady Hope

Moore conjectures that when Fegan fell ill in the summer of 1881, he asked Lady Hope to take over the running of his tent meetings. This would then place her in Downe when she could have visited Darwin.

As the examination continued, it became clear that this link between the two at Downe at this time did not exist. Fegan never mentions that he had asked her to take his place, whilst in the Bole letter, Lady Hope specifically states that she was holding cottage meetings in the area, that Darwin heard of this and invited her to see him (M:87f). At the time, she was living in Beckenham, only 6 miles (9km) away (M:45). Neither mentions the other. In addition, Fegan would hardly ask a lady to run these meetings for one writer described the heat and stench in the tent from the crowds of farm workers there (Rob:13). It was no place to invite Lady Hope.

In an exchange of letters with Moore, he explained why he made this link. Lady Hope had written about an evangelist she called "Felix" to hide his identity and he considered that "Felix" was a thinly disguised reference to Fegan - their names being not dissimilar. "Felix", like Fegan, had worked in tent meetings in Kent. Secondly, Lady Hope was working in the area of Downe. From these slim connections, Moore assumes that Fegan asked her to take over his meetings.

It eventually became abundantly clear that everything hung upon Lady

Hope's accuracy in recording what Darwin actually said. In order to see if she was inclined to "embellish" her accounts, her book *Our Golden Key* (Hope) was examined. It was her account, published in 1884, of the experiences of this unnamed evangelist she called "Felix" who worked in a deprived area of London and held tent missions amongst the hop-pickers in Kent. Her account is quite detailed.

It did not take much reading to conclude that "Felix" could not possibly have been Fegan. (a) "Felix" is said to have a "little cottage" with "a young wife and pretty babes." This is hardly the circumstances of Fegan who was not rich but fairly well connected. (b) "Felix" worked for the London City Mission (which is still operating) evangelising the very poor and there is no mention of him working specifically with destitute young boys - who were Fegan's main interest. (c) "Felix" played a portable harmonium (as did Lady Hope) but there is no mention of Fegan playing such an instrument. (d) "Felix" worked in tent missions to hop pickers. Fegan's tents were for evangelistic meetings of the Downe area and used for housing his boys in the summer. He does not appear to have worked specifically with the hop-pickers. (e) "Felix" worked from an LCM "Mission-room". Fegan started his own orphanage and organisation.

Furthermore, Lady Hope makes no mention of any work she may have done in these tent meetings. She does say that "Felix's" tent preaching "seems to have been very attractive" (Hope:107) which suggests she was not present herself. She also says that "A lady in the part of Kent that we have described... started a coffee tent... and took ..no less than EIGHTY (her emphasis) pounds" (which was returned to the poor as gifts of food). This may have been herself but it seems unlikely. She later refers to taking pains with "*our* tea and coffee", (p116) but this seems to refer to one of her London "tea shops". Had she participated in Fegan's tent meetings in 1881, she would surely have mentioned it in a book that refers to this work published in 1884.

In order to identify who "Felix" was, the London City Mission was contacted. Amongst other things that came to light, they mentioned that it was not until the turn of the century that they actually identified their London evangelists by their names. Before then, they only referred to "our worker in (location)". Thus, the reason for Lady Hope using a pseudonym was to comply with the policy of the LCM at that time and preserve his identity. It was *not* to hide Fegan's name. Indeed, why should she do so?

The LCM could not identify "Felix" from their records, but their Magazine dated 1st. May 1884 (p100) locates the "Mission-room" in Brixton. Fegan worked in Deptford.

We would therefore contend that Moore is incorrect in identifying "Felix" as Fegan. If this is accepted, then Moore's claim that Fegan used Lady Hope to run the tent meeting during his illness can be dismissed.

Thus, *Fegan had no connection with Lady Hope at this time and was away ill when she visited Darwin! Fegan's assertion that "the interview... never took place" is therefore invalidated.*

This raises one question. Why should Moore, who read *Our Golden Key*, contend that Fegan was "Felix", when it is abundantly clear from the book that "Felix" could not possibly be Fegan?

Furthermore, having made the link, Moore then contradicts Fegan's claim that the interview never took place, for he contends that she *did* visit Down House. It is her account of what was said that he dismisses. One is left wondering why Moore should have gone to the trouble of forging a link between Fegan and Lady Hope in the first place.

Fegan's assertion that "it never took place" is not stated from direct knowledge. Fegan made this statement not by questioning Lady Hope but on the basis that Francis Darwin, whom he considered most trustworthy, had claimed this. Moore points out that Francis was not present at that time and could not make this statement from first-hand knowledge.

Robson's review of Moore's book

Robson, in an article in *Faith and Thought* (April 1997.Rob) questioned whether Fegan had any connection with Lady Hope at that time. He is also critical of Moore on several points. He notes that in order to support his claim that Lady Hope *did* visit Darwin, Moore has to contradict Fegan who said the visit did *not* take place. Moore then says "Fegan's reliability as a witness, no less than Lady Hope's, is open to question." Robson, vigorously and rightly defending Fegan's integrity, suggests Fegan was naive to accept Francis's word that Lady Hope never visited Darwin. Robson quotes from Fegan's letter regarding Francis and "the high standards of truth which the Darwin's inherited from their father... a most honourable, chivalrous and benevolent gentleman". Robson comments: "Desmond and Moore's picture of Darwin and family [in their book *Darwin* (Desm)] is very different." He infers that they were not as honourable as Fegan (and Moore) would like to portray them. We also dispute Fegan's accolade but Desmond and Moore's book hardly ever questioned the family's integrity, although *The Darwin Legend* gives a few examples. Darwin's basic dishonesty was to concoct "evidence" for evolution from pure speculation. Surprisingly, for such a detailed book, *Darwin* omits all mention of Fegan.

Robson also mentions Moore's recording of Pat Sloan's two articles (in 1960 and 1965) in *The Humanist*. In these, Sloan surprisingly admitted that "Lady Hope may have visited" Down House (Moore:68).

Fegan's denial that Lady Hope ever visited Darwin can therefore be discounted. What remains of importance in Fegan's letters are his comments on Lady Hope's character.

Darwin's last days

In February 1881, the Duke of Argyll pointed out to Darwin that there is obviously a mind behind the beauties of nature. "He looked at me very hard and said: 'Well, that often come over me with overwhelming force, but at other times,' and he shook his head vaguely, adding, 'it seems to go away'." (Rob. and Desm:649). In the summer of 1881, Darwin was gloomy and depressed which a holiday had failed to dispel. He wrote "I am rather despondent about myself" and "life has become wearisome to me." Wallace wrote that he was gloomy "on the future of humanity on the ground that in our civilisation natural selection had no play and the fittest did not survive" (Croft:104). His thoughts may, therefore, have turned to Christianity by the late summer of 1881. With Fegan away ill, he may have asked Lady Hope, who he heard was in the area, to visit him.

Croft speculates that in seeing that man was kindly to man, Darwin may have realised that this might be a reflection of the kindness of God - and that Paley may have been right after all! If Darwin did entertain such thoughts, then his desire to talk to a fervent Christian as he neared the end of his life is understandable. Darwin may also have wanted to meet Lady Hope in view of her stand against drunkenness. Both his grandmother and great-grandmother had died of alcoholism and he had a dread of its effect (p115). This seems a slim reason, and it leaves open the very important question: *"Why did Darwin invite Lady Hope to his house in the first place?"*

LADY HOPE'S CHARACTER

There are several criticisms that have been made of her character. It is implied that she married Sir James Hope for his title. He was 69 and she was 35 - a mature woman it should be noted - and they did share a great interest in the temperance movement. When he died, she continued to use the title of "Lady Hope" even after marrying Denny when she should have used his name, but her retention of her title for the added prestige that this would have given to her evangelism in those days is understandable. She appears to have been very imprudent in handling her finances, but it must be emphasised that the money went on good causes, and at the end she seems to have been bankrupted by a defrauder. In one instance, she spent money on setting up hostels for the poor that were unsuccessful.

In those days, to be bankrupt was a serious social stigma and the most probable reason why she went to America. In view of this, her claim that she had left England to avoid the anger of the Darwin family and to overcome the grief of losing her husband (LA affidavit) are understandable "white lies". It was also the most likely reason for Fegan refusing to give her a letter of commendation.

Apart from the criticisms expressed in the Fegan letters, these are about the only other direct accusations that that cast shadows on the character of Lady Hope, and how small they are can be judged. As we have maintained, it is extremely unwise for anyone, a Christian particularly, who values their reputation, to invent or embroider a story about a famous man, for it can easily be checked, and their reputation would be ruined.

One can hardly think that she would have been accepted as a close friend of people like Sir Robert Anderson and Fegan or have strong connections with such eminent men as Lord Shaftesbury and Moody and Sankey had she been the least bit untruthful with a tendency to embroider her activities and those of others as Moore accuses her of. This would have soon been apparent to these intelligent and spiritually sensitive men and the acquaintance quickly curtailed.

Dr. David Rosevear received a letter saying that, in a history of old Dorking, she is described as keen to evangelise the local people, holding services, temperance meetings and many other activities. The picture all these testimonies paint is of a woman who was a fervent evangelist, and this was consistently maintained throughout the rest of her extremely active Christian life. The impression one gets is far different from someone who would fabricate such an important story.

Everything hung upon her accuracy in recording her conversation with Darwin. In order to see if she was inclined to "embroider" her accounts we read her book *Our Golden Key: A Narrative of Facts from "Outcast London"* (Hope).

I was impressed with her heartfelt concern for the poor which was overwhelming. She frequently used emphasised words on the state of the poor in order to reach to the heart of the reader. What became obvious was her interest in the work of *others;* there is hardly any reference to the work that she was undoubtedly carrying out at that time. She does begin by an imaginative description of "Felix" wandering into the darkness of the area he would be working in, and she paints vivid pictures to capture the reader's imagination. However, there was no indication that she "added to" any of the many incidents she records of Felix's work which she obviously obtained directly from him. Had she not reported them accurately he would surely have registered his disapproval.

Furthermore, in correspondence with the LCM, their 1884 report, referred to above, also reproduced a review of this book that appeared in *The Record* on March 28th 1884 which gave it very warm praise.

We also read her books *Loving Work in the Highways and Byeways* (Nelson 1888) and *More About Our Coffee Room* (Nisbet 1878). In his introduction to the latter book Lord Shaftesbury said she was a "pious, amiable and accomplished young lady" whose exertions were "founded on an intense love of the Gospel." Furthermore, she is critical of those who run coffee rooms and almost force those attending to "sign the pledge" for they often do not return. We give her comments with her emphases:

> We need tact, and caution, and *love*, in all our dealings with human souls. Nothing should be done to vex or give unnecessary offence.
> We also need zeal, earnestness, diligence, self denial, for this mighty struggle against A NATIONAL SIN.

These are hardly the words of someone who is an overzealous Christian lacking a balanced view of life. They also do not give the impression of someone who would have deceived her husband or the public by fabricating stories.

Moore accuses her of "embroidering" her accounts "with spiritual senti-mentality" - *but this is not the same as inventing incidents*. I found her books written in a vivid style to highlight the condition of the poor, but could detect no evidence of *fabrication*. Her self-effacement and her humour that comes through at times do her great credit. Her other writings, therefore, give some support to her record of her conversation with Darwin.

Lady Hope's attitude.

Following the meeting, she appears to have mentioned it to Sir Robert Anderson at some time, but to how many others whilst here in England is not certain and we discuss this below. In America, far from immediately regaling them with her story, she was there for two years (1913-1915) before she casually mentioned to a lecturer who had been speaking about Hebrews that it was Darwin's favourite book in the Bible. It was this that caused so much local excitement that culminated in her writing her account of the visit for the Watchman Examiner.

If she did say little about the visit to others whilst here, this gives the grounds for the charge that she fabricated the account when she got to America, principally to impress her new friends. In thinking about her (possible) slowness in telling others about the visit, it struck me that one explanation could be that *she attached less importance to it than we do today.* At that time, like many women, *she may have been far less concerned about the implications and effects of evolution* than many evangelicals are today. That the "founder" of evolution was now reading his Bible was of interest to her, but not of such great importance that she should broadcast the fact to all and sundry as soon as possible. However, the possibility that she *did* tell others about her visit soon after the event we discuss later.

Her conversation with Darwin

What is impressive in her account is the restraint of what they discussed - as Moore acknowledges (p55),. Had she wanted to cause a sensation, she would have claimed that Darwin was truly "converted" and written a vivid account of his testimony. In fact, she merely records his views on Hebrews and delicately raises the subject of Darwin's evolution contradicting Genesis. There is no claim of any conversion, but simply a record of Darwin's renewed interest in the Christian faith.

Moore's work and viewpoint

Moore has amassed a huge amount of information in his book, and we acknowledge our considerable debt to his researches. He is quite generous in some instances, even asserting that there was much that supported her account. However, he has little sympathy with "fundamentalists" and "evangelicals". (Incidentally, when any writer use the word "fundamentalist" one can be reasonably certain he is using it in a derogatory sense.)

He says that Lady Hope was "a skilled raconteur, able to summon up poignant scenes and conversations, and embroider them with spiritual sentimentality"(p53). As we have said, if by "summon up" he means "fabrication" then he presents not a scrap of evidence in its support. We would mention that Moore admits that Lady Hope *was* able to distinguish between fact and fiction when she wrote her biography of her father (pers. comm.). Her husband, Mr. Denny, is described as "having made his fortune in pork, larded the coffers of many evangelical enterprises" (p43). Thus, the family fortune was diminishing before she was later swindled out of her remaining money.

Moore also makes a disgraceful charge against Lady Hope's father, a godly man who did much for the people of Madras. Captain Cotton provided an irrigation system in the Godavari district in India and invited a series of missionaries out there who established orphanages and hospitals and much else that must have brought enormous benefits and prosperity to the area (Rob). Yet Moore's comment on Cotton is that he was "the man who wrung more revenue out of the Madras plantations than any previous administrator" (M44).

Moody and Sankey are "a gifted duo like their English contemporaries Gilbert and Sullivan" (p43). Thus, Moore diminishes these famous evangelists to being just mere entertainers. Moore is rightly exercising his freedom to criticise these Christians for he lives in a nation whose tolerance they had no small part in bringing about.

Moore's dislike of evangelicals and fundamentalists is so very apparent that one is left wondering whether this has affected his objectivity in dealing with the story of the evangelical Lady Hope.

He also noted "There is no doubt that Lady Hope was making comments about Darwin to her religious friends long before the story was published". From this, one would have expected at least three or four such incidents might be mentioned. This is important, for if she did freely talk about her visit to others shortly after, it would give very strong confirmation that she did hold such a conversation with Darwin. Yet he only refers to Sir Robert Anderson's note that said she was "much with Darwin". Were there other conversations?

We raised with Moore (a) the Fegan-Felix misidentification, (b) whether there were other records of her conversations and (c) that his bias against evangelicals could be interpreted as damaging his reliability for fair reporting.

His replied that he was very busy and that "numerous leads remain to be followed up" and, somewhat surprisingly, that "vindicating Lady Hope's story" was for him a "chimerical task"!

Moore spent 20 years collecting his information, travelling to several continents, and was funded by the Open University. Would that Christian researchers could call upon such financial resources to support their investigations.

THE EVIDENCE AGAINST

In all my reading of Darwin's last days, *it must be admitted that I found nothing whatsoever that gave any support to Lady Hope's record of her visit.* There is not a single reference to it by Darwin or any member of the family. One might have expected just one passing mention in a letter letting slip that Darwin was reading the Bible or some note of a visit by a Christian lady etc. We will therefore examine this aspect with relevant comments.

The two accounts

There is one important point that appears to have escaped all who have followed Moore in criticising Lady Hope's character. Moore is clearly critical of Lady Hope, yet he admits that Lady Hope *probably did* visit Darwin, for she gives an accurate description of his clothes, facial expressions, the room, etc. Yet he also quotes the Darwin family's total denial that she ever entered Darwin's house.

Now Moore, and all who have adopted his conclusions, cannot have it both ways. *Either* Lady Hope *did* go to Darwin's House or she did not. As Moore admits that she *did, then the total denial of the Darwin family of any knowledge of her visit(s) or even of any knowledge of her existence, is a falsehood.* Emma at least, must have known of them, and if she visited Darwin several times, it is unlikely that no other member of the family ever got to hear of her visits. If Henrietta and others did not know of her visits as they were absent at that time, then they should not have denied it so vigorously. It is my conviction that several members of the family *may* have known of the visits but the implications were too traumatic for them to accept. It is this that seems to be the most likely cause of them maintaining their denial. *We would therefore contend that if Moore is right in saying she did visit Darwin, all the family's vehement denials of her visit(s) were false, whether wittingly or unwittingly.* It raises, once again, their integrity.

The "death-bed" conversion.

His daughter Henrietta wrote "I was present at his deathbed. Lady Hope was not present during his last illness, or any illness. I believe he never even saw her, but in any case she had no influence over him in any department of thought or belief.... The whole story has no foundation whatever."

Now Lady Hope never claimed that she was "at his deathbed", and those who quote this are describing a fabricated scene in order to discredit her.

Darwin's agnosticism

Most of Darwin's letters and writings, far from indicating a return to Christianity, show that, even at a late stage of his life, he remained an agnostic. This greatly troubled his wife Emma and his daughter Henrietta. They insisted, against fierce opposition from the brothers, principally Francis, who were Rationalists and Freethinkers, that any anti-religious passages should be removed from the official collection of his letters.

Moore makes a noteworthy comment on this censoring of Darwin's letters for he says "With her [Emma's] guidance, *the world would know only the 'Darwin' the family chose to reveal*" (p24). This could be particularly significant if Lady Hope's visit was unwelcome as we will see.

What is not disputed is Darwin's approval of Church activities. Only a few weeks before he died he sent a donation to the South American Missionary Society in view of the good effect of the missionaries in Tierra del Fuego (Croft:105). One of his life-long friends was a High Anglican Churchman, and he helped with several "good works" for the poor in Downe, working in conjunction with the Church (M:16) and highly approved of Fegan's work. *His support for Christian activities is far greater than one would expect from reading his more public letters of this period* - as we will now consider.

Darwin's letters

That Darwin remained an agnostic to the end of his life is mainly based upon the letters he wrote at that time. Seven letters have been quoted (Q12/2:99) that show he still accepted evolution and there is little reference to any moral dilemma or Christian thinking.

Lady Hope visited him in late 1881, and any interest in Christianity would only date from about that time. *All previous writings can therefore be discounted as they cannot refer to a change that occurred later*. This would apply to the first four of the letters quoted that are dated between 1873 and 1879 (the letter to the German student) and Darwin's "Autobiography". However, even then he was admitting that he "fluctuated" and that he had "never been an Atheist in the sense of denying the existence of a God" (1879). He said that "the impossibility of conceiving that this grand and wondrous universe, with our conscious selves, arose through chance, seems to me the chief argument for the existence of God" (1873). He also stated that one's faith is a private matter for the individual alone.

There are three letters dated February 1882 written two months before his death in April of that year. In all three he affirms his continuing belief in evolution, but this cannot be construed as confirming he was not a Christian; the two subjects are quite separate. The nearest he comes to touching matters of faith is when he wonders whether the existence of God can be proved from the laws of nature, which is "a perplexing subject, on which I have often thought, but cannot see my way clearly".

It is agreed that there is nothing in these last letters that actually indicates any return to faith, but neither is there anything that flatly denies it.

Darwin's dilemma?

In order to fully appreciate the comments that follow, we would pause here and ask the reader to place himself in Darwin's position. Within his own lifetime, he had become world-famous for his theory, and was one of the most prestigious men of all time. He was well aware that his theory undermined Christianity, but now, facing death, he may have sought the certainty and reassurance of the faith that he had first studied in his youth. Had he publicly admitted that he had returned to the Christian faith, let alone a truly evangelical faith, the repercussions would have been cataclysmic - both for him and the whole family. The uproar it would have created would have been unbearable to his family - both the religious and anti-religious sides. It is little wonder, therefore, that he should have decided that any interest in a true (evangelical) Christian faith should be kept very private, such that it was not even discussed with family members. Almost certainly, they would have become aware of his new interest, but there could have been an unspoken agreement that it should be completely ignored; they also would have been well aware of the repercussions.

Darwin may have maintained his stance of agnosticism for the benefit of his public image, but asked Lady Hope, whose vibrant evangelical faith was obvious to all, to visit him and discuss her faith with him. As I contended in a previous work, Darwin seems to have had one attitude for his atheistic contacts, and another for his local acquaintances. Was he hoping to have the "best of both worlds"?

Emma Darwin

Some have suggested that Emma herself was behind the "Lady Hope story", but this does not bear critical examination. That Lady Hope wrote the account for the Watchman Examiner is beyond dispute.

Moore notes (p119) that Emma was "reportedly present" on 28th September, when he suggests Lady Hope came. Whatever day she visited, we can be fairly certain Emma was present in the house.

Emma Darwin's silence does present a problem. She was keen to get Darwin to read his Bible, and if he was reading it when Lady Hope came, surely she would have rejoiced and referred to it at some stage. Yet she is silent. She was also sympathetic to the Band of Hope, entertaining them in the house, as she wrote on 18th August 1881, about the time when Lady Hope would have been visiting. Also, Fegan wrote that sometimes members of the family came to his Gospel services. That they did not go regularly suggests that they did not have an evangelical faith - a crucial distinction in the eyes of this writer at least, which may explain much that seems inexplicable at this distance in time.

She wrote to Darwin in 1838 when they were courting, begging him to read his Bible and referred to "our Saviours farewell discourse" in John's Gospel. The family attended the local Anglican church but in 1871 left for another when a boorish new vicar came. However, she held firmly to the Wedgewood family's Unitarian beliefs and Moore says Emma was "Unitarian by conviction, Anglican in practice" (M:14 and Desmond:403).

Emma's silence about a change in Darwin's faith is against Lady Hope's account, but Moore notes that in 1881 she said that "nothing can be said too severe upon the doctrine of eternal punishment for disbelief" (M:36).

That none of the family were evangelical leaves the possibility that they may all have been disturbed by any deep change of heart by their famous father.   Even Emma, who rejected evolution and was concerned for her husband's beliefs, "would not have tolerated anything so intrusive as personal evangelizing" (M:57).

The date of her visit

Moore gives no evidence for his suggestion that she came in the afternoon of the 28 September - the same day as Darwin's visitors. There was very good weather on 14, 16-18 September and 28 September - 4 October. Fegan fell ill in early July and Lady Hope could have visited Darwin several times during his absence, with her last and most memorable visit that took place in the late sunny period being the one she most clearly remembered and recorded.

There is one important point. Moore notes that none of those in the family who so strongly denied Lady Hope visited Darwin were actually living there at the time, and that when her story surfaced in 1915, no adult was alive who had been regularly present during 1881-2. Thus, no one could give first hand evidence that she had *never* visited Darwin (M:97).

Darwin's illness

Some have contended that his debilitating illness may have been due to catching Chagas's disease while in S. America, but medical experts say that his symptoms do not conform to this. Croft's book is revealing in just how serious Darwin's illnesses were, yet he was very fit and walking seven miles a day whilst on a "water cure" away from home. His symptoms returned when he came home and started work again. From this, we would contend that Darwin's debilitating symptoms were entirely due to his stress of working and particularly in his propagation of evolution which he knew was destructive of Christianity and good moral influence; a view with which Moore and Croft agree. *If this is so, then we are dealing with a man with a tortured conscience whatever may be said.* Like many before him, it would be only natural that he should seek relief from his sense of guilt from One who had come to earth for that very purpose.

Even Moore admits that Darwin's thoughts may have turned to religion, for his brother Erasmus had recently died, and "his own health was giving 'much cause for uneasiness'" (M:56). During these last months he "thought much on the eternal questions - chance and design, providence and pain" and looked forward to death (M:27). Darwin was not the first to review his life as death neared - and he was certainly not the last.

In June 1881, just before the Lady Hope visit, he was taken ill while on holiday, and wrote that he was looking forward "to Downe graveyard as the sweetest place on earth" (Croft:108). When Darwin suffered a heart attack on the day of his death, he whispered "I am not in the least afraid to die" (M:29). Did he now have faith or was he simply not fearful of his future?

We would make one small observation. Lady Hope records that "his fingers twitched nervously" while she was speaking to him. Now this was a known characteristic of Darwin "when he was lost in thought" (M:55). What could be more natural that now she knew Darwin more familiarly after several visits, she should gently broach the subject of evolution and its detrimental effect upon Christianity? Darwin's nervous reaction was noted by her - and the whole account begins to "hang together".

Did he become a Christian?

What, then, can we say about Darwin? Let us be clear: He never *publicly* recanted from his theory of evolution or professed a new Christian faith.

Moore dates Lady Hope's visit as (possibly) Thursday 28th September 1881 - the very same day that Darwin was visited by Buchner and Aveling (Karl Marx's son-in-law). According to all the records of Darwin's comments during this meeting he said that Christianity "was not supported by evidence" and "I never gave up Christianity until I was forty years of age", mainly due to his father's and his daughter Annie's deaths (Desmond:658). This gives not an inkling of a return to a true Christian faith. We would, however, note that these comments were made to two very belligerent anti-Christians and if Darwin was keeping any change of heart from his family, he was hardly likely to tell his visitors of it, but would maintain his agnostic front. He and Emma strongly disliked the two men.

What is strange is that Emma, writing a letter of the events of this period, mentions several visitors but not the quite important visit of the two men or Lady Hope. Moore considers this was because both visits were "fraught".

For whatever reason, it shows that there was much that might be deliberately ignored if it was unwelcome. If the visit of these two important people went unrecorded, *this could explain the failure to record Lady Hope's visits she may have made at Darwin's request.* Indeed, *I would contend that Emma's failure to refer to these visits, one of which (Buchner's) is known to have taken place, is a perfectly satisfactory reason why Lady Hope's visits also went unrecorded.*

Emma's reaction is understandable. The chasm between liberal and evangelical Christianity is as deep as it ever was. As one who has been on both sides of that bottomless divide, I can speak with some experience.

In meditating on this absence of any reference by the family to Lady Hope's visits or Darwin's change of faith, I can only suggest that there may have been a quite deliberate agreement within the family to say nothing whatsoever about what would have been a late and very unwelcome turn of events. Originally Darwin's letters were heavily edited by the family and that *all* the information in books and letters about his life has been filtered through hands that have no sympathy with evangelical Christianity. This may well be a significant factor in all these records of his life.

The main point in support of her account are the many verifications of Lady Hope's sterling Christian personality and honesty. Even Fegan, after criticising her, said he had "never had an unpleasant word with Lady Hope. Up to the end, we were on friendly terms." There are also the independent references to Darwin's change of heart that were reported soon after his death. *Sir Robert Anderson's note is particularly important.* Furthermore, Darwin must have invited her to see him as she describes the house and Darwin's situation and mannerisms so accurately.

On the other hand, she was obviously a strong character. Was she a spendthrift with money - albeit for good causes? Were Fegan's comments on her character valid? Might she have been a trial to her husband? Did she "elaborate" her discussion with Darwin to impress her American audience? Why did Darwin never speak to Fegan or Emma of his faith?

We would have liked to conclude that, on balance, her account is truthful, but there is also much against it, and we cannnot come to a firm conclusion either way. Whichever side is right, it leaves unanswered questions on the other side. We have presented the evidence for and against, and must leave the reader to decide. No doubt, as ever, the prejudices and bias with which each one comes to this controversy may have already predetermined the result of their conclusions.

Whatever decision the reader may come to, it would be as well to repeat the comments I made at the end of an earlier examination:

> However, even if it were eventually to be proven that Darwin did return to the Christian faith in his last years, let me hastily add (lest my creationist colleagues raise their "hurrahs" too soon) that this would have little effect upon the convinced evolutionist. He will most likely simply dismiss it as a weakness of Darwin in his old age. Furthermore, it will make absolutely no difference to his "scientific" outlook.... He has enshrined the dogma of "evolution in some form" and to it he must hold - for he has nowhere else to go (Bow88:192).

SECTION 6.7
GOD'S HIDDEN PRESENCE

It is interesting to realise that in all subjects dealing in some way, even remotely, with the existence of God, no final compelling evidence can ever be, or has ever been, produced. So frequently did this become evident in research in a wide range of subjects that it was felt worthwhile to list some of them and then examine the theological reasons for this situation.

The following are just an outline of some of the subjects where a clear conclusion has not as yet been reached, and it seems unlikely that it ever will be.

1. Factual arguments in evolution and creation

Neither creationists nor evolutionists can provide irrefutable evidence for their differing viewpoints. All the crucial events occurred in the distant past, and cannot be subjected to any laboratory re-run of the "experiment". Each side can therefore only present their interpretation of what evidence exists today. The listener is then "at liberty" (?) to decide which has the better evidence in its support. However, people do not realise that their minds on this subject have already been made up by the place that the concept of God has in their basic view of life in general - a subject dealt with more fully below.

We would also note that there are some features that seem to support evolution, such as the similarity of apes to men and the apparent "evolutionary" sequence of the fossil record. It is almost as if God is allowing those who insist on following a false view of life to use false evidence in its support. This is their own deliberate choice, against the true evidence, and their condemnation will be that much greater (Matt. 13:10-16).

2. The existence of God.

No purely rational argument for the existence of God can be logically set forth. One of the postulates in the line of reasoning must include the word "God" and whether He exists or not is the very point that is to be proven. All that can be done is to point to a wide variety of evidence that is best explained by acknowledging that God exists.

All such evidence is countered by the existence of suffering in the world, and Christians are frequently challenged to reconcile this with their claim that God is all-powerful and good. Yet God placed suffering at the very heart of the Cross, and from this there is a perfectly satisfactory theological reply to this apparent paradox (Bow92).

3. Chaos theory.

We can never predict what the final outcome of any complex series of events will be i.e. the weather. To make an accurate prediction requires virtually perfect knowledge of the starting conditions. These are never known with anything like complete or adequate knowledge and these imperfections make the predictions increasingly less accurate very rapidly indeed as we try to predict over longer periods of time. Predictions can therefore only cover a very short time span. The problem rapidly becomes *intractable* and no computer can handle the massive amount of information that is needed to predict any event in the long term. We refer to this again in Appendix 2.

4. Geological formations

Neither evolution nor creation can describe the precise sequence of events that have produced the present geological formations. Their form and structure are phenomenally complex, and it is possible that there may have been conditions existing at the time of the Flood that are either not present at this time, or are so reduced that at their present low level, they would be quite inadequate to bring about the conditions now visible.

It is possible that a full explanation may eventually be forthcoming, but, as we will see when we deal with the subject later, the present complexity is daunting.

5. Geocentricity

If it could be proven that the earth was at the centre of the universe, it would be a death-blow to the materialist and humanist. We deal with this subject more thoroughly in Appendix 10, but we will here note that secular scientists cannot actually prove that the Earth travels around the Sun. It is intriguing that God should so form the planetary system that the huge sun *ought* to be the centre around which the planets travel, yet the scientific evidence does not support this interpretation. As always happens, we come to such profound subjects with our preconceptions already formed and it is these that ultimately determine whether we accept the evidence, and not the plain facts themselves.

6. Discovery of the Ark

There have been many reputed sightings of this famous vessel, but nothing substantial has ever been produced. That the most likely site is at the centre where East meets West and the highly charged political overtones that that generates is probably all part of God's plan of which uncertainty of human life is a specific feature.

One might speculate on the repercussions if clear evidence of its existence were ever to be discovered and publicised. It is not impossible that this might occur at some stage - perhaps at a time when there is severe persecution of Christians. Should this ever take place, some might hail this as a great confirmation of their belief at a time when the faith of many might be failing. However, Christ did say that, "it is an evil generation that demands a sign", - and to doubting Thomas, "Blessed are those who see not and yet believe." True faith is a gift of God. It is a rational faith and does not rely upon an unending stream of "signs and wonders" for its continued existence.

7. Accuracy of the Bible.

We have discussed in Section 3.9 - A Biblical Chronology - the differences between the various texts of the Hebrew Old Testament. In that section, we noted that few Christians realise that the text used by Christ and the Disciples was not the Massoretic text from which our Old Testament has been translated. We will not repeat the discussion set out there but mention the subject here as yet another aspect of God not providing an absolute and final authority that is completely free of all problems.

....

The crucial aspect about this seeming lack of certainty in the seven examples set out above - and more could be added - is that they are all part of God's perfect programme. He never intended that we should be absolutely convinced by factual evidence alone. To have done so would have led to an unacceptable form of "Faith by Logical Argument."

It might be thought that each person looks at the available evidence in the world around him and from this draws his own conclusions as to what life is all about; this is really far from what actually happens.

We have all come to certain (pre)conceptions as to what life is about, based upon experiences but more upon an individual attitude that depends upon what extent we allow our self-centredness to dominate our motivation. It is then, from this very personal viewpoint, that *we make our minds up about what we will accept as facts that fit this conceptual framework, and evidence that does not fit is rejected as untrue.* Often there is no rational basis for such a decision - only our "point of view".

When we "see" life from a completely different "point of view" - as a person does when they experiences a true Christian conversion - what has been such a stumbling block before that event (e.g. the Genesis record of "impossible" creation events) suddenly becomes perfectly reasonable once the existence of an omnipotent creator God is accepted. In this, it is important to realise that it is not the facts that have changed, only the attitude of the individual. Many can testify that the experience of true conversion brings an immense sense of the broadening of one's appreciation of nature and the whole of life in general.

As a result of all this it becomes apparent that eventually each man must bear the responsibility for the decisions he makes about many subjects such as the existence of God, evolution, creation etc. whether or not he is familiar with much or little of the facts that are available. It is not the quantity or even the quality of the evidence - which surrounds him on all sides - *but the interpretation that each individual decides to place upon it.*

On a subject as important as creation (that requires a creator) or evolution (by which God can be dismissed) we make our minds up first and only then do we accept or reject evidence for or against the existence of an almighty God. Trying to convince non-believers by purely factual arguments is almost impossible. They know by instinct that if the evidence for crea*tion* is accepted, then there must be a Crea*tor.* It is for this reason, *and no other,* that the non-believer rejects, or more likely ignores, the evidence for creation.

This leads us straight to the writer to the Hebrews who said quite clearly "Through faith we understand that the worlds were framed by the word of God, so that things which are seen were not made by things that do appear" (Heb. 11:2).

For the true evangelical, Bible-believing Christian, it will be found that the only ultimate authority is the internal witness of the Holy Spirit regarding the perfect nature of God. If we *know* that God is perfect, has never made a mistake, and will ultimately bring to glory every single one of those whose name is written in His Book of Life, then we have no need of an external authority to provide us with an ultimate "proof" of our Christian faith.

SECTION 6.8
THE IRRATIONALITY OF RATIONALISM

(In what follows, the terms "rationalist", "materialist" and "reductionist" are virtually interchangeable. A "reductionist" is one who reduces all life to the movement of atoms alone, there being no other activity in existence. A "materialist" believes only the material world exists, there being no spiritual world. A "rationalist" uses only reason, denying that spiritual revelation exists.)

It is the belief of many that the only purely rational approach to life is through the discipline of "science". With its aura of deduction from the hard facts of experimental results, all other approaches to life are considered to retain elements of emotion and philosophical or theological preconceptions.

Science is only one of the many facets of life that impinge upon a person's awareness. It claims, by inference, to be pre-eminently the most rational of all the disciplines, but we will demonstrate that its efforts to isolate itself from external preconceptions is itself irrational.

This is the conclusion of Godel's Theorem in which he proved that a system of axioms can never be based on itself. In order to prove its validity, statements from outside the system must be used. The implications of this are profound and affect *all* disciplines of life. On this basis, Science is possible only within a larger framework of non-scientific issues and concerns. This subject has been well set out by Ancil (Anc) upon whom much of what follows is based.

The important point to grasp is that no system can validate itself by referring only to its own statements. Its authenticity or validation can *only* come from some other area that is outside and superior to itself. Let us look at some simple examples.

(i) There is the well known conundrum of the Cretan making the statement, "All Cretans are liars." If the statement is true, then he also is lying, which makes the statement false. Therefore, if it is true it must be false. The only way in which it can be checked is by someone outside the Cretans investigating their honesty.

(ii) J.B.S. Haldane said:

If my mental processes are determined wholly by the motion of atoms in my brain, I have no reason to suppose that my beliefs are true... and hence I have no reason for supposing my brain is composed of atoms.

From this, the process of thinking, being merely the movement of atoms in our brain, means that anything, even rational thinking, cannot reflect what is really true. This undermines the whole metaphysical basis that science claims it possesses, for it contends its announcements, based upon logical thinking, is an accurate portrayal of the real world. Haldane, however, takes the concept even further by saying that the idea that thinking is solely due to atomic motions in the brain is based upon "scientific" experiments. But we have just seen that thinking is only atomic motion and therefore can prove nothing. Thus, we cannot even be sure that atoms even exist in our brains. We need something outside of ourselves to accept "scientific facts".

(iii) C.S. Lewis showed that thinking is a very special process:

All arguments about the validity of thought make a tacit, and illegitimate, exception in favour of the bit of thought that you are doing at that moment. It has to be left outside the discussion and simply believed in, in the simple old-fashioned way. Thus the Freudian proves that all thoughts are due to complexes except the thought which constitutes the proof itself. The Marxist proves that all thoughts result from class conditioning - except the thought he is thinking while he says this. It is therefore impossible to begin with any other data whatever and from there find out whether thought is valid. You must do exactly the opposite - you must begin by admitting the self-evidence of logical thought and then believe all other things only insofar as they agree with that. The validity of thought is central: all other things have to be fitted around it as best they can." (Lew47).

Ancil comments:

> In other words, reason serves as an external standard to evaluate or validate, a discussion. It can therefore never be the subject of reasonable enquiry.

C.S. Lewis's *Miracles* is one of the strongest and clearest rebuttals of the superficial arguments of the rationalists, materialists and anti-Christians. Usually those who hold to one of these views encompass the other two also. For those who have enjoyed his logical arguments in his *Mere Christianity*, this book is recommended for those who seek to have their minds stretched even further by this master of unanswerable logic in defence of Christianity.

When all the arguments have been studied, it becomes clear that our ability to reason is a direct gift of God, for before creation, the Council of the Trinity declared "Let us make man in our image" (Gen. 1:26). It is by this gift that we can made order out of the world we find we inhabit. It is this acknowledge-ment that it *is* a gift from God that enables us to examine God's world and make sense of it. Those who deny this have no ultimate basis upon which they can logically assess the myriads of "facts" that face them in daily life.

This is very much bound up with the inability of any discipline to authenticate itself; it must always receive this from some external authority. This authority itself must also be validated by some greater authority - and so on - but *not* ad infinitum, for *at the end of all superior authorities it will be found that God is the ultimate authority*. As in science there is a cause for any incident, this chain of causality will eventually end with the Great Uncaused Cause - the Being who has no cause - for he has always existed; i.e. God.

For those who deny the existence of the only Person who could authenticate the reason for their existence, there is no ultimate authority to which they can appeal. They can all be shown to be false *on their self-chosen basis* as we have tried to outline above. Ancil quotes Wilhelmsen who says:

> He looks within and he now finds, after so many centuries, that there is simply nothing there to hold him up, to sustain him, that - looking through the mirage of the rationalist ego - there is only a bottomless pit.

Ancil points out that "The creationist perspective is fully rational for it relies upon validating statements external to science - Divine Revelation. The creationist recognises that science is incomplete and must be based on some thing more profound. Therefore, creationism is the preferred frame of reference within which science should be conducted."

Logic - the Christian's sharp sword!

Whilst meditating on this subject of the illogicality of the rationalist's basic arguments, several other illogical claims on other subjects became obvious. So frequently was this found that one could come to a most remarkable conclusion. This is that *all statements by materialists regarding their materialistic views can be shown to be ultimately illogical and self-contradictory.*

This may seem to be an exaggerated claim but we have seen some of them set out above. Let us look at these more closely and a few other examples that have been collected over the years.

1. Lewis refers to Freud's claim that "all thoughts are due to complexes". The illogicality of this is that Freud clearly assumes that *his* statement is true and is *not* due to any complex *he* has! He is effectively saying he is the only person who is free of complexes - a doubtful proposition indeed.

2. Lewis similarly shows that Marx's claim that all thoughts stem from class-conditioning is illogical. Marx infers that only *his* thinking is a true statement and is free of class bias. With his deceptive philosophy and impoverished background, his writings are full of bitter envy of those who have property and a secure position in life. He is just as class-conditioned as everyone else; in fact even more so.

3. The Rationalist philosopher Hume concluded that it is only reasonable to believe in God, but as we know that God does not exist, therefore human reason cannot be trusted.

His error is that pointed out by Lewis; he is excluding from his generalisation the very statement that he is making which is a rational deduction. In claiming that his reasoning is true, he is effectively disallowing everybody else's but making his rational statement the sole point of reference in the universe.

Hume never extended his arguments to propose what *could* be used as a final authority in men's lives, but left the whole subject "in the air". He thereby betrayed his lack of rationalist rigour, for had he done so, he knew that he would have destroyed the whole basis of his viewpoint. In fact, he hid the weaknesses of his case under a mass of convoluted arguments.

So poor was Hume's case that Paley had no difficulty in demolishing it in his *Natural Theology*. This book was a bastion of strength of the Christian faith. It went through 18 editions and was required reading at Cambridge University until 1922. As we know, Darwin, when studying to be an Anglican minister, delighted in the clarity of his writing and learned by heart many of the logical arguments he set out in support of the Christian viewpoint. With so many thousands of copies having been printed, it is strange that now it is almost impossible to obtain a second-hand copy. What, one wonders, could have happened to them all?

This lack has now been filled by Bill Cooper's *The Sighted Watchmaker* (Coo97) which is a reprint of this classic with minor clarifications and modernisations. The title is a riposte to Dawkins's *The Blind Watchmaker*.

4. There is the argument that "All religions ultimately lead to God." What is ignored is that all religions claim they have an exclusive path to God, and that they are the "only true way". With them all claiming that only they have the right way to god, it is possible that *none* of them are correct, or that one, and only one, *might* be correct in its claim - all others must then be false. What is certain is that they cannot *all* be correct, and therefore the statement is false. In addition, it is not only false, it is misleading, for it gives a veneer of respectability to all other religions and deceives non-Christians into believing they will eventually enter heaven.

There is the opposite argument used that "It is unacceptable that Christianity rejects all other faiths. It must be more tolerant of them."

The illogicality here should be obvious. Before reading further, we suggest that you pause here, examine the sentence and see if you can see what it is.
****

The answer? The speaker is insisting that Christians should be more tolerant, but he himself in *intolerant* of the Christian position. If he is wanting the Christian to be more tolerant, then he should be more tolerant of the

Christian view.

5. There are those intent on denigrating the activities of missionaries. One of the arguments used by such people is that missionaries are destroying the natural culture of the natives they evangelise, and that "they have no right to change the views of the natives."

We will gloss over the fact that the introduction of the Christian gospel brings a freedom from fear of witchcraft and generates peace between tribes. Many tribesmen find the "benefits" so good that they risk their lives to take the gospel to their enemies.

Examining the argument, it has been pointed out that if missionaries have no right to try and change the thinking of the natives, then the critics similarly have no right to try to change the thinking of the missionaries; the critics are doing what they will not allow missionaries to do; change attitudes and behaviour.

The reader might like to exercise his mental muscles by spotting the inherent contradictions in some more paradoxes:

(i) "There are no absolutes."

(ii) "There are only points of view on an issue, and none is *the* point of view."

(iii) "The rules of logic are not absolute."

Richard Dawkins

The present most outspoken advocate of the scientific, evolutionistic and materialistic view, is Richard Dawkins. So extreme are his views that many thoughtful people have realised how weak and narrow his arguments are and they have begun to question the very foundations of "scientific" thinking.

He will have nothing to do with any supernatural, moral or religious influences within his ultra-reductionist viewpoint. What he, and all others like him, fail to realise is that they have cut the ground from under their own feet. As we have tried to show above, materialism can only be validated by something outside materialism. When he, or any other scientist refers to "Nature", it can be taken as a means of avoiding the evidence for design by God.

In his works, Dawkins may use such words as "better", "improvement", "wonderful"; but all these imply some form of value judgement. He should be asked how he derives the concept of "better" from inanimate objects that are only atoms performing their rigidly defined activity. Is he prepared to grant atoms the ability to think and have "aims"?

If Dawkins insists that only atoms exist, why should we accept the motions of the atoms in his brain when he is thinking and speaking as being ultimate truth? If there are only atoms, then there is no such thing as "truth" - only the movements of atoms!

Yet another inherent contradiction in the materialist's case is that they consistently diminish the importance of man in the vastness of the universe such that his cosmic "value" is insignificant. This would then make any opinions he expressed quite worthless. Yet they elevate their own opinions to be superior to all others and to be the final and only acceptable view of life and the universe! (Cust:220). The arrogance of such claims is breathtaking.

In view of the importance of the Christian view of life in undergirding all the scientific disciplines, as we will demonstrate below, the spectacle of people, like Richard Dawkins, fiercely sawing off the very branch upon which they are sitting becomes quite laughable.

We would suggest that those interested in defending the Christian faith by the simple logical arguments set out above might like to develop this form of apologetics. Its skilled use can be a powerful weapon in the right circumstances.

Having said this, its use should always be with the aim of "speaking the truth in love". One can win arguments - but lose an opportunity of presenting the Good News of God's willingness to forgive the listener's rebellion.

SECTION 6.9
THE CHRISTIAN BASIS OF SCIENCE

This may seem an exaggerated claim, but we will show that such a statement is well supported.

It is generally accepted that scientific research assumes that the laws operating this universe do not change. In addition, it is obvious that *how* matter came into existence (even that in the Big Bang) is outside the sphere of scientific experiments as they can only deal with the present operation of the physical world.

What science cannot do is explain how the laws that govern matter (atomic forces, gravity etc.) came into existence. It is perfectly legitimate to ask why scientists should assume that these laws are constant everywhere in the universe. It displays a vitally important fundamental assumption - that these laws are not subject to capricious change by some other agent(s).

The Christian view and the failure of other religions

Eric Snow summarised the work of three authors on this subject (Snow and www4) and listed seven barriers to the production of the scientific approach to nature. Adapting these, we list the positive fundamentals of the Christian faith that eventually gave rise to the scientific investigation of the universe.

(1) The laws that govern the working of the universe were established by God and are unchangeable - apart from miracles, over which He still has sole control. That God is all-powerful and unchangeable is one of the most important basics of Christian doctrine, and this naturally gave rise to the unchangableness of the laws of nature that He created.

In contrast, other religions allowed their gods to change the workings of nature according to their whim. As their will was unsearchable, then any investigation of nature was pointless as the results could vary from day to day. This sense of apathy and fatalism in the face of their god(s) is the fundamental reason why other faiths failed to develop the rational, scientific approach to exploring the universe

(2) The Christian has a strong sense of the progress of time. He knows that the universe had a definite beginning at a specific time in history, and that it is progressing to one final end. This concept gives rise to the sequence of cause and effect that is the basis of the scientific investigation. To highlight this, the concept of Christ having to be offered as a sacrifice for each cycle of reincarnation is both contrary to the Bible and abhorrent to all believers.

Many other religions are caught in the morass of reincarnation. Time is ultimately endless and life is only a repetitive cycle. Such a concept breeds a sense of hopelessness and apathy. This is also the end result when the future is thought to be completely under the control of a changeable "god". There is then no point in struggling against one's fate, which is out of one's control.

(3) The Christian is conscious that he must take full responsibility for his actions and that ultimately he will be held accountable to God.

This involves the concept that man has been created as a special being who can relate to God, unlike animals. Only then does he have true significance and an active and responsible part to play in the running of the world.

For adherents of other faiths, their future is already predetermined, and whilst they may be urged to perform good works, such admonitions are swamped by the pervasive attitude of fatalism when they contemplate their ultimate, unchangeable end. Such an attitude is a powerful barrier to a zealous investigation of the world in which they find themselves.

(4) The Christian is free to investigate the universe for the real underlying causes of its workings. By discovering these basic rules, he is able to predict the outcome of certain situations and conditions. Thus, experiments can be conducted the results of which can be used for the benefit of man.

Other faiths may make a priori explanations of natural events; i.e. the imposition of fables (or the activities of the gods) to "explain" events. For example, in astrology the heavens are considered as alive or divine - they are the habitation of the gods who control man's destiny. This leads to passivity again as there is little point in trying to change what has been determined by "the gods". Scientific astronomy could not arise from such a preconception.

This prescribing of an event to some previous "fabulous" activity gives the impression that the "cause" of an event is known, and it therefore prevents the proper investigation of the event to ascertain the real cause.

(5) Nature is separate from God and it is to be investigated as part of God's command to man to subdue and have dominion over the earth (Gen. 1:28).

The pantheistic view of the world (i.e. even inanimate material has "life" within it) gives nature a false, human-like identity with the implication that man should disturb it as little as possible.

Another false view is that the world is unreal. The aim is to achieve spiritual passivity ("Nirvana") and the world is only an illusion. No one who holds such views will bother to investigate what he does not believe exists.

(6) Christianity has the right balance between reason and faith. The religious leaders should not reject the findings of true science. Equally, scientists need to be aware of the limitations of their sphere of enquiry. They must heed the superior claims of Christianity which alone has the broadest understanding of God's purpose and will, of which science is but one part.

....

The basic concepts of life held by members of other religions have been laid down by their religious leaders - with all the faults and errors outlined above. Any questioning of principles is likely to result in rejection, persecution and even death.

In contrast, the True Christian is free to make what enquiries he will. Differences of opinion will not result in persecution, but should provoke open and honest discussion in order to determine the truth of the subject. Where such truth is earnestly sought, God will always be found at the end of it - for "All truth is God's truth."

Snow reviews the major religions - Chinese Buddhism, Hindu and Muslim - and shows that while they had varying degrees of most of the failings listed above, some had one or more that particularly obstructed the development of a true scientific discipline. The Chinese had the concept of Yin and Yang that overruled all life and they held to the unreality of the world. The Hindus were pantheists, devotees of astrology and considered the world an illusion.

The Muslim religion is free from several of the listed weaknesses and initially produced important books on mathematics, medicine and astronomy, but there was little development after 1200 AD. Snow ascribes this to their theologians emphasising the Koran's teaching on the absolute (and arbitrary) will of God as distinct from his reason (see 6 above).

Some Islamic philosophers also held to Aristotle's misleading teachings which similarly plagued Christian thinking for centuries. It was only when these were eventually overthrown that real progress could be made. Snow says that Islam had no equivalent to Thomas Aquinas who made a philosophical separation between nature and God. However, as Shaeffer has shown, this unfortunately resulted in the eventual dominance of humanistic nature (i.e. Science) over theology as we have today. We will show that it was the Puritan faith that had the right balance between doctrine and reason that was to be the real source of the scientific revolution.

Thus, no other religion could have possibly given rise to modern day science. This should be a sobering thought to any scientist who is not a Christian, for, *whether they realise it or not, when they conduct their experiments, they must temporarily abandon the basic tenets of their faith and adopt a Christian viewpoint of nature.*

The importance of our concept of God

We would emphasise this dependence of science upon a nation's concept of God. That great preacher, A.W. Tozer, in the opening words of his book "The Knowledge of the Holy", made one of the most penetrating and thought-provoking observations this author has ever read when he said:

> What comes into our minds when we think about God is the most important thing about us. The history of mankind will probably show that no people has ever risen above its religion, and man's spiritual history will positively demonstrate that no religion has ever been greater than it's concept of God. Worship is pure or base as its worshipper entertains high or low thoughts of God.

In parallel with this high view of God, the Westminster Shorter Catechism states:

> **God is a Spirit who is infinite, eternal and unchanging in His being, wisdom, power, holiness, justice, goodness and truth.**

No other religion can match such a sublime description of the attributes of the supreme Triune God of the Universe.

Today, there are attempts to return science to an Eastern way of thinking by adopting the teachings of Zen Buddhism, etc. If successful, it will be interesting to see how long scientific progress can survive such a change of its foundations.

In addition, the New Age movement is promoting a pantheistic view of the earth. By a strange, but characteristic, twisting of logic, they now blame Christianity as the cause of the misuse of science that has resulted in ecological damage. That it gave rise to the modern benefits that all New Age followers enjoy is ignored - as is only to be expected in any irrational concept of God's world.

After the giving of the Gospel of Christ and the liberating freedom it provided, Europe was plunged into the appropriately named "Dark Ages" for many centuries when superstition was rampant.

It was only when the Bible was made available in their mother tongue that people realised that God was benevolent and unchanging and gave every man direct responsibility for his spiritual and material progress. Men then began to exercise their freedom of thought in exploring God's creation. Only on this basis could a true scientific discipline arise. The first warrant for this is God's commandment to Adam to fill the earth "and subdue it" and "have dominion over it" (Gen. 1:28) but it is repeated throughout the Bible.

To confirm this, the first major scientific organisation in the world was the Royal Society, formed in 1660. This was founded upon an older "London and Oxford" group, consisting mainly of Puritans, that met in 1645. What is of particular note is that the Royal Society was *"largely composed of Puritan sympathisers"* (E.B. 10:220); they constituted 42 of the original 68 signatories. Where, one might ask, were the materialists, the atheists, and all the many enemies of the much despised Puritans, that they had not already formed their own scientific organisation? Why was it that the first prestigious scientific body was founded by these God-fearing men?

Hooykaas (Hoo) shows that it was the Calvinistic Puritans of different denominations who started the scientific revolution, although he says it was not due to their Calvinism. What he does note is that their doctrine of the "Priesthood of all believers" gave them freedom from external dictatorial authorities - religious or otherwise - which allowed them to study nature. We would, however, contend that their Calvinist doctrine *was* fundamental to the rise of science for this author can testify to a sense of both security and freedom as one of the many life-changing results that came from a reading of Lorainne Boettner's *The Reformed Doctrine of Predestination* (Boet).

It is also interesting that the Royal Society received only moral support from the Crown and in this free atmosphere, development was rapid. In contrast, continental societies were established by the state, but "Their members gained an income but lost their independence" (*EB.* 10:220). Even in those days, it would appear to be unwise to be too closely connected to the deadening hand of state bureaucracy. The fruits of this freedom in our country can be assessed by a 1996 Hansard report which stated that 57% of the world's greatest inventors came from these shores (Bayliss).

Unfortunately, whilst many founding members of the Royal Society may have been Puritans, eventually there was a break between Christianity and Science. The cause was the founding of the Society upon the principles laid down by Francis Bacon that the mind should first be cleared of "idols of the mind" and conclusions drawn only after many experiments. Thus, an approach based on the Scriptures was ruled out from the beginning.

Ian Taylor shows that the Royal Society was not only based upon Bacon's theories but the leaders were Rosicrucians and/or Freemasons. In his *New Atlantis* Bacon refers to Salomon's House and its 33 secret "Orders" which is a clear reference to the 33 Degrees in Freemasonry. Interestingly, he also referred to three higher secret orders called "Interpreters of Nature" (Tay94).

Francis Bacon is a most mysterious man. Taylor outlines the evidence that Bacon was a child of Queen Elizabeth I, and there is also circumstantial evidence that he wrote Shakespeare's plays. Others have claimed that Bacon was the originator of Freemasonry, and of an even more secret group that would control those degrees below, which is indicated by the additional three higher degrees he wrote about. It is clear that those who are in *any* such secret organisations do not appreciate how they are controlled by those above their level. Ultimately, all members at any level of a secret organisation are unaware that they are all tools that are manipulated by the one at the top - who was the very first to rebel against God.

Bacon ruled that the mind should be cleared of previous preconceptions, and Taylor says that in so doing he "unwittingly laid the foundation for humanism" and resulted in Scripture also being abandoned. I do not agree that such a deep thinker as Bacon would have planned any such scheme without being fully aware of its ultimate outworkings. He would have foreseen these well in advance for he knew exactly what he was doing.

The Christian witness

In confirmation of the thesis of this section, a list has been made of famous scientists who held to the Christian religion (ICR Acts and Facts, Jan. 81 and Bow82:219). It includes Faraday, Maxwell, Lord Kelvin, Newton, Pascal and many more. This disposes of the lie that Christians cannot think freely with the implication that they are "narrow minded bigots" who force their science to fit their "blinkered view of the Bible." One of the acknowledged greatest scientists ever was James Clerk Maxwell (1831 - 1879), and it will be a sufficient witness to end with a prayer he wrote out:

> Almighty God, who hast created man in Thine own image, and made him a living soul that he might seek after Thee and have dominion over Thy creatures, teach us to study the works of Thy hands that we may subdue the earth to our use and strengthen our reason for Thy service; and so to receive Thy blessed Word, that we may believe on Him who Thou hast sent to give us knowledge of salvation and the remission of our sins. All which we ask in the name of the same Jesus Christ our Lord (Q21/4:208).

SECTION 7

APPENDICES

APPENDIX 1
THE DECREASE IN THE SPEED OF LIGHT

Background information

In this appendix we would remind readers that for brevity we will be using the symbol for the speed of light used in physics which is "c", and we will also use the accepted abbreviation CDK for the decrease in the speed of light (= c decay!). Purists may object that c has not decayed but has decreased, but it is a useful shorthand term. The present speed of light is given as 299,792.458 km/s.

The subject of CDK was brought to the attention of the creationist world by Barry Setterfield of Australia. His first articles appeared in the *Ex Nihilo Magazine* of March 1981 (v4 n1, 2 and 3) with articles and letters in the following issues. In 1983 the Creation Science Foundation of Australia published his memorandum *The Speed of Light and the Age of the Universe* (Sett83). This covered a wide range of subjects including astronomical and geological events at the time of Creation and The Flood. His colleague who dealt with the mathematical aspects in these publications was Trevor Norman of the School of Mathematical Sciences, Flinders University.

Their work came to the attention of the physicist Lambert Dolphin who was working for the Stanford Research Institute. After considerable research he concluded that their claims were well founded and asked Norman and Setterfield to write an Invited Report for the Institute. For this they compiled *The Atomic Constants, Light and Time* (Norm87) to which Dolphin wrote a foreword which highly commended it.

Setterfield had studied Physics and Geology for three years at Adelaide University, which he left due to ill health. He made a mineralogical study of South Australia for an international mining company and then lectured in astronomy for six years. With this wide range of subjects he had studied, he was well equipped to deal with the diversity of disciplines involved in creationist issues. His abilities in these areas becomes apparent in the various technical aspects that he deals with in his writings, particularly in debate with senior physicists.

1. THE EXPERIMENTAL EVIDENCE

A. Roemer's measurements

Although the ancient world wondered whether the speed of light was measurable, their attempts to measure it failed, and it was generally concluded that it was infinite. In 1675, the Danish astronomer Ole Roemer measured the appearance of Io, one of the moons of Jupiter as it came out of (and into) the shadow of Jupiter over a period of several months when it could be observed. He was able to do this within a second as accurate clocks had been available for some five years. He found that the intervals were very regular, as would be expected, but as the earth drew away from Jupiter, there was a gradually increasing delay from the expected timing. As the earth came nearer to Jupiter, this delay was reduced until it was back "on time" as it would have been when it was first near Jupiter.

He realised that this delay when the earth was further from Jupiter was due to the additional time it took the light to reach the earth as it moved away from Jupiter. He therefore had a measure of the speed of light. Unfortunately, he did not have an accurate value for the diameter of the earth's orbit, so his

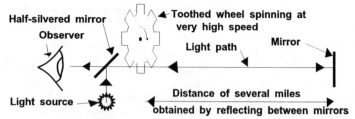

Fig. 1. The toothed wheel method of measuring the speed of light

value for c was badly in error. His timings, however, have been preserved and have been the subject of much analysis, as we will see.

Cassini, in 1693 and 1736, measured these occultations of Io and arrived at a more accurate value for c. Physicists also devised earth-based experiments to discover the speed of light, the most direct being the toothed wheel and it variant, the spinning mirrors.

B. The toothed wheel and mirror experiments

In this, a light is sent through a toothed wheel that is spinning rapidly. The light is made to travel a long distance that has been accurately measured, and then reflected back to the toothed wheel through which it will pass if the wheel is stationary or rotating slowly. As the wheel increases in speed, by the time the light has returned from its long pathway, the gap between the teeth that allowed the light to pass will have been replaced by the next tooth alongside and the light will be blocked off (Fig. 1.).

As the wheel increases in speed, the light will come on again as the next gap has had time to be in the position of the first gap that allowed the light to go through. In this way, by measuring the speed with which the teeth are moving and the distance the light has travelled, a very accurate measure of the speed of light can be made.

The variant of the spinning mirrors is only another way in which the light can be sent out in short bursts when the mirror is at the right angle to send it to the distant reflector, so that by the time it returns to the mirror, it has turned through an angle and the light will not be visible in the eyepiece.

The most famous experimenter using this method was Michelson, who won a Nobel prize for his work on the speed of light. He conducted this experiment several times over many years and noted that generally each time the speed was slightly lower than the last measurement.

There are a number of other methods by which c can be measured, but they are of varying accuracy.

C. Bradley's aberration measurements

In 1726, Bradley was trying to accurately determine the passage of a star directly overhead, and found that the telescope had to be tilted slightly forward in the direction the earth was travelling in order to register the star in the centre. He realised that this was due to the speed of the earth around the sun making him tilt the telescope. This is like having to tilt an umbrella slightly forward as we walk in vertically falling rain. This is discussed more fully in Appendix 10 and illustrated in Figure 7.10.3.

As the speed of the earth around the sun was known, the speed of light could be worked out from the angle the telescope had to be tilted. This is a very small angle but it can be measured very accurately. The present value is

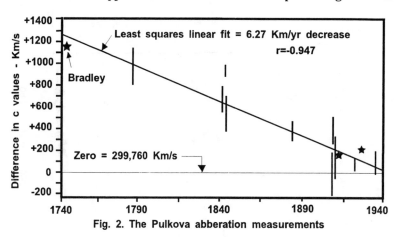

Fig. 2. The Pulkova abberation measurements

20.49552 arc seconds.

Measurements of this small angle has been carried out for many years since his first measurement, and the results also show that it has increased slightly over the years - which means the speed of light has become slower. Fig. 2 gives a graph of these aberration values, all measured at Pulkova observatory, which show a decrease in c is corroborated by this method also. It is interesting that these records were not known by Setterfield until some time after he had published his first articles in March 1981.

D. Electronic methods

There are experiments that involve the charge on a capacitor, Kerr cells and the wavelengths on wires by which c can be measured, but they are much less accurate than the optical measurements. The Kerr cell was an electronic method used in place of the toothed wheel to chop the light very rapidly. There was a time delay of electrons in the complex equipment involved so that c was made to appear slower. However, there was still a measurable decrease in the results over the years even though the value was consistently too low.

The results of the measurements

Setterfield carefully examined the many measurements of c and presented their values in his papers. In some cases it was acknowledged by the experimenters themselves that the result was inaccurate. The Pulkova aberration measurements shown in Fig. 2 were made on the same piece of equipment, and even without correction for a systematic error, the decrease in c is obvious.

As we have mentioned with the Kerr cell, there was an obvious systematic error with the equipment used. Other measurements discussed were the Roemer and early Cassini values and a few others. There was therefore some debate on what should be omitted in the final list of values to be used in the analysis. Critics, however, charged him with "selecting his values" and "rejecting those that did not fit his theory." If, on the other hand, he included all the results, he was accused of "including clearly erroneous values" to support his case! He was in a "no-win" situation.

Fig. 3 is a redrawing of the graph in the SRI report and plots all the most

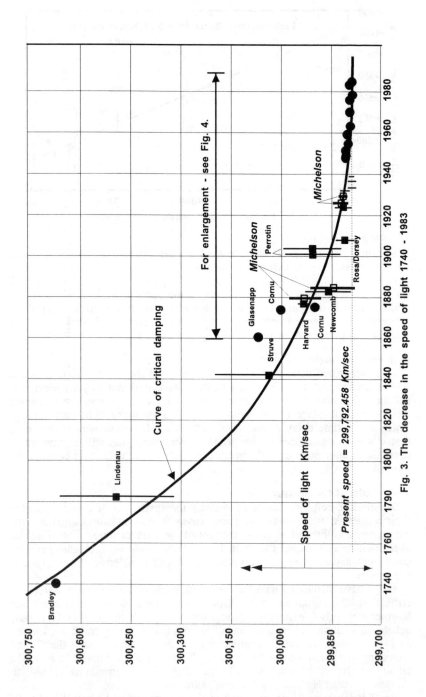

Fig. 3. The decrease in the speed of light 1740 - 1983

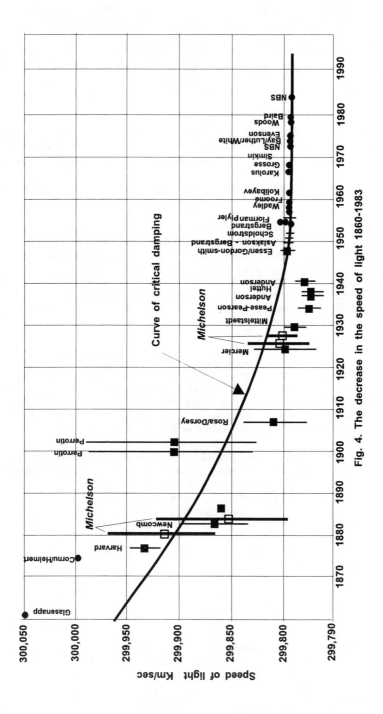

Fig. 4. The decrease in the speed of light 1860-1983

accurate results from 1740. As the graph becomes somewhat crowded at the right hand end, Fig. 4 plots the results from 1870 to a larger scale to demonstrate that c is still decreasing along a curve.

The most controversial measurements were the early ones by Roemer and later workers, on the moons of Jupiter referred to above; this will be considered separately later. The important point is that even if some are omitted, the fact that CDK has taken place is irrefutable.

2. THE SUPPORT FOR CDK

This is a major controversy at this time of writing (1998) and we will spend some time setting out the evidence that shows that CDK has indeed taken place. Once this is established, the many ramifications can be studied thereafter.

As one might expect, the possibility of c decreasing is rejected by the majority of secular physicists. The results are far too disturbing for their peace of mind. Many reputations have been built upon theories that require no change in c, and any suggestions to the contrary are ridiculed and ignored.

There is also the fact - examined later - that CDK has a direct effect upon radioactive decay; it will be much faster and rocks will very rapidly give an appearance of great age when c is very high. Whether scientists realise this when criticising the thesis is not certain, but this would become apparent to them at an early stage. It is little wonder, therefore, that little response is received from the secular academic world. Unfortunately, much of the criticism has come from creationists.

A. The 1930's controversy

Critics point to the fact that c appears to have stabilised in the 1960's and that no experiment today would detect any variation, and the implication is made that this is very convenient as CDK cannot now be disproved! However, in the 1930's there was considerable debate, mainly in the pages of Nature, where c was found to be consistently decreasing with each measurement. Over 35 articles dealing with CDK appeared between 1926 and 1941.

Even earlier *in 1874*, Thomson (Lord Kelvin) and Tait claimed they had *observed* a decrease in c of 8 km/s per century (Barr:236. Their ref: Thomson, W., Tait, P. Natural Philosophy v 1 p 403 1874).

Dorsey, a critic of CDK, writing in 1944, had to admit:

> As is well known to those acquainted with the several determinations of the velocity of light, the definitive values successively reported... have, in general, decreased monotonously from Cornu's 300.4 megametres per second in 1874 to Anderson's 299.776 in 1940 (Dor).

Even after he had reworked many of the results there was still a clear decrease. He eventually claimed that all the experiments were unreliable and on this basis said no CDK had occurred!

Birge (Bir) claimed that c was so fundamental to physical constants that if it were to change, the repercussions on many basic physical values would have been enormous for "the value of every atomic frequency... must be changing. Such a variation is obviously most improbable." Setterfield demonstrates in his articles how each of these would be affected by CDK, and as we will see, most are unchanged.

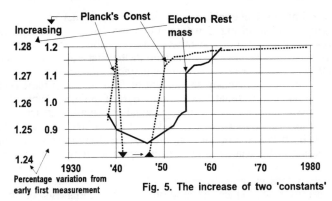

Fig. 5. The increase of two 'constants'

When the subject of the speed of light and its possible decrease was being discussed in the 1930-40's, Birge (Bir) examined many of the experiments to see if there were any errors that would account for the higher values, but any corrections he made resulted in a slightly higher value still. In order to determine the "correct" value for c it was decided to *ignore all values before 1906.* What is important is that all these values were significantly higher than the present value.

B. The consistent decrease
c was measured by many different methods, but all showed a consistent decrease. In several cases, the same equipment was used and each time there was a general decrease in c. This can be seen in the results obtained by Michelson in Fig. 3 which we have highlighted on the graph. Using the same method and in some cases the same piece of equipment, his values were consistently lower each time he made a measurement. The error bars show that they were not as accurate as much later measurements, but nevertheless, the accuracy was sufficient to show that c was higher than today and that there was a general trend of a decrease in the value.

C. The changing "constants"
One of the pieces of evidence that convinced several people that CDK had really taken place is the measured effect that it has upon many of the constants of physics. In his 1983 Memorandum (p39) Setterfield analysed what effect c would have on 17 physical constants, whether they would increase, decrease or remain constant. The result was -

9 remained constant (electron charge, energy, Avogadro's number, gas constant, Boltzman's constant, Rydberg constant, fine structure constant, permittivity and Bohr magneton)

4 increased (effective mass, Planck's constant, h/q ratio and permeability)

2 decreased (specific charge and gyromagnetic ratio)

He then obtained as many values of the measurements made of the these constants as he could and checked if they had tended to remain constant, increase or decrease.

He found that every one tended to follow the CDK changes predicted.

In general, those "constants" that have "per second" in their units have decreased, and those with "seconds" have increased.

Most of these values were not as accurately measured as c, some to only 3 or 4 decimal places. Nevertheless, even within their cruder values, a tendency could easily be seen. In Fig. 5 we have converted some of measurements of the increasing values Setterfield presents in the Monograph, which reduces the actual values to changes in percentage of the first early measurement that was made. The scales are different and enlarged so that the trend can be more easily seen. There is obviously an element of randomness in these results but it should be remembered that they are only part of the total change that is too large to illustrate and still show these gradual but smaller changes. The total change is more obvious when it is realised that the original value (the zero level) is well off the area of some graphs. Of the decreasing values, the most striking is that of the charge to mass ratio (specific charge) which we give in Fig. 6.

These variations in general conform with the CDK prediction and they are in contrast to those which do not change. Measurements of these true constants over many years clearly vary only very slightly around their average values, compared with the more obvious variations of the "constants" predicted to vary.

Some critics have tried to denigrate CDK by calculating what c should be from these less accurate data and showing that it is wildly different from the measured values. This is quite inadmissible and unscientific. One should never work from inaccurate data to check accurate data - only the other way round. Those who have used this argument should know it is unacceptable and are clearly "clutching at straws".

Radioactive half lives

Records of the measurements of the level of radioactivity of 35 elements were collected (Nor:40), the value of the half life being given. This is the time taken for the material to reach half of its original level of activity. These were more random than might be expected but some two thirds showed an increasing half-life which conforms to the CDK prediction. This is despite the increasing efficiency of particle counters which rose from 25% to 80% which would slightly mask the decreasing rate of radioactivity.

D. Troitskii's paper

It was six years after Setterfield had published his first paper that his attention was drawn to a paper by the Russian scientist V. Troitskii that appeared in *Astrophysics and Space Science* (Tro) in 1987. In this very technical paper, he examined various astronomical phenomena (redshift, superluminal jets and 12 astronomical observations) and as a result came to the conclusion that c had been very much higher in the past - in the order of 10^{10} times its present speed. *This was of the same order of high value ($10^{(7-11)}$) that Setterfield had proposed*, in his case, based upon earth-bound experiments of c!

Although differing from Setterfield on certain important features, this is a major independent confirmation of Setterfield's main CDK proposal by a secular scientist whose paper has not been refuted. Needless to say, the claims of this paper have not been taken up by the scientific community - in view of the revolutionary reassessment of the whole basis of physics that it could bring about. Neither have creationist critics ventured to criticise this paper as they have Setterfield's articles.

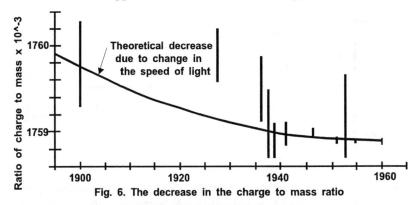

Fig. 6. The decrease in the charge to mass ratio

3. THE CRITICS OF CDK

We have set out above only an outline of the very clear evidence that supports CDK. We will later be examining the wide ranging effects that this has upon many physical constants, the way in which it can explain many phenomena that baffle orthodox scientists but more important, the results that give considerable support to the creationist's viewpoint. With all this in mind, the objections (and/or silence) of the secular critics is understandable, but one is slightly nonplussed by the attitude of many within the world-wide creationist movement.

A. The "inaccurate equipment" claim

One of the most frequent criticisms, by both orthodox and creationist commentators is that the early high results were due to "the inaccuracy of these early instruments" and that as equipment became more accurate, "so the results came closer to the correct speed of light." This claim, however, can be easily refuted by a brief inspection of the plotted results in Figs. 3 and 4.

Before we examine this and similar criticisms made against the theory, the reader is asked to study these two figures carefully. It will be seen that firstly, virtually all the measurements are *above* the present value for c, and secondly, the "error bars" (the vertical lines) of many early measurements are also well above the present value. It is important to grasp this point.

These error bars are an indication of how precise the particular experiment was. When the equipment has been completed, the measurements are made very many times, on different days and under varying conditions. This results in a range of values about an average. If, say, 100 measurements are made, then most of them will be fairly near to the average, but a few will be a moderate amount higher and some about the same amount lower. In order to show how wide ranging these results were, a statistical analysis is made and the error bars cover the middle 68% of the results nearest to the average. An imprecise experiment will give a large error bar and a precise one with many results close to the average, will have a short error bar. It can be seen that the later experiments were more accurate with their shorter error bars.

If c had been constant, this would have produced a range of results that would have been both above and below the actual value. If the early equipment was inaccurate, this would have simply given larger error bars that gradually became smaller as time went by. The resulting graph for such results would then have looked like Fig. 7. Comparing this with Figs. 3 and 4 will

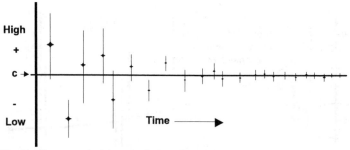

Fig. 7. The expected trend of experimental results if "c" was constant.

make it very obvious that this was *not* the pattern of results actually obtained, and one does not have to be a statistician to appreciate that a decrease has taken place.

The view that the early records of a high level of c was simply due to inaccurate instruments can therefore be dismissed. Those who criticise CDK with this argument are either displaying their inadequate grasp of simple basic mathematics, or, and far more likely in view of the erudition of most of them, are attempting to dismiss and disparage the whole subject for non-scientific reasons of their own.

B. The fallacious "statistical" criticisms

Apart from making major issues from minor (supposed) errors in Setterfield's papers (commonly known as "nit-picking") the main line of attack has been via a statistical analysis of the data he has provided, by which it is claimed that there is *no* decrease in the speed of light.

What has been done is to diminish the effect of the early high values by "weighting" them by a factor that is dependent upon the size of their error bar. Those with a large error are multiplied by a small factor so that their effect in showing that c was higher in the past is greatly reduced. This would be acceptable if they were randomly distributed, but they are not, because the very accurate results were more recent and closer to the present value. This gives them undue prominence in reducing the amount that c has fallen. For example, the early errors were an average of 82 km/s. whereas the later readings were about 0.004 km/s. The ratio between them was 20,500, which means that when the recent ones were heavily "weighted" by this ratio, due to their high accuracy. The early values, although more than accurate enough to demonstrate the decrease, were, by this means effectively "relegated to oblivion".

Even with this method, the result is still a small decrease per year, but this is so small that the critics then claim that it is "statistically insignificant" and therefore c has been constant.

This writer makes no claim to any higher mathematical training, but even with this shortcoming, it was obvious that this "weighting" method was inappropriate for a curve. To diminish results that are quite clearly *more than adequately accurate to prove that c was higher* is mathematically unsound. A re-examination of Figs. 3 and 4 will show, as we have already emphasised above, that the early results are well above the present value, and their error bars show that they were sufficiently accurate to demonstrate that c in the days they were carried out was clearly higher than today's value. These

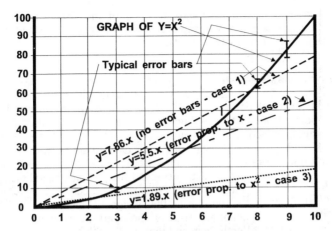

Fig. 8. Graph demonstrating error of 'weighting' curves

experiments were performed by several different experts who were acknowledged world-wide as the senior members of their profession.

If the reader has fully grasped the significance of the high value of the early
results and the clearance of their error bars above the present value for c, then
the following simple mathematical proof of the unsatisfactory nature of this
"weighting" method of error bars is not needed, but it is given for those who
might like to follow the argument used.

C. A simple mathematical refutation of the "weighting" method

If a simple curve is used - say $Y=X^2$, then this can be analysed using the
"weighting" method (Bow89). If there are no error bars, then using the "least
squares" method, we can determine the best fitting "average" of all the results
between 0 and 10 for X and 0 and 100 for Y (see Fig. 8.). Taking 10 values
(X=1-10), the best fitting line for all these results gives a sloping line of
$Y=7.857 \times X$.

Let us now introduce error bars, making each bar equal to a fraction (say
0.1) of the x value. This gives larger error bars as x moves away from the
origin (a reflection of the increasing size of bars as the CDK values are further
in time from the present day).

If those measurements with large error bars are reduced (weighted against)
in their importance by an amount related to the size of the bar, then those
nearer to the origin with small errors will have a greater influence. If a
weighted "least squares" analysis is then carried out, it will be found that the
"best fit" line drops to $Y=5.5 \times X$.

If the error bars further from the origin are made even larger (proportionate
to x^2) then a weighted least squares analysis reduces the slope of the best
line to $Y=1.89 \times X$.

Thus we can see how inappropriate it is to use a weighted method on the
error bars when we are analysing a curve *in which the larger error bars are
concentrated at one end*. What is of interest is that the resulting slope of the
straight line fit is independent of whether we use 0.1, 0.01 or any other factor
to relate the height of the error bars to the Y value. Thus, although the error
bars may all be very accurate, *more than enough to prove CDK*, it is the *ratio*

between them that determines the final slope of the "best fit" line. This indicates even further just how inapplicable this "weighting" method is when used to analyse the curved CDK results.

D. Trevor Norman's riposte

Norman was Setterfield's mathematical colleague who analysed his early results on a powerful computer at Flinders University. In what follows it should be pointed out that he is highly qualified in both mathematics and computers, and has lectured final year undergraduates on both the theoretical foundations and practice of statistics and data analysis with particular emphasis on time series.

After working on the original data, he added little to the general discussion between Setterfield and those who raised various aspects and criticised the results, etc. However, when those using the "weighted" method to dismiss the data of CDK refused to admit any error on their part, he wrote an article that was extremely critical of both them and their method (ENTJ 1991 v 5 n 2 pp 108-112). He noted that to obtain the results the critics were seeking they use one half of a method for the first stage, and then the second half of a quite different method. If they had used one method consistently, as they obviously should have done, their computer would have "crashed". In the articles that followed, no satisfactory answer was given to this criticism.

What is very significant is that there are four experts who have specific experience in statistics - two Christian and two secular - who have investigated the subject and *all* agree that CDK *has* taken place. Those who have used statistics to criticise CDK may have science, maths and computer experience *but not* specialist knowledge in statistics. One expert statistitian was given the data but not told what it related to. Having agreed that they showed a decrease he was then informed that they referred to measurements of the speed of light. He was so impressed that he arranged for Norman to give a lecture on the subject to his department.

E. "Intellectual phase locking"

This is the idea that early values of a constant (not necessarily c, but it seems to be mainly applied to it) were the results of different scientists trying to obtain the same values as earlier workers. To put this clearly in the words of one critic, Dr. Peter Cadush of an Applied Physics department in Australia:

> An eminent physicist makes an initial determination of a quantity, and subsequent workers take that result as a bench mark; the later experiments are "improved" until they yield a result acceptably close to the "canonical" value (Cad).

He suggests this may have occurred with some of the clustering of results following two experiments 46 years apart by Michelson in the data Setterfield uses. In his reply, Setterfield points out that these later results were all lower by an amount four times greater than the order of accuracy; i.e. it was a significant difference and easily detectable.

When scientists report any experiment, it should be with sufficient detail to enable others to repeat the experiment or check for any inadequacies. Therefore any massaging of the results should be apparent to any critic, and is unlikely to be resorted to. In any case, for a scientist to charge any members of his profession with such a practice suggests he has a low opinion of their independence and integrity. This claim of "intellectual phase locking" springs from the same motivation as the charge that "the early equipment was inaccurate." One can be reasonably certain that those who use such arguments are resorting to such "tricks of the advocates trade" (Bow91:213) because their efforts to dismiss unwelcome results lack a sound scientific basis.

F. Goldstein's treatment of Roemer's measurements

In 1973 Goldstein (Goldstein) published the results of his calculations on the possible variation of the speed of light based upon the measurements of Roemer. His conclusion was that the speed of light had not varied by more than 0.5% from the present value. This paper has often been quoted as contradicting the decrease in the speed of light by a number of both evolutionists and creationists in various articles. However, this paper contained not one but two serious errors.

These errors were pointed out my Lew Mammel in 1983 (Mam). He circulated his criticisms by means of the computer network used by the major astronomical centres of the world. What Mammel found first was that in making their calculations for the phases of Io, Goldstein incorrectly adjusted the average *time* of the observations, when they should have corrected the *phases* of Io. The result was that they obtained a value for "c" that was falsely close to the present day value, i.e. their value of not more than +/- 0.5%. After the figures had been corrected by Mammel, the result was that "c" was 8% *slower* in the past with an error of +/- 9%.

A few days later he found there was a major blunder in a simple series of subtractions. Instead of subtracting the calculated from the observed time, Goldstein had subtracted the observed from the calculated. When Mammel amended this error, he obtained a value of 318,000 km/s, i.e. 6% *higher* than today with an error of +/-8.6%. This is a large error but the central point is well above c today.

Thus the Roemer results when carefully analysed support CDK. These published papers and their errors by Goldstein raise important questions. All papers have to be vetted by experts in that subject and one therefore questions just how carefully any such reviews were made. To have allowed two serious errors to pass indicates a low level of examination of this important paper. As Mammel himself said, "Why didn't a referee spot this." It is interesting that Mammel says he "got into this whole thing because this paper was referenced in a creationist work."

There were further confusions in correspondence in creationist journals when Goldstein referred to "a light travel time 2.6% lower than the presently accepted value. The formal uncertainty is +/-1.8%." Now, with a travel time *lower*, i.e. smaller, the speed of light would be *higher* of course. This was later clarified by Goldstein admitting his statement was "ambiguous" and that what he had meant to say was "The new result is that the velocity of light was *slower* in 1668 to 1678 by 2.6% than it is today. I do not think the difference is significant however."

I would suggest that his first statement is not simply "ambiguous" but is in fact very clear in its meaning - the transit time was less than today and therefore "c" was *higher*. The wording cannot be interpreted in more than one way, and is simply a muddled expression on Goldstein's part. In addition, to dismiss a variation of 2.6% as "not significant" when the whole subject hinges on a matter of a fraction of 1% is to try to gloss over the fact that his calculations did show a variation from the present value of c, albeit lower (at that time at least). He and some creationists still seem to be unaware that the second error discovered by Mammel makes the final result *higher* than today.

This does call into question Goldstein's assessment of the whole subject, and whether his scientific objectivity is as impartial as it should be. The two major errors set out above require no further comment, except to wonder, as Mammel does, how his papers passed the scrutiny of the peer reviewers of the prestigious periodical in which they appeared. Questions remain, however, such as - why did Goldstein made so many errors in his calculations and then make misleading statements - all of them in a direction that opposed CDK? Did he know that, correctly calculated, the results actually supported a decrease in the speed of light?

Creationist critics

There have been, unfortunately, numerous articles critical of CDK in creationist journals; indeed, more articles against CDK have been published than those supporting it. These have been very carefully examined by this author and have "been found wanting" in using poor logic or biassed interpretation of results.

One author, chaffing against the mounting evidence for CDK, examined Roemer's data of the moons around Jupiter. He found that the evidence of a secular physicist led to support for CDK. Then, without any justification and quite unwarrantably, simply overturned it saying "But suppose that Lieske was too conservative... Then it would be possible to conclude that the speed of light 300 years ago was the same as today." (ICC 1990:47-52). From this, it could be commented that anything could be "concluded" if contrary evidence is ignored. In another paper, he acknowledged that a graph of Bradley's aberration measurements gave a "best fit" when the speed of light was 2.4% higher than today. This results was again dismissed, this time by claiming that they were not accurate enough to determine whether c was higher. But the fact that Bradley's method is not as accurate as most others, *but still accurate enough to demonstrate the decrease*, was surely known before the investigation was started. Had the results supported the constancy of c, the question of inaccuracy may not have been raised. The article then took this unwarranted conclusion further by claiming that the early results were actually consistent with today's values (ICC 1994:143-150).

Unfortunately, these ICC papers have been quoted authoritatively by several creationists as disproving any change in c, but a careful *critical* examination should have revealed the logical flaws within them. One paper by this author (Bow98) examines these papers and several others in greater detail, highlighting the weaknesses in the arguments used by CDK critics.

Comments on the criticisms

There has been no article in any publication, secular or creationist, that has at any time provided any evidence that has caused this author to doubt the fact that the speed of light was very much faster in the past. Setterfield forwarded a considerable volume of correspondence that he had exchanged with various highly qualified scientists around the world. Having read both sides of these discussions, his ability to answer such high level critics not only raised our level of confidence in his competence but more surprisingly, highlighted the very low level of arguments that these professional scientists were prepared to descend to in order to justify their present opinion.

We have presented one such example in the discussion on Hayward's book in Section 5.3 showing that the criticisms of Prof Billelo were more than adequately answered by Setterfield.

Lambert T. Dolphin and the Stanford Research Institute Report

In his introduction to the SRI Report, Dolphin sets out the very cautious approach he initially had to this subject, but after much study and correspondence with the authors, was eventually convinced that Norman and Setterfield's theory that the speed of light had decreased was correct.

As a result, with the approval of his department head, he suggested that they wrote an "invited report" which is common practice in the institute. *Their SRI report was vetted and approved by several scientists within the institute and two other independent laboratories.* The approval of the head should have been in writing, signing a "sign-off" sheet, but unfortunately this was not obtained, mainly because, due to financial restrictions, the head of his laboratory was dismissed from his post just at this time (August 1987). Dolphin himself was made redundant in September 1987. The new head of his laboratory was strongly anti-Christian.

That there was no "signing-off" sheet was a very common situation, for Dolphin said that there are many reports that have been accepted for publication without this particular document which is considered to be a mere formality. Flinders University in Australia, where Trevor Norman lectured, were also fully aware of the report.

Early in 1988 a very ardent (creationist!) critic of CDK telephoned a high level official in SRI and urgently pressed that the report should be withdrawn. Eventually it was decided to officially disassociate the institute from the report, the lack of any written approval being used as the reason. Yet, as we have said, the report had been approved by the head and others in the institute. Similarly Flinders University denied it any approval and sent out letters to all those who had received copies requesting that they remove the front cover that referred to them as one of the accepted authorities.

Despite all this, legal advice was sought and the conclusion was that the verbal approval of the report by the head of the department was perfectly adequate to give the document legal status as having been accepted by the Institute.

We have set this incident out briefly to give the background of an unfortunate turn of events, so that should it be said that the report was "unofficial" and therefore it had been rejected by the Stanford Institute, the reader will have a more accurate account of what actually took place and that the report has been both independently approved and was legally accepted by the institute.

In 1988, with some degree of trepidation, Dolphin addressed about 60 top scientists of the prestigious Battelle Institute in Washington. He was well received and no one criticised his presentation even though it was clear that if he was correct it would affect radiometric dating and many other "constants". Only a few anti-Christians who quickly spotted the implications were critical! All the others were prepared to accept the very clear evidence that the data proved, no hostility was evident in their attitude and the subject was discussed for several days afterwards. This gives some example of the acceptability of the evidence by those seeking the pure truth in science.

Let us now briefly consider what formula the descending curve of the value of c might be following, and then examine the numerous effects that this high speed would have had and how it supports many of the claims made by creationists.

4. THE MATHEMATICAL CURVE OF THE DECREASE

CDK has been criticised from various aspects, one being the efforts to find the mathematical curve that the plotted results follow most closely. Now it is perfectly legitimate to try to determine which curve fits the results best, but the criticisms come when this is used to assess what the value of c might have been at, say, the date of creation about 6,000 years ago.

This is an extrapolation twenty times the "base line" (300 years of records since Roemer) and critics scorn such a huge extension in time from the comparatively short period over which measurements have been taken. But let us see what their attitude is to radioactivity.

To determine the rate at which a radioactive material is decaying, the number of atoms disintegrating is recorded by a counter for several days or even weeks. When the rate (half life) has been calculated, it is then declared that this has been constant for millions of years - an extrapolation measured in many millions, not just 20! In addition, experiments involving pressure, heat and other factors have shown that the rate of disintegration *can* be varied by a few percent. In fact, a decrease of 28% has also been reported (New Sc. 8 Jan.94:p16). It is therefore *not* as "constant" as most people think, but the half lives are nevertheless claimed to be maintained unchangeable over huge spans of years.

Provided a very close fit to a curve can be made, it is surely acceptable to at least tentatively calculate what the speed might have been in the past, and those following the subject should have sufficient scientific acumen to realise that there is likely to be a wide margin of error with such an extrapolation.

Unfortunately, critics seize upon these extrapolations, charge Setterfield with "poor science" and then use this to dismiss the whole subject of CDK. This is itself "poor science", for the determination of whether c has decreased or not is completely independent of what the curve is that it might be following. We hope we have shown that c *has* decreased. What curve it follows is another matter.

What curve?

When Setterfield and Norman first attempted to find what curve it might follow, they tried many mathematical formulae, some of which gave a very close fit, but not enough to satisfy them. The best fit was found to be a geometrical curve; $c = A.\text{cosec } ^2.kt$. Most surprisingly, the best fit for this curve was when it was virtually infinite at about 4,000 BC. Other curves were examined and in his forthcoming paper Setterfield derives the full curve from the red-shift of light from distant galaxies. The initial value of c is about the same as that derived by Troiskii (see page 298); i.e. about 10 billion times its present value. This curve follows a form of exponential decay which overshot the present value, rebounded, and then returned to the present value. His work involved analysing 1,200 C14 dates to correlate the rise and fall of the last part of the curve. He is expecting publication in a peer reviewed journal and will then circulate his latest findings.

Using this curve reduces the orthodox date of the age of the universe of 15 billion years to a date for creation about 6,000 BC. The subject is technical and we await this paper with interest.

5. SOME QUESTIONS ANSWERED

There are a few aspects that the more technical reader might like to have explained, and we will look at some of the more obvious ones.

A. E=mc^2 indicates an increase in energy with high c

This well known formula (which as we shall see was *not* discovered by Einstein) seems to indicate that energy will rise sharply as c increases. This is not so.

In the classical formulae for m, involving the electronic charge, permittivity, etc., there is a factor of c^2 in the denominator. This cancels with the c^2 in the energy formula above, so the energy remains constant. Incidentally, this mass-energy is known as the "rest mass" and it is this that determines how strongly gravitation pulls on it when near other rest-masses like the earth. It is unchanged with variations of c.

B. High radioactivity would be lethal to all life

This was the criticism of a professor of physics, but Setterfield provided a full answer (Sett83:64-6, Nor:55-6, E84/1:57 and 126). Basically, the emitted rays travelled faster but had the same energy. His forthcoming paper reveals that radiation energy densities are slightly less for a given process for high c values. The damage would be much the same as today.

(i) **Alpha and beta particles.** Penetration distances remain unchanged as c varies and the particles are stopped by 3 ft (1m) of clay.

(ii) **Neutrons.** At the time of creation, with the high value of c, the neutrons from cosmic ray activity would have very much shorter half life (billionths of a second), but their speed would be higher by the same amount. Their high speed makes them less effective in neutron induced fission reactions.

(iii) **X-rays and gamma rays.** The higher the value of c, the less energetic their individual photons become. Therefore the problem caused by this "high energy" radiation is significantly less when c is greater.

C. Would Adam have seen the same colours as we do today?

Yes. The electrons in an atom emitting (say) red light would have been spinning very much faster than today giving a much higher frequency. But the electrons in an atom that was in a receptor in the eye would also be spinning faster by the same amount, so it would be tuned in to be sensitive to the incoming red light, even though it would have been at a much higher frequency than today. Adam would still have seen red light as we do. As c decreased, both sending and receiving atoms would be synchronised at the same (reducing) frequency and light that would be registered in the eye as "red" would always be visible as such. However, light emitted by the sun and stars would have been redder with very high values of c.

Whilst dealing with this subject we would note that with higher c, the frequency is higher but the wavelength remains constant. It is wavelength that is measured in spectra, not frequency. Thus, the sensitivity of the eye to the colours will remain unchanged.

6. THE WIDE RANGING EFFECTS OF CDK

If it is accepted that CDK did take place, it will be found that many phenomena that puzzle secular scientists are solved. More important, other results greatly support the creationist's position in explaining much that took place at the time of creation and at the Flood.

A. ASTRONOMICAL EFFECTS

(i) Red-shift of galaxies

There has been debate on whether CDK does explain the red-shift of light from distant galaxies. Setterfield's latest examination has shown that as c decreased, the introduction of quantum mechanics into the equations results in "jumps" in the output of energy from the atoms. These "jumps" almost exactly agree with the stepped pattern of red-shifts that Tifft has discovered in the galaxies. Another result is that the radius of the universe is static (after an initial expansion). Furthermore, the apparent enormous output of energy from distant quasars is only an artefact of CDK, as in reality they are no more energetic than comparable nearby sources. These points will be discussed in Setterfield's latest paper awaiting publication. The reader is referred to other sources of technical information given at the end of this Appendix.

(ii) Olber's paradox - "Why is the night sky dark?"

If the universe were infinite, then wherever we look we should see the surface of a star, but we only see many millions and the rest is total darkness.

The explanation from CDK is that the light from distant galaxies is shifted towards the red end of the spectrum. For very great distances the peak wavelengths of stars are out of the visible spectrum which is a very narrow band compared to the rest of the complete spectrum (See Fig. 2.2.1). (There is also the possibility that the light from the most distant stars, now that c is much slower, has not had time to reach us yet.)

Thus the night sky is dark because much of the light that started from many distant stars has now been shifted during its passage into non-visible sections of the electromagnetic spectrum.

Distant quasars are small hyperactive centres of galaxies with very large red-shifts in their light. If this is taken as indicative of a great distance (although this is disputed; see section 2.2), then these X-rays from these objects will be greatly red-shifted.

The initial very high speed of light enabled Adam to see many stars very soon after creation and many more as time went by. But there would come a time when the light was so far shifted that few additional stars would become visible - there would be a cut-off point to the visible stars.

(iii) What gave three days of light before the sun?

Genesis records that the sun was not created until Day 4. An early proposal by Setterfield was that many of the larger stars in the centre of our galaxy, known as Type 2 stars, exploded due to their high pressure and the high value of c. These would have provided light like a cosmic firework display.

His latest understanding is that quasars were present in the nucleus of many galaxies, including our own. These ultra-brilliant hyperactive galactic centres would have provided an intense burst of light to the more distant parts of each galaxy. In our galaxy, the light would have reached the earth within two minutes of emission. The outer Type 1 stars like our sun are smaller and are changing more slowly. This sequence would provide light for the 24 hours revolution of the earth before the sun itself was created on day 4.

B. Radioactive dating

c has a direct effect upon the workings of the atom, principally electron speeds are faster. The rate of the motion of the nucleon is also dependant upon c, and this determines the rate at which radioactive decay takes place; high c gives high levels of radioactivity. The result is that when c was very much higher, radioactivity was also very high - in direct proportion to c.

This means that very rapidly a large amount of the radioactive element was converted into the equivalent amount of its particular "daughter" element. As it is the ratio of the element to its daughter that determines the radiometric "age" of the rock, then it can be seen that *with high c the rock will rapidly appear to be very old.* Just how rapidly will depend upon the length of time c is at a high value, and the shape of the curve that it is following.

Setterfield earlier suggested that c was at a very high level for two to four of the days of creation and then fell rapidly. If this were so, then a calculation shows that the "millions of years" given by radiometric dating can be reduced to about 6-8,000 years, which is about the time since creation. We would alternatively speculate that c may have been at a constant value but then began to decrease at the Fall of Adam. This period of high c may have been long enough for a high level of radioactivity to have taken place that would reduce the present apparent "millions of years" to be shortened to only 6,000 since creation.

The other factor is the shape of the curve which can affect how much correction there would be to the recorded radiometric ages. Whatever assumptions might be made, certainly the vast ages that radiometric dating gives can be reduced to a very small percentage of these values when CDK corrections are applied, leaving little time for evolution to occur.

Radioactive dating of rocks is the *only* method used for dating, as it is the *only* method that gives answers in millions of years - all other methods which give much younger ages for the earth are ignored. CDK effectively removes the only method by which the evolutionist can obtain dates of millions of years that are so essential to his theory. It is possible that it is this drastic effect that CDK would have upon radiometric dating that makes it so unappealing to secular scientists. One might have hoped that this factor alone would have made the subject attractive to creationists generally.

Radioactive remnants

If the earth is 4.5 billion years old, then all radioactive elements with a short half-life should have gone through ten half-lives; this is the time after which it is considered there is no more radioactivity left. This, in fact, is what is found and is taken to prove the great age of the earth.

However, if the speed of light was very much faster in the past, then this would produce the same result but in a much shorter period of time. The absence of short half-life radioactive elements is therefore no proof of the great age of the earth.

C. The effect of CDK on atomic properties and the transport constants

This is one of the most fascinating ramifications that CDK has for the creationist. Setterfield has claimed that c affects a number of atomic properties as we have seen above. In a privately circulated paper Setterfield provided mathematical formulae dealing with various phenomena and concludes that the main ones that would vary are photon numbers and electron velocity (both higher with high c). The transport constants that would vary would be viscosity, diffusion and osmosis: both processes would be more efficient with higher c.

It might be thought that these would be directly related to c, but in his forthcoming paper, Setterfield ties this in with the "stepped" red shifts found by Tifft in the light from galaxies (Section 2.2), where he shows that CDK causes atomic changes in quanta stages. The result is that the maximum range of the transport constants is 1:530. As the CDK would have been changing very rapidly to begin with, the average change would be about half this value - 1:250. The precise values depend upon cosmological quantities that are only approximations.

He shows that viscosity would have been about 1/250 of the present stable value which would give higher critical velocities (x 250) for laminar flow, and diffusion would be 250 times more rapid.

(a) Photon numbers

This would be proportional to c. Therefore, in the past, plants would receive a much higher photon level which would greatly increase photosynthesis. This would allow the present-day 9 inch high Horsetail plant to have grown to the 40 ft tree we see in the fossil record. As c decreased, the broader-leaved trees would be able to gather more photon energy and therefore survive better - as we see around us today.

The higher rate of diffusion and osmosis would also encourage rapid growth. With all these factors operating, there would be lush vegetation throughout the world and all plant life would grow rapidly. After the landing of the Ark, plant life would rapidly proliferate to cover the bare earth so that it would quickly become habitable.

(b) Radiation rates

These would be proportional to c and would give very rapid cooling. This would enable hot magmas to cool rapidly. This is in addition to the fact that when deposited they may not have been molten rocks at very high temperatures. We deal with this in Appendix 4 - Geology

(c) Diffusion and viscosity

This has a number of interesting results.

(i) Insect size

Few realise that insects do not have lungs, but receive their oxygen and remove carbon dioxide by means of diffusion through minute tubes that reach well inside their body.

With high c and therefore more efficient diffusion, these tubes could be comparatively long and large insects could survive. There are records of huge insects in the fossil record such as dragonflies with 30 inch (762mm) wingspans.

With c now much lower than it was, diffusion would be more difficult and the gases would not be able to flow as easily as they did with high c. Those large insects with correspondingly long tubes would receive inadequate oxygen and would therefore expire. Perhaps it is a blessing that today we do not have giant flies, spiders and fleas, or cockroaches 12 in (300mm) long!

(ii) Rock viscosity

One of the main problems in trying to find a mechanism for plate tectonics (continental drift) is that the viscosity of rock is far too high for much spreading of large land masses; a subject we will be discussing later. If viscosity was much lower due to CDK, then we may have here a factor that

Fig. 9. The ancient sport of 'Dino jumping'.

will allow such large movements to take place easily. The sub-crustal layer where movement would take place is called the asthenosphere. Its high water content makes it more plastic than the underlying mantle or the overlying crust. Under pressure, its high water content lowers its melting point, and the addition of lower viscosity due to CDK by a factor of 1/250 may have allowed plate tectonics to have taken place (Setterfield: priv. comm.).

(iii) Flying and Pterosaurs

Another important result from lower viscosity is that flying would be more efficient due to lower drag over the wing area. Huge Pteranodons with wingspans 20 ft. (7m) have been found and one humerus bone may have come from one with a span of 51 ft. (16m) (Q17/3:158).

There has been much discussion in scientific journals on whether they could actually fly or could only glide on upcurrents. One of the most interesting and thorough investigations of their flying ability is by Bramwell (Bra). The conclusion of this very detailed paper is that Pteranodon was very near the maximum size of an animal that could fly. Its bones were extremely thin to reduce weight and beautifully designed for maximum strength with such long wings. Every aspect that they investigated showed how very cleverly designed these animals were. For example, the very long protuberance behind the head helped to balance the weight of the large beak and by turning the head, both could be used as a balanced rudder to change the direction of flight.

The authors calculate that it would have had a sink rate of only 0.42m/s (1.5ft/s) and a stalling speed of 7m/sec (23 ft/s), with a ground speed even lower as it would have landed into the wind. They suggest that it would have rested with its claws half way along its wings on the ground. They thought that due to its inability to run into the wind for take off, it might have hung from the edges of cliffs, like a bat does today, and then dropped rapidly to gain airspeed. It might also have been able to rise from the top of a large wave to give its wings enough downbeat.

With all these difficulties, if the efficiency of flying was much higher due to the lower viscosity (drag) of the air, these huge animals would have had a much higher margin for actually flying rather than mainly gliding than these authors would have appreciated.

This paper is a model of how such a study should be undertaken, and we would encourage others to carry out similar examinations of God's beautiful designs in the biomechanics of animals and birds.

(iv) Metabolic processes

With lower viscosity, the blood in the arteries, veins and capillaries would flow more freely. Therefore, the pressure generated by the heart to circulate the blood would be much lower. This would increase longevity and would be yet another factor that would have resulted in the long life-spans of the pre-Flood patriarchs.

The more rapid diffusion rate would mean that oxygen and nutrients would enter the cells more rapidly and the waste products be removed from them. The rate of absorption in the digestive system and the efficiency of many other processes would also be higher. All these would work together to make the body's complex metabolic system very much more efficient than today.

(d) Nerve impulses

Electron and ion movements would be faster, which would increase the speed with which nerve impulses travel. Furthermore, since nerve impulses diffuse across synapses, higher diffusion rates speed nerve transmissions. Thus, an Apatosaurus (originally the Brontosaurus) would receive an impulse from the end of his long tail quite quickly. From this, impish prediluvian children would have been unwise to indulge in the well known "dare" of "Dino-jumping" (Fig. 9.), which involves stamping on his tail and running off before he can catch you!

Adam's high level of intelligence

This high speed of nerve impulses would also have speeded up the passage of nerve signals throughout the whole body, and would have had a particular impact upon the speed with which the brain would operate. As discussed in Section 1.1 on Genesis, early man, and Adam in particular, probably had a very high level of intelligence. Many books describe some surprising discoveries in ancient civilisations and we have no reason to think that our present level of intelligence was fundamentally superior to our ancestors.

SOURCES OF INFORMATION ON CDK

In view of the abundant evidence in support of CDK, which is only briefly covered above, we would hope that the subject will be widely publicised and examined. Setterfield's 1983 *The Velocity of Light and the Age of the Universe* is out of print, but the atomic investigation is a reprint of earlier articles (See ref. Sett83). He has also produced a video with accompanying booklet and chart in which he presents his own chronology which is considerably different to his earlier version and many others (Sett93).

Photocopies of the *Stanford Research Institute Invited Report* (Norm) together with a Christian Supplement can still be obtained by applying to the Creation Science Movement, Box 888, Portsmouth PO6 2YD. Their web site is at <http://www.csm.org.uk>. This author's creation web site has items on CDK - <http://ourworld.compuserve.com/homepages/bowdenmalcolm>

Lambert Dolphin and Alan Montgomery are the main proponents of Setterfield's work in America. Dolphin publicises CDK and many other interesting subjects on his web site <http://www.best.com/~dolphin/> where additional technical details may be found. The site has had thousands of "visits", many by secular physicists. Obviously, all web pages given in this book are only current at the time of publication.

APPENDIX 2
THE ANTHROPIC
COSMOLOGICAL PRINCIPLE

"Why is it you physicists always require so much expensive equipment? Now the Department of Mathematics requires nothing but money for paper, pencils and wastepaper baskets, and the Department of Philosophy is better still. It doesn't even ask for wastepaper baskets." Anonymous University President, quoted in Barrow page 185.

....

Frightening as the title to this appendix might be initially to some (including this author!), it only means that the universe seems to have been designed specifically for the existence of Man.

For many generations, most scientists in those nations that were at least nominally Christian were fully prepared to refer to God in their writings as the author of all the natural laws and activities that they were seeking to unravel. However, following the spiritual darkness of the "Enlightenment" period and the imposition of evolution on the scientific community, fundamental changes took place. Any able scientist had to accept a materialistic/evolutionary philosophy in order to succeed in his work. The existence of God was a hypothesis that scientists did not need.

As the range of investigations widened, some amazing facts were discovered about both ends of the size limitations of the known world. At the atomic level the working of the various elements, the phenomenal ways in which they could combine and interact together, their constituent parts of electron, photons, neutrons etc., all seemed to conform to various patterns that made many of their activities predictable. More important, the often unique properties of many of them and the unexpected special relationships that were discovered to exist between quite different physical constants that allowed life to exist were noted with some amazement.

Similarly, at the other end of the scale in the huge expanse of space, the relationships between the various bodies, the many inexplicable features they exhibited as well as the coincidences necessary for living organisms to operate, also began to provoke fundamental questioning amongst those engaged in their discovery.

Eventually, the possibility dawned upon some non-Christian scientists that there were certain facts that could not be explained away as being simply a coincidence; there were just too many features and interrelationships that had to be the way they were in order for life to exist. In other words, the possibility that the universe was created with an untold number of very special features simply in order that life, and more specifically man himself, might exist, had to be seriously considered.

The question "Was this universe made for Man?" stared the materialistic scientist in the face. How was he to overcome it? In this section, mainly towards the end, we will be tracing the steps that have been taken to avoid the implication that God created the world for man to inhabit.

It is the aim of this appendix to examine numerous areas of science and philosophy where the known universe has many evidences that it was indeed designed and created so that life could exist on this particular planet. One book, bearing the somewhat daunting title of this appendix, is by Barrow (whom we will refer to alone for simplicity) and Tipler (Barr). This is a massive work that examines many spheres of knowledge and philosophy that have any relevance to the subject of the design of the universe that is necessary for life to exist.

The whole book, however, is not only written from a non-Christian point of view, but generally works towards, and eventually concludes with, a Godless interpretation of the ultimate purpose and destiny of this universe. The authors also unreservedly accept the theory of evolution to be a fact, and the corollary that the universe was formed many millions of years ago. However, most of the evidence they produce is a complete confirmation of the design of the universe by a phenomenally intelligent God, and we will reinterpret their book from this point of view. We will also criticise some of their conclusions and expose the underlying philosophical aim of this very lengthy work.

One well known example that points to God's provision for life is the unique collection of properties that are possessed by water. This is such a large subject, that, rather than extend this appendix greatly, it is dealt with separately in Appendix 3.

SCIENTIFIC EVIDENCE OF DESIGN
IN THE UNIVERSE

In this appendix we will not be looking at the numerous examples of design in the natural world of animals. These are given as a proof of design along the line of "Paley's watch" in many good creationist books which can be referred to. We will be considering much wider issues of fundamental physics etc. that some readers may not have met before.

In order to ease ourselves into this potentially complex subject gently, let us first consider two simple relationships relative to sizes in the universe.

1. MAN'S POSITION IN THE UNIVERSE.

In the sense of their ratios of weight, the human frame seems to be set at about the geometric centre between that of an atom and that of a planet. i.e. the ratio between the weights of the atom and that of a man is about the same ratio as that between a man and a planet.

Similarly, a planet is at the geometric mean between an atom and the whole of the known universe. Had man been very much smaller or very much larger (by many hundreds or thousands of times - we are dealing with *very* large numbers in this subject!), then he would have had difficulty in investigating the structure of either the atom or the universe as it would have been too many times removed from his own size. This particular relative location of mans size in the universe is just one indication of his special position in the design of the cosmos - in God's plan. Fig. 1 (after Barrow (Ba:397) and Carr (CarrB:606)) is a graph of the relationships of size from the smallest unit to the largest object.

Barrow shows that atoms can collect together to form a mass until the size is so great that the internal pressure and temperature forces the atoms together that it would burn like a star. This limit is a planet only a little bigger than Jupiter, which means that the earth is comfortably below this unstable size (Ba:307). However, if it were much smaller, then it would lose its atmosphere, as the moon has done (Ba:309).

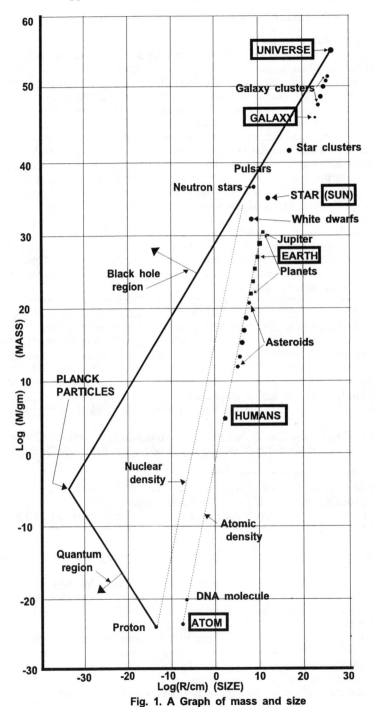

Fig. 1. A Graph of mass and size

2. ASTRONOMICAL EVIDENCE

A. The earth-sun distance

This distance is critical to the amount of heat the earth receives from the sun. There is much anguish generated in the media and by ecological organisations regarding the dramatic effects of only a degree or two increase in the average temperature of the world's climate. The melting of the icecaps and the subsequent rise of the sea, the flooding of lower lands of the nations and the huge problems thus arising are all vividly portrayed by the media.

The sun is 93.5 million miles away = 149.598 million kilometres. This distance is known as one Astronomical Unit -1 A.U. - and is frequently used in astronomical measurements. If the sun were twice as far away, then the amount of heat reaching us would be only a quarter of the present amount. This is due to what is known as the "inverse square law ratio". i.e. the area of the cone of the suns rays that fall upon the earth will reduce inversely to the square of the earth's distance (Fig. 2). If it were half the distance, the sun's heat would be four times greater.

For one percent rise in the amount of heat we receive from the sun, due to the inverse square law ratio, we would have to be only about 1/2 percent nearer than we are; i.e. we need only be just under 500,000 miles nearer. The result would be serious for all life on earth.

The average temperature for the earth is 25° Celcius (=Centigrade). The amount of heat the surface receives from the interior is very small and can be ignored. If the earth received no heat at all it would be at Absolute Zero = -273°C (= 0° Kelvin). The sun therefore heats us to approximately 300°C above Absolute. An increase of one degree rise in temperature would require an increase of 1/300th of the heat presently arriving. This would be the situation if the earth were to be only 1/600th nearer than it is. This is only 156,000 miles (250,000 km) or a mere 0.16% of the total distance between us.

If we were 5% nearer to the sun the seas would boil, and 1% further away they would freeze.

It can be seen how thin is the knife edge upon which this planet has been positioned. This is not the only unique aspect of the sun-earth relationship.

B. The sun is *not* an "average" star

Secular astronomers consistently refer to the "fact" that we are a minor planet (probably only one of many thousands of others in the universe) going round a very average star positioned at an unremarkable place (about half way between the centre and the edge) in our galaxy, which is one of millions of others.

Every effort is made to describe the sun as a very average star but this is not so.

Firstly, the majority of stars produce much less light than the sun, expending a large proportion of their energy in lethal radiations of X-rays and gamma rays. In contrast, the sun is unusual in that its energy output is mainly light and heat.

Secondly, at least half of all stars, and possibly most, are members of a star system containing two or more stars. Had the sun one or more nearby stars, the resulting variations of its orbit would alter its distance from the earth and cause catastrophic changes in the climate.

Thirdly, the sun's heat and light output is very constant, whilst most other stars exhibit very large fluctuations. This may range from 10% to 150,000%

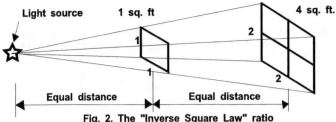

Fig. 2. The "Inverse Square Law" ratio

for some. Life could not exist with such variations.

Almost all other stars are much smaller, cooler, dimmer and less massive than the sun (Unr).

Finally, new (?) stars emit up to 100,000 times more Ultra Violet light than our sun. This would not only kill all life but makes it impossible that life could ever start for it would have destroyed the more complex chemicals in the evolutionist's proposed "primeval soup" (Q21/1:22).

Who said that the sun was "just an average star"?

C. Eclipses

Both the sun and moon are seen as circles of about 1/2 degree angle from the earth. This means that when the moon eclipses the sun, its disc is virtually identical in size to that of the sun, which is completely blotted out from certain positions on the earth for a few minutes.

This may not seem to be an important coincidence, but it is surprising that the very two "lights to light the day and night and for times and seasons" (Gen. 1 v 14-16) subtend exactly the same diameter from the earth. These eclipses were taken to be very significant events for the nation by the priests and astronomers of ancient kingdoms who recorded their occurrence with care. These records have been used by some astroarchaeologists in their efforts to date early records of events, but others consider that such dating methods are misleading.

D. The stabilising effect of our moon

If the earth were perfectly spherical then the impact of quite a small asteroid would make it roll almost indefinitely, producing chaotic conditions on the earth. The equatorial bulge of the earth is quite small but the nearness and large size of our moon has an important effect on it stability (Las), limiting the roll to only a few degrees as shown in Fig. 2 in Appendix 5 that deals with the tilt of the earth's axis.

Furthermore, the moon creates tides that clean our shores regularly. Thus the moon has several special functions and without it, life on earth would be far different and very unstable, which would hardly conform to the "perfect" conditions in which God placed Adam.

E. Bode's law

In 1766 Johann Titius von Wittenburg presented a series for the distances of the planets known at that time from the sun measured in astronomical units (1 AU = distance of earth from sun). This formula was copied by Bode whose name it bears today. The predictions obtained from the formula and the measured values are as given in Fig. 3.

There was originally a gap for the fifth planet. Searching the skies

Planet No.	Series	Result	Actual
Merc. 1	0 +.4 =	.4	.4
Ven. 2	.3 +.4 =	.7	.7
Earth 3	.3x2 +.4 =	1	1
Mars 4	.3x2^2 +.4 =	1.6	1.5
(Ast). 5	.3x2^3 +.4 =	2.8	(2.8)

Planet No.	Series	Result	Actual
Jup. 6	.3x2^4 +.4 =	5.2	5.2
Sat. 7	.3x2^5 +.4 =	10	9.5
Uran.8	.3x2^6 +.4 =	19.6	19.1
Nep. 9	.3x2^7 +.4 =	38.8	30.1
Plut.10	.3x2^8 +.4 =	77.2	28-50

Fig. 3. Bode's Law predictions

eventually revealed numerous lumps of rock circling the sun at the position expected of this planet. It would appear that the planet in this position had disintegrated at some stage into this band of bodies known today as the Asteroids. The only problem with this tidy theory is that the total weight of these asteroids comes to only 5% of the weight of our moon - a very small body indeed. What happened to the rest of the planet? If it exploded, where is the debris? Van Flandern has suggested that they became comets (Section 2.2).

It is in the outer planets, Neptune and Pluto, that the formula fails to work, for it gives 38.8 and 77.2 AU when they are actually at 30.1 and 39.5 AU. Thus, the appearance of great regularity, implying a natural law for their creation is upset by these non-conforming planets.

3. THE EARTH'S THIN CRUST

Anyone who has seen the pictures, and even more impressive, a film, of erupting volcanoes spouting red hot lava high into the air, will have a clear idea of the enormous heat there still is in the interior of our earth, and how comparatively thin the crust of cool rock is that we live on. The tremendous forces that lie not too many miles below our feet are a constant reminder that were some major fault to develop in the crust and these forces released only in part, the results would be an overwhelming catastrophe that man could do little to mitigate.

Much like the narrow band of acceptable positioning of the earth relative to the great heat of the sun, the near instability of the crust on which we live is yet another reminder of the precision, in this case a threatening one, with which mankind has been placed in this universe.

4. DIMENSIONAL ANALYSIS.

Barrow has a fascinating section dealing with dimensional analysis. This is a method of calculating various physical properties using only the ratios of length, mass and time in such a way that the actual units, whether metric or pounds, feet and inches, is immaterial to begin with. With this method he calculates the approximate limiting dimensions due to heat loss, energy output, atomic binding forces etc. of the maximum and minimum range of size animals could exist, the maximum heights of mountains on a planet (=30km), and that the best way for small animals to escape a grizzly bear is to run uphill - the bear uses more energy than they do because of his size!

These and a number of other intriguing dimensional limits he investigates show how well designed our earth is for the inclusion of many varied features that we see all around us - and yet take for granted. The results are only very approximate, within a factor of ten or more at times, but they demonstrate that there are very real upper and lower physical limitations on the size of almost all the various things, living and dead, from atoms to astronomical objects,

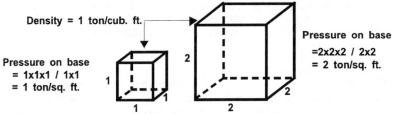

Density = 1 ton/cub. ft.

Pressure on base
= 1x1x1 / 1x1
= 1 ton/sq. ft.

Pressure on base
=2x2x2 / 2x2
= 2 ton/sq. ft.

Fig. 4. The "square-cube" law

that exist in the universe.

As an illustration, the largest size that a land animal can achieve can be very roughly calculated as follows. The stress on the leg bones of a large animal like an elephant = weight/area of bone = (body density x volume)/(2 x pi x bone diameter^2). For an animal L metres long, the body weight will increase proportionate to the cube of this number (L^3). The area of his leg bones, however, will only increase proportionate to the square of this dimension (L^2). Thus as animals get larger, the stress their weight imposes upon their leg bones will increase in the ratio L^3/2 (Fig. 4). Now the near-breaking stress of bones is known and the average body density of animals also. From these factors, the maximum practical size of an animal can be calculated and it is very roughly that of an elephant.

Barrow considers that the huge dinosaurs might have been on the edge of the allowable limits due to their bones being so highly stressed by the enormous bulk they carried. He considers this may have been a contributing factor in their failure to survive in the process of evolution. For the creationist, the changed environmental factors, possibly heat loss or gain, are more likely to have been a major cause of their gradual demise when they emerged from the Ark.

Another calculation he sets out is that for the largest bird that can hover purely by wing action (i.e. a humming bird. Hovering birds such as the kestrel rely on wind power also). Making reasonable assumptions regarding wing area, the energy that muscles can develop relative to the weight of the bird that it has to support etc., he arrives at a figure which is about the 20 grms. weight of a humming bird.

At the other end of the scale, the smallest warm-blooded animal is limited by the amount of heat that very small animals lose relative to their comparatively large surface area. He considers that an animal smaller than a shrew could not eat enough food to maintain its body temperature; its would lose heat too fast through its comparatively large skin area compared with the heat it could get from its food intake rate.

Calculations of the number of heartbeats of different sized animals shows that they have roughly the same total number of heartbeats in their lifetime - 3 x 10^9. Smaller animals have high pulse rates but live shorter lives than larger animals with low pulse rates. The reason for this is as follows.

Animals of length L lose heat proportional to their surface area = L^2 but their heart stroke volume is proportional to L^3. Therefore the ratio of heat loss/heat generation is proportional to (L^2)/(L^3)=1/L. This means that the larger the animal, the smaller the percentage of its volume of blood needed to make up the loss of heat from its skin. Therefore, large animals with their proportionately large heart need only a low pulse rate to keep their temperature constant. In contrast, a small animal needs a high pulse rate to keep his comparatively large surface area (relative to the small volume of his tiny heart) at the right temperature. It is for this same reason of heat loss that mice are not found in arctic regions and why the pulse rate of babies drops as they grow in size.

5. LARGE NUMBERS

The famous physicist A.S. Eddington carried out a number of calculations using basic constants from both the world of atoms and astronomy and determined what are known as dimensionless ratios. These are certain relationships that measured constants of physics have between themselves, and as they are only ratios, then whatever units they are measured in (feet or metres, pounds or kilogrammes) they will always give the same ratios.

He found there was a surprising regularity of certain numbers, particularly 1, 10^{40} and 10^{80}. The total number of atoms in the universe he calculated to be 10^{79} - a value that has not been seriously disputed as far as it is known.

Although his work is not referred to much today, it did spark off considerable interest in the whole subject of the relationships between physical constants. A number of unexpected coincidences were found that became, and still are, matters of considerable debate.

The whole subject is very technical, involving many formula of atomic physics, and it is not proposed to spend time on it. Those wishing to pursue the subject further should refer to Barrow's book and his many references.

The topic has been raised, however, to show that once again, those investigating these relationships in nature began to sense that there were too many "coincidental" connections between factors that seemed to be quite unrelated. This suggested that there was an underlying unity behind the universe. For the Christian, this would come as no surprise, knowing as he does that there was a great Mind behind its design.

One aspect that stimulated great interest was the possibility that many of the so-called "constants" actually varied with time, and we have referred to Thompson and Tait's claim to have observed a decrease in the speed of light of 8 km/s in Appendix 1. Barrow also refers to several other workers who examined the effect that this would have in astronomy etc. They deduced that the *Hubble red-shift of galaxies could be fully explained as being due to a decrease of c* and *not* necessarily to cosmic expansion.

6. IMPROBABILITY OF EVOLUTION BY CHANCE

Barrow notes the very large improbability that just one gene in DNA could have arisen by the free association of nucleotides by chance. The figure is one followed by between one hundred to over two hundred zeros. It is admitted that there has not been enough time even within the assumed millions of years of the earth's history for these random combinations to have been tried out to obtain the final result. The chance of the human genome assembling is a colossal number - up to 1 with 24 million noughts behind it!

The impossibility of the chance arising of life has been pointed out in another work (Bow91:106). The reason for referring to this subject again is the way in which Barrow seeks to overcome this first impassable hurdle in the path of evolution.

Having pointed out this huge improbability, he tries to get round it by saying that this is, however, little different to the improbability of the Queen of England being crowned. He says:

> Even though the probability of a given Briton being monarch is

about 10^{-8}, *someone* [emphasis his] must be. Only for the person who is monarch is it possible to ask "how improbable is it that I should be monarch" (p566).

He then says it is much the same when humans ask how improbable it is that they should have evolved, and in a universe where life *could* evolve, then they clearly have done.

But his analogy is quite false. We would first observe that the fact that we exist is no argument for evolution; creation is just as valid a reason. But Barrow's logical flaw is more serious than this.

It is clearly certain that even if chosen randomly, one person *will* be crowned monarch of England. There is no question of chance of this *event* occurring if it has been decided upon by the leaders of the nation; the event *will* take place. What the particular chances are that any specific individual has of becoming monarch is a completely separate matter that is related only to the number of people in the country. It has nothing to do with the certainty of the event itself taking place.

Barrow quotes a case where an event *will definitely* take place (a monarch chosen from a known number of people) and tries to say this is the same as whether an event *might (or might not!)* take place (evolution by chance).

It surely does not take very much insight to see the gross inadequacy of the analogy that has been presented in an attempt to slide past this impassable barrier that blocks the path of evolution. The authors are clearly very intelligent men who can deal with an exceptionally wide range of extremely complex subjects. Just a brief glance through the book calls forth from this writer, and surely from any fair minded reader, admiration for the scope of the many specialised subjects they have included and the depth to which they have examined them.

With this high mental acumen in mind, it is therefore very revealing that they have had to press into use this very flawed analogy to try to overcome the huge problem that chance presents to evolution. They must have known that the analogy they employed is totally inapplicable and its inclusion was an act of desperation. It surely suggests that these intelligent men are not engaged in pursuing truth but in using whatever arguments they can to put over a particular philosophical viewpoint. What that viewpoint is, and why they should spend so much effort in promoting it we will see at the end of this appendix.

7. THREE DIMENSIONAL SPACE

We inhabit a three dimensional world - of length, width and height.

It is possible to examine the properties that a two dimensional world would have. Such a world would be like a series of lines drawn on a flat piece of paper. Certain rules could be set out up and various mathematical relationships between the "objects" could be formulated, i.e. only a limited number of areas could all be in contact with each other at the same time, and no lines can "cross over", etc.

Similarly, the geometrical properties of a sphere divided into latitude and longitude can be examined and the relationships of lines, angles subtended to the core and on the surface can be defined - this study being known as spherical trigonometry.

In the same way, mathematically, worlds with four, five or more dimensions can also be defined and analysed, working from the basis that they are only an extension of the laws that govern our three dimensional world.

One subject he deals with is Newton's "inverse square law of gravity." This simply means that the gravitational attraction between two objects decreases by the square of the distance between them, i.e. if the distance is doubled, the attraction is reduced to a quarter of its original value. Worlds of various numbers of dimensions have been examined mathematically and it is found that only in a three dimensional world can stable elliptical orbits of bodies be obtained, which are the orbits of our planetary system around the sun.

Barrow examines in some detail the investigations of physicists who have looked at atomic formulae and how they would work in a world of more than three dimensions. They consistently found that they could not exist or function properly. For example, two Russian scientists examined these various worlds with respect to several atomic physical laws to see if they were "habitable", i.e. whether they could exist and whether it would be possible for man to have evolved (?) within them. They found that many of the laws of physics could not operate and concluded:

> ...it follows... that atomic matter and therefore life are possible only in a three dimensional world. (Ba:259)

After examining a number of atomic formulae, Barrow concurs by saying:

> Analysis of these equations indicates that there are no stable bound orbits [for the atom] if N [the number of dimensions] is greater than 3.... Thus we see that the dimensionality of the Universe is a reason for the existence of chemistry and therefore, most probably, for chemists also (Ba:265).

Having placed an upper limit of 3 on the number of dimensions, he then refers to another writer who, using an interesting yet quite different approach places a lower limit on N. He quotes:

> ... it seems to me that the solution to this problem lies in the geometrical structure of the brain.... In three or more dimensions any number of cells can be connected with each other in pairs without intersection of the joins, but in two dimensions the maximum number of cells for which this is possible is only four.

Another quotation he gives is:

> ... our actual physical world, in which acoustic or electromagnetic signals are the basis of communication seems to be singled out among other mathematically conceivable models by simplicity and harmony (Ba:269).

Interestingly, although atoms may vary greatly in the number of electrons and nucleus weight, from hydrogen (1) to the heavy radioactive elements - e.g. Uranium 238 etc. - they are all about the same size. As the nucleus increases the number of its charged particles and weight, the inner rings of rotating electrons are drawn further inwards, keeping the outer electron orbits at roughly the same distance for all atoms (Ba:298).

I am sure that most people have never considered that there could exist anything other than a three dimensional world. Nevertheless, it is interesting that mathematicians should have considered other numbers. That the outcome of their deliberations shows that three dimensions are the only *possible* number is interesting nevertheless. I am sure that we all feel very grateful to them and reassured that we just happen to inhabit a world with the only number of dimensions in which we could exist!

8. CHAOS THEORY

This is the idea that there are many aspects of life that appear to be the final outworkings of apparently random events. The subject is very mathematical as it deals with predicting outcomes from basic starting points that might differ only very slightly from each other. It has been found that changing one value or starting point by only a minute amount, may not give a very slightly different result but a result vastly different to that expected.

Some examples are a pendulum on the end of another pendulum, or a pendulum that is magnetic swinging between two attracting magnets, etc. There are many books are now written on the subject.

When we try to predict the long term future, we cannot construct a mathematical or computer model, no matter how large, that can hold all the necessary information that will enable what will actually take place to be determined accurately. It has been found that models constructed for this purpose are very sensitive to the initial conditions. If these are not known with sufficient accuracy, then the errors in the prediction build up very quickly and the results become totally unreliable.

This is best illustrated by the "butterflies wingbeat" affecting the worlds weather conditions. Given a particular set of conditions, powerful computers can be run and predictions made of what the expected weather patterns would be around the world. It requires only one of the parameters fed into the computer to be slightly altered by a minute amount, for this to affect all the other conditions, until the difference between the new and the old prediction rapidly diverge and present completely different forecasts. It is from this realisation that it has been said that a butterfly's wing flap in Asia can affect the weather in America.

One other paper might be mentioned (amongst very many others). Two physicists examined the behaviour of a particle in a field with friction and jolting added. It either settled into a chaotic motion or went off into infinity. They found that even the smallest change in the starting conditions resulted in a different outcome. The equation is unremarkable and was the first system they tried. They wondered if there were other such elementary matters that were equally unpredictable.

Commenting on this work, William Corliss noted (with tongue in cheek) "What a way to run a universe"!

Barrow gives an insight into the unpredictability of "living beings":

> There is considerable evidence that the behaviour of living beings cannot be predicted for any significant length of time by any intelligent being, no matter how intelligent.... In fact, the instability of living systems... probably makes the calculation of their future behaviour an intractable problem (Ba:139).

He had, however, given earlier how we manage to make reasonable predictions. He noted that it takes 10^{10} bits to simulate a human being, but then:

> We can drastically reduce the amount of data we require to understand our fellows because we know that they will typically react in certain ways to certain stimulus. *but this drastic reduction in the data set is precisely what is accomplished by teleological explanation* [Emphasis his] (Ba:137).

From this, we know how most people react, and we can therefore make a reasonable prediction of their behaviour - making a large saving in the brain capacity we would otherwise need.

It is interesting that the brilliant Christian scientist James Clerk Maxwell recommended that natural philosophers should study "singularities" (single events that arise which have no pattern of recurrence that would enable them to be studied). This was against the prevailing Victorian approach of his time which sought to study stable mechanical states that could be predicted. He was very much before his time, for it is only comparatively recently that the importance of chaos theory had been realised.

This aspect of the virtual unpredictability of many natural phenomena has some interesting theological implications. If we are unable to predict certain events, like the weather, over any long period of time, then it would appear to be a result of pure chance on what the actual conditions will be. This leaves it open for a very small adjustment being all that God would have to do in order to bring about the exact conditions he required at any time. As an omniscient being, He would have no difficulty in ordering it in any way he needed.

This apparent unpredictability of systems is being bent by evolutionists to serve their own ends. They are using chaos theory to introduce spontaneous changes in genetics as a basis for evolution, reversals of the earth's magnetic field, etc. In chaos theory we have speculative theories which are claimed to be "proven" by mathematics. We examine this further when studying Relativity in Appendix 8.

9. ATOMIC STRUCTURES

There are a number of measurements in physics that have surprised those working in this field. They have been struck by the apparently unique or very specific value they had, which, had they been different by even a quite minute amount, the atom would not have functioned at all.

To give just one example, Hoyle's "interest... was provoked by his discovery of a remarkable series of coincidences concerning the nuclear resonance levels of biological elements" (Ba250). Barrow quotes Hoyle's "teleological conclusion from the fortuitous [!] positioning of nuclear resonance levels in carbon and oxygen." (Ba:22). These are of course vital to the existence of life, and in considering this, Hoyle is quoted:

> I do not believe that any scientist who examined the evidence would fail to draw the inference that the laws of nuclear physics have been deliberately designed with regard to the consequences they produce inside the stars. If this were so, then my apparently random quirks have become part of a deep laid scheme. If not then we are back again at a monstrous sequence of accidents (Ba:22).

Barrow quotes another writer, Dyson, with the same view:

> As we look out into the universe and identify the many accidents of physics and astronomy that have worked together for our benefit, *it almost seems as if the universe must in some sense have known that we were coming* (Ba:318).

Barrow devotes several pages to showing the narrow range that many atomic forces can occupy in order for the atom - and therefore us - to exist. Barrow's use of the words "coincidences" and "fortuitous" should not go unnoticed. It is of interest that when Hoyle published a book in which he suggested that life was far too complicated to have begun on this planet, he immediately became persona non grata with the Establishment scientists even within his own University and was snubbed by his former friends (Bow91:175).

As a final example of the delicate balance that exists in the design of the atom, DeYoung (De:113) refers to the mass of the proton, in which a change as little as 0.2% would make the atom, and thus the universe, unstable.

10. MATHEMATICS

Most people tend to take mathematics for granted, for whether adding up the cost of purchases or developing advanced theories, the basis of mathematics is rarely considered. In an article entitled "Why Does Mathematics Work?" Nickel shows that its roots are so impenetrable that most mathematicians avoid the issue (E90(4):147). Bertrand Russell wrote at great length trying to prove the basis of arithmetic; i.e. that $1 + 1 = 2$. He never succeeded.

Nickel, as well as quoting Russell's philosophy of ultimate despair of human endeavour when the world comes to an end, also gives the thoughts of several mathematicians, all of whom admit that why mathematics is so useful in life and why it can predict events is ultimately a mystery to them all. Einstein admitted that he had to recognise it as a "miracle" that he could see no "legitimate way of getting any further." To show that he was not becoming mystical he added "I have to add the last point explicitly, lest you think that, weakened by age, I have fallen onto the hands of priests."

Believing as most do, that mathematics are the product of the human mind, they are then unable to explain what basis it rests upon. Nickel discusses this at length and concludes:

> The mind of man, with its mathematical capabilities, and the physical world, with its observable mathematical order, *cohere* [his emphasis] because of a common creator.

Some have admitted that there is something deeper behind the working of mathematics, and the way in which it operates makes them aware that "the universe is a thought in the mind of a great mathematician" and that they are only "thinking God's thoughts after Him".

PHILOSOPHICAL ARGUMENTS

Cosmologists have two basic principles when dealing with the anthropocentric (man-centred) nature of the universe - the Weak and the Strong Anthropic Principles, which I would simplify as follows.

The Weak Anthropic Principle (WAP): All physical and cosmological quantities are not random but are limited by the requirement that it must be possible for life to exist (or evolve - as Barrow states).

The Strong Anthropic Principle (SAP): The Universe must have those properties which allow life to develop at some stage in its history.

Barrow also states the *Final Anthropic Principle as;* Intelligent information-processing must come into existence, and, once it comes into existence, it will never die out. This seems a strange statement, particularly the phrase "will never die out", but its importance to Barrow's philosophy, which he is at pains to hide until the end of the book, will be seen later.

I will not go into the deeper philosophical discussion that these principles raise, but one point is well worthy of careful consideration, and it is one that occurs at times in Barrow's book. This is that every time a scientists observes a physical value, one important factor often ignored is that there exists observers to make these measurements in any case.

The prisoner's dilemma

This is a fascinating conundrum Barrow mentions (100) which at first sight seems to be far removed from any relevance to the problems of life, philosophy or the Christian faith. But it will be seen that it highlights certain principles where a person's world-view (weltanschauung) will affect the decisions they will make in their relationships with other people.

The situation is that of two prisoners, A and B, in separate cells, unable to communicate and both charged with a crime. They are each faced with the following three alternatives.

(1) If he confesses and the other does not, then he will get off free and the other will get the maximum sentence of five years.

(2) If they both confess, then their confessions are worthless and they will both get three years.

(3) If they both stay silent, then they will be convicted on a minor charge and get only one year.

These options are obviously contrived and unrealistic but have been formulated to place the prisoners in a dilemma. The possible alternatives are set in a table as shown in Fig. 5.

From each prisoner's personal (selfish) point of view, it would be best if only he confessed and got off free. But if at the same time the other confessed also, they will both get three years. It would *then* be better if they *both* kept silent and only got one year - but they cannot tell if the other *will* confess to try and get off free.

This may appear to be a wild and unrelated subject to be examining, but it is important to Barrow for he discusses the Dilemma problem over three pages as a part of the Teleological Argument. In the Concise Oxford Dictionary, teleology is defined as "Doctrine of final causes; view that developments are due to the purpose or design that is served by them."

As might be expected, he interprets the solution of the Dilemma from a materialistic point of view. After some mathematical juggling, he quotes others who have shown that a group of individuals that "cooperate" can successfully invade those who don't cooperate, whereas the opposite does not take place. He concludes with the fairly obvious point that the state of the universe is not just decided by the state immediately before the present (as is usually done in physics), but is a function of all past and future states.

Barrow refers to the work of others, including the geneticist Maynard-Smith, who have examined this problem and its ramifications at some length. That they have spent so much time and effort on this particular philosophical problem raises the question of why evolutionists and materialists should consider it worthy of all this attention.

For the Christian, the answer should be obvious.

Christianity states that there is a God who wants men to love each other and cooperate in their work together. This moral standard has been implanted deep within us all by God as an eternal reminder of His nature and commandments to us.

To explain away this natural feeling, materialists have proposed this artificial dilemma so that they can demonstrate (mathematically!) that cooperating societies will achieve more than non-cooperative ones. By reducing it to selfish benefit they have eliminated the need for God in the process.

Such an artificial concept hardly explains why it should be so deep seated in

Prisoner ——→		A	
		Confesses (Cooperative)	Silent (Non Cooperative)
B	Confesses (Cooperative)	3	A=0 B=5
	Silent (Non cooperative)	A=5 B=0	1

Fig. 5. The "Prisoner's Dilemma" table of options

the human heart, and neither can it explain those who sacrifice themselves for a higher cause. Whilst society may benefit, they personally do not, and therefore their analogy fails. Cooperation is one thing: to choose death is of quite a different order.

This problem is a reflection of the dilemma facing us all in our relationships with other individuals. In the non-Christian world, we would all approach other individuals with the selfish attitude of getting something out of the encounter - one would be the winner and the other the loser - even though it would be better if we each dealt with one another fairly. In the prisoners dilemma, option 3 is the best for them both in the long run. But this requires the vital element of trust.

This trust can be built up by examining the way in which the same prisoner behaves after several "imprisonments" (encounters in life). If he has a record of always confessing, then the other will also confess to limit the imprisonment to three years they will both receive. If, on the other hand, he is known to keep silence (i.e. he is known to be trusting - that the other will keep silent also), then the other will also keep silent and both will get only one year.

What has all this to do with cosmology? I would suggest a very great deal. If, on the old evolutionary teaching, life is only a series of accidental combinations of chemicals that gradually developed their present extreme complexity known as life, then there is no moral force behind the process. If, however, the evidence shows that the whole universe was carefully designed by a creator with a purpose in mind, then moral aspects come into the picture. Which picture we have as a basic world view will inevitably affect how we arrive at certain important decisions, particularly regarding our relationships with others on the same planet.

It is here that the Christian view of life and its ultimate purpose affects how we behave. Christians have a clear injunction to be trustworthy in their dealings with others, so that they establish a reputation for fair play. This then encourages others to deal with them also in a fair way. Thereby, social cooperation is initiated, *even though most of them will not be Christians,* because it will be found by pure experience that such conduct (honest and trusting) benefits the whole society in the end. It is in so doing that Christians will be "the salt of the earth", and their standards of conduct will "rub off" on to others around them. This is not to say that their trust will not be frequently abused, but with patience and God given humility, they will be a beacon to all around them.

Here, we begin to see the importance of the Christian basis to the well-being of a nation.

What is the alternative?

Where there is no clear Christian witness, men will always be suspicious of the motives of others, and automatically tend to assume that others cannot be trusted - and act accordingly. (In our Dilemma, always confessing in the hope that the other does not, but thereby increasing the punishment.) This fundamental suspicion of others is inherent in most other cultures, and is at the root of the weaknesses of their society which displays itself in impoverishment of their social life and lower standard of living *of the vast majority of the citizens.* As with all societies, the strong, powerful and ruthless will still be in comparative comfort at the top of the "pile".

In these conditions, in order to function at all, societies are either in a minor state of independent anarchy, or have to be ruled by strong men wielding power to bring about the essentials of civilised organisation, usually the latter.

This view will be dismissed as a gross oversimplification and a "sweeping statement", and exceptions will be pointed out. Despite this, I would maintain that as a basis, this is a reasonable summary of the international situation. I give one example: Great Britain, due to its Christian traditions, despite its many and growing problems is still considered to be one of the most law-abiding and peaceful nations in which to live. This, unfortunately, is attracting criminal elements to settle here and with the increasing stresses in society from many causes, one begins to wonder how long this "peacefulness" will continue.

Barrow's treatment of this subject is one of the few that has moral implications but he trails off into a vague materialistic statement. This technique of failing to deal fully with the obvious implications of most of the subjects he discusses and changing to another point is one he consistently adopts in his book. By this means, he avoids the most obvious reason for the presence of design in the universe. Indeed, it is amusing to see him almost squirming to avoid the use of the word "God", usually using the euphemism "Design Arguments" in its place. Yet the whole basis of the book points so clearly to The One who created the universe.

Barrow's evasion of considering God in his philosophy is evident in his meandering and inconclusive *Theories of Everything* (Clarendon 1991). We have considered in Section 6.9 the importance of Christianity to the rise of science. Barrow will have none of this, saying no religious basis is needed for scientific investigation. He then puts up a smoke screen which contradicts the whole basis of his book for he says "The real world is immeasurably more complicated: it is a skein of many strands, knotted and tangled, whose beginning is out of reach and whose end we cannot know" (p14).

TEILHARD DE CHARDIN

Those who have read any of my previous books will not be surprised on seeing that his name is making yet another appearance. Some may feel that I have pointed the finger of guilt at him for his many activities in anthropology and philosophy rather more frequently than can be really justified. This I would deny. I have exposed his involvement in the Piltdown Fraud and many other "ape-men" discoveries in an earlier work (Bow81) and quoted the scathing view of C.S. Lewis in a brief criticism of his philosophy (Bow82:162-3).

In this appendix, we will mainly be examining the way in which Barrow deals with his philosophy. In his first reference to Teilhard he says:

> (Monod) singled out the... theory of Teilhard de Chardin as being particularly untestable and hence unscientific.... We point out that far from being untestable, it actually makes a prediction about the nature of thought, *and this prediction has been falsified!* (p127)

Despite such a bad start, Barrow ignores this fall at the first fence and continues by saying:

> Nevertheless, the structure of Teilhard's teleological cosmos has certain features that must appear in *any* [Barrow's emphasis] theory of a melioristic [i.e. improvable by man's efforts] cosmos that is consistent with modern science (p127).

It will be noted, in this apology for Teilhard's false theory that Barrow appeals to, that "modern science" (i.e. the particular view of science that Barrow seeks to propagate) is made the final arbiter of all of man's efforts and aspirations. The absence of any reference to a superior Being, let alone God, should not pass unnoticed.

Determined to support Teilhard's ideas, Barrow devotes a whole section to examining his philosophy, giving far more attention to him than to any other of the very many philosophers that he discusses.

Teilhard's philosophy of life

It is here that we might set out a synopsis of Teilhard's philosophy, so that the reader might be aware of what he claimed to be a combination of the "scientific" and "religious" areas of man's existence.

For him, the earth was first covered as a "biosphere", where life existed before the evolution of man. When he arose as the first thinking animal, he formed a cogitative (thinking) layer which Teilhard called the "noosphere". The biosphere he imagined as acting as a tangential force on a circle and the noosphere as an inwardly working radial force of a spiritual or psychic nature. This latter at the moment is still growing and is engaged in "planetisation" (fully covering the planet) or "development" (evolving). As it becomes more complex, it increasingly develops an effective life of its own that gradually becomes independent of the biosphere. As this radial force operating towards the centre of the circle becomes stronger, the diameter of the circle decreases. The final state of reaching the "Omega Point" we will leave Teilhard to describe:

> ... taking a series of sections from the base towards the summit of a cone, their area decreases constantly; then suddenly, with another infinitesimal displacement, the surface vanishes leaving us with a *point* [Teilhard's emphasis].... what was previously only a centred surface became a centre... Thus by these remote comparisons we are able to imagine the mechanism involved in the critical threshold of reflection (Ba:202).

The "Omega point" that Teilhard consistently refers to in many of his writings is of course a deliberate misappropriation of the phrase Christ used when he claimed to be the "Alpha and Omega". These are the first and last letters of the Greek alphabet and He was effectively saying that He was the beginning and end of the whole meaning and purpose of human life and of all creation. Teilhard takes this saying and uses it in his pseudo-philosophical nonsense that is so highly praised by some.

I have elsewhere recorded C.S. Lewis's dismissive letter of his ideas (Bow81:34-5) and his ridiculing of all such "Life-Force" philosophies (Bow82:163). Barrow quotes an even more scathing comment by Medawar who said Teilhard's *Phenomenon of Man*:

> ... cannot be read without a feeling of suffocation, a gasping and flailing around for sense... the greater part of it is nonsense tricked out by a variety of tedious metaphysical conceits, and its author can be excused of dishonesty only on the ground that before deceiving

others he has taken great pains to deceive himself (Ba:197).

Why should Teilhard de Chardin be so frequently praised by the scientific establishment? This nebulous group is sometimes referred to as the Scientific Mafia - for the way in which certain "politically correct" theories, such as evolution, are forced upon colleagues which they must accept or be ridiculed - or worse.

There are several reasons, of which I will mention three.

1. The "heat death" of the sun

One of the main problems facing materialistic philosophers is what is called the "heat death" difficulty. This refers to the accepted fact that, although it may take millions of years, eventually the sun will cool down and life on this planet will no longer be able to exist. Thus, all the struggles of life, the attempts to find any true meaning or eternal purpose behind the whole of human existence will fail. As T.S. Eliot put it:

This is the way the world ends,
 This is the way the world ends,
  This is the way the world ends,
   Not with a bang, but a whimper.

This is obvious to any thinking person, and the Bible makes clear the futility of all human efforts for its own end. At this point, it is relevant to comment that it has only recently dawned upon this writer that ultimately, only works carried out for God will ever last for all eternity. All purely earthly achievements are ultimately doomed to non-existence. The reader might like to ponder on this point in relation to his own life and work.

Some have suggested that eventually man will be able to colonise another planet around another star when our own star, the sun, begins to cool down. But this seems a philosophy of desperation, for not only have no other stars with planets ever been found, but the travel problems are insuperable.

The existence of this seeming unavoidable barrier renders all human efforts as ultimately purposeless. It is here that Teilhard springs to the rescue. To the great relief of the materialist, Teilhard sidesteps the problem by claiming that "mind" (noosphere) is in the process of developing self-existence and will eventually not require any physical or biological support in order to operate. It will achieve this state of pure mind when the Omega point is reached.

2. The scientific/religious combination

Teilhard is revered for the way in which he can speak "with authority" as one who is highly qualified in the fields of both science and religion. He provides a view of the whole of the process of life which is aimed to satisfy those who have a scientific background and at the same time look for some religious/spiritual meaning to existence. Most thinking people like to have a comforting sense of being "part of the great drama of the life force that is operating in the universe" - or some such nonsense.

Teilhard's credentials as an authoritative scientist have little support. He was at the centre of the many discoveries of fossil bones that are held to be evidence of man's evolution from apes, but his involvement in the Peking Man and other frauds, and particularly in the Piltdown Hoax should have left this side of his reputation in tatters. This is little referred to in the adulatory writings that are published about him, however.

In contrast to his philosophy, the first steps of humility and seeking God's forgiveness as required by the True (Evangelical) Christian faith are far less attractive, indeed repulsive, to the natural human mind. As C.S. Lewis said about the impersonal forms of "Life-Force" philosophy like Teilhard's:

> The Life-Force is a sort of tame god. You can switch it on when you want, but it will not bother you. All the thrills of religion and none of the cost. Is the Life-Force the greatest achievement of wishful thinking the world has yet seen? (in Bow82:163).

3. Teilhard's supporters

By presenting such an "uplifting" yet godless philosophy, Teilhard appeals to many, and is therefore strongly promoted by those intent upon subverting the Christian faith. These forces are extremely powerful and control virtually all aspects of present day life, as I have shown in other works (Bow82, Bow93, Bow94).

To give one example in earlier years: In 1864, five years after the publication of Darwin's "Origin of Species", no less than 717 scientists signed a manifesto entitled *The Declaration of Students of the Natural and Physical Sciences*. The signatories included 86 Fellows of the Royal Society and in it they all affirmed their confidence in the scientific integrity of the Scriptures.

With such strong opposition, it is surprising that evolution should nevertheless eventually take over our universities and institutions. This becomes understandable when the clandestine activities of the X-club are examined. This consisted of only nine men but they were in extremely powerful positions - presidents and secretaries of all the major institutions. It first met in 1864 and continued for almost 30 years (Bow82:112). With evolutionists in firm control of the true "levers of power", the number of opponents becomes irrelevant unless the members can retake control of these senior positions of patronage for themselves. This is still the situation today, the main difference being that we have had many generations that have been completely protected from examining the contrary evidence. As a result, they are convinced that evolution is "scientific", and therefore criticise creationists, sincerely believing that they have the "truth".

....

Teilhard has always been the "darling" of the Establishment, who take great pains to shelter him from any implication in the various scandals that have surrounded him during his controversial life. I give just two examples.

(i) Following the exposure of the Piltdown fraud, the local solicitor, Dawson, was "set up" to take the blame. In order to cast doubt upon his integrity, some very inadequate thermoluminescent tests were carried out on some Roman tiles he had found in 1902. Despite various problems and the fact that the method cannot date so very accurately, the results were said to prove that the tiles were recently fired and therefore forgeries - by Dawson of course. At the end of the report of the tests, the quite unnecessary comment is made that:

> It has been suggested that Teilhard de Chardin was the author of the Piltdown hoax, but since he did not meet Dawson until 1908 he could have had no part in the Pevensey forgery, which weighs against this to some extent. (in Bow81:40)

The implication of this comment is that Dawson was a forger (which is untrue) before he met Teilhard. Teilhard was therefore unlikely to be the forger at Piltdown, as one "forger" (Dawson) was already present and filling the necessary role!

(ii) When the identity of the hoaxer was being investigated in 1953, Teilhard later arrived at the British Natural History Museum and virtually refused to answer any questions about the part he played in the "discovery" of the fossils so many years ago. Instead of having their suspicions roused by his evasiveness and therefore questioning him even more closely, it was said that as they were "unable to advance the case against Teilhard.. attention was shifted" to other suspects! (Bow91:190).

This is hardly the action of people truly intent upon discovering the real truth behind the hoax.

Teilhard's contacts were world wide and he held a powerful position in the field of palaeoanthropology (the discovery of fossil "ape-men"). This resulted in him having a hand in virtually all the well known fossil discoveries around the world. As his biographer put it:

> One has the impression of a vast web, of which Teilhard held in parts the threads, where he served as liason agent, or better still, as chief of staff, able, like a magician, to make American money flow, or at least to channel it for the greatest good of palaeontology (Cue:163).

As an illustration of the support Teilhard's godless philosophy enjoys, I have elsewhere (Bow91:193) described the "Teilhard de Chardin Centenary Exhibition" held in July 1983 in the Chapter House of Westminster. The patrons were the heads of the Anglican, Roman Catholic and Church of Scotland denominations.

For the reader's interest, Fig. 6 charts the life-spans of some prominent people in science and philosophy.

Barrow's proposals

Now to return to Barrow's book. This is very large (700 pages), is a real "*tour de force*" on the subject of design in the cosmos, and in it he examines various cosmological theories, past and present, in considerable detail. A careful reading, however, shows his support for Teilhard's philosophy.

At the very end of the book, Barrow gives some space-time graphs known as Penrose diagrams, and noted how similar was Teilhard's only drawing of the Omega Point.

> Teilhard made only one drawing of the Omega Point (Diagram 4 in *The Phenomenon of Man*), and amusingly, it is quite similar to the Penrose diagram for a closed universe whose future c-boundary is a single point..! (Ba:203)

It is doubtful that such an "amusingly" similar diagram was accidental. Concepts that are foisted onto an unwitting public by degrees, such as evolution, have a long history of "sitting on back burners" cooking gently. These are then served up when the customer's digestion has been suitably prepared for their ingestion - and subsequent indigestion!

Barrow gives an example of how "influences" are passed from one "thinker" to another:

> The most significant contribution of Bergson was to make French Philosophy take evolution seriously....Bergson's influence upon on such French evolutionary philosophers as Teilhard de Chardin was immense. (Ba:189).

Barrow also noted that the final theories he (Barrow) develops in a later chapter in this book were not the same as Teilhard's as "being closer to the "neo-Marxist" theory" (p203) which differed from Teilhard's in expanding it

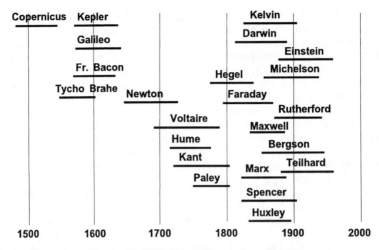

Fig. 6. The life-spans of some prominent men

to include the whole universe rather than limiting it to this earth. Is there here a hint of where Barrow's basic ideology has sprung from?

In the very last paragraph to the whole book, given below with his emphasise, he uses Teilhard's concept of the Omega Point being the ultimate end of all existence. I quote:

> At the instant the Omega Point is reached, life will have gained control of *all* matter and forces not only in a single universe, but in all universes whose existence is logically possible; life will have spread into *all* spacial regions in all universes which could logically exist, and will have stored an infinite amount of information, including *all* bits of knowledge which it is logically possible to know. And this is the end (p667).

His note to the penultimate sentence says "A modern day theologian might wish to say that the totality of life at the Omega Point is omnipotent, omnipresent and omniscient!"

Here, then, is revealed at long last the whole purpose for which this interesting and lengthy book was written. It is devoted to propagating the concept of a godless world that will eventually achieve an eternal life of the mind that can exist without matter. It is the materialist's quite inadequate answer to the most obvious fact that this beautifully designed universe could only have been brought into existence by a phenomenally intelligent and powerful God. Such a God is likely to make moral demands upon his creatures. Therefore, those who cannot accept the existence of a God like this will cling to such a non-judgemental philosophy as presented by Barrow. That it is metaphysical nonsense will be ignored.

This is only a more scientific version of what is today called the "Gaia Hypothesis". As this is the current phase of a more popular philosophy, it would be as well to examine it at least briefly, so that we may be aware of the latest philosophical propaganda.

The New Age "Gaia Hypothesis"

This philosophy is a direct product of the New Age Movement that is so pervasive today. The basic concept is that this earth - "Mother Earth" as it is sometimes referred to - is a living organism that is evolving. We humans, as part of this impersonal organism, need to protect the many delicate balances that allow the organism to live and develop. In this way, we are all encouraged to join ecological groups and "protect the environment". This acts as a great rallying point and all are urged to engage in the many activities to banish pollution etc. Schoolchildren are particularly targeted to become involved.

All this is very praiseworthy and it will seem churlish to criticise such public concern in any degree. It must be said, however, that they are used at times for ends which seem to be more political than ecological. In addition, it helps to create the atmosphere that protecting this material world for future generations is the most important activity that has implications of eternity that humans can become engaged in. Young children in particular will unwittingly absorb the philosophy behind these organisations and be distracted from questioning the basis behind it.

Oard has commented "These groups wish to dethrone man from his preeminent place in nature and bring him down to the level of the rest of nature" (Q28/3:108). The whole philosophy is that of pantheism - God is only seen in nature. Furthermore, proponents blame the Judeo-Christian culture for destroying the peaceful goddess-orientated culture where nature was virtually worshipped in early cultures. They deny Darwinian evolution and show how the many activities of nature fit together in a self-sustaining way. That they were created this way by God is denied.

There are numerous New Age Movements that cover very diverse subjects and they all appear to be fairly independent organisations who express concern for the way in which modern life is destroying the ecology and propagate alternative ways of living.

Far from being independent, the real roots of these organisations have been fully exposed by the monumental work of Rev. Alan Morrison in his book *The Serpent and the Cross* (MorrisA). There are a number of existing organisations under this umbrella title but he considers that they all spring from such diverse groups as the Theosophical Society, the Anthroposophical Society, Rudolph Steiner schools, Camphill Trust, the very influential Lucis Trust, the Findhorn Foundation and the New Thought Movements - all of them supporting similar philosophies to those of Teilhard de Chardin. The Theosophical Society is rooted in the occult and in it heyday is considered to have been responsible for passing its poisoned chalice to over 100 organisations in the U.S.A. and Europe (MorrisA:106)

These New Age organisations are behind such activities as the Greenpeace Movement, the World Wildlife Fund, many forms of alternative and holistic medicine such as Homeopathy, Acupuncture, Radiesthesia, Iridology, Kirilian photography, hypnotherapy etc.

We would reserve judgement on these medical practices for, as with all things evil, the bad is carefully mixed with some tempting portion of good. It is a major problem for the Christian to discern those parts that he can accept and what he should certainly avoid in view of possible unrealised spiritual influences. Unfortunately, research on this subject to clarify the situation for Christians drew virtually a complete blank (Bow94).

....

Returning once again to Barrow's book, I have given these extracts to show how the minds of materialistic philosophers work - or rather how they write for the public consumption. That intelligent people should actually believe such nonsense is surely astonishing.

In his introduction to the book, Barrow claims to be impartial, saying:

> Scientists feel no qualms about suggesting different but mutually exclusive explanations about the same phenomenon. The authors are no exception to this rule and it would be unwise of the reader to draw any wider conclusions about the author's views from what they may read here (p15).

I do not accept this. I consider that the underlying aim of this major work is to ultimately promote the philosophy of Teilhard de Chardin or a very similar version. Tipler, in fact, has written a whole book devoted to explaining Teilhard's philosophy (Tip). Here we see yet again the hand of those intent upon the diversion of attention from a truly Christian examination of the purpose of life.

What is needed is a similar work, using the same information, formulae and scientific approach, but recasting the whole subject from a Christian perspective. Such a book would not necessarily be very large, for many of the ideas proffered could be eliminated, leaving only those that conform to real life and practice. Before I am trampled to death in the stampede to answer this clarion call to such an undertaking, I might mention that aspirants will need to have a very high ability in mathematics, atomic physics, astronomy and Christian doctrine and theology! Are there still any takers?

A CRITIQUE OF ALL
NON-CHRISTIAN PHILOSOPHIES

There are several criticisms that could be made of all rationalist ideas of the meaning behind and the future of the universe. I give the following few examples to highlight the inherent weaknesses they posses that may not be realised by some.

The hidden assumptions of modern philosophies

Barrow's book is a classic example of the tendency of scientists and materialists to arrogate to themselves the position of final arbiter of the meaning of life. This is done on the basis that the scientist deals only with "hard facts" and the materialistic philosopher comes to the subject with no preconceptions.

However, as we have shown in Section 6.8 - The Irrationality of Rationalism - any logical argument must start with *some* assumptions, and these assumptions themselves must be unjustified. Therefore *all* efforts to argue "from pure reason alone" are logically unreasonable. As Barrow himself points out:

> Antony Flew, who is the most profound of the contemporary critics of theism [that God exists and operates the universe], points out that not only is the principle of sufficient reason unjustified, but it is actually demonstrably false! *Any* [emphasis his] logical argument must start with some assumptions, and these assumptions must themselves be unjustified.... At some point we have to just accept some postulates for which we can give no reason why they should be true. Thus the nature of logic itself requires the principle of sufficient reason to be false (Ba:104).

From this, the scientist's claim that his "experimental facts" are the only consideration is an unacceptable assumption. It ignores the spiritual realm. It is also clear that to claim reason alone (and to them this means reason based upon scientific "facts") is the only acceptable basis is but another unprovable assumption - a subject discussed in Section 6.8 above. God can work and communicate to man in many other ways.

Creeping Pantheism

Beneath these modern "scientific" philosophies of the universe lies the idea that the universe is itself god. This is also the basic views of the New Age Movement and the "Gaia hypothesis" that have been discussed above. That this is the view of Barrow becomes increasingly evident throughout his book, and he calls upon "twentieth-century theologians" for support:

> If the universe is by definition the totality of everything that exists, it is a logical impossibility for the entity of "God," whatever He is, to be outside the Universe if in fact He exists. By definition, nothing which exists can be outside the Universe. This is a viewpoint which more and more twentieth-century theologians are coming to hold: they are beginning to adopt a notion of Deity which insofar as questions of existence are concerned, is indistinguishable from pantheism. As Paul Tillich succinctly put it, "God is being-itself, not A being" (Ba:107).

The materialistic world view of both Barrow and Tillich in this passage is clear - as is the inadequacy of their philosophy. They make the false assumption that "existence" only means physical (material) existence. But are they incapable of imagining that there may be a *spiritual* being who is outside the material universe and brought it into existence? Note that they are only required to *imagine* that such a person *might* exist - and allow for this in their philosophy. They are not required to accept it as a fact.

Such a concept does not, indeed cannot, enter their particular philosophy. The wide ramifications and moral implications that such a step would engender cannot be handled by those blinkered by materialistic preconceptions. I would apply this criticism also to Tillich and any pseudo-christian philosopher: it is unwarranted to grace them with the description of "theologians" - there is no "theo" in their "ology'.

What is paramount throughout this lengthy work of Barrow is that every fact that clearly points to a designing deity is carefully by-passed with a godless interpretation and another related subject is then discussed. To illustrate Barrow's muddled thinking, we note that in the passage above he places God as part of the material world. Yet in the passage below in which he quotes Hegel with approval, all is mind, not material:

> In fact Hegel contended the struggle of the Universe to become aware of itself was the purpose of human history: "... the final cause of the World at large, we allege to be the consciousness of its own freedom on the part of Mind (Geist), and ipso facto, the reality of that freedom. ...substance is essentially subject...the Absolute is mind...Mind alone is reality" (Ba:157).

Either God is the material world or he is pure mind above it; he cannot be both. Barrow will quote either case but not once suggest that He is a superior Spiritual Being outside it all.

The ignored subjects

There is one aspect of modern materialistic philosophies which, to my mind, renders them worse than useless, indeed positively misleading and deceptive.

Any philosophy worthy of careful consideration should at least include within its orbit *all* the major facts of life as experienced by human beings the world over. There are two areas of life that are *always* either completely ignored or glossed over, yet they are absolutely central in everybody's experience of life.

I refer to human sin and human suffering.

Some have tried to deal with these problems but they have never been accepted as providing an adequate explanation. For example, Tipler attempts to deal with profound subjects such as these in his book *The Physics of Immortality* (Tip) but to a Christian his efforts are, frankly, ludicrous. For example, to answer the question "When will the dead be raised?", his reply is:

> when the computer capacity of the universe is so large that the
> amount of capacity required to store all possible human simulations
> is an insignificant fraction of the entire capacity (Tip:225).

This example of his level of argument was chosen virtually at random as the book is full of similar "profound" statements.

It is unacceptable for *any* philosopher, such as Teilhard de Chardin, Tipler or any other, to ignore these factors, gloss over them or say that they are only the "growing pains" of the evolutionary process. The important "facts of life" are far too predominant and central to each individual to ignore them for some abstruse concepts that are ultimately meaningless. Far from the world becoming more peaceful and conducive to a good life for all, it is clearly becoming increasingly menacing to ordinary citizens. This totally contradicts the idea of "the perfectability of man". This is what might be called "Rousseau's Great Lie" on which all man-centred philosophies are based.

I did not find in Barrow a single reference to the subjects of sin and suffering. If philosophers are challenged with this, most would probably reply that these subjects are "outside the scope of scientific investigation" or "growing pains of evolution" or similar excuses. But this is precisely my challenge, which is that any philosophy worthy of the name should give the right amount of emphasis to *all* the major factors in life. The Christian view of life puts these questions at the very centre, and when God's answer to them is realised, *all* other phenomena then fall into place - making a more harmonious concept of life. These factors obstinately remain at the centre and create a major philosophical difficulty, and it is for this reason that they cannot be ignored or "explained away" by the materialists.

I would therefore contend that this glaring omission renders all such godless philosophies worthless and they forfeit any claim to credibility. To emphasise this, I would ask of all who are followers of non-Christian religions - "As heaven is perfect, but everyone has sinned -

What do you do with your past, present and future sin?"

APPENDIX 3

THE UNIQUE PROPERTIES OF WATER

One of the most abundant chemicals upon this earth is water. It is a simple combination of two atoms of hydrogen bonded to one of oxygen. Yet this combination possesses an amazing array of very special characteristics that make it unique compared with any other material known.

1. FREEZING

Almost all materials decrease in volume very slightly as they get colder. Water also reduces in volume as the temperature drops towards its freezing point of 0°C (= 32°F). However, as it reaches the temperature of 4°C a strange thing happens. As the temperature falls below this level, the volume of the water actually *increases,* as shown in Fig. 1. This has very important results in nature.

Imagine a lake with fish in the depths of winter. When the air temperature is below zero, the water at the top gets colder and decreases in volume, making it slightly more dense than the water just below it. It therefore sinks to the bottom of the lake. (Incidentally, this circulation of the water is important as it brings oxygen dissolved at the surface to the lower depths of the lake for use by the lake bottom organisms.)

This process continues until the whole depth of the pond has reached 4°C. Now as the surface water is cooled below this temperature, it *increases* in volume, making it *lighter* than the water below. It therefore has no tendency to sink but stays at the top of the pond. This top layer eventually freezes and acts as an insulation layer against the very low temperature of the air above the lake.

If water did not have this unique property, then it is easy to see that it would continue to sink to the bottom of the pond until the whole pond was a fraction of a degree above freezing. The ice would form at the top, but the whole pond could freeze solid quite quickly as the low temperature penetrated the depth of the pond. All fish and living creatures in the pond would be killed, because most animals, unless designed for low temperatures, would have their cells disrupted by the needle-like ice crystals that form in the water within the cells. As the water turns to ice, it expands, and the cells would burst.

The ice in the pond now floats on the top, having a density that is 9% less

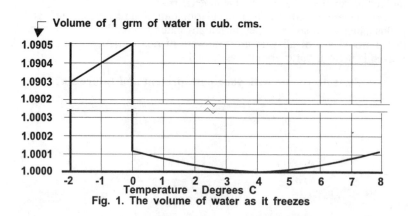

Fig. 1. The volume of water as it freezes

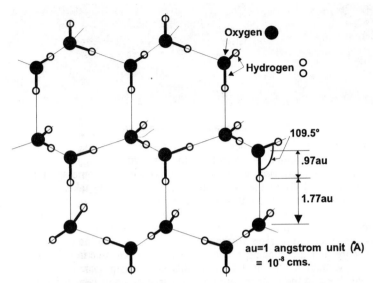

Fig. 2. The tetrahedron shape of water molecules in ice

than water. It is for this reason that icebergs float with most of their volume below sea level.

When water freezes, it expands by 9% of its minimum volume at 4°C. We are all too familiar with this effect upon uninsulated water pipes in winter. However, it has many beneficial effects in nature by breaking up hard earth. The rain or dew penetrates the soil and when it freezes, the water expands in volume and the soil is shattered into small particles. This prevents the soil from becoming too hardened and crumbles it to provide a suitable state for seeds to germinate in.

Why does water behave in this strange way? It is all to do with the unusual bonding relationship between the two atoms of hydrogen with the one atom of oxygen as shown in Fig. 2. In what is known as a hydrogen bond, the oxygen strongly attracts the two single electrons of the hydrogen atoms, leaving the positively charged hydrogen nuclei fairly free to attract other negative atoms. It attracts the oxygen atoms in other water molecules and due to this linkage, large frameworks are formed.

The angle of 104.5° between the hydrogen and the oxygen atoms (Fig. 2) is almost exactly that of a perfect (but warped 3 dimensionally) 6 sided tetrahedron shape (109.5°) and it can therefore take up this shape with little stress in the bonds. The strong inclination for these molecules to bond with others, both in front and behind, results in large 3 dimensional tetrahedron frameworks being formed which are being constantly broken and reformed. These hydrogen bond frameworks are important in many ways, particularly in biochemical reactions, as will be seen.

When frozen, the tetrahedron lattice becomes solid, and as it has a very open shape it makes the ice lighter than water and, therefore, floats. This molecular structure of ice does not allow other chemicals to be included,

Fig. 3. The hexagonal pattern of snowflakes

which is why sea water is desalinated by freezing it, removing the ice and melting it. The product has no salt or other impurities in it.

As the temperature rises above zero, the molecules become agitated by the heat and about 15% of the bonds are broken as melting takes place. These broken portions are able to fit between the open lattice of the ice and amongst themselves more compactly, thus making the water slightly more dense than the ice at low temperatures. The maximum compaction is at 4°C.

As the temperature rises further, the heat begins to agitate the molecules even more and the spacing between them increases, making the water *less* dense now than it was at 4°C. It is this mechanism that accounts for the unusual shape of the temperature/volume curve of water near freezing.

As the temperature increases to boiling point, the distance between the molecules increases, and more of the links are broken, but not all. It is the extra energy required for the final breaking of all the links as the molecules leave the surface that is the cause of the high heat of vaporisation that water possesses, a subject discussed below. Some of these links still exist in steam.

2. SNOW

Water vapour is a clear gas, which, as it cools in normal conditions, condenses and forms into water droplets. At high altitudes, water vapour can cool to below freezing, but without a small amount of impurity such as dust around which it can collect, it will remain in this state. When an aeroplane passes by, the dust and gases thrown out by the engines allow the supercooled vapour to condense around them. The result is the long white "con" (condensation) trails of ice crystals that we see at high altitudes marking the path of the plane.

When ice crystals form, the molecules of water arrange themselves in a specific pattern that is determined by the tetrahedral shape of the molecule in the frozen state discussed above. As further molecules join those already frozen, they give up their high amount of latent heat of freezing. This melts the adjacent molecules which reform to a shape depending on the local conditions of air temperature, wind currents, humidity etc. Thus, the growth of each snowflake pattern is unique to itself, but always based upon the hexagonal bonding pattern of the ice crystal as shown in Fig. 3.

Snow is also important in the ecological cycle. When it falls it filters dust out of the air, absorbs nitrogen which enters the soil, and acts as an insulating blanket to the plants and roots in the ground. The difference in temperature between the air and the ground covered by a two foot (0.6m) thickness of snow can be as much as 40°C. When the snow melts, it requires considerable heat to effect this, and therefore it only melts slowly. This lowers the rate of production of the melt water, reducing the flooding that can occur in the

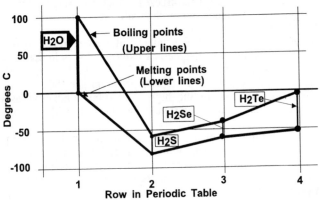

Fig. 4. The unexpected melting and boiling points of water

spring to much less than it would be if the latent heat of freezing were lower.

With all these unique but natural properties, snow has the added ability of reflecting all the colours of the spectrum to give a pure white. Who can but be awed by the sheer beauty of a pristine carpet of snow covering a glorious landscape? Who can doubt the artistic nature of a God who not only provides such an important element of the natural world with such properties, yet still gives it such wonderful features that can bring joy to the hearts of men throughout all ages.

3. THE THREE PHASES

Most materials can exist as a gas, a liquid and a solid at various temperatures and pressures. For most of them, one or both of the particular temperatures where they change from one state to another are rarely met with in practice, being too high or too low to be of any use in normal life. Water, however, is useful in all of its three states, and can be changed from one to the other comparatively easily.

As an indication of how unusual this is, Fig. 4 is a graph of the properties of hydrogen when combined with three other elements. The three elements, sulphur, selenium and tellurium, all have six outer electrons and appear in the same column of the atomic table. The graph shows that if we were to know the freezing and boiling points of these three molecules, we would expect the combination of hydrogen with oxygen to have a boiling point of -75 and a freezing point of -85°C. As we know, these figures are actually 100 and 0°C respectively.

4. HEAT PROPERTIES

A very important characteristic of water is the amount of heat involved when it changes from one phase to another. If water is gradually heated, when it reaches 100°C, it will boil. But to turn it all into steam, a great deal more heat is required to actually make the change. This additional heat is known as latent (hidden) heat, or heat of vaporisation. For water it is 540 calories per gram, which is far higher than any other substance. Thus, one gram of steam at 100°C contains much more heat than one gram of water at 100°C.

Similarly, the latent heat of freezing (or fusion) is the amount of heat that has to be extracted when a substance freezes, which for water is 80 calories per gram. Again, this is much more than all other substances - except ammonia, for which the figure is 108.

Even if water remains a liquid, the amount of heat required to raise the temperature of one gram by one degree is 1 calorie. This is in fact used as a standard for defining the unit of heat which is measured in calories. Only ammonia has the higher value of 1.2 calories per gram per 1°C.

In addition, water has one of the highest thermal conductivities of all liquids. This means that heat can be transmitted fairly quickly throughout a large body of water.

These last two features are of immense importance for the working of so much that we take for granted. Water has an immense capability of transferring heat from one area to another without much change in its own temperature. Sea water warmed near the equator by the sun circulates the oceans and gives up its heat to the cooler regions in the north and south. We in England have to thank the Gulf Stream that is warmed in the West Indies for the mild temperatures that we have so far north. Julius Caesar remarked upon our lush greenery and tourists still say the same today. The general temperature of the whole world is regulated and moderated by this enormous heat reservoir, preventing excessive temperature differences arising between the poles and the equator that would be even more extreme than they are now.

This property is used in many ways both by man and nature. We use it in our central heating systems to carry heat from a central boiler to the various rooms in a house, and to cool the hot engines of our cars by the radiators. Our bodies consist of some 70% by weight of water which is maintained at a steady 98.4°F (36.9°C). The heat energy used for the evaporation of perspiration greatly cools the body after any activity or in hot climates. Drinking hot tea removes ten times more heat from the body by evaporation than the heat in the tea itself (DeY)!

The extremities of our limbs are kept warm by the heat of the blood pumped to these colder parts. Very many other uses could be cited. As can be seen, without these amazing properties of water, life, if it could have existed at all, would have been be quite different from its present form.

The atomic basis of these properties

Why should water have so many unusual properties? The reason lies in the uniqueness of the hydrogen atom which has only one electron circulating around its nucleus of one proton. It can either share this electron with other elements or attract an electron from them - and even do both at the same time (Ba:543). No other element has this property to this extent. The oxygen strongly attracts the electron from the hydrogen leaving it as an almost bare proton which is then very attracted to the electrons in another atom. This gives the very strong hydrogen bond that generates these unusual properties and as a result hydrogen has more chemical combinations than any other element.

The elements that are not in the first row of the periodic table are attracted to each other by van der Waals bond - the much weaker attraction between the positive nucleus of one atom and the cloud of electrons of another. This is more easily broken than the strong hydrogen bond between water molecules, which require more energy from heat, hence water's higher boiling and freezing points. This is also the reason for the high specific heat of water. A

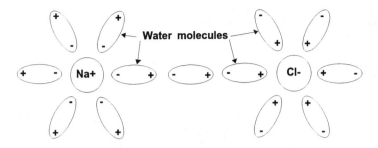

Fig. 5. The separation of salt (NaCl) in water

lot of heat is used used in breaking down an increasing number of these strong bonds, so much more energy is needed to raise the temperature which is measured by the thermal agitation of the liquid.

5. SOLVENT PROPERTIES

Water is able to dissolve more substances than any other liquid. Plants use nutrients dissolved in the sap that transports them throughout the system. The oceans act as a reservoir of gases keeping the atmosphere stable. If the amount of carbon dioxide in the air increases, more is absorbed by the sea water. It is alternatively released should the level go down. The use that we make of its ability to dissolve so many substances ranges from the humble cup of tea to complex chemical reactions.

If two substances are to react together quickly, the best way is to dissolve them and mix them together so that each molecule can be placed very close to the other. This, of course is an important factor in the huge number of chemical reactions between the complex molecules in living organisms. One example is the rapid reactions of enzymes that combine other chemicals at a phenomenal rate (3×10^5 molecules/sec. (Nee:263)), all carried out with little or no raising of the temperature.

The property of a substance to dissolve chemicals depends upon its Dielectric Constant, which for water is far higher than any other substance. This is a measure of the difference of charge when the hydrogen shares one of its (negative) electrons (and therefore becomes positively charged) whilst the oxygen shares the hydrogen's electron (and becomes negatively charged). This high charge difference between the ends of the molecules enables the substance being dissolved to be broken into positive and negative parts (ions) and keep them apart from each other. This is illustrated in Fig. 5.

A very small number of molecules break into a positive H ion and a negative OH ion. The loose positive H ions join to other molecules to become positive H2OH ions leaving the negative OH ion free. These ions are important in chemical reactions and their transport is greatly speeded up. In addition, in water at room temperature, there are very long links of the molecules stretching across large distances. These ions can travel rapidly along these chains by a series of exchange "hops". From this, any change in acidity (pH level) can be transmitted very rapidly throughout a solution. It also gives water a fairly high conductivity to electrical currents (Ba:539). Its actual conductivity can be adjusted by the addition of various electrolytes, allowing extremely fine control of the electrical conditions in cells for their numerous chemical reactions (Nee:20).

In addition, two of the six outer electrons of the oxygen atom are shared with the two hydrogen atoms, leaving two pairs for bonding with other chemicals. These are important in the solution of non-ionising solutes such as sugars (Nee:18).

Regarding the fine balance necessary for life, it is important that the conditions are neither too acidic or alkaline, and the measure of this is the pH value - neutral being 7.0. This only has to vary a fraction of a unit from this level for life to become impossible. To control this there are buffering systems, one of the most interesting being amino acids which deal with positive ions at one end and negative at the other (Nee:22).

At 300°C and under pressure, the molecule disassociates to produce a positive hydrogen ion and negative hydroxyl (OH) components. The result is that there are both acidic and basic features which makes it extremely active in chemical reactions. If it is under pressure it will also remain in a liquid state adding to the efficiency of the whole process, for under differing conditions it can act as a solvent, a catalyst and a reagent (Pen:124). It is this property that makes hydrothermal (supercritical) water able to form solutions of rocks deep in the earth's interior as will be discussed in Appendix 4.

6. SURFACE TENSION

In the liquid state, the hydrogen atom is also attracted to the oxygen atoms in other molecules, causing them to "cling" to its neighbours. This attractive force is higher than all other materials except mercury. On the surface of the water, this tendency to stick together results in "surface tension". This makes the surface behave like a thin film that allows small loads to be supported. Light objects, such as pins, will float on the top of a glass of water if placed there carefully. Many insects exploit this property to scud across the surface of a pond without getting wet or breaking through it.

Due to this surface tension, free floating water droplets are automatically pulled into a perfect sphere, this being the shape that gives the minimum surface to contain a specified volume. Similarly, soap bubbles form into a sphere for the same reason.

Capillary action

This tension within a liquid, also known as cohesion, is also able to raise water up a very fine capillary tube.

Where the liquid meets the side of a vessel, the molecules will also be attracted to it. If this attraction is larger than the cohesion between the liquids molecules (as with water) then the edge of the water will curve upwards, making an angle with the container wall. For pure water in a very clean glass this could be 0°. However, even contamination by air would increase this to 25° or more. For mercury, the internal cohesion is greater than its attraction to the walls of vessels and the curve is downwards, giving an angle of 148 - 140° (Fig. 6).

This angle at the edge gives an upward pull on the liquid below and the liquid will rise as a result. It will continue rising until the weight of the water below the surface equals the upward total force from the curved meniscus at the top. With a large diameter tube, the force is large due to the large circumference, but this is more than offset by the very large volume of water that it is trying to pull up. With a very fine tube, however, the perimeter at the top is smaller but the volume of water below is very much smaller, so the rise

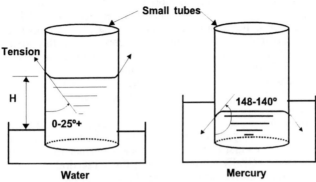

Fig. 6. The capilliary forces of water
and the reverse effect of mercury

will be much greater. For very fine tubes, such as are present in cell structures, the tensile force can raise water to over 100 ft (30m) which is necessary for the growth of tall trees.

7. MOLECULAR ACTIVITY

Just how wide a range of roles water plays in many reactions has only recently been realised. A very interesting article (Pen) summarising recent discoveries gives the following little known facts that are changing the fundamental ideas of physicists and molecular biologists. Far from being a passive medium of solution, it is being found that it has a very active role in many reactions.

a) Organic activity

As referred to above, the oxygen atom attracts electrons from the two hydrogen atoms, making itself negative and the hydrogen atoms positive, which give the molecule a wide range of uses. In many complex (organic) molecules there are charged sections with which the water reacts. The uncharged, non-polar, sections that do not react with the water molecules, however, form into isolated "droplets". They are squeezed together by the surrounding water molecules that are attracted to each other and tighten themselves around these droplets (Fig. 7). Now the energy required to form a

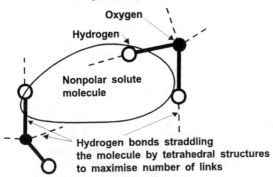

Fig. 7. The shaping action of water molecules

tight cage around two "droplets" is more than if they were combined into one larger droplet, and so there is an attraction between them and they come together in a "hydrophobic bond", reducing the number of links required.

The water molecules also tend to align themselves so that their negative ends are near the positive ends of other chemicals and their positive ends near the negative. This brings the surrounding chemicals into an aligned position and the hydrogen bond linkages take effect and tend to maintain this formation. In this way water interacts with some amino acids and affects protein structure.

With certain molecules, the linkage actually shapes them. This is the case with enzymes, that bring about many chemical reactions in organisms. It is the shape of the enzymes that brings the chemicals together for them to interact, and this shaping is actually brought about by the tetrahedral linkages that push the enzyme into the correct shape (Ba:539).

Does water have a memory?

There may also be a connection between these shaping properties of water, or some other not yet discovered, that may explain the results of Bienveniste in his examination of homeopathic treatments for illnesses. He found that solutions of certain potions, diluted to such an extent that none of the original material could be present, nevertheless had a measurable effect upon immune cells. Could the water retain a "memory" of the shape of the chemical or an electrical "profile" of its charged surface? From what is now known of its properties, this is not an impossibility.

Needless to say, the Establishment professionals decried such results and undermined his credibility by sending over a trio of most unusual "experts", one of them being a magician, to find flaws in his very technical experiments (see Ref. Davenas). Creationists are not the only ones to find their efforts to seek the truth fiercely opposed by orthodox "science". It should not be inferred that this gives any endorsement whatsoever of homeopathic treatments, but it has been mentioned in this section because there may be yet another amazing feature possessed by water which is still undiscovered.

b) Protein structure.

When you have a protein composed of a very long chain of amino acids, it is not a long thin strand as might be expected. Because of the many different links between the various sections of the chain, the final shape is very convoluted, with many deep crevasses and bumps etc. As the protein molecule forms, these crevasses can hold water molecules that can make up from 27 to 77 percent of the final weight of the protein. These molecules can enter into and out of these grooves at the incredible rate of a million times in one thousandth of a second. This is similar to the billions of reactions per second that we have noted that enzymes can operate at.

The water can link up into long chains that can influence the fine-scale structure and function of the protein.

Due to the complex folding of the protein molecule, it is possible that the folds might be so tight that the surfaces would touch were it not for the water molecules keeping them apart in the deep grooves. Thus the water keeps the surface of the protein open to other chemicals, and the main areas of activity are these deep grooves in the protein molecule. In addition, the activity of the water in these sites is different to its activity elsewhere around the protein molecule. Furthermore, the "backbone" of the protein is the peptide chain, and surprisingly, this has been found to be as active, if not more so, with water than the side-chains.

It is this new factor of the importance of water to the whole way in which proteins operate that is having to be taken into account by biochemists. What is of interest to the creationist is that these amazing properties are consistent across many different species. One enzyme had the same water-related mechanism whether it was from yeast, cows or humans.

c) The formation of fossil fuels

We will examine the whole subject of coal and oil in Appendix 4, but here we will look at the very important part that water plays in their formation.

For both coal and oil, it has long been thought that it takes at least thousands of years to produce their complex chemicals from the mass of decaying organic compounds in the earth. What has been a puzzle is that out of the original phenomenally complex organic components, nature manages to break them up and recombine them in the still very complex molecules of coal and oil that have such useful properties for us today.

To re-examine the whole sequence, organic chemicals were heated to see how they broke up, but no matter how hot they made them, certain important bonds in the organic molecules would not break and the chemicals produced gave poor heat output. It was only when water was added was oil produced (Pen:124).

It seems that it is the dual acidic and basic nature of hot water that is the main agent of forming oil - acting as a base in breaking up the long molecules at particular points, and then as an acid in accelerating different reactions. The products then attack other parts of the molecules. The whole process can be very rapid and takes place at a much lower temperature than first thought, with water a most important agent in the whole activity of producing oil.

As a result of these new discoveries of the property of water, scientists are now suggesting that it may be used to improve the quality of certain types of coal and oil, break down petroleum based environmental contaminants and be used as a catalyst in many chemical reactions. The very important role of high temperature water (supercritical water) in the formation of the rocks in the earth's strata, discussed in Appendix 4, is obviously due to its particular properties outlined above.

Those engaged in oil discovery base their methods of searching for deposits on the evolutionary assumption that it can take millions of years to form the oil. They are now very reluctant to accept these findings that it can be produced in a comparatively short period of time. Had they listened to the creationist evidence, they would have known this fact many years ago.

8. BODY TEMPERATURE

The body is maintained very accurately at 36.9°C (98.4°F). We have mentioned that water has an extremely high capacity to absorb heat with minimal raising of temperature (i.e. high specific heat). Now this varies for different temperatures and *it is at its lowest value at precisely the body's temperature*. This means that the molecules can be more easily mobilised for each unit of energy supplied (Nee:10). Other properties of water and its solutions also show turning points about this temperature.

Needham notes that insects warm up to this temperature before taking flight and under bacterial action, compost and damp hay tend to this temperature also. It is surely amazing that the body's temperature is at this very fine point

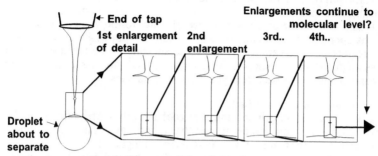

Fig. 8. The repeated patterns in a dripping tap

where the properties of many chemicals are at their most efficient.

9. ONLY A DRIPPING TAP!

Scientists have studied the formation of a droplet of water as it leaves a tap (D.Tel 26.10.94 p18) . What they have found is that a flat disc forms in the thin water link just as the drop separates from the water in the bottom of the tap above. Just below this is an even smaller disc, and below that a smaller one still, and the series seems to go on until it reaches the dimensions of the water molecule itself (Fig. 8).

This repeating series of ever smaller patterns is very much like the "fractal patterns" that are found in plots of certain mathematical formulae. Even in something as simple a dripping tap there are surprising patterns to be discovered.

10. ABUNDANCE OF WATER

One might have expected that this wide ranging collection of quite unique properties, all possessed by this one substance, would make it a very rare molecule, possibly only manufactured in a laboratory with great difficulty. The reality is, of course, quite the opposite, for the total volume of water on this planet is 340 million cubic miles. In addition, to the surprise of geologists, deep boreholes have shown that there is a vast amount of water at a depth where theoretically the pressure should have closed all the pores in the rocks (Ker).

That such a unique substance should also be so abundant is surely at variance with what might be expected by the normal laws of chance. It is also completely transparent, tasteless and odourless. Had any one of these simple properties been absent it is difficult to imagine how different life would be. Just imagine the situation if water was either opaque, or had a taste or smelt - or all three!

SUMMARY

We have briefly set out the major properties of water, an element that clearly plays such an exceptionally important part in the ecology of the earth and the metabolism of living organisms. The innumerable ways in which these unusual properties are used throughout nature are either unnoticed or taken for granted.

Surely it obvious that it has been specifically designed for this very wide range of roles in nature. One wonders how any materialistic sceptic reading such a list of properties - and the evidence produced in the previous appendix - can nevertheless maintain an atheistic position. It does raise the question of just how much evidence it would take in order to convince them that an infinitely intelligent designing God most surely exists. One can only conclude that, despite their claim to only be convinced by "facts", the truth is that they ignore them when they point towards a creator. This exposes their real motive, which is *not* the seeking of truth, but the avoidance of God.

APPENDIX 4
GEOLOGY

This is one of the most important fields of investigation into the natural sciences, central as it is to the theory of evolution. The invariable appearance of the standard geological column in one form or another in all books about evolution, with its time scale of "millions of years", gives an impression of scientific certainty to all that follows within their pages.

There are many creationist books that can easily demonstrate the numerous weaknesses and contradictions when the evidence is examined more closely. Even many articles by geologists admit to their puzzlement when confronted with evidence that conflicts with the standard evolutionary interpretation of strata or fossils in the rocks. The theory could be destroyed by quoting from these sources alone. Indeed, lacking funds to do original research, much of the information in creationist journals springs from this source.

To replace the evolutionist's interpretation of the geological column, tidy and convincing as it seems, with a "young-earth", scriptural, catastrophic creationist model, however, is far from easy. For one thing, the actual sequence of strata of the rocks around the world, and the fossils they contain, are far more complicated than the neat "column" implies. This alone makes *any* comprehensive interpretation extremely difficult.

For this appendix it would have been adequate to have presented an outline of the model that was able to describe how and when the various geological strata were formed within a Biblical framework but this cannot be done at present. The main difficulty with so many models is that they leave too many major questions unanswered.

It is easy to provide a sweeping picture of how rocks were formed, received their fossil content, were covered and redeposited, etc. to provide the present scene, but too often, ordinary mechanical constraints appear to have been ignored or contradicted, and just how certain geological features were formed was far from clear. Several versions were examined in detail but the result was often one of increased confusion on the precise way they would operate. Unfortunately, in the opinion of this writer, no satisfactory model able to explain even the major features of the strata has yet been produced.

In fairness it must be said that the problems facing creationist geologists are formidable. There are many deposits that almost defy any explanation that sounds reasonable, and we will be looking at some of these. However, we will first deal with certain subjects in order to set the scene for much of what follows.

We would here note that few readers will have any specialist knowledge in geology. Although some technical terms are used, we trust they will be able to follow the main points. This appendix, however, may be of particular interest to creation geologists as some ideas, mostly proposed by others more expert in this subject than the writer, are described in some detail in the hope that, if found viable, they might be incorporated into future creationist models.

A. Geological Problems

1. CREATIONIST ASSUMPTIONS QUESTIONED

The geological column is generally used as a starting point by creationists. Fig. 1 gives a typical diagram indicating the various fossils in the different strata.

When creationists read in a journal that a certain strata was, say, Jurassic, they automatically relate this to its position in the column, placing it after

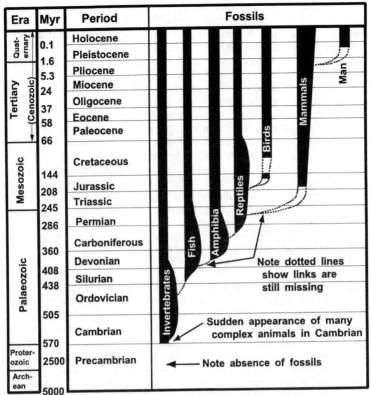

Fig. 1. A typical evolutionary geological column

certain strata and before others. But the factor that is often overlooked is that this label really has nothing to do with time. It has been called "Jurassic" *only* because of the fossils it contains. The researches of Woodmorappe show that a large percentage of the earth's surface is covered by only a few of the ten main geological periods (Cambrian to Cretaceous + Tertiary). Fig. 2 is a recasting of Woodmorappe's Fig. 1 - CRSQ, v 20, n 3, p 135. The graph shows (for example at X) that only 13% of the land area has 5 of the 10 main geological periods above it. Other values can be obtained from the graph.

From this graph it can be seen that 50% of the earth has only 4 or less geological periods over it, and even those will not always be in proper sequence for they will have missing periods between them. In some locations certain periods will be in reverse order to the column sequence.

These strata could have been laid down at almost any time relative to another one with similar fossils some distance away. The only criteria is that in any one location, obviously the upper layers were laid after lower layers. This allows the sequence in which local strata were deposited to be determined. There may then be much upheaval and erosion, further deposits, etc., but the sequence in which they were laid can generally be determined.

What is questionable is the correlation of the deposition of the strata that may be on different continents. This is usually by the fossils they contain, or by radiometric dating. Correlating by fossils assumes that on all continents each group of animals (Invertebrates, fish, etc.) were inundated at the same stage of the Flood. This is quite possible but is nevertheless a large assumption. Correlating by radiometric dating, as far as creationists are concerned, is far too inaccurate - as can be seen from Fig. 1 in Section 4.

At times, this is not always appreciated, and false conclusions can drawn by creationists when using these labels in the geological column. It is not denied that there appears to be a general progression of fossils as shown in this chart but it is far more varied than the stylised drawing suggests. It is possible that the frequent reference to these named strata may be one of the major causes why creationists have difficulty in interpreting the evidence on scriptural lines. Each area needs to have its individual interpretation of geological events applied to it without too much reference to the evolutionary labels the strata carry. In addition, it may be an important factor to know what layers (if any) are above and below the strata in question and if they are conformable.

Whether the geological column is a reliable reflection of the actual geological strata is a subject of considerable debate between creationists at the time of writing. Some contend that it is a concocted series rooted in evolutionary interpretations and should be treated with great caution. Others claim that it is a satisfactory summary of the strata and creationists can refer to it with reasonable confidence.

2. UNIFORMITARIANISM AND CATASTROPHISM

Lyell wrote his *Principles of Geology* in the 1830's and established his Theory of Uniformity - that the gentle processes of erosion of the mountains and land and deposition at the river estuaries going on today is the same process that has laid down the great depths of strata over millions of years. Since then, geologists have consistently interpreted the rock strata based upon this assumption of gradual wearing down of rocks. It was assumed that this process would at the same time encase a small percentage of most of the creatures living at that time that would then be fossilised and provide the evidence for the slow progress of evolution.

Alternatively, in more recent years, creationists have maintained that all the geological column has been laid down under catastrophic conditions of earthquakes, volcanic eruptions, lava flows, etc. The evidence for this mechanism is very clear in the strata but has been consistently ignored in the long-age assumptions of virtually all geologists who have been evolutionists to a man. To have been otherwise would have meant total rejection by one's peers.

The evidence for catastrophism has been so clear, however, that a few geologists have suggested that some of the column must have been due to brief periods of much activity followed by long periods of inactivity. One of the earliest to say this clearly is Derek Ager, who was a Professor of Oceanography and Geology at Swansea University. He set his views out in his book *The Nature of the Stratigraphical Record* [Ag73]. He later wrote a sequel *The New Catastrophism* [Ag95] but this added little more than his first book.

He makes many criticisms of the uniformitarian interpretation of the strata, and describes various huge deposits of chalk, limestone and coal, etc. that can stretch across several continents. He refers to the conclusions by the highly respected American geologist J. H. Bretz of how a glacially-dammed lake in Montana broke and produced the present scenery over a distance of 430 miles [Ag73:46].

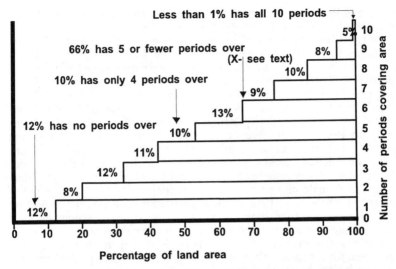

Fig. 2. The coverage of the earth by the ten geological periods

What is interesting is that this description was presented by Bretz in a paper in 1923. He was summoned to a "kangaroo court" by the Geological Association of America and his work was described as "incompetent" and "preposterous" [SF(Book Supp.)113]. In 1969 he reinvestigated the evidence with modern techniques and proved that his earlier interpretation was fully supported. In 1965 the area was visited by a geological party from the International Association of Quaternary Research who subsequently sent him a telegram which concluded "We are now all catastrophists" [Ag73:467]. In 1979 the Geological Association of America presented him with their highest award!

Ager's books have interested many orthodox geologists, but whether they will have any lasting effect is doubtful. They have also been widely quoted by creationists, but this greatly annoyed him. He said in his first book:

> This [catastrophism] is heady wine and has intoxicated palaeon-
> tologists since the days when they could blame it all on Noah's
> flood. In fact, books are still being published by the lunatic fringe
> with the same explanation. In case this book should be read by
> some fundamentalists searching for straws to prop up his preju-
> dices, let me state categorically that all my experience (such as it
> is) has led me to an unqualified acceptance of evolution by natural
> selection as a sufficient explanation for what I have seen in the
> fossil record. I find divine creation, or several such creations, a
> completely unnecessary hypothesis (p19).

He was even more emphatic in his second book for in his preface in bold print he says:

> ..in view of the misuse that my words have been put to in the past,
> I wish to say that nothing in this book should be taken out of
> context and thought in any way to support the views of the
> "creationists" (who I refuse to call "scientific").

Stephen J. Gould was similarly annoyed when creationists used his

"Punctuated Equilibrium" theory to support their claim that the fossils linking the major groups simply did not exist.

Why Gould and Ager should feel like this is understandable. But what are creationists to do? Ignore their works? We are simply referring to Ager's work as additional evidence of the obviously catastrophic nature of geological depositions. This is something many creationists have been claiming for years, *long before Ager (or Gould) put pen to paper.*

Ager's thesis is not just a minor quibble but a criticism that strikes at the heart of the present-day interpretation of geology. The evidence has been staring the experts in the face for generations, but they have all been too blinded by uniformitarian dogma to take any notice of it. And now, when one of their own people "breaks rank" and admits that this evidence has been there all along, are creationists to keep silent out of respect for Ager's finer feelings? We would also point out that creationists do not quote him out of context: the whole of his book is about the evidence for catastrophe and we merely refer to his considerable evidence as a belated confirmation by a secular geologist of a view creationists have held for many years.

Surely we have every right to use his book to support our case, as it is exceptional for a member of the geological Establishment to publish anything that concurs with the creationist's viewpoint. On the very rare occasions when they do, they should not be surprised by the response.

3. THE UNRELIABILITY OF SEISMIC PREDICTIONS

The KTB project.

There has been a long term investigation of geological strata by very deep boreholes. The Russians drilled to 12 km (7.5 miles) and the Germans were trying to reach the same depth. A report of this latter project shows that the results obtained were far different from those expected (Ker93).

The first surprise was that the rise in temperature with depth was much greater than expected. Another was *the huge amounts of water that flowed in* at depths where the rock was expected to be so fully compressed due to the weight above that there would be no voids left for water. What was found at depths as great as 6 km was a large quantity of water with a concentration of salt twice that found in sea water. It has been estimated that there is four times the volume of the surface water within a depth of 400 km (*New Scientist* 30.8.97).

This has implications for the present salt content, for it suggests that the first outpouring of water was fairly fresh. When this deeper, more salty water came later, it would then have increased the saltiness to its present level. With fresh then salty water coming from the depths of the earth, their dispersal over the face of the earth may have been arranged by God such that both fresh and salt water fish could have been preserved following the Flood. This was discussed when answering critics in section 5.1.

Yet another surprise was the strength of the rock continued to increase with depth. It was expected that the increase in heat would eventually make the rock softer, so that the crust would be stronger than the deeper strata. The lower rock was found to be stronger than the crust - which has considerable implications for earthquakes and plate tectonics, etc. for it has always been assumed that the deeper levels were more plastic to allow the plates to move. Similarly this questions the cause of earthquakes. If the lower levels are harder, how can they be caused by the much publicised "subduction" of the upper crust beneath the continents? One expert asked "Does the top drive the bottom or the bottom drive the top?"

The electrical conductivity of some parts of the strata was also higher than expected, and furthermore, it was not by graphite in the rocks but by another component. The biggest surprise was the failure of the predictions from seismic studies. They had expected at 3 km depth to go through two tectonic plates that had "collided" in the past. This junction had not been found even at 7.5 km (4.7 miles), the depth of penetration at the time of the report.

The Deep Sea Drilling Project - Leg 138

This project, like the KTB, also failed to confirm seismic predictions. One scientist said "Once again, we discovered you should take seismic interpretations with a grain of salt" (Oard92A, Ref; Ker91).

Oard's article reports several other failures of drilling to find what was expected from seismic reflections. One failure was thought to be the reflections from a water level in the rocks. If this is the case, and certainly *something* caused the recorded result on their instruments, *then all seismic records that claim to detect differences in the rock strata are under suspicion.* This means that the diameters of the solid and fluid cores at the centre of the earth, important in many subjects such as the earth's magnetism, may not reflect reality at all. The core could be solid throughout and no dynamo activity could take place.

Creationists consistently claim that an interpretation of the geological evidence from a purely evolutionary standpoint is greatly at odds with the evidence that stares any independent investigator in the face. These unexpected discoveries indicate that it is the establishment geologists who badly need to reconsider the whole framework from which they view their subject. Creationists are more likely to be nearer to the truth.

It should be noted that all these unexpected results in the field of geology are paralleled by the surprises that confront astronomers when they study the data received from spacecraft regarding the planetary system or the observations of the universe by very powerful telescopes. Each time they are baffled by what they find. Yet popular scientific articles rarely mention these anomalies that regularly arise and for which the scientists have no satisfactory explanation. At all times it must appear to the populace that "Science has the answer" and can be trusted as it is "objective" in its search for "truth".

4. THE INADEQUACY OF SEDIMENTARY THEORIES

Almost all geologists, both evolutionist and creationist, assume that most strata have been formed by the erosion of uplifted land washed into the sea and lakes where it laid down the sedimentary strata. The evolutionists would claim this is a very slow process. These sediments would harden and are then lifted up to become the new strata that are in turn eroded to form the next era of sedimentary layers. In this way, secular geologists provide an unending sequence of events as a background to the long slow process of evolution over millions of years. Most creationists would accept erosion as the source of the strata but would say this was achieved in a very short, catastrophic period.

Plausible as this might sound, there are fundamental problems for the long timescales required by evolutionists.

Nevins (Nev. *ICR Impact* No. 8) has shown that by taking the estimated volume of material deposited into the sea annually (27.5 billion tons) and dividing this into the amount of land above sea level (383 million billion tons) then it would only take 14 million years to erode the whole land area to sea level. Yet the geological column gives the total time since life first appeared in the Cambrian as about 600 million years. There is enough time for these strata to have been eroded many times over, removing or repositioning the earlier fossils. This fact destroys the credibility of the evolutionary geological column with its evidence of slow but steady progress from amoeba to man. Nevins similarly calculated that it would take only 30 million years to deposit the total amount of sediment present today in the oceans. There is therefore something badly wrong with the very long time geologists claim for the deposition of the present geological column.

Problems for the creationist "erosion" model

For creationists, however, the "erosion" model requiring the deposition of most of the strata in the catastrophic conditions of the Flood within one year presents just as great a problem, *for the turbulence of the Flood could not produce the present formations either.* We present the following evidence in defence of such a controversial claim.

(i) **The turbulence of the water.** In order to sweep the soil off the existing land surfaces, the force would have had to have been very powerful. This power could easily be supplied by the emerging subterranean water as the "fountains of the deep" broke up. However, it is this turbulence that would have caused very considerable mixing of the various constituents. It is claimed that the material would have been sorted by the various sizes settling out in order of size - gravels, then sands, then silts and finally clays. But this has problems also.

(ii) **The sedimentary pattern.** If the contents of the Flood waters settled out as assumed above, then, as we followed along the deposit, we would see a very slow gradation from the gravels to the clays, with much mixing of the different sizes; e.g. sand dropping from the top of the sea level would be mixed with silts and clays that had been suspended near the bottom of the sea but already deposited. There are a number of strata that do display such a gradation, but there are far more where there is a sharp boundary between different sizes. Often, there is little mixing even where they touch; usually one strata gets thinner along its length as another one becomes thicker - with little intermixing (See Fig. 4 later).

There is one aspect that creationists appear to have overlooked regarding the formation of deep strata of sand. If the grains of sand have been reduced to their present size by the crushing and rolling of larger stones, this requires a very considerable amount of energy to have been expended by water as it flows down from the mountainside towards the sea. Could this action provide the sorted sizes today? It is suggested that it could not do so as we will see in the points below.

(iii) **Sand and clay - the source problem.** Almost all sands (and gravels) are extremely hard and take a very great deal of grinding to produce a smaller grain size. Those who have polished stones in a grinding machine will know that it has to be kept working for several days just to remove the initial roughness of most stones. What comes out of the machine is not a mixture of stones and sand but a slightly smoother stone and a very fine dust which is silt *and not the much finer particles of clay.* On a pebble beach the stones have been continually washed backwards and forwards for a few thousand years at least, but no sand sized particles seem to be produced. There may be sand in the vicinity but can it be established that it actually came from the grinding of the stones nearby? Close inspection would probably show that it is of a quite different composition.

In addition, inspection of grains of sands in deserts show that they still retain their sharp edges (Q22/1:47). If they had undergone any grinding action for a reasonable length of time, these edges would have long since been rounded off.

It is therefore suggested that sands and clays are not generated by the breaking down or grinding of gravel; the product of such action is only smaller gravel and silt.

(iv) The energy problem. The only mechanisms for breaking down hardened rocks into sands and gravels is either on their passage from the mountain tops to the sea, where the products are sorted by differential settlement over the sea floor, or by grinding on wave-swept beaches. Now let us consider this whole scenario in stages as it applies to a single Flood period.

Let us assume that the lower 2/3 of the geological column at least was laid down during the one year period of the Noachic Flood (we will see below that upper layers may have been formed later). In these strata there are many deep beds containing vast quantities of sand. According to the above assumptions, it could only have been produced during its descent from a mountain area, or possibly by wave action on a beach. Once a material is below the wave level, as the vast majority would have been in view of the depth of the waters of the Flood, the conditions would have been far too tranquil to have any effective grinding action. But all these Flood deposits, complete with their entombed fossils, were laid down in less than one year *and there was no time for mountains or beaches to be formed* that could have produced the sand by pounding rock against rock under the assumed conditions! Even if they had been formed, it would have taken far more than one year to have produced the vast quantities of very uniform sized sand granules in the strata. How then could this sand have been formed if there was insufficient time or mountain height available to produce it?

(v) The colour of mixed deposits. At the estuary of all large rivers there are mud flats and possibly sandbanks; all fairly uniform for great distances and reasonable depths. If this were the usual way in which strata were formed, then by now the whole earth should consist of muddy mixtures of a fairly uniform grey/brown appearance. Any heavy rainfall removing the soil from the land would contain a range of minerals that would be the usual dark mixture. If you mix all the colours of a paint box you will have a brown mess, not a brightly coloured result.

But this is not what we see in the various strata. In some places there are enormous volumes of great depth of pure, light coloured clay with a uniform texture which could not possibly be the result of the washing out of a mixture of land material. Similarly, there are large sand deposits of a very uniform grain size and texture with virtually no admixture of clay or pebbles. To my knowledge, no geologist, whether creationist or evolutionist, has ever discussed the significance of this fact.

Whilst there is some re-deposition of previously laid materials - such as in conglomerates - *it is contended that all models, whether orthodox or creationist, that refer solely to "erosion" as sufficient to produce the huge volumes of very uniform clays and sands we find in the strata are not realistic.*

When giving an explanation of how strata were formed, geologists, somewhat airily, call upon the Flood waters to perform some strange acrobatics. One moment they are required to exhibit enormous force to break rocks, smash bones till they no longer exist. Then, to explain the strata immediately adjacent, they need to be tranquil for a long period to allow the slow settlement of clays to take place.

When creationists ascribe the present strata to the action of violent Flood waters, we can only suggest that they are unaware of the huge problems that their "erosion" model involves. To confirm this claim, we would suggest that they are asked to answer three problems -

(1) If the grinding of rocks does not result in clay but only in silt, where do the vast deposits of pure, light-coloured clays come from?

(2) At the mouths of rivers there is either dark mud or sand bars. How could the deposits of light clay have been kept so pure and free from mixing with other darker minerals?

(3) Can they demonstrate *in detail* how Flood waters can lay a complex sequence of strata such as a series of coal seams? The inherent contradictions in the sequences are likely to become apparent.

If the material of the strata did not mainly come from existing land surfaces, where did it come from? Having seen that there are still vast quantities of hot, compressed water in the interior, we will now consider the very important role that a large quantity of pre-Flood superheated water deep in the earth's interior would have played in the formation of the geological strata.

In considering the acceptance by creationists, both qualified and unqualified, that the present strata were formed by the turbulent Flood waters from the products of erosion, one cannot but wonder whether they have unwittingly imbibed a fundamental feature of the uniformitarian philosophy of Hutton without realising it? To be trained for a long period by uniformitarians could make it difficult to see "the wood from the trees".

B. The Importance of Hydrothermal Water

Barry Setterfield is widely known for his work on the decrease in the speed of light, particularly the Stanford Research Institute Report which he coauthored with Trevor Norman (Nor). This was preceded by a larger but less well known publication "The Speed of Light and the Age of the Universe" published in 1983 (Set83). In this he covered a wide range of subjects including an extensive geological scenario. Much of this material also appeared in the Creation Ex Nihil Technical Journal 1984 v1 p52-69.

The subject of particular interest here was his proposed source of the minerals that formed the strata we have today. Setterfield, basing his view upon a very important paper by Stanton that we examine later, suggested that the majority of this was *not* material washed off the land that then settled in the waters of the Flood to form the "sedimentary" strata. He contended that most of the rock minerals were brought to the surface from the interior as a solution in extremely hot water known as "hydrothermal" water (HTW) but sometimes called "supercritical" water.

The effect of hydrothermal water

When water is heated to a high temperature, above 374°C, and is above a pressure of 224 kg/cm^2., its acts like a gas and can expand indefinitely, but the molecules are still close together, making it behave like a liquid. In this form it is called "hydrothermal water" and it has an extremely high capacity to dissolve a wide range of substances, including all the chemical compounds that make up the strata we have today.

The most obvious explanation for the source of the majority of the present strata is that it was hydrothermal water that was the prime medium by which much of the rock strata were transported to the surface. With its high solvent properties, masses of minerals would flow out over the land and sea surfaces to form the new strata.

In some cases, the flow would be huge and great deposits would be laid down. In other cases, the rising minerals would be carried to the surface by separate "bubbles" of rising compounds. When these reached the surface they would spread out and cover a limited area, and other rising material would cover it or overlap it on the edges. If there was any turbulence, then they would become mixed and provide a gradual transition from one type of strata to another in a short distance.

If the rising solution were to meet a hardened upper layer, it would force itself sideways beneath it, forming a "magmatic intrusion". The role of water "in the behaviour of magmas is becoming increasingly appreciated, quite apart from its dramatic lowering of their melting points". (Set83:73 quoting from Krau:84f).

Setterfield's Memorandum (Sett83) set out the important activity of HTW as early as 1983 and he deserves recognition for highlighting the importance of this subject at that early date. The subject was referred to in an earlier work (Bow91:147f), more recently Snelling has written on the subject (Snell94B) and we refer to Cox's models later. Almost all others, if they do mention it, do not appear to realise its importance and the difference it makes to the whole process of how geological strata are produced. For this reason, we will set out the evidence in some detail.

The work of R.L. Stanton

At this point we will examine the quite revolutionary paper referred to by Setterfield that first pointed to the crucial activity of hydrothermal water. This is by R.L. Stanton and is entitled *An Alternative to the Barrovian Interpretation? Evidence from Stratiform Ores* (Sta). Stanton was the Professor of Geology at the University of New England, Australia, and he has presented this paper at a number of meetings of geologists throughout the world.

The "Barrovian Interpretation" refers to the work of George Barrow who mapped a number of metamorphosed rocks (i.e. changed by heat and pressure). Stanton pointed out that there were many so-called "metamorphosed rocks" lying immediately adjacent to *un*metamorphosed material - in some cases as close as 1mm. He considered that heat and pressure could not be the main cause of the difference between these two closely associated rocks. He provided considerable evidence and then said:

> It is concluded that the fluctuating seafloor interplay between warm, acid, concentrated hydrothermal waters with cold, alkaline, dilute seawater during stratiform ore formation, together with diagenetic processes, leads to the formation of a wide range of clay/chlorite ...precursor materials and hence, later, to the complex assemblages of metamorphic minerals closely associated with some stratiform ores (Sta:11).

We have, then, a mechanism for the formation and deposition of many clays and minerals. His proposal for this *chemical* deposition of strata is set out on his page 22. I give extracts below, but the interested geologist reader is referred to the whole of this important article.

It appears that most stratiform ores are formed by the contribution of mineral-bearing hot springs to the sea floor in areas of volcanic activity. The waters of the hot springs are, of course, at relatively high temperature; they are also slightly acid, have a high dissolved solid content, and a low Eh. As they debouch onto the seafloor they encounter the water of the sea which is cold, slightly alkaline, possesses relatively low dissolved solids and which may or may not have low Eh. Added to this, the output of the hot springs is likely to be somewhat *pulsatory*, and the motion of the seawater likely to vary with variation of the slow bottom currents of the locality concerned, these two factors leading to a fluctuating interplay between (them)...It is this interplay... that leads to the development of the bedding of the stratiform ores.

However, the contribution of the springs involves more than the ore minerals. As well as iron, calcium and other metal compounds, it usually includes substantial quantities of silica, alumina, and silica-alumina gels, the basic materials of the clay minerals and, through its acid nature, it also involves the variable breakdown of detrital feldspars and other minerals to a variety of clays. This activity may continue on well after the deposition of the stratiform orebody itself. It is plain that it may lead to the accumulation of sediments not only of highly varying chemical composition, but also containing a wide variety of *clay* and associated chemical/ detrital minerals (Sta:22).

The theory that metamorphosis of rocks was by heat and pressure was, and still is, the current view.

However, Yoder noted that his experiments showed that changes of a few percent in composition (including water) may produce a great difference in mineralogy; that mineralogical differences interpreted by Eskola and others as resulting from changes in pressure and temperature-pressure conditions might actually be, for the most part, results of subtle changes in bulk composition (Sta:27).

Yoder surprisingly said "This conclusion, based on experimental fact, appears to be at variance with field observations", but Stanton points out that his experiments really confirm what has actually been found.

We would here, in passing, notice once again the vital part that water plays in the formation of these compounds, both as the transporting medium and within the chemical reactions - a subject discussed in Appendix 3.

Lest it be thought that Stanton is dealing with only small scale deposits, it is important to understand the huge quantities that Stanton considers as having been laid down by this method. In one map he gives the gradation of deposits as they spread across the surface. The point from which they flow is from the direction of John O' Groats and they cover virtually the whole of the North of Scotland.

It must be emphasised that many rocks are usually interpreted as being *igneous* rocks, i.e. once molten, but Stanton claims that they are precipitated *solutions* in outpourings of HT water. This is a very important aspect, for geologists have always assumed that these rocks were once molten liquid at a very high temperature. They have studied these rocks under a microscope and labelled them as such. Stanton, a very highly qualified geologist lecturing to other expert geologists who would have ridiculed him had he been badly wrong, is nevertheless claiming that their source was quite different. This is an important aspect that should be bourn in mind in all that follows.

With distances and depths such as he gives in his map of Scotland, combined with a totally different source of the material, we have a major tool for the reinvestigation of *all* the present geological formations.

Confirmation of this source of geological compounds is given some support as granite cannot be made in the laboratory so it was assumed that the crystals took millions of years to grow. However, granites could be synthesised "in a few hours in hydrothermal conditions" and "biotites...had been synthesised in a few hours on 'hydrothermal conditions'. "

Regarding clays, all the various types have been formed in the laboratory *under hydrothermal conditions* (Roy). It would therefore appear that all the major types of strata can be produced by hydrothermal conditions.

Supportive views

In a paper (U.S.) discussing the surprisingly high conductivity of the earth, it was suggested that there were three possibilities - water, magma and conductive minerals. One expert favoured "a supercritical saline water explanation". Reference was made to "fluids released from mantle-derived magmas crystallizing higher up in the lithosphere", and that the critical temperature of water "is also in the temperature range at which various minerals (particularly quartz) would precipitate to create an impermeable seal."

Thus, the HTW model proposed would also solve the high conductivity of the earth and other features.

Appreciating the scale of geological activities

Whilst dealing with the subject of the enormous volumes of various deposits around the world, this all needs to be held in perspective. To say that a deposit is a mile deep gives an impression of a vast quantity. But when compared with the size of the globe on whose surface it lays, it is minute. The radius of the earth is 3,964 miles (6,378 km), and therefore a layer 1 mile (1.6 km) deep is a thin layer of only 0.025% of the total depth below - say about as thick as one layer of onion skin on an onion! They *are* huge deposits, but still small in comparison to the size of the earth that provided them. Therefore we should not be overawed by quantities of rock that could be laid down during the Flood period; it was small compared with the quantities below.

If this proposal of the important activity of HTW in *chemically* producing the majority of strata from the earth's interior is accepted as the most viable, it can provide a far better explanation of many geological formations such as those following.

1. THE FORMATION OF SAND

The main constituent of sand is silica, a compound of silicon and oxygen - SiO_2. These elements are abundant in the rocks and the earth's interior. They would therefore be a prime constituent of the mineral load carried to the surface by HTW. There would be some loads that would be almost pure silica that would be deposited or alternatively, the silica would be precipitated out at a certain level where the temperature had fallen to a critical point. The result in either case would be a vast volume of solid crystallised silica - the component of sand.

What happened then has been discussed by Douglas Cox (Cox75) in an early 1975 article in which he proposed that the mass of silica then shattered into sand particles in stages beginning from the top. In what follows we would point out that Cox has since modified his theory for one in which the sand is produced by crystallising out of an amorphous state. Whilst this is a different mechanism, the production of sand *from a fluid state* is the same.

Some creationists with geological qualifications have strongly criticised these proposals of how sand is produced. We have examined their comments with care but consider that they have failed to give adequate answers to the problems with the "erosion" models set out above. We are, therefore, outlining the following evidence regarding the production of sand as answering the majority of problems regarding the deposition of these strata. With these warnings ringing in the readers ears....

The sand bedding planes

Cox noticed that in some sands the bedding lines were very sharply curved as shown diagrammatically in Fig. 3. It is obvious that there is something unusual about these sharply curved "beds" and even in geological descriptions there were layerings referred to as "false bedding". There are some 15 different types of bedding but this particular classification has since been abandoned as being "obsolete" - but we would question this. Clearly, there must have been at some stage a form of bedding that could not be attributed to water flow, and was therefore called "false". Have geologists now found a way in which they were laid down under flowing water? What compounds the problem is that Cox, in his article, notes that sedimentologists using flumes were unable to produce many of the beddings found in nature. This, therefore, leaves open the question of how some sand beds were formed. Some strata have certainly been laid down under water, but for other patterns, until they can be replicated in the laboratory, the assertion that "all beds have been laid by water" is not as fully supported as might be imagined from the confidence with which it is stated.

What Cox proposed was that these are not always lines of "bedding" but lines of fracture and he quoted experiments on glass under high pressure that produced similar patterns of close fracture lines. If glass and quartz were placed in water and subjected to very high pressure and then suddenly released, the glass shattered in the well known "brittle fracture" form. In one experiment, a thick-walled capillary broke into layers "like onion skins".

> A similar effect would apply in geology if there had been former high pressure on the rocks of the earth's surface due to great depths of burial under water, and rapid elevation of these rocks again to the surface (Cox75:170).

Cox pointed to dolomite which he describes as "chemically precipitated rock" formed "under deep burial and high pressure", which if brought to the surface, would shatter, just as discovered in the experiments. I would, however, question whether any large volume of rock could be "rapidly brought to the surface" as he describes. It would be difficult to see what force could be called upon to produce such a result. Far more likely is the rapid removal of overburden which could have occurred in the turbulent conditions of the Flood. This release of pressure may have taken place during later, more local, catastrophes after the Flood.

I would suggest that HTW could not only have been the means of

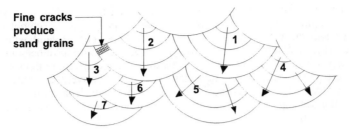

Fine cracks produce sand grains

Fig. 3. Crack propagation in crystallised silica producing sand grains

transportation the silica from the depths, but may have had yet another part to play in this subject of "release of pressure".

If the transportation of the silica that formed the sand was as an HTW solution or a gel, then it may not be necessary for the pressure to be released by removing the overburden. There are several factors that could produce intense internal pressures within the suddenly solidifying silica which would still contain much of its transporting water. Instead of expansion of the water trying to be released under rapidly lowered external pressure, it is possible that the contraction on cooling of the silica mass may have put high pore pressure on the contained water - which would have much the same effect. There is also the possibility of phase changes involving volume changes within the material that could produce very high stresses in such a bulk. It would be interesting if this possibility could be examined by an expert in this field.

The sequence of cracking that Cox gave is interesting. The vertical pressure inside the rock structure itself would be less at the top than at the bottom, due to the extra self-weight of the mass itself. If the pressure at the top was sufficiently low that it could not resist the internal pressure of the water, the top layer would be burst off first releasing the local water pressure. This would immediately make the next layer down the top of the solid mass under internal pressure which would in turn burst off - and continue for the whole deposit. In this way, and very rapidly, the whole bulk could shatter throughout its full thickness as each layer had the pressure above dramatically released.

An additional factor is that the cooling would have taken place most rapidly at the top, and this would have shattered first if the internal pore pressure of the water was increased by contraction of the solid.

Even the crack fracture angle is interesting. Cox quotes an experiment that showed that:

> In compression, the most severely stressed crack is inclined at about 30° to the axis of compression. Such cracks, when either isolated or placed in an array, grow along a curved path which becomes parallel with the direction of the compression. When this direction is attained, growth stops, unless applied compression is increased considerably (Cox75:171).

This starting angle of 30° and the curved path the crack follows agrees with the pattern commonly found in these "false bedding" lines as shown in Fig. 3. In examining this figure, it is easy to visualise the pattern of cracking spreading rapidly down from the top and producing a curved pattern which could be mistaken for "bedding planes".

This pattern is preserved in some beds but for most locations it would require only one large jolt from an earthquake (and there would have been many at the time of the Flood) for this delicate pattern to be completely destroyed and the whole strata made into a uniform bed of sand with no layering evident. Where there is obvious layering, this could have been in the outpourings of the HT water giving levels of slightly different compositions which were preserved after the fracturing period. Alternatively, the stratification would have been preserved if there has been any cementing material between the sand grains that would have preserved them against moderate earth movements.

Cox's later views

As we have noted, Cox has since modified his ideas and suggested that the sand crystallised out of a hydrous amorphous material in subsurface sills, during compaction of the Flood deposits. This crystallisation occurred in successive layers that produced patterns of stratification that are typical of sandstones. He also notes that this can result in very rounded grains of sand as distinct from the sharp edged sands in many deposits.

We would suggest that both methods of deposition could have been operating to produce the different types of sand. They could also have worked together; the mass of silica could have cooled to produce the solidified liquid (like glass) which then crystallised into the sand grains we see now. There could have been slightly different conditions that produced a wide range of sands.

The important aspect is that both models rely upon material being brought up as a solution which then cooled and not from the slow erosion of hard rocks.

Cox now places great emphasis upon "disintegration" of deposits to explain a wide range of strata, some of which we examine later. Having proposed this model, he subsequently discovered that Raphael Pumpelly, a very experienced and widely travelled geologist of the last century, came to a very similar conclusion. Cox's "disintegration" model has been a subject of controversy, but his evidence has yet to be adequately refuted by creationist geologists.

Caves formed by rock disintegration?

It is generally accepted that caves are formed by solution in water passing through the rocks. However, several geologists have noted that certain features do not conform to this theory. They are formed on joint lines and not on faults; they can occur in mountains well above any long term water-line; deep "potholes" are formed in the *roofs* of huge caverns; they can be filled completely or pockets left on high levels; their pattern is often a network on the same level throughout and not sloping downwards,, etc.

At the suggestion of the then editor of the CRSQ, Harold Armstrong, who had read his articles on sand, Cox examined the problem. He concluded that, in the same way as sand was produced, the fill and the formation of the caverns was due to the sudden release of pressure along the joint lines permitting the shattering of the highly pressurised material (Cox76, Cox77). This provided the fill in the caverns that in most cases would then be washed out to leave the strange patterns of caves we have today. We will not elaborate on this but refer the reader to these articles for further information.

Salt domes

How salt domes were formed has always been a problem to uniformitarian geologists. Nutting of ICR had proposed in 1984 that they were a product of hydrothermal water (Q26/1:15) and that even earlier, Nevins had proposed a similar source in 1974 (Q10/4:244). We would consider that deposits of sand have the same subterranean hydrothermal origin that salt has. The wider implications of these papers does not appear to have been appreciated by creationist geologists for they contradicted the orthodox (!) creationist view that the strata are produced by erosion.

2. SANDSTONES

Cox proposed that these are also produced by migration of HTW laden with silica, but as this rises it precipitates its load in layer formations, giving the appearance of stratification (Cox86). Material in HTW rising later through the deposit would have cemented the sand into the harder sandstone.

The Franciscan sandstone

In support of the activity of HTW, we quote an early edition of the CRSQ (6/4:161) that reviewed a book (Bail) dealing with a huge deposit in California of a mixed sandstone of sand and clay called greywacke. The quantity was such that it could cover the whole of America to a depth of 600 ft (182m) - a huge volume.

The report refers to "lack of abrasion" and "lack of sorting" and the conclusion is that they have not been "blown, tumbled, rolled nor washed on the beach". The report notes:

> Such heated, silica-enriched water would rise, be cooled, and quickly become oversaturated with respect to silica. Silica would then be polymerized and precipitated as a gel..and it would rain down onto the sea floor forming a mass of impure silica gel. Subsequently, by a process of diffusion and crystallization, layers that superficially resemble normal sedimentary beds would form.

All this is in complete accordance with the mechanism of HTW set out above. One Christian geologist asked "Where did all the sands come from?"

It is suggested to all geologists that the action of hydrothermal water is used in interpreting the source material of those strata labelled today as "igneous", "sedimentary" and "metamorphic".

3. PEBBLES AND GRAVELS

The formation of gravels according to standard theory is much the same as for sands. Rocks are assumed to be shattered and ground down to become smooth pebbles by being transported along river beds. Similarly, beach action may be called upon to produce the rounding of the pebbles, but as with sand, there has been neither the time nor the available mountain height or beaches that could produce these rounded hard stones within the Flood year.

Cox confirms this, for he notes that there are stones already within some sand deposits (Cox75). There may be stones that have fallen out of these strata and may be laying in the nearby streams, but this does not mean that they have been shaped by the small amount of rolling they may have received. He also notes that where the "false bedding" planes meet an internal concretion, they do not "flow" around the obstruction as might be expected in a sedimentary deposition, but finish butting tight to the face of the inclusion. This suggests that the inclusion has already solidified, was harder, or at least of a different material to the shattering silica around it, thus preventing the cracks from propagating further.

Cox suggested that pebbles are formed by a cementing material being precipitated out in nodules and forming a shape that minimised their surface area - as a soap bubble does (Cox86). This would explain how gravels are formed within sandstones.

There is yet another method of producing a "rounded" product from a uniform strata. Rusch describes the weathering in some exposed basalt faces and says:

> ...a criss-cross pattern of vertical and horizontal fissures develops, that gives rise to a rounded type of cobble formation. The cobbles then fall to the base. General examination fails to reveal any obvious variation in the basalt (Rus:163).

Anyone inspecting these cobbles would assume that they had been rounded by friction and tumbling - *and they would have been wrong.*

This unexpected way in which rounded cobbles can be produced demonstrates that long periods of grinding are not necessary. There are strata that have two or more independent "structures" within them. There may be what appear to be "bedding planes" in one direction, but quite independently, there may be an isolated area that may have lines of "weathering" or fissures possibly filled with another material, or there may be a colour or texture difference. One or more of these may be present and all these may have no relationship to the first lines. This is more easily explicable by allowing a local area of the HT water mixture to have a slightly different chemical composition to the rest of the strata when deposited. The difference in the weathering along internal stress lines, as seen in the production of sand and in these cobbles may be another fruitful line of enquiry on the formation of pebbles.

The rapid formation of stones and sand on the shore of a reservoir has been described (Lamm) but these were in a comparatively soft sandstone and the very rounded pebbles that are on many beaches did not seem to be prevalent. These were local events on a shore, but what has to be explained is how whole separate beds of sand and rounded pebbles could have been formed and placed in their specific positions.

I would agree with Cox that gravel and stones could be a product of small, local "concretions" within the rising solution in the HT water. They might be of a different material to the majority of the solution and would hold together by being more viscous, etc. They would also have a different temperature at which they solidify, and might therefore be precipitated as distinct "lumps", even with veins running through them, before the surrounding material itself solidified.

This method of generating gravel might also explain how they can be admixtures within other geological deposits. Thus "conglomerates" are a cemented form of gravel within a matrix, often limestone. Probably, the gravel was flooded by the rising limestone that was precipitated and solidified between the stones. However, it may be possible that the gravel compound solution became mixed with a limestone solution on their way to the surface. If the dissolved gravel compounds did not easily mix with the limestone matrix, like oil being mixed with water, it would naturally form roughly spherical shapes (due to natural surface tension) and we have the formation of gravel already within the strata when the whole mixture cools and precipitates out its components.

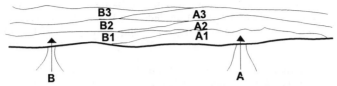

Fig. 4. The "interfingering" of different strata

4. DEPOSITION OF FINE CLAYS

If a fine clay is washed into the sea, it could take a very long time for it to all settle to the bottom - in some cases probably far longer than the whole period of the Flood. This would be for only one layer and it requires calm water, which is hardly the condition prevailing during the Flood! When there are other, different, clay layers over them, the time required would that much longer still. The time taken to settle through deep oceans is very great indeed, and with the slightest turbulence there would be considerable mixing with other settling sediments by the time it reached the bottom. Flocculation - the clumping together of several particles - would give a more rapid settlement time, but it is doubtful if even this would be sufficiently quick to allow many distinct layers to settle.

If, however, the material was brought to the earth's surface by the hydrothermal water, it would react with the sea water and could form a moderately dense precipitate. This could easily spread out over the sea floor and no long time would be required for its settlement - it would already be virtually "in place".

Even the very fineness of the particles of clay is interesting, for they are so small that even water has difficulty in penetrating between them. As discussed above, a fine, uniform size of particles is easily produced as a *chemical precipitate*.

5. INTERBEDDING AND "INTERFINGERING" OF STRATA

If it is imagined that there are a number of rising "bubbles" of material containing different chemical assemblages, they will spread out over the sea floor at different times, giving rise to the interbedding that can be seen in some formations, as illustrated in Fig. 4. If deposit A1 was laid first, then B1, A2, B2, etc. the formation would be gradually built up.

The publications of William Corliss are considered later, but in his volume of Geological Anomalies there was a striking picture of vertical lines of flint stones in a chalk face at Norfolk (Fig. 5.). The only reasonable explanation for these is that there was a stream of rising "bubbles" of material through the chalk, which was unable to progress further as the chalk became sufficiently compressed or cohesive to "freeze" the progress of these blobs in their tracks. It may be objected that the present flint is heavier than the chalk, but this may be a later transformation by chemicals seeping into the volumes created by the rising material. However the flint was formed, the formation of these apparently rising blobs is, on a small scale, some confirmation of Stanton's proposal of rising HTW through existing strata.

6. DOWNWARPING OF LAND MASSES

When the rising water with its load of chemicals reaches the surface, there is automatically a void created in the earth and the land sinks to fill this void.

Thus, for every volume of material coming to the surface, there must be exactly the same volume by which the land must sink. Therefore, there is no need to search for great depths of deposits compressing or forcing down local areas for they will naturally subside into the hole created by the rising material.

It is this mechanism that would have inundated the local animals and plants in specific areas. Had they been washed a considerable distance into the sea, then there would have been much greater mixing of both fossils and deposited material.

Dry land "inundation'?

An additional important factor is that this inundation could have taken place over dry land. Considerable water would have been provide by the HTW and the land would have subsided into the cavity vacated by the HTW - *and all this could have taken place above the existing sea level*. It would not have been necessary for the land to subside below sea level to be inundated from the sea, and then rise again to become dry land again as it is today. The material could have poured out over the land with much or little free HTW accompanying it.

If this proposition is accepted by creationists, we can begin to see just how radical the reassessment of geological activity would be when all the aspects of Hydrothermal Water are taken into account.

7. THE FORMATION OF KIMBERLITES

These are vertical "pipes" of material that have obviously risen from the interior, the most famous of them being the diamond mine at Kimberley in South Africa which is almost a mile wide in diameter. The material within them has come from below 200 km (125 miles) deep and at a great speed, tearing off portions of the rock walls through which it has travelled, bringing them to the surface as xenoliths. We would suggest that this rising of interior material through well known kimberlites is a more obvious example of the remains of a vertical conduit used by HT water.

It is usually claimed that diamonds were formed under great heat and pressure deep in the earth's interior. The recent discovery that microdiamonds have been found in crustal rocks in Norway (E96/10(1):1) is just one more fact that baffles geologists.

8. REWORKING THE LANDSCAPE

Once a number of strata had been laid down, the violence of the Flood or further subterranean flows of water could have swept across some areas to produce the erosion of layers laid down earlier. As they were only recently deposited, they would still be soft and easily eroded. This would explain the very sharp, straight interfaces in many unconformities, where one set of rocks are at a distinct angle to later bedded layers as shown in Fig. 6. Had the rocks had time to harden, they would have been differentially eroded as we see on some headlands today, and the meeting line between these two surfaces would have been very irregular as a result.

An important point is that any clay, sand or gravel strata deposited by HTW could be eroded and the new areas they settle in would look precisely as if it was an ordinary sediment, to be classed as such by geologists. What is maintained is that the *origin* of the material is *not* a long term erosion of land but the product of HTW. As we have emphasised, there was not enough time

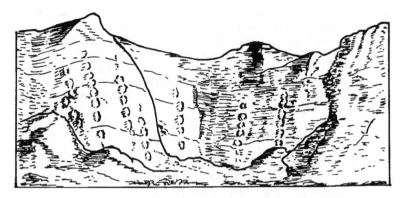

Fig. 5. The rising pockets of material through chalk

in the Flood for much erosion of a continental mass that could have produced the huge sedimentary deposits we have today.

The rising HTW could engulf animals and fossilise them quickly in the warm solution rich in chemicals, that would have destroyed the flesh. If reworked, additional fossils could be incorporated from another area.

By various mixings of the chemicals and reworking, etc., it should be possible to explain such deposits as greywacke, conglomerates and many other deposits.

Engulfing of animals

In the strata, there are numerous fossilised bones of animals. Some are "articulate"; i.e. they are positioned as they would be in the animal, from which the flesh has since decayed, leaving the form of the animal still visible. Others are just isolated bones. This would be where the animal has been dead sufficiently long, possibly floating on the surface of the sea, for the flesh to have decayed and its bones to have been separated, to then become entombed and eventually fossilised.

It might be asked how fish could have become engulfed, as the sea is their environment. There are several ways that this could occur.

(i) There could be many areas where the land might (temporarily) rise with the upsurging material, and this would have dried out local lakes containing fish, leaving them stranded and they would die within minutes.

(ii) The upswelling of the hot hydrothermal water with its chemical load would be enough to ruin the delicate metabolism of the fish who would be used to cold water free of major contaminants.

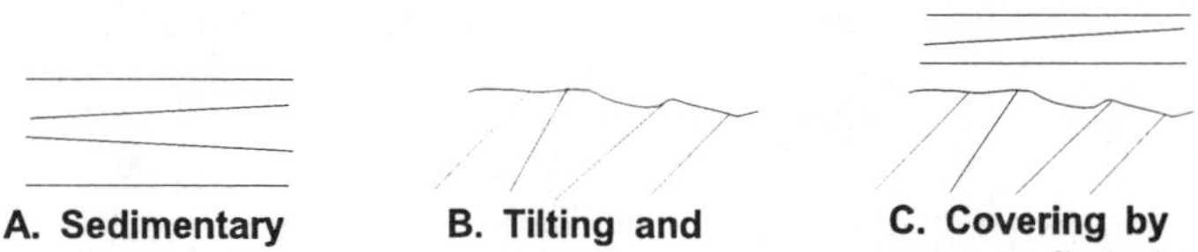

A. Sedimentary layers   B. Tilting and erosion   C. Covering by more sediments

Fig. 6. How unconformities are produced

(iii) More effective in causing widespread destruction of aquatic animals would be the chemical deposition of the material in the hydrothermal water. As HT water with clay bearing minerals reacted with the sea water, vast quantities of clay would be generated that would quickly suffocate all marine creatures in the area. That this could take place very quickly is indicated by many fossils that show fish caught in the act of giving birth or swallowing other fish at the very moment of their death. One of these is illustrated in Fig. 7.

There are examples of huge numbers of fish being buried in contorted positions and covering vast areas. That burial was very rapid is indicated by the twisted position of many fish as though they were dying in agony, their bodies passing through several thin horizontal layers. These layers must have themselves been laid quickly otherwise the protruding parts of the fish would have rotted before they were covered and protected.

Another indication of rapid burial is that some fish have their defensive spines erect as though fleeing in fear, and other examples of this nature could be given.

9. COOLING OF MAGMAS

Davis A. Young has noted that a particular intrusive strata - The Palisades Sill adjoining the Hudson River - would have taken a few hundred years to have solidified from a molten state (You), whereas - according to his understanding of the Whitcomb-Morris sequence, the sill would have had to cool within the Flood year, be eroded and then have fossil-bearing Triassic strata laid upon it.. He quotes other examples with long cooling periods - up to 200,000 years. He says "The burden now lies with flood geologists to explain.. just how igneous bodies.. could succeed in completely solidifying during the flood". Let us see if an answer can be given.

(i) **The material of the rock.** The layer just referred to, in the HT water model presented here, would not be a white hot outpouring of liquid rock, but an outflow of hydrothermal water that precipitated a particular solution known today as "diabase".

On this, we have already shown above that the work of Yoder, as used by Stanton, shows that the constituents of what are called "igneous rock" could equally be provided by hydrothermal water, as indicated by the "igneous" or "metamorphosed" rocks of Scotland which Stanton contends are the product of HTW.

(ii) **The temperature of the rock.** The most obvious consideration is that the HTW solution would never start from the very high temperatures of over 1000°C that Young assumes. The critical temperature of water is 374°C. As soon as the temperature dropped slightly, the solutions would be precipitated to form the various "igneous rocks" we have today.

There is a further possibility. If concrete is mixed and kept continually agitated, it will remain fluid long after it should have set. If it is then poured out onto the ground it will set within seconds as the agitation prevents the chemical links from forming. Something very similar could have happened with the rising HTW "mush" of dissolved material. The turbulence of the rising fluid would have prevented it "setting" even though cooled well below the temperature that it should have done so. Once it reached the surface, it would have "set" very rapidly, producing the "frozen in activity" appearance that many articulate fossils seem to possess. This would explain the position of polystrate fossilised trees laying at an angle through several strata.

Fig. 7. Sudden death at dinnertime!

In confirmation that the temperature may have been quite low, it has been claimed that "Once the "favourable" conditions obtained, the minerals crystallised easily, in hydrothermal conditions *as well as in normal conditions of temperature and pressure"*. From this, the dissolved materials could be precipitated out at the ordinary temperatures that would prevail on the earth's surface.

As an indication of the dramatic effect that water can have on the properties of rocks, it is reported that the time taken for a magma to cool to a solid decreases ten-fold between water contents of 0.5% and 4% (E96/10(2):177).

It is hoped that the above may be an adequate reply to Young's challenge to flood geologists.

We would finally question whether this sill is really an intrusion. It is very thin compared with its large area, and an intrusion between two strata would surely bulge upwards where there was any weakness or lower pressure. To force apart two strata for the same thickness over a large area is difficult to imagine. The dimensions of the sill are far closer to being a surface deposit. If this is correct, cooling would have been even more rapid.

10. THE FORMATION OF COAL LAYERS

The standard evolutionary explanation of how these were formed is that they were forests that subsided below sea level and were then covered by one or more sedimentary strata. Later the land arose above sea level and a new forest grew again, which in its turn, sank below the sea and became covered with more sediments. This process would have to repeat itself very many times to provide the sometimes hundreds of coal measures that lay above each other. One slight variation debated is whether each layer of timber actually grew in its present position, or whether each was brought there as a mat of floating wood that eventually settled in its place. Often the lowest layer has upright tree trunks with the roots going into a layer known as the "seat earth", which gives the impression that they grew in this position.

Whichever view is taken, it is clear that there would have to be very many risings and fallings of the sea level to produce the present strata. For this to happen so many times and over such vast areas as the coal measures cover is surely stretching credulity too far.

Is there a sequence that could produce these multiple layers in a short period that could be encompassed during the period of the Flood? What follows provides a possible answer to this.

The proposal is a combination of three separate aspects;

(a)The floating rafts of timber

There would be floating rafts of timber torn from the land. Dr. Steve Austin suggested that these would gradually become waterlogged, and the continual rubbing of the trunks in the waves would produce a "rain" of timber onto the sea floor (Orig). Scheven points out that the lower layers of bituminous coal in the Palaeozoic are composed of lycopod trees. He suggests that these were actually floating on the sea and were not a land plant, and that they had a a variety of amphibia living on them also (Sch). The coal in the Mesozoic was of ordinary modern trees that were swept into the sea and became the lignite coal in these later strata.

(b)The timber "rain"
The waterlogged timber and whole trunks would sink to the bottom. This action has been confirmed by those investigating the Mount St. Helen's explosion, a subject covered more fully later. They have found tree trunks with roots in an upright position on the newly formed lake floor, giving the impression that they had grown in that position (Aust86). From this, claims that the tree trunks embedded in the "seat earth" prove it was grown in position are disproven. Close examination shows that the roots do not penetrate into the "soil" very far - they have just settled into the soft material as they descended from the surface.

(c)The action of hydrothermal water.
The various geological layers between the timber debris would have been provided by the hydrothermal water arising from the interior and flowing out over the layers at periodic intervals. We have noted above that Stanton specifically refers to the "pulsatory" emergence of the HTW. This would explain the repetitive nature of the series of strata between coal strata. This is not to say that the sequence should always be identical. As we have discussed with the interfingering of strata (Fig. 4), different outpourings would overlap and emerge at different frequencies to produce the repetitive yet varied sequence of strata observed.

This whole sequence of events is set out in Fig. 8.

There are few alternative theories of how coal could have been formed. There have been proposals that they were laid down by the cyclic action of either (A) tides or (B) waves. Each inundation of water would deposit a timber layer that becomes covered by a strata, the next wave laying down a further timber layer, etc. That the layers were laid down as a whole is indicated by the intertwining of the branches found in the Carboniferous seams which contradicts the "timber rain" proposal we have made above. However, there are major problems with such models.

(i) The areas covered by coal seams. The laying down of a raft of timber by tidal action alone is difficult to picture in actual practice as the previous layer would float again as the next tide returned to fill the area. If the tides were beating against a beach, they would just make a vast pile of timber debris along the shoreline and could not produce a thin flat layer over vast areas.

It is the enormous areas covered by one coal seam, some of them extremely thin, that is a problem that needs an adequate answer. The tidal deposition would not produce such a result and there would be inadequate time for the laying of the depths of sediments between each layer.

To suggest that it was wave action that deposited each coal layer would give even less time for the deposition of each layer and its covering by strata. The "wave deposition" theory is quite untenable.

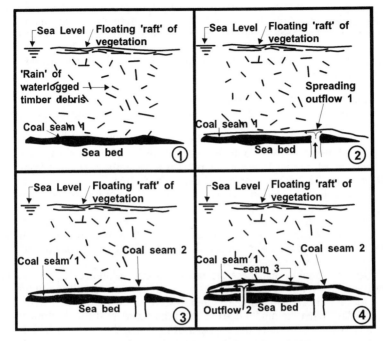

Fig. 8. Proposed formation of coal seams

In an interesting article by Morton (Mort84B:27) there is a description of the Pittsburgh coal seam: about 2 ft (0.6m) thickness of coal uniformly spread over 15,000 square miles with a very level top surface, covered by an unbroken layer of shale only 3/8 inch (10mm) thick, above that 4 inches (100mm) of coal, another 3/8 inch thick shale layer and then 3-5 ft (0.9 - 1.5m) of coal. A comment by a uniformitarian geologist was "That sounds like a precipitate, as ridiculous as that would be." Morton agrees; "There is no known mechanism for such an occurrence."

The thinness of these strata when the huge area they cover is a major problem for both evolutionist and creationist explanations, but they are solved if these strata were *chemically* precipitated.

(ii) **Violent and tranquil water.** The main problem is the contradiction between the rapid flow of the water necessary to drain away from large areas to deposit the timber on the "dry" ground, and the tranquil conditions required for the slow settlement of the clay or similar strata in between layers. Much rushing of the water as it drains away from and into an area is not conducive to the depositions of fine clays and other sediments. Any turbulence of the water would stir up sediments laid only a short time before.

(iii) **The introduction of the sediments.** There remains the question of where the sediments came from (if eroded from the land), and how did they get between the coal layers as such thin strata?

(iv) **The rapid production of coal.** Evolutionists usually assume that the timber layers took many thousands of years to be gradually converted into coal. This is now known to be incorrect. Coal has been produced from vegetable matter by heat and compression in a few hours (Hill). It has also been suggested that clay can act as a catalyst to produce coal in a much shorter period than usually assumed. An even more rapid conversion of timber to coal has been suggested by experiments. These have shown that with high temperature and the added factor of vibration, the hydrogen atom of the cellulose can be split off, making it pure carbon, with the clay acting as a catalyst in this operation (Kar).

Problems with the "timber rain" model

There are two problems with the proposed model that must be acknowledged at this point.

The first is that it can take a very long time for floating timber to become waterlogged and sink. We would suggest that the conditions prevailing may have greatly reduced the time for this process to take place. Heating from the HTW or other factor(s) may have had the desired effect.

The second is that Scheven reports that the members of the lycopod trees in the Flood strata are entangled together, which would not be the situation if they had descended piecemeal as each member became sufficiently waterlogged to sink. Again, it is possible that they may have sunk as a mat from the same cause that might have produced the rapid sinking of the material of the floating raft timber suggested above.

It might be thought that these are unsatisfactory solutions, but we would point out that it requires only a factor in the unique and turbulent conditions of the Flood to bring about a more rapid descent of the timber than we could expect today. What the model does solve is the far more difficult problem of *how* these vast yet virtually flat deposits of coal could have been laid down with the slow settling and easily disturbed clayey strata between them; problems that are almost insuperable to the "tidal" and "wave" models.

There will no doubt be criticisms of this model, such as the presence of volcanic ash clay that forms many seams. If it is assumed that it has come from a volcanic eruption, this would indicate that the layer below it was exposed to the air at that time. Even here, however, it could be that this settled through shallow water to lay on the previous layer.

There are still several problems to be solved before a satisfactory model could be presented of how coal was formed. Meantime, the action of hydrothermal water in conjunction with this suggested proposal may go some way to achieving that end.

A chemical source for coal?

In an article headed "The Carbon Problem" (Mor84A), Morton points out that there is nearly seven times more coal in the world than could have existed in the pre-Flood forests. He suggests that some coal deposits are not of vegetation but are mainly due to chemical deposition.

He notes that the *Encyclopaedia Britannica* says that coal is so compressed that no plant remains are found in many strata. They are found underlying the strata and sometimes overlying. They may not be directly involved with the coal as fossil plants are found that are unconnected with any coal. Prof. Gold has suggested that rising methane produced deep in the earth inorganically may be triggered by passing through a plant layer to produce the various thicknesses of coal seams.

We have noted that Prof. Gold has already claimed that gas and oil may not be due to the decay of vegetation but from an inorganic reaction. Proof of this has been found at a depth of 9,000 ft (Bow91:149).

We summarise some of the evidence Morton quotes.

(a) **The great thickness.** There are seams of coal up to 30 ft (10 m) thick. It is estimated that the ratio of depth of vegetation to the final thickness of coal is about 10. Therefore, this layer represents a mass of vegetation 300 ft (100 m) thick. How such a huge thickness of vegetable matter could have been laid over a large area in one operation is difficult to imagine.

Oard reports a seam 75m (250 ft) thick (E96/10(1):5), the second deepest in the world. This is divided by claystone layers indicating periodic deposition of each layer. Even so, the thickest continuous depth is 20m., which would require a depth of vegetation of 200m (660 ft). These are huge depths that are hardly likely to have existed.

At the opposite end of the scale, we have described above the 4 inch (100mm) coal seams covering 15,000 sq. miles.

There would be no problem with either thickness of coal if they were due to rising methane or, as we would propose, a HTW *chemical* deposition like any other strata. This latter proposal would also explain how the vast coal deposits could have been formed with other strata in between: each was part of a series of cycles of deposition.

We have noted that Scheven has described the lycopod trees remains in the Palaeozoic levels showing that vegetation was identifiable in these strata, but much of the coal seam could have had a chemical source as suggested above.

(b) **Vertical stacking.** There are many coals seams vertically stacked one above the other in comparatively limited areas and spanning many geological periods. This fact could be explained by a deep source of the rising methane which repeatedly rose through the strata to produce the oils, gas and coal over a specific area and stacked one on top of another.

(c) **Precambrian "coal"!** There are coal-like deposits in the Precambrian very similar to anthracite called anthraxolite. As these strata were laid down long before forests existed, their origin *must* be inorganic. This deposit is found in veins and fissures in the Precambrian rocks, some up to 10 ft (3m.) thick, showing that the deposit from the inorganic rocks below had penetrated them after they had been laid down.

Furthermore, one Carboniferous coal strata of a similar material was mined from a seam that cross-cut other strata and was not laid down as a sedimentary bed like other coal seams.

As Morton suggests, at least a partial inorganic source for coal should not be dismissed too lightly. If confirmed, it would solve the problem of coal deposition in arriving at a satisfactory scriptural geological model. Although some coal layers have vegetation, does this mean all layers must be derived from coal? It is for those who hold to the orthodox view to explain Morton's evidence.

11. THE RADIOMETRIC DATING OF THE STRATA

We have already pointed out in Section 4.1 on the age of the earth that due to the decrease in the speed of light the millions of years ascribed to the strata by radiometric dating would be reduced to only thousands of years.

In the same section we have also provided a possible explanation of the apparent increase in age with the deeper rocks in the geological column.

C. Additional Geological Features

Having outline the importance of HT water in producing strata and its many

Fig. 9. The 'fit' of the continents

important ramifications, we will examine some other geological subjects.

1. PLATE TECTONICS

If you look at a globe, the continents have shapes that can be made to roughly fit together. This apparent fit of the continents is well known and was first suggested by Sir Francis Bacon in the 16th century. A better fit can be made if the continental shelves are included in the shapes to be fitted. Fig. 9 is based upon Ballard's ideas, but to obtain a good fit, Africa had to be shrunk 40% (BrownW:85).

The possibility that whole continents could be moved as one mass was ridiculed by orthodox geologists for generations until Wegener, a respected *meteorologist* incidentally, proposed this in 1912. It gradually gained support and is now the generally accepted theory by orthodox geologists. Such is the fickleness of "fashion" even in a staid profession such as geology! Is this a case of using a "new" theory to oust the "Old Guard" as evolution was used by Huxley and others in his day?

The question is; Have the continents moved or not? There seems to be evidence on both sides.

Although the majority of orthodox geologists accept the theory, there is still a small number who do not. Amongst creationists, it is a subject of discussion but only a few seem to commit themselves one way or the other. Those creationists that accept it point to the time of Peleg, "for in his days the earth was divided". This could refer either to the dispersion of mankind at the time of the Tower of Babel, or to the physical dividing of the earth's surface from one large land mass into the continental divisions we have today. The Biblical evidence appears to support the latter view.

In popular books about geology, neat diagrams of the convection currents in the mantle are shown, pushing the continents around and creating the mountain ranges, whilst mid-ocean ridges are claimed to provide a "tape recording" of the earth's magnetic reversals as the upwelling magma spread outwards. This all looks very convincing, but there are both large and small problems with the theory. Fig. 10 gives a simplified view of the principle plates and mountain ranges.

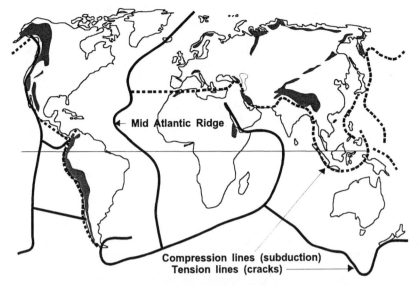

Fig. 10. Crustal plates and mountain ranges

(a) The evidence used.

Some of the criticisms of creationists are as follows (Snell95 and others):

(i) Regarding the Mid-Atlantic ridge, there are areas along the ridge that show no regular pattern of magnetic striping, whereas all the ridge should have the same pattern if it is all supposed to be splitting apart uniformly. In fact, drillings on the ridge give a far more varied pattern of magnetism than the "stripes" recorded by towing instruments over the ridge that have received so much publicity.

Furthermore, if the sea floor were spreading, a deep smooth crack would be expected, but it rises as it approaches the edge of the crack. In fact, there are many fracture zones that are displaced hundreds of kilometres, and this has caused several geophysicists to reject the theory that the sea floor is spreading (Q20/3:132). It has been claimed that the pattern of the cracks is more consistent with the sea floor being thrust upwards. It has been suggested this was due to the weight of the huge ice cap (Cook66 and Q30/4:186).

Another point is that checking the age of the mid-Atlantic ridge using Potassium-Argon dating shows that there is no increase of age as you move away from the ridge; i.e. there has been no sea floor spreading (Q16/1:10). In fact, the west side near America is dated at 160 million years but only 110 m.yrs. on the east side near Africa.

(ii) The deep trenches off the coast of Chile should be filled with highly compressed and distorted layers that would be scraped off as the mantle descended under the continent. In fact they are soft and flat lying without compression features (Nev).

(iii) An examination of the various crustal plates around the world show that there are some places where there should be compression actually show tension features and vice versa.

(iv) Although there are claims of measured movement between the continents, this is far more problematical than is realised. Often the amount is within the accuracy of the instruments used and it has been stated that no movement has actually been detected! (Snell95:17).

(v) One of the most surprising claims regarding the "magnetic stripes" is by Walter Brown (BrownW:79) who says that the magnetic field does not "flip" from one direction to the opposite direction, but only varies around a particular value. A line was drawn through the centre of these variations and from this the claim was made that the direction was reversed!

The main problem with examining secular evidence on both sides of the argument, is that they all assume that the earth has existed for millions of years, and generally that the geomagnetic evidence of reversals and pole wanderings is valid, and much else that is dubious to say the least.

One of the best surveys of papers critical of plate tectonics is by Wesson (Wes). The interested reader is referred to this paper for the extensive Bibliography he provides.

On the magnetic evidence, he notes that some experts had "illustrated the possibility of crustal stresses having influenced the direction of all palaeo-magnetism, thus rendering one of the postulates of the palaeomagnetic method invalid" (Wes:321). This is one of several points made by Barnes in his critiques of the assumptions of interpretations of magnetism in the rocks (Bar72).

Wesson also mentions that a standard interpretation of magnetic evidence would indicate "such apparently ludicrous geomagnetic events as the rotation of the State of Oregon (!)" [exclamation mark his] (Wes:322). This is surely indicative of the unreliability of using geomagnetic evidence for major geological theories such as plate tectonics.

Often biological similarities between continents that were thought to have once been together is claimed, but Wesson refers to one expert who competently criticised tectonic theory and said:

> This work, together with that of Axelrod, who shows that an unbiased examination of fossil floras suggest stable as opposed to drifting continents undermines the whole field of continental drift hypothesis (p329).

There is a similar lack of correlation in the magnetic fields of the two sides of the Atlantic (Q16/4:218).

There are, however, said to be similar strata on both sides of separated continents, particularly the Atlantic, but this evidence needs to be checked. This does suggest that they were once together and then separated. It is possible that the large expanse of what is now the Atlantic was washed away rather than the continents becoming separated but this would then raise the even bigger problem of where the eroded material was deposited.

(b) The fit of the land masses

Various experts have shown how the continents fit together. This is easy for the continents on either side of the Atlantic, but even here, there are different arrangements. Should the continental shelves be used or the main land mass? It is in other areas that the fit is much less certain. Complete reorientations of land masses have to be assumed to make some fittings. It then becomes more difficult to explain how the various continents could have turned and moved to their present positions.

One extreme case is the view that India travelled some 4,000 miles (6,500 km) from near the Antarctic up to Asia where is "crashed" into it and produced the Himalayan mountain range. This we would dispute.

Firstly, it is an enormous travel distance for a comparatively small landmass and no other land appears to have been affected by this long range travel. Secondly, had it done so, we would expect to see the Himalayas arranged in an arc around the top of India. In fact, the mountain range is curved in the opposite direction, centred on the northern side. In addition, there is an irregular line of mountains running from the western end of the Himalayas up to the Sea of Okhotsk. This suggests that the activity producing the Himalayas was more likely centred in China, pushing the mountains towards India.

(c) The problem of the driving force

This is an intractable problem that all continental drift theories have yet to solve. The stiffness of the mantle that is supposed to be moving the continents is many orders higher than the lowest value that could possibly allow any movement at all. To allow convection, the viscosity assumed by Wegener was 10^{16} cgs. units, whereas the actual values range from 10^{24} to 10^{26} cgs. units (Wes:322). His value was $10^{(8 \text{ to } 10)}$ too low.

An assessment of the mantle viscosity has been obtained by measuring the rise of Sweden. This was said to have been covered by a glacier and when it melted, the land arose. Measuring this rate of rise gives an indication of the viscosity. It has been found, however, that this has been miscalculated and that under the oceans it should be 10 to 100 times smaller. The result is that the forces generated at the bottom of the strata would be too small to cause any movement (Blu).

We have examined the effect that a higher speed of light has in reducing viscosity in Appendix 1. As the speed was possibly higher by a factor of 10^7 or more, it might be thought that this would so reduce viscosity by an inverse proportional amount which would enable continental drifting to take place. From the latest work by Setterfield this may have varied in repeated steps to a minimum of 1/530 of its highest value and given an average of roughly 1/250. This would have had a large effect upon the metabolism of living organisms but it is still far too small a change to give the $10^{(8-10)}$ (say 1 billion fold) decrease that is necessary as discussed above.

In addition, there is Lomnitz's Law mentioned by Burdick (Bur80). This says that the amount of creep in rocks under stress is logarithmic with time; i.e. with constant stress, the amount of movement decreases with time, giving eventually very little progress at all. This is hardly ever referred to by supporters of the theory, and the *Encyclopaedia Britannica* gave no entry under his name.

In confirmation, an article in *Nature* (225:1007) notes:

> Convection demands the elastoviscous law, which is contradicted by all the available evidence. Similarly, to maintain continental drift, in any way, at a constant rate would require a steadily increasing force.

This factor is a most formidable barrier to the orthodox convection theory of continental drift.

Asteroid impact?

Some articles propose that continental drift was brought about by the impact of an asteroid. The two sites of large asteroid impacts most frequently proposed are near Madagascar on the east coast of Africa and Yucatan on the north coast of South America.

The problem with such sites is that the surrounding land masses do not exhibit the features one would expect if the results were the world-wide movements of whole continents. For example, if the site were Madagascar, why should it have the whole continent of Africa on one side and the expanse of the Indian Ocean on the other. If the force was sufficient to push America away from Africa, the latter should hardly exist as a result of the huge forces involved in such a long distance effect across the Atlantic.

Asteroid impacts of this size can neither provide sufficient force nor explain the present dispersal of the continents or mountain ranges.

Benard cells

Another major problem is the dimensions of the convection currents that are supposed to be driving the continents apart. If a pan containing a liquid is heated, convection currents will be generated as the heated bottom liquid rises to the top. It has been found that fairly "square" "Benard" cells develop, in which the circulation path around each "cell" is roughly a square equal to the depth of the liquid as illustrated in Fig. 11A.

The problem then arises that the continents are much further apart than the assumed depth of the circulating currents. Thus, even if there was enough pressure to move a continent from A to B, it would then meet opposing circulation tending to hold it at B. The Atlantic is about 4,000 miles (6,400 km) across, and, allowing for the widths of the continents, to drive the continents apart on either side would require a "Benard cell" about the same depth, which reaches to the centre of the earth. This is an unacceptable situation as other continents would also have to be driven by "cells" of much the same depth and working in different directions. The flow of each cell would be much deeper than the normal square shape of a Benard cell (Fig. 11B).

It is here that the results of the deep drilling projects discussed at the start of this section become important. We have seen how many "facts", that geologists for many years have assumed to be fully confirmed, have been completely contradicted. From the results of years of seismic records, they have built up a pattern of what the various major levels are in the depths of the earth, only to find that even a comparatively shallow probe did not reveal the meeting of two different plates, showed there was water where it should not be and that the rock is far harder than they expected. As one expert has reported:

> You can devise all these models, and no one even tests them, except in sedimentary rocks. But, invariably, when somebody drills, it messes it all up.... It's ridiculous.... We have these thousands of kilometres of [seismic] reflection profiles, and we don't know what they show (in Oard92:28).

What these results do is to place a huge question mark over all seismic interpretations. The existence of the crust, mantle, core and other discontinuities are all based upon this technique, and therefore it must be questioned *whether these "boundaries" exist at all*? Such a fundamental change in geological theories would no doubt be strongly resisted by establishment geologists, but this change of concept might be of benefit in a creationist model.

These seismic surveys do show several deep horizontal layers due to some cause, which argues against the existence of very large vertical currents sufficient to move continents (Cox81).

There is yet another factor against Benard cells developing which is how

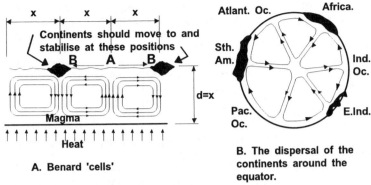

A. Benard 'cells'

B. The dispersal of the continents around the equator.

Fig. 11. "Benard cells" of circulation

the circulating currents are generated. We have described the rising of heated liquids due to their being less dense than the surrounding liquid. *Experiments have shown that this most obvious explanation is not the true cause;* it is due to the differences in surface tension that causes this flow (Bluth and Block). The effect upon convection currents is that the lighter crust counteracts the surface tension effects of convective cell formation. Some geologists have said that if Block's evidence had been known before his 1956 paper, convection theory would never have been accepted, although others disagreed.

Contradictory evidence such as that set out above badly damages any confidence that might be placed in geological theories. This is particularly important for the creationists who rely upon publications written by orthodox geologists. I fear that their uniformitarian basic principles can all too easily be assumed unwittingly by an investigating creationist. To have undergone a course in orthodox geology could result in imbibing incorrect concepts that are founded on weak evidence and contrary to the truth that should result in a Biblical geological model finally emerging. It may be relevant that one seismologist said to this author that the geologist he worked with was useless in trying to predict what the soundings and boreholes would find!

Runaway subduction

This is the proposition that slabs of the cooler surface of the earth under the sea plunged into the weaker, hotter depths of the mantle. As they descended, the heat from the movement reduced the strength of the mantle further resulting in a catastrophic "runaway" condition. In two very technical papers Baumgardner (Bau) made a computer model and showed how this could take place and proposed that this operated during the Flood and provided the power that caused the continents to separate.

It is questionable whether the slight increase in density due to the cooling of the surface could produce enough force to allow the slightly denser rock to sink.

The key factor is the viscosity. The value chosen gives velocities that "are in accord with current observed plate velocities of a few centimetres a year" (Bau:74). This seems a little dubious and there is a degree of vagueness in dealing with this major factor. Other factors are based upon seismic results, the unreliability of which we have discussed above. Furthermore, he uses a "power law creep" factor that produces the "runaway" condition - the heat of the friction reduces the viscosity and increases the descent of the slab of rock. This seems to contradict the "Lomnitz Law" of increase in resistance with shear movement in a rock.

One paper by Vidale (Vid) is referred to in its support. This is a review of another paper in which a descending slab of mantle is said to have been discovered - again by seismic records. It could only be detected by careful correlation of many records to omit "overprinting", etc. and as a result it was estimated that it was descending about "1cm. (1/2 inch) per year"! This is hardly the catastrophic descent that would produce "runaway conditions" but it was based upon a 50 million year period so the true rate may be much higher - if it *is* a slab of descending mantle.

Also contradicting the idea that the mantle has moved the crust is the claim that a conduit found beneath Brazil that has existed since the separation of the continents (VanDec). This indicates that they have been locked together throughout that period and that any movement of the mantle must be at a very much greater depth than usually assumed.

Brown is also critical of subduction theories, and his analysis of the forces required shows that subduction would not occur (BrownW:216).

Baumgartner's theory may be viable but it should be critically examined by experts in this field.

In reading the evidence in support of the theory, particularly regarding palaeomagnetic, biological and fossil evidence of links between continents, one has the feeling that the evidence is both slim and selected, and could be criticised by a competent expert. It was therefore interesting to read about a very full critique by Meyerhoff (quoted in Bur80:113) who expressed the same thought regarding the selectivity of the evidence presented. This does not mean that continental drift has not taken place, only that the evidence is far from being as convincing as the general public are led to believe.

Some creationist geologists have examined the evidence and have come to the conclusion that the orthodox, uniformitarian model of slow creep of the mantle was unable to produce the dispersal of the continents, but that the tectonic activity was extremely fast and took place during the Flood (Aust94, Snel95:15). Others have claimed that there is much evidence against the theory (Reed).

Brown's "hydroplate" theory

One very interesting proposal is Walt Brown's hydroplate theory which he presents in his excellent book *In the Beginning: Compelling Evidence for Creation and the Flood* (BrownW). This contends that the early surface strata were supported by a layer of water that flowed upwards and irrigated the earth - the "Fountains of the Deep". At the Flood, the earth split where the mid-ocean ridges are today (see Fig. 10), the water shot out high into the atmosphere where it froze and descended as hail - killing the mammoths as we have mentioned in Section 3.2. The lifting of the continents at the ridge resulted in them sliding rapidly, riding on the water beneath them. As the water flowed out, the leading edge grounded on the rock beneath first, the friction rose sharply and this buckled the American continents to produce the Rockies and the Andes. However, as with all models, there are problems in explaining how and when mountain ranges were formed which we discuss later.

We will not give the details of Brown's hydroplate theory, which is one of the few that gives a reasonable model of the major forces that must have been operating, but highly recommend his book to the reader.

Apart from Brown's explanation, the main problem facing supporters of the theory is to provide a reasonable force that could have moved the plates. Are there any factors that might provide this? Before answering this, we must briefly examine one theory that some have proposed.

The "expanding earth" model

In view of the problems with crustal plate movements, some geologists have proposed that the earth expanded, creating the large oceans between the continents. One article by Unfred (Unf) catalogued a number of weaknesses in the accepted plate tectonic (PT) theory, and noted that the "expanding earth" theory had sufficient support for two secular conferences to be held on the subject in 1981. He claimed that there is a good fit of the continents on an earth only 60% of the present size, but gave no source of energy for this expansion.

Morton (Mor83) suggested that the force came from a change in the permittivity of space which would increase the size of all atoms but not uniformly. There would be a difference in the expansion of the mantle and the crust that would provide the required amount of surface expansion.

This appears to be a possibility, but as with many alternative "explanations", they can produce more problems than they solve.

(i) Any crust expansion would be very uniform and cracks would appear between the continents as they parted. However, PT models require considerable *rotation* in addition of some land masses to arrive at their present positions.

(ii) An expansion of the earth's diameter from 60% of its present size would slow down its rotation to 60% of 24 hrs (14.4 hrs.). In contrast, we will see that the earth may have *increased* its rotation from 360 days in a year to 365.24 days in a year at the time of the Flood.

It is suggested that any expanding earth model would have to address these problems in its presentation.

Returning to the high resistance of the rocks to deformation there are two factors that might have operated at that time.

A possible solution?

An important discovery from the deep drillings is the unexpected hardness of the rock. Could this have been more fluid in the past?

The first factor is the very subject we have majored on in this section - the profound effect that hydrothermal water has had on the geological system of the earth's crust. If there were huge quantities of this liquid-like gas arising from the depths, we may here have an effective force for driving the continents apart and a means of "floating" them to their present positions.

The second factor is the moderate effect upon viscosity due to CDK. Combined with the fluidity of the uprising HT water, this may have enabled plate tectonics to take place. This does not remove, however, the evidence provided by Wesson and others we have summarised above that indicates that it has not occurred.

These two factors of HT water and lower viscosity, are, of course, put forward as possible solutions for the "drifting force" problem. It must be recognised that they may raise problems of their own. For example, are the high temperatures recorded in the deep drillings an indication that HT water

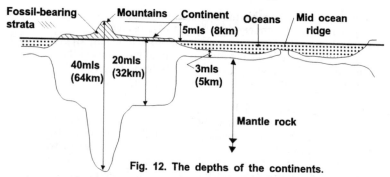

Fig. 12. The depths of the continents.

may have been involved but with a lower rock viscosity than today? The problem of the size of the Benard cells would still remain, and the "Lomnitz Law" or the "power-law creep" of decreasing movement would still operate.

Mountain building

Whether the continents have drifted or not, there is still no explanation of where the force could come from that could raise the mountains to their present considerable height. These two events are not necessarily connected; plate tectonics is basically tearing continents apart - mountain building involves compression of the crust that buckles the strata.

There are some unusual aspects about the locations of mountains. Some are well inland (e.g. the Urals in central Russia) and others on ocean coasts (The Rockies and the Andes). The Rockies are near the main tension crack yet the Andes are well away from it (see Fig. 10). The Alps are near the Mediterranean but separated from it by Italy which runs into the Mediterranean, on the other side of which is a flat desert. What could have thrown up the almost isolated great Rock of Gibraltar? Any general theory of mountain building would have to take these varied formations into account.

The sequence is also important. If fossil-bearing mountains are buckled, the strata must have been laid down some time before the mountain was upthrust. This is a criticism that applies to many models. The major mountain ranges *must* have been formed some time *after* all the various strata had been laid, and there were earlier periods of buckling and "weathering" to produce the unconformities (Fig. 6.) before the whole mountain range was eventually upthrust. Yet some models have the continental split and the subsequent buckling of the mountain ranges as the first event, before the many strata in these rocks could have been laid down.

The relative thicknesses of the continents and oceans needs to be kept in mind. Fig. 12 (see Q26/4:133) is vertically to scale and shows the deep "roots" that lie under mountain ranges - if seismic evidence is to be accepted. Note that the "sea mountains", however, are due to the rising of the crustal floor. More surprisingly, the fossil-bearing strata of the Flood *are on the raised continents*, not in the deeper oceans as might be expected. All these features would have to be addressed in any acceptable creationist geological model, and we consider this later.

ANCIENT MAPS

Not unrelated to this subject of the continents is the study of ancient maps. Some of these show very different positioning of the continents and these are

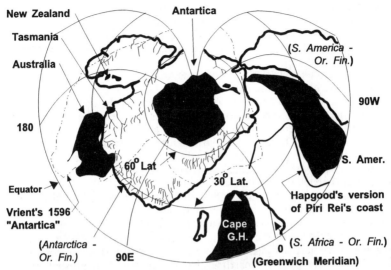

**Fig. 13. Oronteus Finaeus' 1532 map of the South
Pole with the correct locations of the continents**

thought to indicate considerable movement due to drift. Others have the continents correctly shown but they were drawn some time before the area had been explored. It is thought that ancient map makers may have had knowledge that has since been lost until the area was explored within the last few centuries.

This was the view of this author and various maps were examined to highlight this. One of the most interesting was a 1531 map by Oronteus Finaeus - his Latin name. (Correct French name: Oronce Finé). This showed the whole of the Antarctic area covered by land with ranges of mountains and many rivers - all free of ice cover! As this area of the globe is now known to be all land, just as this map shows, it may have been copied from a map made by men many generations earlier who were far more knowledgeable than we give them credit for. Accordingly, the Oronteus Finaeus map was drawn for the readers interest as shown in Fig. 13.

As a check on the accuracy of the map, the correct locations of Africa and South America were plotted.

Oronteus's map, although using an unusual Cordiform projection, shows the degrees of latitude and longitude very clearly at 10 degrees intervals, but his zero longitude is where our 20°W is today - just off the west coast of Africa. We assumed that the Cape of Good Hope at the south end of the African continent was correctly located at 20°E. From this, the positions of the other continents could be plotted relative to South Africa. To have taken the Greenwich Meridian as his 20°E (which goes through England on his map) would move all the present (black) continents 20 degrees further to the west (anticlockwise).

It was only then that serious anomalies became apparent and the following became obvious:

(i) Latitudes are fairly easy to determine with quite simple equipment, and this has been known for millennia. The latitude given for the Cape and S.

America are quite accurate. However, relative to Africa, South America's longitude is wrong and it is almost touching the polar continent.

(ii) The actual area of the map's polar continent is huge compared to the present land area. The decrease in area could not have taken place since the date of the map.

It was when the correct positions of Australia and New Zealand were plotted on the map that the most serious error became obvious, for Australia was touching the edge and New Zealand was within the continent. It cannot be said that he used very ancient maps as his source as he described it as "Southern land: Recently discovered but not yet fully explored". The continent could not have reduced so much that Australia and New Zealand were left isolated only 200 years later when surveyed by Captain Cook. There is no evidence that Antarctica ever covered such a vast area and the geological changes required are enormous.

It was at that point that this author lost any trust in the reliability of this ancient map, at least in its depiction of Antarctica.

Subsequently, Hapgood's extensive examination of this map and many others in his "Maps of the Ancient Sea Kings" (Hap) was read. In this he contends that Finaeus's plan of Antarctica can be "adjusted" to comply very closely with the present coastline. He enters into a confusing maze of "redrawing", "turning", "proportioning", etc. that covers 11 pages. He proposes that the Antarctic Circle (latitude 66.5°) was incorrectly assumed to be the 80th parallel of latitude, yet the Antarctic Circle is clearly shown in its correct position on the map. We would suggest that any map that made an error of latitude of this order cannot be relied upon. With all these many adjustments, there is still no close correlation between his final map and the present coastline.

An important point is that latitude could be measured fairly accurately, even in ancient times. Therefore any map that was seriously in error on this score should be treated with considerable reserve.

Hapgood subjected Piri Re'is Map, drawn in 1531, to a not dissimilar treatment. He notes that the numerous "portolan" lines that cross maps of this era were usually for compass directions from one port to another. However, he unwarrantably rejects this and says that they were for constructing a grid of latitude and longitude in order to combine separate maps into one large map. Yet these grid lines themselves do not appear on the map.

Again, after many "adjustments", there is little convincing correspondence between Hapgood's final map and the known coastline. He admits there is a loss of 16 degrees of latitude down the east coast of South America, and where Drakes Passage between South America and the Antarctic should be, a solid barrier of land is shown. If this map is so grossly inaccurate regarding latitude - which is easily measured - at this position, how can it be trusted for the remainder? We have plotted this coastline on Fig. 13 as redrawn by Hapgood in his Fig. 18.

In summary, Hapgood's "reconstructions" are quite unacceptable and these maps are unreliable. Accordingly, we do not believe that Antarctica was free of ice when surveyed by men. The Ice Age probably developed soon after the Flood, and Antarctica has been covered by ice ever since.

Where ancient maps accurately record correct land positions and details known today, then this suggests that they had been explored by some early traveller. As we have mentioned, there is considerable evidence that the east coast of America was known to Europeans in view of the many relics that they left on that continent. If many of these ancient maps are studied, the information near Europe is moderately accurate, but as you go further afield, although considerable detail is still shown, it becomes increasingly at variance with the known layout. We would suggest that there is a reason for this.

Map making was a very competitive business in those days and legal cases were fought over the copying of information from maps by rivals. One can imagine a map maker would be tempted to add great detail, on the flimsiest - or no - evidence, to imaginary lands in order to sell his wares. He would appear to be very knowledgeable in the subject and this would add to his prestige - and income.

Lister noted that "French cartography had not been impressive" but did consider Finaeus "outstanding" although no reason is given (List:28). Furthermore, their reputation did not improve for he says of a later period:

> Yet one should qualify the claims for the accuracy of eighteenth-century French maps by stating that many of their makers engaged in a certain amount of guesswork rather than leave blank spaces (List:30).

To demonstrate that Finaeus was not alone in fabricating lands, we have plotted the "Antarctica" shown in Vrient's 1596 map of the world, using the Cape as a common landmark again. It can be seen that the coast of his "Antarctica" almost reaches the equator!

Any cartographer inventing unknown land in unexplored areas would be fairly safe for his patrons were unlikely to travel to these remote places relying on his maps. If any did, then their comments to him on their return go unrecorded - which, perhaps, is just as well!

2. THE REVERSALS OF THE EARTH'S MAGNETIC FIELD

When rock cools in the presence of a magnetic field, below a certain temperature, known as the Curie Point, it can retain the direction of the field even though the external field may later change. The direction of this field in many rock samples is said to be in the opposite direction to the earth's present field.

Geophysicists have now produced an "agreed" sequence of magnetic reversals - and the brief "excursions" of opposite polarity within them - that cover the whole of the geological periods and strata. They are used to correlate strata across the world by profile matching to this accepted standard.

The theory can be criticised on a number of points. For example, in one single strata, all laid down at the same time, a reversal of the field can be found. Another is that there are several ways in which the rock's field can be changed without the earth's field changing.

In the *Scientific American* article by Carrigan and Gubbins referred to in Section 4 - The age of the earth - when discussing reversals of the field, they say "Any successful account of geomagnetism must explain what caused the pole reversals at various times in history." But only a few sentences later they admit "No one has developed an explanation of why the sign reversals take place. The apparent random reversals of the earth's dipolar field have remained inscrutable" (p98). Thus, by their own admission, none of the explanations by geophysicists are satisfactory - not even the "only viable" model of a dynamo.

Indeed, it is almost impossible to even imagine how, in the dynamo theory, the massive volumes of circulating magma in the core can so quickly change their direction of flow such that they can regenerate either a field that is suddenly switched in the opposite direction, or alternatively, decaying to zero and then rising to a new value in the opposite direction. This is one of the principle objections to these reversed polarities in the strata being caused by *any* major activity in the core - whether electrical currents or fluid movement.

The sun's reversing dipole magnet?

Those holding to the dynamo theory point to the fact that the sun regularly reverses its magnetic pole. Barnes rebuts this saying that no one has demonstrated that the sun has a dipole field similar to the earth's. It appears that the sun has numerous localised magnetic "storms" over its surface giving both north and south fields. There seems to be a regular congregation of "north" poles periodically, but there is no evidence that a dipole moment exists within the sun. Furthermore, the fly-by of the satellite Ulysses has shown that the sun has no "south" pole. As the satellite flew past, the field strength remained "absolutely constant" (*New Scientist*. 24.9.94 p11).

The offset magnetic axis

Wesson, in his paper on plate tectonics, commented in passing that the magnetic field does not go through the centre of the earth but is tangential to the (solid) core. In 1975 the north magnetic pole was over the north of Canada (latitude 75°N, longitude 101°W) and the south magnetic pole was on the edge of Antarctica just below Tasmania (lat. 67°S, long. 143°E). This is illustrated in Fig. 14 but is better appreciated if these points are located on a globe.

Not only is the magnetic axis offset from the centre of the earth, but the strength of the south pole is 21% more than that of the north pole. (Wesson said they differ by 40%) (Wess:320). The magnetic axis of both Uranus and Neptune is offset and skewed by roughly the same amount.

This is a surprising departure from the normally assumed closeness of the geographical and magnetic axies, and at first it was intended to merely mentioned it as a point of interest. Further thought, however, showed that it would have a profound effect upon the two models of how the earth's magnetic dipole was generated, for it showed that it was very unlikely to be due to convection currents in the earth's molten core.

If the axis of the magnetic field went through the centre of the core, even if it was at an angle to the true poles, it would be possible for it to be generated by magma flows circulating axially around the core centre. At present, the axis is considerably offset, which greatly restricts any circular flow pattern. In addition, the possibility that there is a small circular flow of magma not central to the core is unlikely and probably could not be sustained for any great length of time before either decreasing or becoming axially centred. We would therefore contend that magma flow in the core cannot generate the present offset magnetic field. This leaves only one possibility; that the field is generated by circulating *electrical* currents that can flow through both liquid and solid rocks in order to produce the field on the present offset axis.

The situation is further compounded by the imbalance of the polar strengths, which would displace the centre of the magnetic field towards the south pole (Fig. 14). The path for circulating magma would still be restricted to a small area of the liquid core, which is highly unlikely. A circulating electrical current is by far the most obvious generator of the magnetic field.

In addition there are two further complications; there is evidence that (i) the solid core might be crystallised, and that (ii) it is slowly rotating faster than

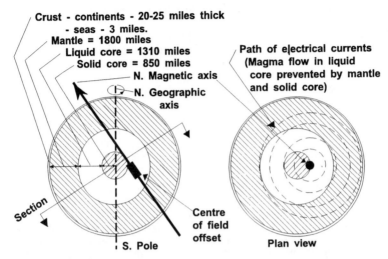

Fig. 14. The eccentricity of the earth's magnetic axis

the liquid core by 1.1 degrees per year.

The reversals of the magnetism in rocks

As we have set out above, Barnes proposed that these reversals were generated within the rocks themselves. An alternative theory of magnetic reversals arising from magma flows in the liquid core has also been proposed. In this, hot core fluid rose to the outer surface of the liquid core, and this deflected the magnetic flux, so that "waves" of flux gradually rose to the surface of the earth. However, an equal volume of fluid must also fall from the surface of the core and this would surely have produced "waves" of flux of the opposite polarity, thus cancelling most of the flux generated by the rising magma. In addition, these "waves" of flux rising towards the surface of the earth would have only produced local magnetic reversals, not the global wide-world "flips" that secular geologists contend have taken place.

No "reversals"?

The discussion about magnetic reversals usually assumes a complete "flip" of 180°. Yet one chart plotting the reversal of the magnetic polarity of a 600m. deep deposit shows that the inclination is +60° at the top, varies across the middle depth to reach -60° at the bottom. This is only a swing of 120° and is far from being a complete reversing "flip" of 180° as is claimed.

This supports Walt Brown's surprising contention that the mid Atlantic Ridge "reversals" are only *variations about a mean value* (BrownW:79). He points to maps of these magnetic "anomalies" that notes the results are after "the earth's smooth field has been removed". He discussed his views with a senior geologist specialising in geomagnetism who could not fault his claims (BrownW and pers. comm).

Magnetic effects

DeYoung relates that a large magnet suddenly lost its power just before an earthquake in Tokyo in 1855, but regained it afterwards. In Lisbon, the earthquake of 1755 caused magnets to lose their power and magnetic needles to fluctuate (Q20/3:188). He suggested this might be a cause of local reversals. Corliss notes that just before the Kobe earthquake in 1995, the local magnetism at one Japanese University changed in a southeasterly direction for 30 seconds, whilst at another site, it changed in a northwesterly direction (SF100). We would suggest that it is forces of this nature that are far more likely to have caused the magnetic "reversals" in the strata.

There are many reversals in the various strata which may have been generated by local electrical currents - themselves possibly generated by a magnetic disturbance. Observing this, Chui points out that in the design of electrical transformers, if the core were solid metal, then large, unwanted currents would be set up that would heat up the core (Q26/2:65). The core is therefore split up into thin sheets insulated from one another to reduce this current into many smaller independent circuits.

A similar process might be operating when an earthquake generates local electrical forces. The current and the magnetism it induces could be restricted between insulating strata, thus producing a sequence of reversals with depth, as illustrated diagrammatically in Fig. 15. However, the theory faces the same problem as the "rising flux" theory does; the magnetic field is predominantly parallel to the surface and would not necessarily *reverse* the direction of the dipole field over most of the earth's surface.

The unreliability of the data

Oard wrote an excellent article that casts considerable doubt on the reliability of these reversals (Oar85), and we will only briefly give the main points he makes. Although his paper is about deep sea cores in sediments, much of what he says covers other strata also and he is particularly critical of the way in which the evidence is used to correlate strata. We would accept that even if reversals are present (and we will see that there is doubt about this), then they are very localised and are not due to any major change of the earth's magnetic field allowing world-wide correlations to be made. Oard notes the following.

(a) **Dating method.** In order to date when these reversals took place, the Potassium-Argon radiometric method of dating is usually employed. The unreliability of this as a basis for the dates has been discussed above and is one of the many factors that can be "adjusted" to give the results that are "expected".

(b) **Fossil correlation.** It is far from being an independent dating system, for fossils are still used to date local events. Palaeomagnetism is only used for correlating world-wide events. In order to do this, they have to resort to "curve matching" of results to get a correspondence between two widely separated areas. What might be really a poor fit could be claimed as evidence of a satisfactory "correlation".

(c) **Magnetic "treatments".** One of the main sources of "variability" is "overprinting" of the original magnetic field by later forces producing "chaotic" results. "These secondary overprints must be eliminated, *presuming one 'knows' what must be removed and what must be kept"* (Oard85:172). They are removed by heating or applying an alternating magnetic field of moderate intensity. The possibility of affecting the final results are obvious and this is admitted by experts. Just how weak the magnetic fields are that are measured can be seen by the fact that the earth's magnetic field is 0.5 gauss whilst that in sediments is only 10^{-4} gauss. So weak is this field that Cook,

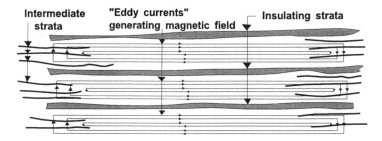

Fig. 15. Possible "Eddy current" production of magnetic reversals

writing in 1966, considered it "too small to be significant... Therefore only igneous rocks are of value in studying palaeomagnetism" (Cook66:282).

(d) Unknown effects. There are numerous problems in obtaining an accurate measurement of reversal of magnetism in a sample of sediment. Amongst them are - determining the actual level from which the sample was taken due to slumping, plastic flow, etc. - coring operations can rotate, twist the sample and in some cases even reverse the order - storage and manipulation of the core can affect the magnetism of the sample. Even when settled their magnetism can be affected by local events.

(e) Effect of oxygen. One discovery that has disturbed the whole basis of palaeomagnetism is that *oxidation of igneous rocks can cause reversals.* It has also affected red clay samples (Oard85:175). If a chemical reaction can have this effect, then no change in the polarity of the whole earth is necessary. This is a major problem that could completely undermine the whole subject.

HTW and reversals

With all these criticism, the data cannot be used for correlating strata. We would suggest a quite different cause - the activity of oxygen on strata deposited by hydrothermal water. At the time of the Flood huge quantities of material would rise from the depths and pour out over the surface. Once this moving mass was stationary, as we have suggested above, it could have hardened very rapidly indeed.

Oxygen is a major component of many of the compounds in magma; sand consists of only Silicon and Oxygen. In many of the chemical reactions there must have been some free oxygen at one stage. Depending on the quantity (it may not have required much) and the state of the chemicals in the strata at the time, the oxidation could have changed the direction of the magnetic field of the minerals that were susceptible. Some strata would have been affected, others not, each case depending on the chemical stages involved.

We note that the Curie Point is between 500 - 700 degrees C, but that the critical temperature for hydrothermal water is 374 degrees C. These may seem to be unrelated, but it is possible that the continual agitation of the rising HTW prevents the compounds from aligning themselves with the earth's magnetic field, even though it might be well below the Curie temperature. Once it "sets" (like the delayed set of agitated concrete we described earlier), it will then align itself with the dipole field. Any free oxygen may then change the direction quite rapidly.

The codifying of the "chaos" of the results

Oard mentions some 19 ways in which the magnetism of the sample could be affected, and quotes several experts who voice their concern about the unreliability of the results that these factors create. One journalist, referring to a committee called to coordinate the field said "With all these problems, can palaeomagnetic 'magic' still be taken seriously?" (BroG). Having a vested interest in the subject, their answer was somewhat predictable. He also noted:

> The general character of the palaeomagnetic record is now so well established that claims to discover new "anomalies"...must pass rigorous standards of analysis before they can be considered seriously (BroG).

This suggests that the present "accepted" sequence of magnetic reversals has become sacrosanct, despite being founded upon fundamentally unreliable methods. With so many variables that could be applied, there will be little difficulty in ensuring that any future "reversal anomalies" can easily be rejected - or corrected to fit the accepted pattern.

In summary, Oard's paper leaves the whole subject of magnetic reversals with little credibility. Having quoted an expert who said that many "excursions" could not be proven, Oard concludes "This suggests a strong possibility of non-geomagnetic mechanism(s) for excursions, and even for reversals" (p173). With all the many criticisms given above, one wonders if a complete discipline has been generated out of minute variations in the remnant magnetism in rocks.

3. BLACK SMOKERS

In the 1970's vertical "pipes" were discovered on the ocean floors that poured out mineral rich water at temperatures up to 400°C (Lee). The pipes themselves were precipitated sulphides of various metals, forming chimneys up to 15 ft (4.6 m) tall and on mounds of minerals up to 60 ft (18.3m) high (Fig. 16.). What was most surprising was that around them there were colonies of clams, mussels, worms, crabs and limpets. These were the first animals to be discovered that did not obtain their energy by way of photosynthesis. An examination of their metabolism has shown they possess very specific digestive systems as might be expected (Q30/1:35).

The growth rate of the chimneys was very rapid; 5-10 cm (0.5 - 1 inch) per day was witnessed. At this rate a chimney could be built in about 70 years. They are surrounded by a glow that is 19 times stronger than can be accounted for, the source of which is unknown.

Most of these smokers are on the lines of the Mid-Oceanic ridge system and it is estimated that the total flow could fill the present oceans in as little as 1.4 million years. The water is not recycled sea water but subterranean water, as it has more He_3 isotope content than sea water and the thermodynamics that produce a steady flow (geysers are intermittent) do not allow downwards percolation of sea water to be the source.

One problem they present is that if the division of the Atlantic Ocean had been going on for millions of years, you would expect to see thousands of old "smokers" dotted all over the sea floor. That they are concentrated along the present ridge line suggests that they have only recently been active.

4. SURTSEY

This was an island that appeared out of the sea in 1963 off the coast of Iceland. What surprised the experts was the speed with which this island

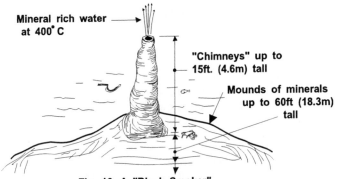

Mineral rich water → at 400° C

"Chimneys" up to 15ft. (4.6m) tall

Mounds of minerals up to 60ft (18.3m) tall

Fig. 16. A "Black Smoker"

became "mature'. Within a few months, flies appeared and birds were soon nesting. In April 1964, lava flow began which gave the island a hardened cap which protected it against erosion by the sea. In June 1965 the first rooted plant appeared. Normal beaches with sand and gravel are reported, yet there would have been insufficient time for then to have been produced by years of rolling by the waves. This means they were formed by some other process which supports the rapid production of sand and pebbles by HTW we have proposed above.

This island is a witness to the way in which rapid outflows of material can quickly cool and become indistinguishable from land that has existed for "millions of years".

5. THE MOUNT ST. HELEN EXPLOSION

This was a major explosion of a mountain in Washington State in May 1980. The force was from superheated water and it generated huge mudslides and devastating waves in a nearby lake that swept trees away 850 ft (259m) above the waterline. As with the rapid development of Surtsey, there was a similar rapid recolonisation by plants and animals. A later mudflow produced a 100 ft (30m) deep miniature version of the Grand Canyon. There were two interesting features to creationists.

a) The sunken "forest'

Aqualung divers found waterlogged tree roots standing in an upright position on the lake floor. Above was a floating mat of timber logs that was gradually depositing its debris onto the floor. There were also floating stumps in an upright position. These had grounded on the shoreline and were they later to become buried, it would have been assumed that they had grown in their present position. In Yellowstone Park there are several levels of tree stumps buried in this position which are claimed to be evidence of their growth and subsequent covering to form coal. The rapid production of trees similarly upright at Mt. St. Helen's shows this to be unwarranted. They were probably swept to this location by a repeated series of outpourings of stumps, water and material to produce the layers of upright stumps now seen.

b) The rapidity of the formation of strata

Off the flank of the mountain there were mudslides of volcanic ash debris that produced 25 ft (7.6m) of thickness in the centre of the main pit in one day. Later, a further mudslide occurred within this deposit and the exposed section showed that it contained many layers that varied from 1mm (1/25th inch) to over 1m (3.3 ft) in thickness. This shows that numerous layers are no guide to the time taken to produce them.

6. CHALK

There are huge deposits of chalk around the world and they are all made from the skeletons of two minute organisms known as planktonic foraminifera and coccolithophores. As these animals die, their skeletons sink slowly to the bottom of the oceans to form a component of the ooze on the sea floor.

The present rate of this slow build-up is estimated to be 0.5 - 4 inches (1 -10 cm) per 1,000 years. The chalk beds in England are about 1,300 ft (400m) deep and are thought to have been laid down in about 35 million years during the Cretaceous period. This gives a rate of about 0.5 ins (1.2 cm) per 1,000 years - agreeing with the lower estimate of the present rate. This slow rate is held to completely contradict the proposal that the age of the earth is only a few thousand years as there would be no time to lay these great depths of chalk.

This evidence has even troubled some creationists but has been effectively answered by several writers, one of the most recent summaries being by Snelling (Snell94A). We must once again point out the uniformitarian basis of this method of dividing the thickness by the *present day* rate of production of the "chalk" on the sea floor. This is the main error in these assertions of great age.

These creatures can, under suitable conditions, reproduce very rapidly indeed. Present-day foraminifera can produce 300 ft (100m) in 1,000 years and the coccolithophores this same depth within only 200 years. Taking all the Limestones in the Upper Cretaceous and Tertiary as chalk (it is only a proportion of this), Woodmorappe has shown that with high rates of reproduction, only 2.5% of the earth's surface would be needed to produce this quantity over 1,600 years - the period from the creation to the Flood.

Snelling places these chalk beds within the strata laid down during the Flood. They must, therefore, have been generated rapidly and deposited during that comparatively brief period.

These creatures can reproduce so rapidly that they give the water a white "bloom". Under the catastrophic conditions of the Flood, there would be warmth from the volcanic activity which might also have provided carbon dioxide outpourings from the depths or chemical reactions between the various constituents that formed the strata. In particular, there would be abundant food from the vegetation and flesh of decaying animals killed by the Flood. The great depth could be accounted for by the rapid "blooms" covering a huge area being killed by the solutions brought up by the hydrothermal water and then swept into an area of the ocean that subsided into the void left by the rising HTW.

A creationist critic of his paper (E95/9(1):29) gave rough calculations that indicated a few thousand years would be needed for the thicknesses of chalk existing, but Snelling rightly pointed out that the coccoliths that constitute the chalk are almost all extinct, so their rate of reproduction cannot be checked. It requires only that their rate to be much higher than the present for the huge volumes to be fully explained. It would appear that they accumulated over a period of time and were then swept into their present positions. This is indicated by the cross bedding and slumping of the heaps that can be found in some areas. They were also produced in shallow seas, and with the effect of

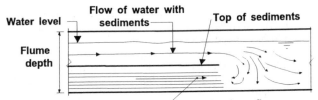

Fig. 17. Rapid deposition of stratified layers in flowing water

flocculation, the time required to settle out would be very much less than the many years calculated by geologists for settlement in the deep oceans.

Tyler has commented (Tyl96) that these chalk deposits were actually laid down in several distinct periods within one complete deposit. These periods between the layers were sufficiently long for some animals to establish a position and grow. It is for this reason he, with others, have proposed that strata above the Carboniferous were laid after the Flood - a subject discussed later.

A rapid deposition in stages is a far better explanation than that of the evolutionists who ask us to believe that these huge deposits were slowly built up over millions of years without a single intrusion of any other deposits that would disturb the great purity that these chalk beds display today.

7. SEDIMENTATION THEORIES

(a) Guy Berthault (Bert)

These have been described in another work (Bow91:130) but a brief description will be given here. Berthault mixed sand and a fine dust of different colours and poured them into water. He found that they automatically sorted themselves into laminations about 2.5mm thick *after* they had been deposited on the bottom. He found a similar action even if dry. In flume experiments, he poured the mixture in at one end and found that it again segregated in to layers that appeared as the deposition of the sediments progressed along the flume length (Fig. 17).

His experiments provide yet another way in which stratified deposits can be quickly formed. These fine laminations may have a bearing on the very thin varves found in the muds of lakes that form at the foot of some glaciers. Whether it is applicable to the majority of strata is debatable.

(b) Walt Brown's "liquifaction" theory

Brown experimented with rising water through strata and found it produced layers. This is similar to Cox's contention that it was rising water depositing cementing minerals in sandstone which gave a similar layering, falsely ascribed to horizontal bedding planes when the material was deposited. Brown also proposed that the rising water could raise and sort fossils to their present levels, producing the appearance of an evolutionary sequence, but it is doubtful if it could produce the reasonably consistent world-wide result of the present distribution of fossils.

8. VARVES

Varves are fine layers that are considered to be the result of one season's deposition of fine clay due to the glacier melting. As there can be many thousands of varves in one deposit, this is held to be evidence of great age.

However, there is evidence that more than one layer can be generated in one season (Oard92B). Berthault's work shows another way in which these laminations could have been quickly formed.

It has been reported that there are examples of a single varve dividing into several varves like the tributaries of a river. This shows that one varve cannot be the result of one years deposition, but such evidence is ignored by the "experts" in this field.

9. ICE AGES

There is a general acceptance that at some stage much of the earth was covered by very thick glaciers of which the polar ice caps are but a remnant. Some creationists, however, suggest that all the evidence could equally be due to the action of massive flows of water transporting soil and rocks, etc. - a subject examined later. The orthodox view for very many years claimed that there were four ice ages - Gunz, Mindel, Riss and Wurm - separated by three warmer interglacial periods. This held sway for decades and many results were held to "confirm" this strongly held view by what is now called the "reinforcing syndrome". Eventually, sea core evidence conflicted with this interpretation and now up to thirty ice ages are proposed by some.

A major problem, even for evolutionists, has been to find a cause for these ice ages and the most frequently used theory is that of Milankovitch who pointed out that the slight eccentricity of the earth's orbit that varies the earth-sun distance might be correlated with each age. By linking this with the small variation of the tilt in the earth's axis and many dubious extensions of climatic factors, eventually a good fit between the astronomical data and the "ice ages" was "proved". As it was the only available explanation, its popularity was strong, but it later waned. More recently it has revived due to its so-called correlation with the analysis of deep sea cores.

Michael Oard has made a special study of "ice ages" and in several articles has pointed out the many flaws and assumptions Milankovitch's theory is based upon. He shows that it requires considerable manipulation of the various factors that are often only guesses, many of which are given unrealistic values simply to produce the desired result (Oard84A). Some experts have agreed that the theory is unsatisfactory.

Oard describes how the experts have tried to correlate ice ages with cores of the sea floor using the Oxygen-18 isotope. Oxygen's normal atomic weight is 16 but 0.21% is Oxygen18. It is thought that the amount of O18 can be affected by the temperature of the oceans allowing a correlation with the "ice ages" in past years. Oard again shows that this correlation is only achieved by considerable fudging of the many factors involved (Oard84B).

Attempts have been made to correlate the earth's "magnetic reversals" with the core data, but Oard again demonstrates the very poor basis on which the whole of the theory of these reversals exist (Oard85).

As result of his extensive investigations, Oard, a meteorologist, concludes that there has been only one ice-age (Oard79). It has been proposed that this arose when the sea was warmer and evaporation was high. This would have produced high precipitation at the cooler poles, starting the ice age. However, this cannot provide the very rapid temperature drop necessary to freeze the buried mammoth as discussed in Section 3.2.

Polar ice cores

Deep cores of the polar ice caps have been taken and it has been claimed that they would have taken 160,000 years to form. This has only been calculated from the present rate of snowfall of 1 inch (25mm) per year in Antarctica (Vard). Oxygen 18 and other trace substances indicate annual deposits, but this increase is so small that the lower layers are not buried quickly enough to avoid contamination from the atmosphere. As a result these variations are "smoothed out" and an annual cycle becomes undetectable. In Greenland, the rate is some 5 ft (1.5m) /yr. and assuming this has been constant, the whole depth could have been laid down in 6,000 years. If, as most geologists agree, there was at least one ice age, much of the depth of the snow at the poles could have been rapidly deposited, greatly reducing the time needed to produce the present depths at the present rate of snowfall.

One further complication is that huge lakes of water have now been discovered under the Antarctic ice cap (Kap).

Ice caves

One little known geological feature are the ice caves that exist in several locations in America (Q3/1:68). These are caves containing solid ice that is sandwiched between layers of lava and have provided ice for local residents for many years. It is a major problem to explain how they could have been formed, and how they could have remained frozen for some four thousand years. This is yet another puzzle that both creationists and evolutionists have avoided or overlooked but nevertheless should be included in any proposed geological model.

Were there thick glaciers?

The present evidence for an ice age was originally interpreted as the results of the Flood in the early 1800's, but William Buckland and Louis Agassiz proposed they were due to glaciers in the mid 1800's. This was refuted by Dawson and Howorth who produced considerable evidence of water activity, but their works were ridiculed. What is interesting is that even today, the objections of Howorth have not been answered. His book *Ice or Water* is still available from William Corliss (See Appendix 9).

After 1840 the slow action of glaciers was eventually adopted rather than the violent activity of a global Flood. As we have seen with Lyell's uniformitarian theory, the evidence of a world-wide flood was ignored. Howorth, in fact, claimed that the theory was deliberately seized upon by Lyell's supporters as a means of encompassing the evidence into uniformitarianism so that they could neutralise any evidence for catastrophism (Cox76A).

Thus we see that the glacial theory has a very dubious origin.

Criticisms of the glacial theory

We could give a long list of the evidence against the theory, but will limit it to the following (Cox76A, Cox77A, Cox79, Mol). By way of explanation, the following deposits are said to be due to glacial action.

A DRUMLIN is a streamlined mound of boulder clay, sand or gravel.

An ESKER is a winding deposit mainly of gravel or sand thought to be the bed of a stream in a now melted glacier.

A KAME is a mound of gravel or sand said to be the outwash of a stream from the glacier.

BOULDER CLAY (or TILL or DRIFT) is said to be the ground-up material at the bottom of the glacier that is left as a deposit when it melted.

The evidence against the land being covered by a great thickness of ice is as follows:

1. The "drift" deposits are not easily explained by glacial action. There are no drifts over the northernmost parts of Greenland and some islands in the Canadian Arctic where one might have expected them as the ice would have been thickest in these areas. However, they are found in the tropics. Oard agrees that "till" deposits were not necessarily due to glacial action.

Evidence of "glaciation" has been found in such unlikely locations as the Sahara desert, South Africa and even the Precambrian (Mol). This again suggests that what is interpreted as the action of glaciers is probably due to the activity of fast moving water, rock slides, etc.

2. The assumed location of the thick ice-sheets are not centred on the poles, but are greatly displaced from them.

3. The cause of the ice age is still unknown. However, as we have said, Oard has claimed that it can arise from the unusual weather conditions following the Flood.

4. Ice flows downhill under gravity. However, it is possible that where there is a sufficient depth of ice, the lower layers may be forced upwards over small barriers. The problem is how large boulders can be "picked up" by a glacier and left much higher than their original level as well as being transported for many miles. Some stones have been carried as much as 1,000 km (625 miles) (Cox77A:48).

5. Cox has quoted a geologist who calculated that it would take 75,000 years for an ice particle to travel 50 km (31 miles) to the edge of the ice sheet. This demonstrates that any erratic rock in a glacier could not travel the huge distances that has been recorded for some (CRSnet).

There is the additional problem that a large "erratic" rock would migrate to the bottom of the glacier under its own weight. How it got "into" the glacier in the first place is a further problem

What has also been found is that loose rocks can flow across long distances and these are sometimes interpreted incorrectly as the results of glacial action (Mol). Some rocks show cross striations, which are hardly likely to have been caused by a change in the direction of the ice mass.

5. Some drumlins are bedrock but others are till or sandy mounds in a streamlined shape. They would have been completely flattened by a glacier. Yet many sandy drumlins have clear cross bedding patterns indicating they have not been disturbed since their formation. Some eskers have vertical cores of clay which could not have been the results of glacial action.

6. Deposition of boulder clay and many other features attributed to the action of huge glaciers can equally be due to fast flowing water (Cox79) or to gravity flows (Mol). The amount of rock that a glacier can remove is very small because when it applied pressure to a rock to grind it or move it, the ice would melt into water and flow round the object.

7. Many fossils found in glacial areas are more suited to a warm climate.

Cox has suggested that as the pressure of the Flood reduced when the land was uplifted, the drift expanded and disintegrated, pushing up the kames, drumlins and eskers (Cox77A:52). These features often reflect the type of strata below, and if the expansion was confined horizontally, then ridges would be pushed up, forming these shapes. At one location, a boulder disintegrated and merged into sand within an esker, indicating some form of expansion had taken place as we have discussed earlier regarding the production of sand.

There are creationist articles that set out the usual (secular) evidence for glaciation (e.g. Q14/4:222), but they do not address the criticisms of the theory Cox and others have raised. We would suggest that they need to be adequately replied to if the proponents of the glacial theory seek to have it incorporated into creationist chronology.

....

We would conclude by pointing out that even with the huge drop in temperature necessary to freeze the mammoths so rapidly, there was no accompanying glacial activity in the areas of Siberia and Canada where they are found for it would have destroyed the mammals and changed the landscape as it moved. This sudden drop in temperature may have triggered a very cold period with perhaps heavy snow and some glaciers but not necessarily a deep ice sheet that is said to have covered vast areas and landscaped the continents as it flowed over them.

There is also the possibility that the wind referred to in Genesis 8:1 may have triggered the ice age but it is unlikely to have caused a sufficient drop in the temperature to deep freeze the mammoths so rapidly. This passage also suggests that the wind was for the reduction of the water level, but its precise action is not clear.

D. Flood Sequence Models

One subject of debate is whether some of the upper strata were laid down some time after the Flood. At this time of writing, there are three views giving different levels in the geological column above which the strata are considered to have been laid after the Flood.

1. Model I (MI) - The End-Pliocene Model - All the strata up to and including the Pliocene are Flood deposits. This is virtually the whole geological column and is the model proposed by Whitcomb and Morris in their *Genesis Flood*. Generally, those who propose this model do not accept that the geological column reflects the true situation, but is a collection of fossil-bearing strata arranged to conform to the theory of evolution.

2. Model II (MII) - The End-Cretaceous Model - The Flood deposits are those up to the top of the Cretaceous strata. The Cenozoic were deposited after the Flood. This has been proposed by a group of American and Australian creationists (Aust94). This has much the same strengths and weaknesses as MIII below. There is a recognised break in the geological column at what is known as the KT boundary; the Cretaceous/Tertiary boundary which marks the extinction of the dinosaurs.

3. Model III (MIII) - The End-Carboniferous Model. Proposed by a group of European creationist geologists (See ref. Scheven). They generally accept that the geological column is a reasonable reflection of the world-wide sequence of the fossil bearing strata.

....

MI is fairly easy to understand, as the sequence of all the fossils is roughly in the order in which they would have been inundated in a world-wide flood. The small, slow moving sea creatures are at the bottom in the Cambrian strata. As the water rose and then covered the land, there is a progression through fish and amphibians to the slow moving reptiles, with mammals and man at the top of the column. This has been the predominant model since it was proposed in "The Genesis Flood".

Unfortunately, there is geological evidence that this model cannot explain, principally that at one or more periods dry land appeared during the deposition of the upper strata of the column. This would seem to contradict the claim that the Noachic Flood covered the whole world for the duration of the Flood period. It is this evidence that has prompted the production of MIII, which, like MII, allows post-Flood depositions of the upper strata of the geological column.

The two main pieces of evidence in support of MIII are -

(a) Footprints made by air-breathing land animals (amphibia, dinosaurs, etc.) appear in all strata from the Devonian upwards. These could only have been made in shallow water in soft material and then gently covered with a protecting layer of sediments that hardened over time.

(b) The presence of dinosaur nests complete with eggs in the Upper Triassic and above. These also require the ground to be above water and conditions to be stable for a sufficiently long time for the dinosaurs to lay their eggs and allow them to hatch. In the Gobi desert, nests were found at five levels in cross bedded sandstone with 80 ft (50 m) between the top and bottom levels. This indicates successive periods of geological stability above water allowing egg laying at least to take place.

Further evidence of dry land are; **(c)** termite nests in the Triassic; **(d)** oyster beds on the top of the Cretaceous and below a Jurassic unconformity, which appear to have grown close together naturally; **(e)** 70 sq. km of unbroken starfish (which are extremely brittle) in the Jurassic that must have been covered gently with sediments. Other examples are given in the relevant articles (Schev).

Tracks of reptiles and amphibia are often found near coal measures. In view of this, one of the proposals is that floating masses of trees housed these animals and when the trees grounded, the animals it carried spread out over the land leaving these early tracks. The trees later became coal strata.

The ocean deposits

There are no ocean deposits that are older than the Mesozoic (Q27/3:98) and this indicates that there may have been a drastic change after the Carboniferous period. However, this is only based upon marine microfossils such as plankton, etc. and radiometric dating, as no land animal fossils have been found. If this dating is nevertheless accepted as correct, then it suggests that the continents parted after the Carboniferous (almost the last age of the Palaeozoic era) had been deposited, and all subsequent depositions involved sea creatures only. No animal fossils appear to have been swept into the oceans in any abundance. This would require all Mesozoic strata and above to be deposited on the various continents (now separated) by individual local inundations.

A major problem for creationists

The fact that there are virtually no land fossils in the ocean strata raises a difficult problem for both creationists and evolutionists. The erosion of the strata should have washed most fossils into the sea, but as we have indicated on Fig. 12, they are almost all positioned over the land which is above the sea level. In addition, it cannot be said that they are on sections of the ocean beds that happen to have risen above the sea, for Fig. 12 shows that beneath the land masses, and particularly under the mountains, the rocks below penetrate a very great depth into the mantle. How could the land and marine fossils finish up on high land over great depths of rock leaving almost nothing in the oceans? I have posed this to creation geologists and have never received an adequate explanation. We would suggest that creationist geologists should first deal with this problem and other very fundamental ones that we have raised in this appendix. If these are solved, then they may find that many other lesser problems can be dealt with more easily. The whole subject needs a very fresh view to be taken from broad principles first.

....

Returning to the two models, MIII certainly highlights evidence of post-Flood dry land above the Carboniferous that received further inundations, and this must be taken into consideration by any final creationist model. Like all such proposals, however, this model does have its own problems, amongst them the following.

A. The missing fossils

One major problem is that there are no fossils in the Carboniferous and below of air-breathing land animals or humans. To explain this, it is claimed that they were all completely "destroyed" in the Flood such that there were not even any fossils left.

The proposers note that the Bible uses "*machah*" for the "destroying" of all air-breathing animals, and this is also used for God's "obliteration" of our sins - i.e. they will no longer exist.

However, "*shachath*" is also translated "destroy" and means "decay, ruin, batter, cast off, perish", etc. and in its context does not mean to totally annihilate as "*machah*" does. Yet it is used to describe this very same event three times, in Gen. 6:13 and 17 and 9:15. This makes this their scriptural interpretation of total destruction somewhat less certain.

For the means of the total destruction of the fossils, they quote the extreme "violence" of the Genesis Flood. However, we would contend that it is impossible for the bones of millions of animals and humans to be disposed of in this way. To destroy just one bone, very considerable force has to be exerted for a long time; try reducing one to dust with a hammer! Bones would sink to the bottom of the sea, and once below the waves, would be in very tranquil water. Those buried in deposits, whether on land or under the sea, would remain undisturbed. The only place where such energy would have been exerted is in large waves on a rocky shoreline, and the inadequacy of this force has been discussed when considering the production of sand and gravel. Whilst a number of bones might be badly smashed in this narrow area, it could not possibly have smashed every bone to dust such that it could no longer be recognised as such.

Some bones may have been consumed by marine predators, but it is very unlikely that every single vestige would have been disposed of as their Biblical exegesis requires.

As the Flood waters could not have disposed of the bones of air-breathing animals, then the only means left of removing them is an Act of God. As creationists try to use only non-miraculous means for Biblical events, to have to revert to this when there are other explanations for the present distribution of fossils, renders their model less acceptable.

A possible solution?

One proposal that might explain the absence of animals and man in the Palaeozoic strata is that there were actually few of them and they were possibly located in a comparatively small area of the globe or that the numbers migrating to distant areas were few - both animals and man. Their corpses may also have been devoured by sea predators. We have discussed this more fully in answering critics of creationists in Section 5.1.

Human artefacts

There are many evidences of cultured objects being discovered in very early strata. These, understandably, have been ignored by the press and scientific establishments and therefore the supporting evidence is sometimes poor and incomplete. They cannot all be fakes and hoaxes however. Some of the most interesting are:

(a) A nail in Cretaceous rock (Fan:16)

(b) Human skeletons in Cretaceous rock (Bur75 and Q10/2:109). These are the earliest human fossils known to this author. Understandably, their authenticity has been disputed by evolutionists. Dr. Marwitt took the skeletons away but later returned them without comment. He subsequently contended that they were burials placed in a rock crevice but they had fallen to the bottom! However, the original report shows that the skeletons were found under 15 ft (4.6m) of overburden, and the site was carefully inspected for any evidence of them having been buried, and none could be detected.

(c) Jawbone of a child in Miocene coal (Fan:16). Many artefacts have been found in coal mines but, as mentioned, clear proof is sometimes lacking.

Very many more examples could be given and we would refer the reader to Fange's article (Fan) for a wide ranging survey of such evidence. Some of his examples have poor documentation and have been criticised for this, but there are too many for them all to be dismissed. As we have noted, such evidence will be ignored by the scientific community and the national press. Creationists may only hear of these discoveries some time after the event when the first-hand evidence has been lost.

These fossils do not contradict MIII but we record them to show that there is evidence for human existence in deeper strata than just the more recent geological strata.

B. The continuity of the fossil evidence

A geological chart is provided in the ENTJ article (Fig. 1 p33 v10 n1) setting out MIII, the end-Carboniferous model. However, examination of the fossil content of the various periods gives no indication that there was any dramatic change between the Flood strata of the Carboniferous and the Permian and Triassic immediately above. One would have expected to see a sharp change in both the numbers and types of fossils above and below this boundary line.

C. The submerged lands

In MIII, the continents were basically formed during the Flood and the strata laid down to the level of the Carboniferous Flood boundary. This means that all sediments above it were laid down after the Flood. Vast areas of land above sea level supporting the normal rich complexity of life must have suddenly sunk below sea level. Then the arising HT water would deposit its sand, clay and minerals over the area, entombing the animals and plants to form the particular period in the geological column. It would then have to rise again to become the present land surface containing these more recent fossils.

There are many such strata above the Carboniferous Flood boundary, covering huge areas of Europe and the Middle East. These would have been laid down under violent, catastrophic conditions. Such catastrophes as these must have happened many times, making life in the adjacent areas extremely precarious. Yet the Bible only records the gradual progress of mankind and makes no reference to any civilisations being swept away in these catastrophes. The silence of the Bible does not mean that it did not take place but one might have expected some reference.

There is, however, the evidence of the catastrophe that drove the Amalekites towards Egypt where they met the Israelites coming out at the time of the Exodus as discussed in section 3.8 above. More violent repercussions than this might have been expected, however. There is also the possible implication of geological activity during the time of Peleg "when the earth was divided". This, however, was a "one off" event.

The geological "see-saw"

For MIII, the land would have to be above ground to receive the footprints and for the laying of the dinosaur eggs but then sink below the sea level in many areas for the deposition of the Mesozoic strata and above. This would have to occur many times to give the stages of dry land and undersea situations MIII requires.

How all these conflicting features can be incorporated into any one model is difficult to visualise. I have never seen any attempt to demonstrate, by a series of drawings, how the pre-Flood land mass could change by several stages to result in the geological strata that we find today. It would necessitate the rising and submergence of the land many times.

Creationists have rightly criticised geologists for proposing just such multiple risings and fallings to explain the many layers of coal with sediments between each of them, but it would require a similar repeated series of inundations to produce MIII. We have suggested above, however, that it is possible that hydrothermal water was able to inundate an area and deposit its load of material even though it might be well above sea level.

It is only when we begin to look for the answers to fairly simple yet basic questions such as these that the complexity of interpreting the geological formations on a Scriptural basis becomes apparent.

D. The Ararat mountains.

Burdick (Q4/1:5) reports (as does Holt in ENTJ v10 n2) that the main deposits covering eastern Turkey are Palaeocene and Miocene limestone, whilst the mountains themselves are basaltic and andesite lava that burst through the limestone creating mountains 20,000 ft (6,100 m) high. The lava is shaped in "pillow" form indicating that it was extruded under water. On this basis he contends that they were all laid down at the time of the Flood.

This, of course, contradicts MIII in which the Mesozoic was laid down after the Flood. Therefore, according to this model, Ararat did not exist at the time when the Ark grounded on a mountain. To overcome this, it is proposed that it landed not at Ararat but in Asia and Noah moved into the Fertile Crescent of Shinar "from the east" as the Bible mentions.

This would mean that the ancient names and traditions of the Ark landing on the mountains called Ararat today are spurious. Yet many Early Fathers contended that the Ark was on Ararat in their day - Berosus (257 BC), Josephus (1st Cent.) referred to it three times, Theophilus (180 AD), Bishop Epiphanius of Salamis (4th. Cent.), Chrysostom (4th. Cent.) Isidore of Seville (610 BC).

One possible solution is that the Ark landed on the original Palaeozoic deposits that had been upthrust during the Flood, and these were later burst through by the present rocks that engulfed their Mesozoic fossils, and these rocks became contorted in turn to provide the present formations. This, however would involve considerable geological activity that would have affected all life for many hundreds of miles around, yet there is no reference to such catastrophic events in the Biblical record.

E. Absence of meteorites
Meteorite impact sites have only been found above the early Pleistocene, which would indicate that below that level, the strata were all laid down rapidly, giving little time for meteorite impacts. It has been claimed that some have now been discovered in earlier strata, but the evidence supporting this is slim and we do not consider that it affects the original proposal. This gives some support to MI.

THE MIII PROBLEMS - POSSIBLE SOLUTIONS
The evidence for MIII is obviously against MI. Can adequate explanations be provided that supports MI?

Dinosaurs and tracks
Oard has examined the dinosaur problem (Oard95) and has plotted where the tracks of dinosaurs and their nests are in America. He found they are confined to a strip of land, parallel and just to the east of the Rockies, stretching from Alaska to almost the Bay of Mexico. He has suggested that this is a portion of land that emerged briefly during the early stages of the Flood, and the dinosaurs laid their eggs in hasty nests. There was enough time to hatch but all were later swept away. He notes that there were only very young or adult dinosaurs, and that tracks were always straight as though running away.

The Bible gives little indication of any break in the rising flood water. It is just possible that the descent of the rain for 40 days covered all of the land, leaving the dinosaurs swimming, but then when some land appeared, it was quickly colonised whilst it existed. Then the major quantity of water was released at a particular stage of the breaking up of the "fountains of the deep" that then covered all land for 150 days.

Oard mentions that these tracks were found at more than one level which requires that this land was exposed, occupied by dinosaurs, re-inundated, exposed again and then reoccupied once more - to give one cycle only. This finding of tracks at more than one level is paralleled by the nests found at five levels in the Mongolian sandstone beds discussed above.

That there was evidence at more than one level arose during this writers investigations of the "ape-men" fossil discoveries in the Olduvai Gorge in Africa. What seemed to be groups of three bolas stones were found at several levels in Pleistocene strata - the roughest shaped at the bottom and almost perfect spheres at the top (Bow88:185). How could land be inundated and covered with several metres of sediment, which would have obliterated all trace of previous habitation, then be occupied again? This seems to have occurred not only on more than one occasion but the report seemed to assume that they were located over the same spot each time or reasonably close by. Where were the inhabitants whilst the land was under water, and why should they return to the same area? I had no answer then and still have none today.

Which model?

In examining the evidence produced so far, it is difficult to choose which is the more acceptable model. On balance, MI, the Pliocene Model, seems to have fewer difficulties overall. MIII, the Carboniferous Model, has to make too many adjustments to become viable - the annihilation of the land animals, the huge inundations that did not effect the nearby early post-Flood human settlements, the late deposition of sediments of the Nile delta before it was eventually inhabited, the re-siting of the landing position of the Ark from Ararat to some other location, etc. MI has only one major problem - to provide land above the sea for certain periods and localities that would allow one or more brief recolonisations during the Flood. If this can be accounted for in a reasonable way by its proponents, then their model would be adequately proven.

What is important is that all the evidence for MIII, the Carboniferous Model, is dealt with and not brushed to one side. To point out these problems with the Pleistocene Model is only one of the many difficulties creationists must solve in seeking to close that large gap that, unfortunately, still exists in the correlation of the Biblical account with the record of the rocks.

Final Comment

As we hope has been demonstrated, the present situation in geology is one of complex evidence that is difficult to interpret and some of which contradicts other features. It is for this reason that we have not presented a model that can satisfactorily combine most of the evidence to fit a Biblical model. What we have done is to highlight certain features that may not be fully appreciated by creationist geologists in the hope that they may be incorporated into future models that will be able to to replace the discredited evolutionary theory of how the geological column was formed.

APPENDIX 5
THE TILT OF THE EARTH'S AXIS

We are all familiar with the circular arrangement of large stones at Stonehenge. These were obviously used for recording the movement of the heavenly bodies throughout the yearly cycle. Of particular interest were the days on which the sun reached the furthest points north or south when it was rising and setting, as these would mark the days when it would then return for the next yearly season. These were important days in the life of a nation as they marked the time for a change of season.

There are many similar stone circles here and in other places around the world, all basically for a similar purpose; the recording and predicting of the change of seasons. It is for this reason that astronomers were held in such high esteem in ancient civilisations. As well as observing the sun they also recorded star movements, comets and other events in the sky.

One of the most accurate instruments used in those early days were gnomons. They were simply a vertical pole, often a standard 8 ft (2.4m) high that was used to measure the position of the shadow cast by the sun on the ground which had been carefully levelled. As the sun passed across the sky, the position of the shadow would move across the ground that had been marked out for each period of time - hourly in Europe. The tall obelisks of the Egyptians and others were for accurately recording the time to regulate the daily events as well as seasonal festivals etc. Some have been transported to other countries, and there is one on the Embankment by the Thames.

These gnomons were extremely accurate, and could record time to minutes if needed. What we will be examining, however, are the records of the lengths of the shadows at midday on the longest and shortest days of the year, when the sun was at each end of its yearly passage. The reason for this is that from these figures we can obtain both the amount of tilt on the earth's axis, and the latitude of the position the gnomon is situated. This is obtained as follows.

The gnomon measurements

If you set up a vertical pole (you could do this in your garden!) and measure the length of the shadow at midday on the longest day of the year and six months later, on the shortest day of the year, you will have the dimensions in Fig. 1. By drawing to scale or by calculation, you can obtain the value of the angle between the two shadows (WXS). By bisecting this angle you can obtain two important angles; the angle of tilt of the earth (WXL and SXL) and the latitude of the pole (LXG). We will not go into the geometry of why this should be so but it can be obtained from a consideration of the tilt of the earth as it goes around the sun. If there were no tilt, then the midday shadow line would not vary with the seasons and would give a direct reading of the latitude the year round.

The ancient gnomons

Some gnomons were very large and accurately constructed. The accuracy of the base was ensured by flooding it with a thin layer of water and checking its depth. The pole would be carefully plumbed. The top might be a small circular hole or some similar shape to cast as sharp a shadow as possible. They were able to record to an accuracy of less than 5 minutes of arc.

There is a very good check on the accuracy with which these measurements were made. From the length of the shadows, the latitude of the observation position could be accurately determined. In every case, this was *precisely* the known latitude of the city in which the observations were made. Thus the

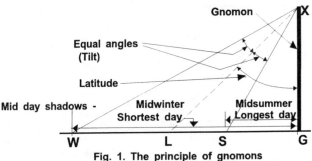

Fig. 1. The principle of gnomons

records were accurate, which means that the tilt observations were also reliable.

Thus, very accurate records of the sun's movements were made over many centuries. The importance of this we will see later.

The variation of the tilt

If a top is spinning clockwise, its axis will slowly trace out a circle anti-clockwise. Similarly, the earth "precesses" with a period between 26-40,000 years, during which the tilt varies between 22 and 24.5 degrees of arc. This is due to the pull of the moon, sun and the planets on the bulge at the earth's equator. This variation has been calculated by Stockwell and the past and future tilt angle is shown in Fig. 2. His calculations were later modified by Newcomb but they only apply from 2000 BC onwards.

Prof. Dodwell's investigation

George Dodwell was the South Australian Astronomer between 1909-1952. He was a leading expert with an international reputation and worked on several important projects. In 1934 he became interested in the obliquity of the ecliptic (the tilt of the earth) and collected 66 records of the sun's movements, almost all from old gnomon records over the past 4,000 years.

He wanted to check the tilt of the earth against these predicted values and therefore calculated this angle from the ancient records with various modern corrections to obtain the true angle of the sun. When he plotted the results, he found that they diverged significantly from the predicted. They were on a distinct curve that gradually departed from the predicted tilt as you went back in time.

This departure is shown in Fig. 2 and to a larger scale in Fig. 3. This shows some of the tilt angles obtained from these ancient records related to the date they were made.

It is interesting that several other experts had looked at these discrepant measurements, and it is somewhat amusing to read of their puzzlement over results that were so harmonious amongst themselves but departed so far from the "correct" values calculated by astronomers. Why could they not see what was so obvious to Dodwell?

Dodwell examined the shape of the curve and found that it precisely fitted a curve which is the path taken by a rotating body that has been struck as it returns to a stable position. By mathematically projecting the curve back further, he found that it became vertical *about the year 2345 BC*. Clearly, the earth had a severe impact, presumably from a meteorite, at that date. Only comparatively recently had it recovered its stability, and was now at a stable

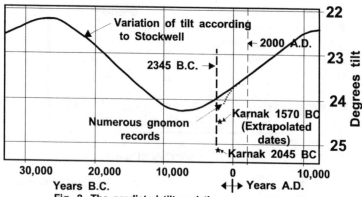

Fig. 2. The predicted tilt and the gnomon records

position at a larger angle of tilt to that which it had before the impact.

In addition, Dodwell noticed that the results varied around the main curve, and he analysed this "wobble" which had a period of about 1198 years. Many early astronomers had referred to the cycle of "trepidation" of the stars for they found that they increased their longitude for 640 years and then suddenly reversed this movement for a further 640 years. This was a puzzle to present-day astronomers. Dodwell appears to assume that these variations about the main curve (with a 1198 year period) explained the "trepidation" (with a period of 1280 years) of these early observations.

What was the original tilt?

What the angle of tilt was before the impact may be inferred from the 18° angle that the moon's orbit makes with our equator. Almost without exception, the moons of other planets revolve round the equator of that planet, no matter what that angle is to the ecliptic - even for Uranus which is at almost 90° to the ecliptic. This suggests that the earth's original angle of tilt was only 5° (=23-18) to the ecliptic; enough to give a small seasonal variation each year.

Regarding the stability of the moon's orbit, Setterfield points to Psalm 89:37 which speaks of the moon being a "faithful witness in the sky."

There is confirmation of these changes by one present when they were still large enough to be measured. This was Manilius, who lived in 14 AD, and was a close observer of gnomons for 30 years. He noted these changes might be due to "the discordant course of the sun itself, and some change in the sky, or through some change in the universal earth, by which it has moved away from its centre, as I have detected myself and I hear of also in other places."

There could be no doubt of this movement as he used the great 75 ft (22.9m) high obelisk in Rome. This had a golden ball at the top and he could measure its shadow to within 1/16 inch, but the shadow was up to 1/2 inch different to what he expected.

Something clearly happened to the earth in 2345 BC, and Dodwell wondered what this might have been. He made enquiries of his professional colleagues, but it was not until he was pointed to Professor McCready Price's book *The New Geology* (1923) and the chapter called "Hypothesis of a World Catastrophe" that he felt he had found the cause of Noah's Flood! Using the Biblical chronology, Price's date agreed with his 2345 BC.

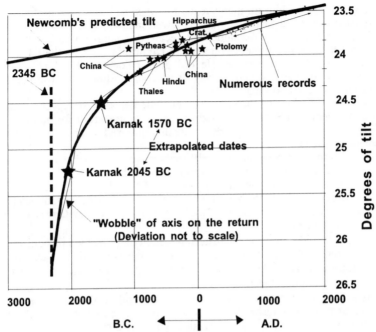

Fig. 3. The changing tilt shown by the ancient gnomon records

The opposition

He made a preliminary report of his findings and in 1935 he forwarded it to the Royal Astronomical Society in London. *They rejected it, claiming that the results were due to "observational errors".* This was ridiculous, as the graph is a very clear curve, with few contradictory points away from it. We have met this very inadequate argument before in the dismissal of the results in the past measurements of the speed of light. For such a prestigious body as the Royal Astronomical Society to have to stoop to such a low level as using this unacceptable reason for rejecting his results indicates just how revolutionary his findings were. To have found the cause of Noah's Flood would be most unwelcome in this (pseudo) "scientific" age.

In view of the charge that the readings of these old astronomers were "inaccurate", Dodwell carried out several experiments. Nine observers took 172 readings of the shadows using different shapes at the top of the pole. They were able to achieve an average accuracy of one or two minutes of arc. As the departure from Newcomb's values was over one degree, then "inaccuracy of observations" can be dismissed as an explanation.

In 1936 he mentioned that his work was being prepared for publication in his report to the Government of South Australia, but for some reason this never took place. A few years before he died, he wrote to Rene Noorbergen about his discoveries who referred to it in his book *Secrets of the Lost Races* (Noo:27).

Not only did the Royal Astronomical Society reject his paper, but he had considerable opposition from his professional colleagues at Adelaide University. Professor Sir Kerr Grant bluntly told Dodwell "You're mad", but clearly the subject bothered him for many years, for when he was on his deathbed he unexpectedly referred to the subject. Dodwell mentioned the subject to the Anglican Archbishop of Adelaide and received a similar retort. After his death in 1963, his family never referred to Dodwell's work on the tilt as the response was always the same. He did give a copy to the Archbishop's successor - who quietly stored it away. It was only following a bush fire that the manuscript came to light again!

It was Barry Setterfield, then a theistic evolutionist, who was given the copy by the Astronomical Society of South Australia to prepare it for publication. Setterfield's summary of the work eventually appeared in an ASSA bulletin (September 1967).

A copy of this and some of Dodwell's papers were forwarded to this author by Setterfield and it is mainly these documents that have provided the basis of this section. A synopsis of them was written as Pamphlet 236 for the Creation Science Movement and this was eventually noted by Corliss in America (See Section 9). He reviewed it in issue No. 30 of his *Science Frontiers* (Nov-Dec 1983), and he commented:

> One would think that such startling data, compiled by a recognised astronomer, would be the subject of intense study in archeo-astronomical circles; instead, it is an English creationist tract that discusses the subject.

There have been several efforts to have the full work published, and a number of times a publisher has agreed to produce the book, but each time, for some reason, the deal has fallen through. It is therefore hoped that this section will give some reasonable coverage of the subject until that full work appears.

Having given the background to this interesting research, let us examine some of the subjects that it affects and the explanation it provides for conflicting facts that have puzzled experts for years.

1. The temple at Karnak

As worshippers of the sun, the Egyptians built long temples that were accurately aligned to the sunrise or sunset on the longest day of the year. One of the longest and most magnificent was that of Amen-Ra at Karnak. This building is one third of a mile long down which the sun shone on only one day of the year (Fig. 4).

At a yearly mid-summer ceremony of "The Manifestation of Ra", the king and priests would assemble in the dark sanctuary on the only day that the sun was at its most northerly point. Just as it was setting and in line with the long axis, the doors would be flung open and the whole sanctuary would become a blaze of light reflected from the gold on the walls and on the robes of those within. The sight must have been very impressive at this ceremony when the sun once again blessed the Egyptian Sun-God king.

Over the years, as the tilt reduced, the sun failed to reach its former most northerly position by an increasing amount. From this, if the angle of the alignment of the pylons is known, then from the tilt obtained from the theoretical curve, we can check when the temple was built by reading off from the graph the amount of known tilt and obtain the corresponding date.

To obtain this date, Lockyer carried out a survey of the alignment of the temple columns and concluded that the oldest part of the building, the sanctuary, was built in 3,700 BC. However, his description of how he arrived at this date is very confusing and I failed to understand how he could have

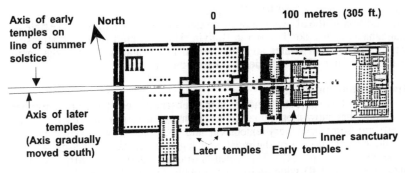

Axis of early
temples on
line of summer
solstice

North

0

100 metres (305 ft.)

Axis of later
temples
(Axis gradually
moved south)

Later temples

Early temples

Inner sanctuary

Fig. 4. The varying alignments of Karnak temple

obtained it from the information he gives in his book (Loc:119) for the various angles he obtains are all greater than Newcomb's lowest value of 24.2°.

Michael Garton, a creationist friend, came across an interesting paper in the British Museum by Richards who had carried out an accurate survey in 1914 (Ric). He found the line was for a tilt of 25.1°, but we can see from Fig. 2 the maximum theoretical tilt is 24.2°. *So theoretically the sun should never have reached the far end of the temple.* Richards confidently concluded:

> There is thus no reason to suppose that the temple of Amen-Ra at Karnak was originally laid down to have any relation whatsoever with the position of the setting sun at the summer solstice (Ric:8).

Yet at the base of one of the pylons there is a hieroglyph saying, "[The sanctuary] is a flood of shining splendour when the sun shines between the two [pylons]. It is seen an endless number of miles off" (Loc:106).

As the sun set further south of its old position, later additions to the temple had to be aligned slightly more to the south, and this slight realignment can be seen in the two later phases of the building. However, for some unknown reason, the outermost "pylons" (actually massive walls with huge doorways) were slightly aligned 0.53 metres more to the north than would have been expected. There is no explanation for this at this time but probably the temple was extended, ignoring the setting sun which was then too far to the south to enter the central sanctuary by that date in any case.

Realising that the largest theoretical tilt was still less than the alignment angles of "tilt" measured at Karnak, Dodwell extended the curve from the other ancient records to meet these angles. This gave the two dates when the different sections of the temple was built, and these are the "extrapolated" values of 2045 and 1570 BC in Fig. 3. The last alignment gives a date of 320 BC which is not shown on the graph.

It is interesting that these dates are much more recent than those used by Egyptologists, but they are closer to the "reduced" chronology for the Egyptian dynasties proposed by Velikovsky (Vel73) and Courville (Cou). Both of these contend that the period should be shortened by some 700 years, a subject previously dealt with in Section 3.8.

2. Stonehenge

Archaeologists and historians date this structure about 350 BC. Astronomers have calculated from the alignment that it was built about 1900 BC. By using the alignment and applying this to Dodwell's curve, the date agrees with that of the historians; 350 BC.

In addition to the above, Dodwell investigated the ancient Solar Temple at Tiahuanacu, near Lake Titicaca in Bolivia. This was built for observations of the sunrise at both winter and summer solstices, and they gave the same results of greater tilt as recorded by these other temples.

Ancient stone monuments

Whilst on this subject of ancient stone "observatories" there are a number in Europe that show most remarkable alignments with sun and star positions. These are sometimes very extensive, and there are a very large number around Aberdeen. One of the most amazing is in Brittany at Carnac (Is the name just a coincidence?). This consists of over 3,000 stones arranged in 12 lines, 100m (330 ft) wide and nearly 1,000m (3,300 ft) long. They show a knowledge of the Pythagorean 3-4-5 right-angled triangle in the setting out of two oval shapes at each end. Quite what the purpose of this pattern of stones was is not clear but certainly a high level of intelligence was required.

There has been very great controversy on how intelligent the constructors of these elaborate stone structures were. Francis Hitching quotes one writer, John Michell, who reviewed the history of astro-archaeology (as it is known) and said:

> Resistance to astro-archaeological theory has been intensified by the understanding that, if ancient people of Neolithic culture are credited with an astronomical science far in advance of mediaeval, and even in some respects of modern, standards, current faith in the unique quality of our own scientific achievement is undermined. Yet evidence of a remarkably developed and widespread Stone Age science continues to accumulate (Hit:60).

One can understand the bafflement of modern physicists and archaeologists when faced with these complex and very accurate stone observatories, for it does not fit in with their picture of man emerging from ape-like ancestors through an ignorant and illiterate cave-man period to the "intelligent scientist" as the ultimate achievement of evolution.

If they were to admit that man has always been intelligent ever since the creation of Adam, limited only by the natural materials he had to hand, all would be solved. But such a revolutionary explanation is unacceptable.

3. Eudoxus

Eudoxus was a Greek astronomer who lived about 350 BC. who wrote a poem on the position of the stars. Astronomers point out that the positions he gives the stars apply to a period about 1900 BC and arrogantly claimed that he either used data from an earlier period or was an "armchair" astronomer, never venturing to study the stars themselves. Again, using Dodwell's curve the positions agree with the dating of 350 BC.

Is there Scriptural evidence?

Setterfield has suggested that the precession, the "trepidation" variation of the stars and the "wobble" of the returning axis, would have produced a "beat difference" that would have occasionally, at specific times, affected the movement of the heavens as seen on earth. The effect would have depended upon the position of the observer, with a maximum effect at the poles and zero effect at the equator. The result would have been to make the heavens appear to briefly "go back" at intervals of 742 years. He refers to the "going back of the sun" in Hezekaiah's day (2Kings 20:8-11) about 1453 BC, Joshua's long day (Jos. 10:12-15) about 711 BC - 742 years before, and the Crucifixion - 32 AD; 742 years later. A further 742 years brings us to 774 AD, and although the effect would be smaller, there are reports of long days from Britain, Europe and Africa.

This is of interest, but these variations are quite small and seem incapable of making the very large alterations in the movements of the heavens as recorded in the Bible. This is a phenomena that could be investigated in greater detail by those with the specialist knowledge in this subject.

Days in the year

In the pre-Flood world there may have been 360 days in each year; 12 months of 30 days each. There is some confirmation of this in Genesis 7:11 and 8:3,4. We read that the Flood began on the 17th day of the second month and "abated" after 150 days on the 17th day of the seventh month. 150 days over 5 months gives 30 days per month exactly. In addition the circle is divided into 360 degrees of arc which may have been derived from the sun's progress across the signs of the Zodiac taking 360 days for a full circle.

In addition, most, if not all, prophesies are based upon a 360-day year (Twelve 30-day months). For example, in Revelation 11:2-3 it refers to a period of 1,260 days and 42 months which gives 30 days per month precisely. Some use a 360-day year in the 483-years prophecy of Daniel to correct this to 478 years to obtain agreement with the years between the restoration of Jerusalem (444 BC?) and the entry of Christ (33 AD?) (Cris).

We would here mention an intriguing fact. When God created the circle, He automatically determined the ratio between the diameter and the circumference; i.e. pi = 3.14159... - a non-repeating and endless number. At the 360th position the three figures 360 are centred exactly at that point! This is a chance of 1 in 1,000. The figure 365 is positioned 51 placed later (CSM pamphlet No. 319). Does this indicate that the 360 degrees of the circle were originally given by God to mark the days? We leave the reader.....

The 360 day year was possibly the calendar used before the Flood, for there is no reference to changing the calendar reckoning until Moses gave the Israelites an observed calendar in Deut. 16:9 as discussed in Section 2.3.

It is therefore possible that the impact of the asteroid increased the turning rate of the earth such that there were now 365.24 days in a year instead of 360. Newton and other astronomers have discussed this subject but there is surprisingly little written about when the change was first noted. A change in the year of this magnitude would have been quickly apparent, probably within a few years after the Flood. Although Velikovsky and others have claimed that the change took place several hundred years later, Brad Sparks has investigated the evidence and concluded that the original documentation does not support such a view.

We would suggest that only the impact of an asteroid could have effected such a drastic change. The near fly-pass of another body, such as Velikovsky proposed, could not bring this about. Additional factors that could increase the speed of rotation is the collapse of the Water Vapour Canopy and the collapse of the crust if it were sitting on the water that provided the "fountains of the deep". This movement of heavier material towards the centre of the earth would, in both cases, have increased the rate of rotation. We discuss below the possibility that they occurred at the Flood which may have been at a different time to that of the asteroid impact.

What caused the impact?

It is generally thought that the impact was due to one of many meteorites or asteroids that are wandering around in space. However, van Flandern has made a very good case for both comets and asteroids being created by the explosion of the "missing planet" where the asteroid belt is. It is his contention that this planet (named Phaeton by some) exploded and threw its debris into space. These lumps of material, depending on their trajectory and the gravitational effect of other planets on their course, became the asteroids, meteorites and comets that we have today.

It has been speculated by some that this might have taken place at the Fall, and that therefore Noah's Flood was planned for and predicted well in advance of it actual occurrence. This would be entirely in keeping with God's Plan for His universe and the very central role of man in that scheme.

Had the asteroid hit the pre-Flood earth, then any crater would have been engulfed by the subsequent deposits welling up from the depths when "the fountains of the deep were broken up", having been triggered by the impact.

It has been proposed that the impact of a meteorite that resulted in the extinction of the dinosaurs is marked by a trace of iridium at the top of the Cretaceous strata that is world wide. However, six other levels have now been found, which virtually eliminates its significance as a marker of an impact (Q31/3:136).

Where did the meteorite land?

There are various sites that have evidence of meteor impact; Yucatan on the north coast of South America; off Madagascar etc. There is one large area where it could have struck and left evidence around the edges; this is the Pacific Ocean. This was the site originally referred to by Dodwell and Setterfield.

When a meteorite of large size crashes into the earth, it liquidises the rocks at the point of impact and breaks into pieces that flatten out and penetrate the interior. When this happens, the hot magma pours out of the earth's interior through the broken crust and covers the area around the impact. This outpouring levels off and a flat area will then remain. We can see this in the craters of the moon that have also filled with magma.

If a map of the bed of the Pacific Ocean with the water removed is examined, it will be seen to be surprisingly flat for such a huge area; almost one half of the total area of the earth. Only small islands appear above the surface, such as Hawaii.

In addition, the Pacific is surrounded by what geologists call the "Ring of Fire". This refers to the many volcanoes and earthquake areas that there are around the Pacific. There are the earthquakes in Japan, The Russian coast, South and North America and Alaska, and eruptions in the Philippines and the huge explosion of Krakatoa in 1883.

It is interesting that in a book on the impact of meteorites on the earth, the author noted that "It has been suggested that the Pacific Ocean could be the scar of a meteorite's impact" and calculated it could have lengthened the day by 3 hours, 17 minutes, 39 seconds (Gal:81).

We do not know the plan of the land areas after creation, and therefore we have no means of knowing whether it struck land or water. It is fairly certain that there was not as much surface water then as there is now, as huge additional quantities were released from the interior by this impact that shattered the crust. In addition, we read that the waters were "gathered together into one place" (Gen. 1 v9). If the impact did trigger the Flood, there is less likelihood of it generating vast waves that would have smashed the Ark before it could float properly.

In addition, there would be, of course, two places on the earth where this sharp tilt would hardly be felt. These are the two points either side of the point of impact forming the axis of the tilting movement. It could be speculated that this might be where the Ark was situated so that its "launching" as a floating vessel could be quite gentle as the Flood waters gradually poured into the area.

Further calculations might show if the orbit of the earth might have been affected, whether it could have caused the lengthening of the years from 360 days to 365.24 days, and the amount of tilt - which would depend upon the angle that it struck the earth.

Did this trigger Noah's Flood?

We discussed this in Section 3.9 "A Biblical Chronology", where we pointed out that the impact may have caused the Flood about 2345 BC, but that Sparks's revised chronology places the date of the Flood earlier at 2517 BC. This leaves the possibility of the impact occurring in 2345 BC, causing the "dividing of the land" in the days of Peleg. The collapse of the Water Vapour Canopy and the splitting of the crust to release the "fountains of the deep" would still have been at the time of the Flood in 2517 BC.

There is one problem with an impact triggering the Flood. Wherever it impacted, one would expect to see the whole globe covered with the different strata. In fact, only the present land has the most significant strata; the oceans have nothing earlier than the Mesozoic, and even this appears to be obtained from radiometric dating, not from any fossil content. The problem of explaining this in a creationist geological model we have raised in the previous appendix.

Final comment

The full information on the tilt of the earth's axis is still awaiting the publication of Dodwell's book, but meanwhile it is hoped that until that time this appendix gives an adequate outline for the interested reader.

APPENDIX 6
THE GOSPEL IN THE STARS

The immediate reaction of some people when raising this topic is to wonder whether they are being invited to dabble in a Christianised form of astrology. Let me reassure the reader that no such aim is intended, in fact it is quite the opposite. Far from foretelling the future for personal knowledge or gain, the names of the zodiac tell the sorry story of man's fall and the glorious way of redemption prepared for believers.

Much of what follows has been obtained from Bullinger (Bull) and Seiss (Sei), and both of these acknowledge their debt to Frances Rolleston's foundational work *Mazzaroth, or the Constellations* (Roll). Their reliance on this early work can be seen in the number of times both authors have almost the same wording. They were writing in 1893 (Bullinger) and 1882 (Seiss) but modern reprints are still available. There are other smaller books but they are synopses of these earlier works. What follows is also a synopsis and the interested reader can obtain either of these books for further information.

Before examining each of the constellations on the ecliptic, (those through which the sun passes during the year) we will discuss the evidence that indicates that they were named for a spiritual purpose.

1. Astrology a deceptive replacement

If the meaning behind the names of the constellations and stars were to be a reminder of God's plan of salvation for fallen mankind, we would expect this to be attacked by Satan. He would adopt his usual tactic of transforming it into a deceptive practice so that its original meaning became totally obscured. This is probably the reason for the rise of astrology and its use of the constellations to delude those who are ignorant of the Christian message they contain.

2. A Biblical basis for this approach?

Bullinger refers to Rom. 10:18 where Paul is saying that the gospel was clear to all men:

> But I say, Have they not heard? Yes verily, "their sound went into all the earth, and their words unto the ends of the world".

Paul is quoting from Psalm 19 which reads as follows:

> The heavens declare the glory of God; and the firmament sheweth His handiwork. Day unto day uttereth speech, and night unto night sheweth knowledge. There is no speech nor language where their voice is not heard. Their line is gone out through all the earth, and their words to the end of the world. In them he hath set a tabernacle for the sun, which is as a bridegroom coming out of his chamber, and rejoiceth as a strong man to run a race (Ps. 19:1-5).

In this passage we see the glory of God set forth for all to see. Now this may be in the awesomeness of space and of the uncountable numbers of stars. These are there for all to see and wonder. But it is also possible that it was in the names of the constellations and stars that the real message lay that Paul could have been referring to. Indeed, this is far more likely when we are told that it was God himself who named the stars in Psalm 147:4:

> He telleth the number of the stars; *he calleth them all by their names.*

We will see the spiritual significance in very many of the names given to the stars in what follows, but if God gave them their names, surely this is added evidence that they were named not just for identification but so that He may set out His plan of salvation for fallen mankind.

3. The Universality of the names of stars and constellations

Bullinger says that "the twelve signs are the same, both as to the meaning of their names and as to their order *in all the ancient nations of the world* (emphasis his)" (Bull:9). He then refers to the antiquity of the Chinese, Chaldean and Egyptian records but gives no evidence. Rolleston (Roll), however supplies more on this.

She notes that all constellations began with Aries - in Latium, Egypt, Arabia, India and China (p 11). Astronomers also measure their star positions from the "First Point of Aries". In the Chinese names, nine of them were obviously connected to the present system. The Sanskrit was also said to have a complete correlation. The Buddhist system, which started with Aries, had eleven with similar names (p27). Traces of the zodiac were also found in China, India, Egypt, South Seas, Etruria (Etruscans) and Mexico (p15).

Several ancient authorities state that they had a spiritual intention. The Arabic astronomer Albumazar said that "many attributed to them a divine and prophetic virtue." Cicero said that "The signs are measured out, so that in so many descriptions divine wisdom might appear."

Depuis, in *L'Origin des Cults* had collected a vast number of traditions prevalent *in all nations* of "a divine person, born of a woman, suffering in conflict with a serpent, but triumphing over him at last, and finds the same reflected in the figures of the ancient constellations."

4. The ancient origin of the names

Rolleston says that the zodiac is attributed to Seth (the son of Adam) and to Enoch. She suggests that the Jews kept the word and the prophecy, the Arabs preserved the names of the stars while the Greeks and the Egyptians transmitted the figures to which they belong (p11).

Persian and Arab traditions and Josephus ascribe its invention to Adam, Seth and Enoch (Bull:10). The Jews called Enoch the Great Scribe who wrote books on sacred wisdom, particularly astronomy, and he is quoted in Jude vv 14-15.

The Chaldean Epic of Creation says that the great god Anu created the "mansions in the sky". Again we see the naming of the constellations was by the supreme God himself and not by a human being.

With the names being so widespread, then, as with the folk stories of the Flood, we can assume that their origin was before the dispersal from Babel. If the traditions are accepted, then we are dealing with God's revelation to Adam of the way of redemption after his Fall.

We have set out the ancient origin of the names in order to support the claim that that they have been given by God, particularly in view of Psalm 147:4 quoted above. We can, therefore, expect them to have particular significance for fallen mankind.

The languages most frequently mentioned are Hebrew, Latin, Arabic and Persian and it will be obvious that these are all fairly near each other geographically. We will give the various names of some of the stars which have the same meaning in different languages when they are provided.

5. Critics of the Gospel interpretation

Seiss notes that secular anthropologists acknowledge that many ancient cultures had mythologies that were remarkably similar to the basic events of Christian history. They often have a god who is born to a virgin mother, slays a dragon to save mankind, was entombed and rose again, eventually ascending to heaven. So similar were these accounts that Volney tried to claim that Christ never existed and was only a mythical character who embodied these concepts.

One critic is Allen (Alle) who is dismissive of those who read the gospel into the names. He charges them with attempting to "alter the sky figures" for their own purpose and calls them "iconoclasts" of the accepted scheme. However, having listed twelve notable authorities, he specifically comments; "The recent efforts of Miss Frances Rolleston...and Dr. Seiss are especially remarkable" (Alle:28). This is almost his only comment on her work and he seems to be according it grudging approval for its scholarly research. Bullinger is not mentioned.

His only other reference to what he admits is her "singular" work is to criticises her explanation of how the name of one star was derived (p201). Her work may contain other errors he chose not to mention but as this was the only fault he points to, it could indicate the thoroughness and reliability of her work.

6. The pictures and constellation shapes

One of the most surprising aspects of any constellation is the almost complete absence of any correlation between the shape of the star pattern and the picture painted around them. About the only constellation to which this would not apply is the Southern Cross which is obvious, but for all others there seems to be no relevance.

For example, who would have made the shape of a flying horse, Pegasus, from one bright star and few others in the constellation? Indeed, take any of the constellations and see if there is much connection between the positions of the few stars in it and the picture around it in Fig. 1.

How could these ancient pictures have become attached to these specific groups of stars? One can only conjecture that this was yet another gift from God to mankind for all generations. It is possible that he has presented these pictures to Adam of His redemptive plan and they have been transferred in these forms down through succeeding generations.

Obviously, it is also possible that they are the figments of man's imagination for godless purposes, but as we examine the names of the stars the evidence gradually supports the proposal that they have a deeply spiritual Christian meaning.

7. Modern names

There were efforts in the 17th century to give names to groups of stars not within the known constellations. The banality of such names as the Air Pump, the Telescope, the Indian, the Balloon etc. only served to highlight the more significant and meaningful names that the ancient constellations possessed. Of all the many aspects of life that could have been portrayed in the names of the constellations and stars, it is significant how many refer to "judgement", "strong saviour", "weighed in the balance" etc.

As the true meaning of the names was lost, nations such as the Greeks gave some of them spurious names which they acknowledged. However, the original names can be obtained from older cultures.

Bullinger points out that if the names were given to enable astronomers to identify the stars, then *all* the stars would have been included. In fact, the reverse is the case for certain stars are used to identify the pictures - the more important consideration.

8. Did Abram "tell out" the gospel story?

In Genesis 15:5, in the Authorised Version, we read that God told Abram to "tell (Hebrew "*caphar*") the stars, if thou be able to number (*caphar*) them: and he said unto him 'so shall thy seed be' ". This is usually translated in more modern versions as "count the stars" and the NKJV adds "so shall your descendants be." (NIV - "offspring").

It is noticeable that the word "*caphar*" is used for both "tell" and "number" and to translate it as referring to "counting the number of the stars" is perfectly acceptable, but should it be used in this passage?

The Hebrew word "*caphar*" can also mean "recount, commune, account, declare, shew forth, speak, talk, tell (out), writer" (Strong's Complete Concordance). All these imply more than just counting a number of objects but can allude to recounting a story.

Furthermore, Paul examines this passage in detail in Galatians 3:16 where he says "He saith not, 'And to Seeds', as of many; but as of one, 'And to thy seed, which is Christ' ". He is at pains to point out that the word "seed" was singular in the Hebrew and referred to Christ (as the Coming One). Now if the word "seed" is singular, it does not fit with the translation of this passage as referring to counting innumerable stars and saying "this is how many descendants you will have".

There is therefore an *alternative,* or *additional,* view of this passage as Paul considered it. It could refer to the future advent of one person - the Saviour. God may have told Abraham to "read out" the story in the stars of the gospel record of future events that was apparently also known by ancient peoples. Accordingly, this passage could therefore be loosely paraphrased:

> Go outside your tent and recount to yourself [and to future generations?] the story that is in names given to the stars and constellations. They will tell you of one person, descended from you, who will come - Christ - who will save His people.

9. Job's witness.

The oldest book in the Bible was written by Job who lived about 2150 BC, not long after the Flood. Already the names of the stars and constellations are fixed for he refers to Orion (38:31), Mazzaroth (the zodiac) and Arcturus (38:32). His reference to "binding the Pleiades" (38:31) is interesting as this group of stars are unaccountably stationary in their relative positions and not moving away from each other as expected. How did Job know this? This particular question struck Barry Setterfield forcibly before he became a Christian and made him rethink his life.

In Job 26:13 we read:

> By His spirit He hath garnished the heavens; His hand hath formed the crooked serpent.

The first reference is the to the heavens but it is not clear whether the second reference is to living serpents or the "fleeing serpent" in the sky (Hydra). If the latter is intended, as suggested by the first statement, then it is God Himself who shaped the constellations, and then gave them the spiritual message that they contain.

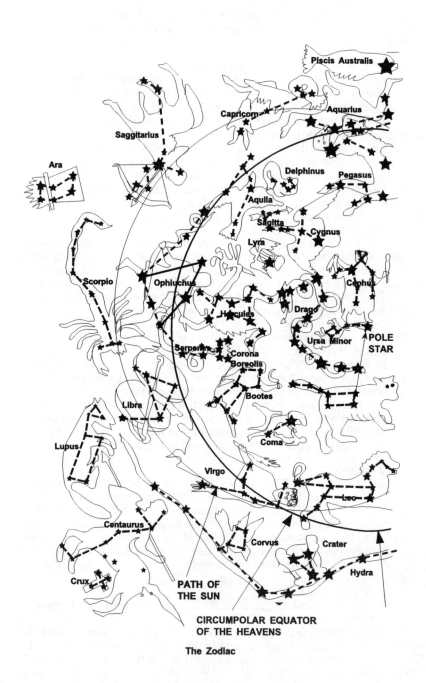

The Zodiac

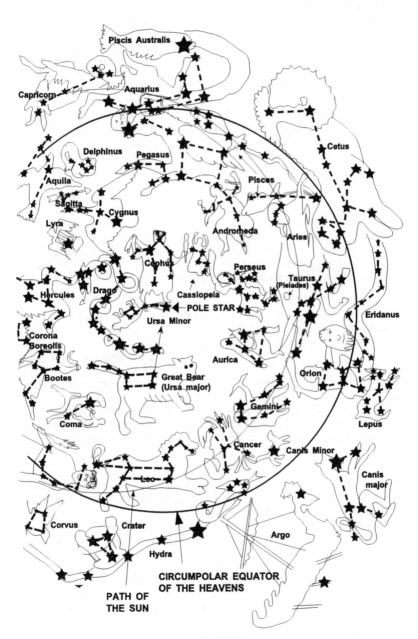

The Zodiac

10. The Tower of Babel?

Before continuing, we will examine one doubtful reference by Bullinger.

In the Authorised Version, the incident of the Tower of Babel refers to men "building a tower whose top *may reach* unto heaven". In the original the "may reach" is not there and has been added to make sense. It literally reads "a top unto heaven" and could indicate that the top of the tower would be dedicated to heaven, i.e. the worship of heavenly bodies. It is this that would have angered God more than just the building a high tower.

Bullinger quotes a Lieut.-Gen. Chesney who excavated the ruins of Babylon and who described the mound known to the Arabs as Birs Nimroud. This is 153 ft. high and the square base has 400 ft. long sides. He claimed that there were seven stages made of bricks in different colours each representative of one of the planets. On the top was a tower on the summit of which were the signs of the Zodiac.

This sounds very interesting but Bullinger obtained the information in a very roundabout way; from the sermon of a preacher who said he had copied it from Chesney's private notes. One would have thought that this very specific archaeological evidence, that considerably alters our understanding of this important event in the Bible, would have been corroborated by other excavators and become more widely known. As this seems to be the only reference it should be treated with considerable reservation.

11. The days of the week.

For the reader's interest, this might be the best point to give the origin of the names for the days of the week. They are all based upon the names of the planets that were those of Saxon gods and Seiss gives the following:

Sun-day, Mun (moon) - day, Tue (*Tuisco* - Anglo-Saxon name for Mars) - day, Wed (*Woden* - A. Sax. for Mercury) - day, Thurs (*Thor* - A.S. for Jupiter) - day, Fri (*Friga* or *Freiya* = A.S. for Venus) - day, Satur (*Saturn*) - day.

That a seven day week has been known from the earliest days of antiquity and have been followed in most civilisations is evidence that they were based upon the six days of creation and the seventh day of rest as we read in Genesis 1.

THE ZODIAC

With that introduction, we will only briefly refer to the various Christian aspects of the names etc. We would mention that for each main constellation in the Zodiac on the path through which the sun passes, there are generally three other constellations, associated with it, called "decans". These are listed A, B and C under each constellation. In what follows we will be brief and use only a "note" form.

In both books, each author gave the name of many stars and then would say how this was relevant to some aspect of the Christian faith. At times, these connections were somewhat forced and one had the impression that virtually every star name had to be fitted into the system somewhere. There is sufficient evidence of the spiritual nature of the Zodiac names without forcing every name to comply.

Those given below are only a selection of the best of those where the relevance is clear. The Christian allusion will be obvious to most, but we give some of the biblical references. There are a number of "strong men", such as Hercules, Ophiuchus, Centaur etc. who are symbolic of the coming Christ and the various names and roles relative to the Gospel hardly need explanation. Surprisingly, I could find no star chart that gave both the lines joining selected stars used in astronomical charts and the figures of the zodiac. The zodiac chart illustrated on pages 420-1 was compiled with some difficulty by carefully combining these two sources.

The start of the Zodiac.

Although Rolleston said that the constellations start with Aries, Bullinger and Seiss start with Virgo, the woman, and the last one is Leo, the lion. Bullinger contends that this is indicated as the starting point in the Egyptian pantheon of gods by the Sphinx, which has the head of a woman and the body of a lion. Thus the two ends are joined to complete the circle.

1. VIRGO

This is the first constellation of the circuit which the Greeks wrongly renamed Ceres. A virgin (Is. 7:14) holding a branch (Jer. 23:5-6) and an ear of corn. Corn = seed (Latin = Spica, the modern name of this bright star. Old name was Arabic Al Zimach = seed). Star Zavijaveh means "gloriously beautiful" (Is. 4:2).

(A) Coma. Woman with a child on her lap - Name means "Desire of all nations"

Albumazer, an Arabic astronomer of the 8th century, said that the Persians, Chaldeans and Egyptians said this was a young woman (Persian = virgin) on a throne nourishing an infant boy, having a Hebrew name Ihesu which in Greek is called Christos. Shakespeare referred to this as "the good boy in Virgo's lap" (Titus Andronicus Act 4 Sc. 5).

Original Egyptian name Shes-nu = the desired son. Renamed by the Egyptians as Coma Berenice = The hair or wig of Berenice.

The possible connection of this decan with the Star of Bethlehem will be discussed at the end of this section.

(B) Centaur. Half man - half horse. Said to indicate the two natures of Christ (?). Hebrew name is Beza or Al Beze (Arabic) = the despised (Is. 53:3)

(C) Bootes. A man with a spear and sickle (Rev. 14:15-16). Name = The Coming One (Ps. 96:13). Arcturus, the name of the bright star in the left knee= the keeper (of those) going up on the heights. Star Nekkar = the pierced (Zec. 12:10).

2. LIBRA

Latin = Libra (scales). A pair of scales (Heb. = Mozanaim). Arabic - Al Zubena (= purchase or redemption).

Star names; - lower scale - Zuben al Genubi - Arabic (the price which is deficient) (Ps. 62:9) - upper scale - Zuben al Chemali - Arabic (the price that covers). Alternative name - al Gubi = heaped up (the value of the redemption). Zuben al Akrab - The price of the conflict.

(A) Crux = the cross

(B) Lupus or Victima (Beast slain or victim)

(C) Corona = A crown

3. SCORPIO = A Scorpion.

Coptic = Isidis (the attack of the enemy)

(A) and (B) Ophiuchus and Serpens. The "strong man" Ophiuchus (=serpent-holder) wrestles with the serpent who is reaching for the crown. The scorpion is stinging the heel of Ophiuchus, who is treading on the scorpion (Gen. 3:15). In his heel is the star Antares (= wounding).

(C) **Hercules** - the mighty vanquisher. Foot is placed on the coiled dragons neck. Star Ras al Gethi = the head of him who bruises (Gen. 3:15).

4. SAGITTARIUS - The Archer.

Same meaning in several languages (Rev. 6:2). Star Naim = The gracious one.

(A) **Lyra** - The harp. The name indicates the praise of God. Brightest star is Vega = He shall be exalted. (Ps. 21:13)

(B) **Ara** - the Altar. The burning fire prepared for His enemies.

(C) **Draco** - The Dragon. The name comes from the Greek = Trodden on (Ps. 91:13). Brightest star Thuban = The subtle. Names of other stars all refer to similar aspects of the dragon.

5. CAPRICORNUS - The Sea Goat.

Ancient pictures are half goat - half fish; i.e. the sacrifice and those who it is sacrificed for (Christians use of the fish as a symbol). Second brightest star Deneb al Gedi = the sacrifice cometh. Others have similar meanings.

(A) **Sagitta** = The Arrow that pierces (Ps. 38:2).

(B) **Aquila** = Eagle. This has been wounded by the arrow. Names of stars are "wounding", "piercing" etc.

(C) **Delphinus** - The Dolphin. The one who rises.

6. AQUARIUS= The Water Bearer (Is. 44:3)

(A) **Piscis Australis** = The Southern Fish. Star Fom al Haut = the mouth of the fish

(B) **Pegasus** = The Winged Horse

(C) **Cygnus** = The Swan. Brightest star Deneb = The Judge or Adige = flying swiftly.

7. PISCES = The Fish.

Star names indicate "the fish (multitudes) of those who will follow"; i.e. The Church (Ps. 115:14).

(A) **The Band** - (that unites the two fish) (Hos. 11:4)

(B) **Andromeda** - The Chained Woman (who will be delivered).

(C) **Cepheus** - The Crowned King.

8. Aries - The Ram or Lamb (John 1:29).

Brightest star El Nath = wounded, slain; (others similar).

(A) **Cassiopeia** - The Beautiful Enthroned Woman. The captive woman now delivered. Brightest star Schedir (Hebrew) = freed. 2nd star Caph = The Branch (of victory). (Is. 54:1-8, 62:3-5).

(B) **Cetus** - the sea monster. The enemy bound.

(C) **Perseus** - The Breaker. Hebrew = Peretz. Greek = Perses (Micah 2:13). Winged feet = coming swiftly. Head he carries wrongly called Medusa by Greeks; Hebrew Rosh Satan = Head of the Adversary.

9. Taurus - The Bull.

The Pleiades = The congregation of the judge.

(A) **Orion** - The coming Prince. Hebrew Oarion = light. He holds a club and the head of "the roaring lion" (1 Pet. 5:8). Betelgeuz = The coming of the branch. Rigol = the foot that crushes. Al Nitak = the wounded one.

(B) **Eridanus** - The River of the Judge. Star names refer to "flowing" etc. (Dan. 7:10; Nahum 1:8).

(C) **Auriga** - The Shepherd (Is. 40:10-11). Hebrew root = shepherd. Star

Capella (Latin) = she goat.

10. Gemini - The Twins.

There is some confusion of the pictures for this constellation in the different languages, but they generally refer to two people. Probably referring to the two natures of Christ and his eventual victory.

(A) Lepus - The Hare (the enemy); trodden under Orion's foot. Star names refer to "the deceiver" etc.

(B) Canis Major (The Dog) or **Sirius** (The Prince). Sirius is the brightest of all stars. (Is. 9:6).

(C) Canis Minor - The Second Dog. Star Procyon = Redeemer.

11. Cancer - The Crab.

There are a variety of pictures for this constellation. The meaning is uncertain.

(A) Ursa Minor - The Little Bear. No bears found in any ancient Zodiacs. Confusion may be from Hebrew Dohver = Sheepfold, Dovh = Bear.

(B) Ursa Major - The Great Bear. Possibly "Sheepfold" as Ursa Minor as Al Naish = "assembled together"; Dubhe = "Herd of animals or a flock" etc. Many stars similarly named.

(C) Argo - The Ship. Became part of Greek Argonaut story. Meaning is the "Return of the travellers".

12. Leo - The Lion.

The Lion of the tribe of Judah (Rev. 5:5). Hebrew name means "Lion hunting down its prey". Name in other languages similar. Denebola = Judge who cometh.

(A) Hydra - The Serpent. Hydra means "He is abhorred". Star names similar.

(B) Crater - The Cup. The pouring out of wrath on the wicked (Ps. 75:8).

(C) Corvus - The Raven. Birds of prey devouring the Serpent.

....

Truly, "Their sound went into all the earth, and their words unto the ends of the world'." Mankind is left with no excuses..........

THE STAR OF BETHLEHEM

Before leaving this study of the heavens, we should briefly deal with the various explanations for the star of Bethlehem that guided the Magi to the Christ. The most frequently mentioned are Kepler's suggestion that it was the conjunction of Saturn, Jupiter and Mars in 7 BC, whilst a Dr. Martin suggested that it was a conjunction of Jupiter, Venus and the star Regulus in 3 BC.

Morris (ICR Impact 150) dismisses these, pointing out that they could not be called "*His* star". Similarly, comets and meteors could not be called a star. He suggests that supernova (very bright star explosions sometimes visible during the day) may have been the sign but these are very rare and well noted. He mentions three occurring long after the birth of Christ, in 1054 (Chinese), 1572 (Tycho's) and 1604 (Kepler's). Morris suggests that it was a star that appeared in Virgo that the Magi saw.

Bullinger claims it was a new bright star, whose presence at the time of Christ's birth was attested by Ignatius (69 AD), presumably on the report of someone who had seen it. It was in the decan Coma, possibly in the child on the woman's lap. Thus it would be very specifically "*His* star". The latitude of Christ's birth would be that of the star and the longitude by the fact that he was to be born in the land of Jacob from whence a star would rise (Num. 24:17).

Bullinger relates (p38) the "beautiful tradition" that the Magi, resting by David's "Well of Bethlehem" saw the reflection of the star immediately overhead, so they knew that they had reached His birthplace. He appears to have overlooked the fact that had they done so, their heads would have obscured the light from the star!

Seiss similarly contends that there was a brilliant star in Coma and referred to Hipparchus seeing it 125 years before the time of Christ. He also says the Chinese record it but this conflicts with Morris's rejection of this observation due to the dating.

Bouw investigated this subject in considerable detail (Q17/3:174). He rejected the appearance of a supernova flare, conjunction of planets, comet or other such appearance and concluded that the star was a miracle.

In all, it would appear that the most likely explanation was the appearance of a star, probably in Coma, that initiated the travels of the Magi.

It should be noted that the Magi "saw His star in the east" but then had to travel west to go to Judea. For most of their long journey they were therefore *not* following the star, which only reappeared near Bethlehem. There is also the question of who the Magi were. There is the distinct possibility that they were Jewish astronomers ("wise men") who were descendants of those in the Babylonian captivity. They had stayed behind after the general return to Jerusalem but had not forgotten the promises in the Scriptures of a coming Messiah.

The Bible record implies that they were guided to the exact place of His birth. How a star could have done this is difficult to conceive, but with so many supernatural events surrounding this climactic time, it is likely that this was one also. The star may have been over Christ's birthplace no matter from which direction it was observed, and in addition, may have only been visible to the faithful and believing Magi - as Christ's glory is to the Christian.

APPENDIX 7
NUMBERS IN THE BIBLE

On reading this heading, some might wonder whether we will be dealing with mystical numbers, magic squares or similar subjects with occult or cabbalistic overtones. No such ideas would be entertained.

What we will be looking at are three subjects. The first is the main one which is a study of gematria. This deals with using the letters that represent numbers used by both Hebrew and Greek and obtaining the numerical equivalent of certain passages and words.

The second subject, only dealt with briefly, is the significance of certain numbers that often appear in the Bible such as 3, 7, 40 etc. This is only for the reader's general interest.

The third is an addendum dealing with words found by stepping out letters at regular intervals in the Old Testament - known as Equidistant Letter Sequences - ELS. This has recently achieved public prominence.

THE JEWS AND THE OLD TESTAMENT

Before discussing this subject, it would be as well to explain the very great care with which the Jewish scribes - the Massoretes - made copies of the OT scrolls. The importance of this will become obvious as we examine the subject of gematria closely and we will see that even the slightest inaccuracy in copying would quickly destroy many of the intricate patterns of numbers that are still found after over a thousand years of copying from an approved original version.

When copying, the scribes would be scrupulous in making sure that there were no mistakes. To ensure that there were no omissions of letters or words, they would count the number of letters from each end of both the original and the copy and check that the central letter was the same for both of them. As an indication of how sacred the scriptures and the name of God were to them, before writing the holy name of God - Javeh or Jehovah (known as the Tetragrammaton - the four letters YHVH), they would bathe themselves, change their clothing, and use a new nib in their pens. They would then repeat a short phrase before writing the name.

If letters touched or a mistake made in the name of God or the sheet had three mistakes it was destroyed. Any scroll that was badly copied or old was not destroyed but placed in a Genizah - a burial ground for unusable religious articles. This burial of a seemingly inanimate object surely echoes the New Testament which says the word of God is "living" (Heb.4:12).

Practices such as these indicate the extremely high regard they had for their sacred scrolls, for they were rightly conscious of the fact that they were dealing with the very word of God Himself to mankind. However, we have discussed in Section 3.9 on Biblical Chronology that the Massoretic text we have today was not finalised until about 1500 AD. How close this was to the original texts as written is debatable, but we can be assured that the present text is fulfilling God's purposes for this present generation.

OLD TESTAMENT GEMATRIA

When we want to write a number, we have specific symbols, adopted from the Arabic system, for each figure - 1, 2, 3 etc. In both Old Testament Hebrew and New Testament (*Koine*) Greek, neither had specific symbols but used letters of their alphabet to represent numbers. What each letter represented in each of these languages is given in Fig. 1. In the Greek, 90 and 900 were two special symbols - Koppa and Sampsi, which would not, of course, appear in any text.

Numbers were made up by placing the correct letters in a group. That they were numbers and not a word would be obvious both from the context and that generally the word would be meaningless.

This process can, of course, be reversed. Each letter in a word could be given its numerical value and the summation of the whole word would be its Numerical Value - NV. It might be thought that this would be a meaningless number, but in the Bible, this is far from the case, for very significant values were found for words and phrases. This was known by Jewish scholars for centuries, but Ivor Panin extended the subject and wrote prolifically on it.

Ivor Panin (1855-1942) was a Russian revolutionary who plotted against the Tzar. He fled to America and entered Harvard University, where one of his friends was Ralph Waldo Emerson. He became a Christian and in 1890 he discovered the numerical patterns in the New Testament, following this with an examination of the same features in the Old Testament (MooJ:84).

He spent the rest of his life in examining thousands of words and revealing the pattern of prime factors that he repeatedly found. Now it must be stated that he became completely obsessed by the subject, and tended to see relationships where really there was none. He exaggerated some features and this tended to discredit the whole subject. Moore (who wrote about Lady Hope) referred to his work as "cabbalistic" (MooJ:85), but this is not correct. It is misused by Jewish cabbalists but our interest is only in the mathematical constructions within the scriptures.

There was no need to go to such extremes, for we hope to prove that there are more than enough obvious "patterns" that could not possibly be due to mere chance or coincidence. Let us then proceed, first by examining one of the most significant verses of the Bible - its opening sentence in the Old Testament.

"In the beginning God created the heavens and the earth".

In Fig. 2 we give the Hebrew and the numerical equivalent for each letter which are then summed for each word. (The "*eth*" is an untranslatable particle in Hebrew grammar.)

One of the best examinations of this sentence is by Charles Ozanne in a section of his book *The First 7000 years* (Oz) and I give a summary of the findings he presents. We will see in the last section of this subject that 3 and 7 have a particular spiritual significance. In this sentence we will find that the summation of the Numerical Values (NV) of various combinations of the words will have many common factors, but we will concentrate on the prime factors of 7, 37 and 73, and show that they occur far more frequently than can be by pure chance.

The prime factors are, of course, those numbers that cannot be factorised further - 1, 2, 3, 5, 7, 11 etc., but it must be mentioned that mathematicians consider that 1 is not a prime number.

In what follows, a reading of the many analyses of the phrases examined with their repetitive numbers might induce a sense of boredom or "heavy going". But this is the whole essence of this section, in that there are not just a few mathematical cross relationships but very many, even in one passage, far more than could possibly be a minor coincidence or a contrived result in one phrase only. Ozanne gives 87 significant patterns in this one passage, but we will give just a short selection of the more striking examples.

HEBREW

1	Aleph	א	30	Lamed	ל
2	Beth	ב	40	Mem	מ ם
3	Gimel	ג	50	Nun	נ ן
4	Daleth	ד	60	Sameck	ס
5	He	ה	70	Ayin	ע
6	Waw	ו	80	Pe	פ ף
7	Zayin	ז	90	Tzade	צ ץ
8	Heth	ח	100	Qoph	ק
9	Teth	ט	200	Resh	ר
10	Yod	י	300	Shin	ש
20	Kaph	כ ך	400	Taw	ת

GREEK

1	Alpha	α	50	Nu	ν
2	Beta	β	60	Xi	ξ
3	Gamma	γ	70	Omicron	o
4	Delta	δ	80	Pi	π
5	Epsilon	ε	100	Rho	ρ
7	Zeta	ζ	200	Sigma	σ
8	Eta	η	300	Tau	τ
9	Theta	θ	400	Upsilon	υ
1	Iota	ι	500	Phi	φ
2	Kappa	κ	600	Chi	χ
30	Lambda	λ	700	Psi	ψ
40	Mu	μ	800	Omega	ω

Fig. 1. The Numerical Values of the Hebrew and Greek letters

Examining just the numbers of letters in this passage, there are:
1. Seven words
2. 28 letters = 7 x 4
3. First 3 words contain 14 letters = 7 x 2
4. 4th and 5th words = 7 letters
5. 6th and 7th words = 7 letters
6. First 5 words = 21 letters = 7 x 3
7. Middle word and one before it = 7 letters
   Middle word and one after it = 7 letters
   Examining the Numerical Values (NV.) I give the following selection -
8. The 3 nouns (God, the heavens, the earth)=14 letters
9. Their NV = 777 = 7 x 111
10. Their first last and middle letters = 427 = 7 x 61
11. The NV of the first, last and middle words = 1610 = 7 x 230
12. The remaining letters = 560 = 7 x 80
13. First and last letters of all the words = 1393 = 7 x 199
14. First and last letters of the first and last words = 497 = 7 x 71
15. NV of letters in prime number (1,2,3,5 etc.) positions = 301 = 7 x 43
    For the factor of 37 we have -
16. *NV of the whole verse = 2701 = 37 x 73, both prime numbers.*

The earth	and	the heavens	...	God	created	In the beginning
ha'arets	we'eth	hashamayim	eth	Elohim	bara	Bereshith
ץ ר א ה	ת א ו	ם י מ ש ה	ת א	ם י ה ל א	א ר ב	ת י ש א ר ב
90 200 1 5	400 1 6	40 10 40 300 5	400 1	4 10 5 30 1	1 200 2	400 10 300 1 200 2
296	407	395	401	86	203	913

Fig. 2. The gematria of Genesis 1:1

17. The first five words = 1998 = 37 x 54
18. The last two words = 703 = 37 x 19
19. Sixth word = 407 = 37 x 11
20. Seventh word = 296 = 37 x 8
21. First six words = 2405 = 37 x 65
22. The three nouns = 777 = 37 x 21
23. First, last and middle letters of the first and last words = 999 = 37 x 27
24. First, last and middle (2) letters of the first word = 703 = 37 x 19

The letters used in this sentence are exactly half of the Hebrew alphabet, and even the letters that are *not* used, when arranged in alphabetical order have 37 as a significant prime factor.

There are geometrical patterns of the letters in each word - reading left to right - 4-3-5-2-5-3-6. Only the first and last do not correspond exactly.

If the letters of the alphabet are arranged in alphabetical order, there is a quite amazing symmetry as seen in Fig. 3. Again, it is only the last and first in the sequence that do not match exactly.

Examining the NV of the levels in this "pyramid" we get:
25. Of the first, fourth and top stories = 1332 = 37 x 9 x 4
26. Of the second, third and fifth stories = 1369 = 37 x 37
27. First, third and fifth stories = 1971 = 73 x 9 x 3
28. Second, fourth and sixth stories = 730 = 73 x 10

In addition, the value of "the earth", (296 = 8 x 37) is related to "Jesus Christ". In the Greek, Jesus = 888 = 8 x 37 x 3 and Christ = 1480 = 8 x 37 x 5. We know that Christ was the creator of the earth from John 1:1.

But why should 3 and 7 be found with such frequency in these factors? The three persons of the Trinity obviously spring to mind. We will see later that there are particular numbers in the Bible that have a symbolic spiritual significance and that three represents Divine Perfection and seven Spiritual Perfection. When combined they confirm the divine spiritual perfection of the Word of God.

It is interesting that (counting 1 as a prime number) 13 is the 7th prime number and 37 is the 13th! 37 has the unique property that when multiplied by multiples of 3, up to its third power (27) it unifies the product - 37 x 27 = 999. Some interpret this as signifying the ability of the Bible to unify all the races and classes of mankind.

There are many more intriguing number patterns that are embedded in these few Hebrew words and their values. For example, as we have shown (No. 16 above) the total of 2701 factors into the two very significant numbers in gematria of 37 x 73! 37 is the number of God and 73 is the gematria of "wisdom" in Hebrew. In Rev. 13:18 "Here is wisdom" has a Greek gematria of 73 and in this sentence, the first letter is alpha and the last is omega; i.e. Christ's claim in Rev. 1:8,11, etc.

In the very centre of the sentence is the untranslatable word "eth" consisting of an aleph and taw - the first and last letters of the Hebrew alphabet!

One can begin to see that there are many hidden patterns in this sentence but as this section is only an introduction to the whole subject we will leave others to write on it in greater detail.

Before going any further, let us pause and consider what we have here. We have analysed the opening sentence of the Bible and have found that there are arrangements of factors that are far above anything that could be attributed to pure coincidence.

Line totals

					Lamed 30x1=30	30
				ל		
Yod 10x3=30		י י י	ם ם ם		Mem 40x3=120	150
Waw 6x1=6		ו	צ		Tsade 90x1=90	96
He 5x3=15	ה ה ה	ה ה ה	ר ר	ר ר	Resh 200x3=600	615
Beth 2x2=4	ב ב		ש ש		Shin 300x2=600	604
Aleph 1x6=6 א א א א א א			ת ת ת	Taw 400x3=1200	1206

Fig. 3. The pyramid of letters of Gen 1:1 when arranged alphabetically

Ozanne sent these points to a Cambridge mathematician teaching statistics who discussed *only* the possibility of the figure 37 being a factor by pure chance. He concluded that the chances of 37 occurring as frequently as it does is just over a million to one. One cannot help but smile at his somewhat cool conclusion (as befits an academic) "Other explanations than mere chance are therefore to be considered."

God, surely, has put His stamp of authority on His book in this opening sentence.

The Shema

This is the name given to the verse in Deuteronomy 6:4: "Hear O Israel, the Lord our God, is one Lord."

The total value of this passage is 1118 = 2 x 13 x 43 or 13 x 86.

13 is the NV of "one" and 86 the NV of "God". Thus the total value of the sentence mirrors the teaching of the sentence - that God is "one God".

On this subject, we would notice that where most European languages have singular and plural, Hebrew has singular, dual (two) and plural (three or more). In this passage, "Lord" is singular, but "God" is plural. Therefore, every time the Jews repeat this passage, they are unwittingly testifying to the fact that God is both one and a triune God also!

To go into further detail might be too boring for the reader (who was warned) and therefore, out of a vast number that have been analysed, we will set out just a few other Old Testament words and verses with their NV. If we look at some of the verses that follow the first we find their NV are as follows:

Gen.1:2B "And the Spirit of God was hovering over the face of the waters" NV = 1369 = 37 x 37

"Then God said 'let there be light'; and there was light. And God saw the light and that it was good." NV = 1776 = 2 x 888 = 37 x 48

This figure of 37 can be found in several of the subsequent passages to v 28 "and God blessed them...I have given every green herb for food (v 30)" NV = 10,804 = 37 x 73 x 4

Some of the OT names for God reveal a pattern of 13;

Jehova = 26 = 13 x 2
Adonai = 65 = 13 x 5
Ha'elohim (The God) = 91 = 13 x 7
Meshicho (Anointed or Messiah) = 364 = 13 x 7 x 4

Mal'akh Ha'elohim (The Angel of God) = 182 = 13 x 7 x 2

The important phrase "And God said..." occurs frequently throughout the OT. Its NV is 343 = 7 x 7 x 7

We could quote very many other passages that have been analysed but will draw a line at this point and touch on one other feature of the OT before examining the NT.

Jewish poetry - the Psalms

Although not connected to numbers in the Bible, it is interesting that the Hebrew form of poetry was not by rhyming words, but by word plays, such as repeating statements in two different ways or expressing the opposite situation ("the good will be rewarded, but the wicked will be punished", etc.)

To translate ordinary poetry into another language is extremely difficult, and important aspects can be lost simply to achieve both the scanning rhythm and rhyme. With the Hebrew form of poetry, however, there is no difficulty in conveying the concepts into another language.

This is yet another example of how God ensured that all of His book would be easily understood even after translation and therefore could speak to the hearts of "many peoples, nations, tongues (languages) and kings."

Regarding this method and gematria generally, there was no possibility that there could have been any collusion between the authors, for the OT was written by at least 22 different people between the 15th and 4th century BC.

Similarly, no collusion could have taken place in the writing of the New Testament which has similar gematrial patterns, as this was written by eight different writers between about 50 to 100 AD. To this we will now turn.

NEW TESTAMENT GEMATRIA

In examining the NV's of the New Testament it would be well to add a note of explanation. These numeric values are for the singular nominative case in the Greek. Where the Greek word is in another case, giving a different ending to the word, then its numerical value is altered. It would not then have the significant values we have given here, but where the gematria of the whole sentence has significance, this changed value would be an integral part of it.

The very first passage in the New Testament of 17 verses is the genealogy of Christ. Verses 1-11 cover from Abraham to the Captivity and 12-17 from the Captivity to Christ.

Examining the first section:
1. It has 49 words (7 x 7)
   28 (7x4) begin with a vowel
   21 (7x3) with a consonant.
2. There are 266 letters = 7 x 2 x 19
   140 (7 x 20) are vowels
   126 (7 x 18) are consonants.
3. 35 (7 x 5) words occur more than once
   14 (7 x 2) occur only once

Regarding the gematria of the vocabulary used in the whole 17 verses, the NV of the 72 words used in the passage is 42,364 (7 x 6,052).
4. As with the OT names for God, the Greek names for Christ have a significant gematria;
   Jesus = 888 = 37 x 8 x 3
   Christ = 1480 = 37 x 8 x 5
   (Note; 8+8+8 + 1+4+8+0 = 37)

Jesus Christ = 2368 = 37 x 8 x 8
Son of man = 2960 = 37 x 8 x 10
Lord of Hosts = 1813 = 37 x 7 x 7
Christ our Passover = 3700 = 37 x 10 x 10
The Door = 518 = 37 x 7 x 2
Godhead = 592 = 37 x 16
Logos (Word) = 373
Truth = 8 x 8

There is a pattern of 13 in names and passages that deal with rebellion against Christ and the Apostles. The following are just a few names:

Simon Magus (with art.) = 1170 = 13 x 90
Elymas = 676 = 13 x 13 x 4
Hermogenes = 481 = 13 x 37
Philetus = 1118 = 13 x 86
"The Antichrist" = 1911 = 13 x 147
Wormwood = 1040 = 13 x 80

We give just one way in which the gematria of a passage could be considered to have spiritual significance. Ian Mallet examined the names of those on the Mount of Transfiguration (Matt. 17:3), and found the total gematria of Moses and Elijah is 3865 and that of the Jesus, Peter, James and John is 1497. The difference between these two numbers is 2368 - the gematria of Jesus (888) Christ (1480). This could be looked upon as Christ being the difference between the dead and the living (or between the OT and the NT). This may be dismissed as fanciful, but the odds against this being a numerical coincidence are high.

"666" - The "Beast" of Revelation 13:18

John's wording of this passage is strange. He says:

> Here is wisdom. Let him who has understanding calculate the number of the beast, for it is the number of a man: His number is 666.

The persecution of the Christians was beginning under Nero and many of his readers would have realised the significance of "the number" of a name. But the Greek for Nero Caesar (*Nero Kesar*) does not give 666 but 616. This, in fact, is the number that is given in some New Testament copies. However, in Hebrew the correct spelling is Neron Kesar, and this *does* give 666 precisely! Is it possible that John, exiled by the Romans to Patmos, wanted to bypass any Roman censor who would remove any damaging reference to Nero that he noticed? Perhaps this would explain John's reference to "him who has understanding" suggesting the Jews in the local Christian congregation would have the correct answer.

Incidentally, if John was referring to Nero in this passage, then this would date Revelation between 65 AD when Nero began persecuting Christians and 68 AD when he died. As Revelation was the last book of the NT to be written, this would place all the NT writings before the fall of Jerusalem in 70 AD, a view that is gaining support. This could profoundly affect the apocalyptic interpretations of Revelation and all other books of the NT.

WRITINGS OF DISPUTED AUTHORITY

If the gematria of a passage or book is so extensive in significant values, it clearly indicates a divine author, for no other could bring such coincidences to pass. Assuming the reverse of this, could it not be used to check whether certain passages are inspired or not by whether they display these same characteristics? We believe they can.

1. The Apocrypha.

These are fifteen books or parts of books written between the last book of the OT and the times of Christ. Only one book is in the original Hebrew, the rest are Greek translations for the Jews of their day who only spoke Greek. They are rejected by Protestant churches, although the New English Bible contains them. They are accepted by the Roman Catholic church as authentic writings to be used alongside the Bible. But were they written by men who were "carried along by the Holy Spirit" (2 Pet.1:21)?

These books have been extensively tested *and no patterns of numbers were found.* On this basis they can be discarded as having no evidence of any inspiration in the same way that the accepted books of the Protestant Bible have demonstrated.

2. The last twelve verses of Mark

These verses have been called "a forgery", but an analysis of this passage shows some *sixty* features, amongst them:
  a) Words 175 = 7 x 25
  b) Vocabulary of 98 words = 7 x 7 x 2
  c) Letters 553 = 7 x 79

Thus it can be taken as an authentic part of the Gospel.

There is one other interesting point. Panin produced his own version of the Bible, *The Numeric Greek New Testament.* This was based upon Westcott and Hort's texts which give many alternative versions of words and passages. He examined each of these alternatives and decided, by their gematria, which was the most likely to be the original version. When you take the first, middle and last words of his *New Testament*, they are biblios, zoe, agion - "The book of, the living, Saints" (P. Bluer; priv. comm.).

Criticisms of Gematria

There are critics of gematria who contend that it has no valid basis. J.J. Davis made such criticisms in his book *Biblical Numerology* (DavisJ). In the chapter dealing with gematria, headed "The Mystical Use of Numbers" (p125-149) he spends considerable space criticising gematria in general terms. Every one of his objections and examples can be adequately answered. However, he fails completely to address the mathematical odds against these patterns being only due to chance.

What Davis and other critics cannot overcome is the statistically impossible odds against so many patterns of significant numbers appearing so frequently. Consider one simple example. We have shown above that the Greek word for Christ has the very significant factor of 37. That for Jesus also has 37 as a factor. The chances of both these words having this factor is 37 x 37 = 1,369 against. The chances that 7 names used for Christ have 37 as a factor is nearly 95 billion to 1 against.

With odds of this order in this one example, one can only wonder what one would have to do in order to convince Davis and other critics of the validity of *Biblical* gematria. He completely fails to address this aspect adequately which indicates that, for whatever reason, he has not grasped, or does not wish to grasp, why gematria demonstrates the inspired basis of the Bible. This omission renders his criticisms void.

One statement he makes is "A careful study of these numeric patterns, *according to this theory*, will give the student insights into Scripture which he could get in no other way." This we would deny. Gematria reveals some amazing numerical patterns that demonstrate that the Scriptures could only have been written by the Holy Spirit - *and this alone.* We have given one or two which do appear to have some spiritual significance, but to read into them any deep hidden messages that affect doctrine or practice, as some cabbalistic Jews have done, is both unwarranted and dangerous.

As we have said elsewhere, *any* form of Christianity that claims to have "special" knowledge whether from "oral traditions", "secret traditions handed down" or even gematria, is partaking of the heresy of "gnosticism" or "secret knowledge" that the Bible frequently warns against. The whole of the Christian faith is an "open secret" that can be read in any Bible. Davis's assertion is unwarranted as it does not apply to all who accept the findings of gematria.

SIGNIFICANT NUMBERS IN THE BIBLE

It is obvious to any full reading of the whole Bible that there are certain numbers that repeatedly arise in the narrative. Examples are:

3 - The Trinity, temptations of Christ, temptations of man (1 John 2v16), groups of people (e.g. Shem, Ham, Japhet etc.), Christ's offices (Prophet, Priest and King), etc.

7 - days of creation, clean beasts in the Ark, churches, seals and trumpets in Revelation.

10 - Noah the tenth generation, commandments, tithing, plagues in Egypt.

12 - Patriarchs (Seth to Noah and Shem to Jacob), apostles, gates in Jerusalem.

40 - Years in wilderness, days of Moses in the mount, spies in Promised land, Elijah in Horeb, Jonah and Nineveh, days of Jesus's fasting and temptations, days Jesus seen after resurrection.

The various numbers in the Bible have been investigated by many scholars and they suggest that there is a pattern of spiritual significance to them. Where there is a number that is a multiple or compound of two smaller numbers (i.e. 37) it is thought that this might be a combination of the significance of them together.

The spiritual pattern that has been proposed to the basic numbers is as follows:

1 = Unity, primacy. The Unity of God. One is divisible into all numbers; God is "in" everything.

2 = Difference and the number of witnesses; 2 shall bear witness etc. Strength, help, confirmation.

3 = Divine perfection. God often works in three stages.

4 = Material creation.

5 = Divine grace: Man's body (five senses).

6 = Man and his sin.

7 = Spiritual perfection; the seal of God's approval.

8 = Regeneration, Christ. The first perfect cube (2x2x2=8) = gematria of Christ.

9 = Judgement and finality. Combined with other numbers; **19** - Finality with God or judgement; **29** to witness to a finality, etc.

10 = Numerical perfection and man under earthly rule (10 Commandments).

11 = Disorganisation. Disciples before Pentecost.

12 = Governmental perfection on earth. No. of Disciples
13 = OT names of God and Satan's rebellion; the claim to be God - both true and false.
40 = Judgement and testing. The periods of 40 days, nights and years occur many times in the Bible.

A CAUTION

We give this list of symbolic meanings that have been attached to these numbers, but as with all such lists, there are many passages and incidents in the Bible that do not conform to these patterns. That the Bible is full of numerical significance cannot be denied, but questions arise where a particular interpretation is being forced into a passage where it does not really apply. I leave the reader to make what use he will of this list, but would warn against too much involvement in a subject that can be very time consuming and ultimately may be less productive in spiritual growth than other activities he could be engaging in.

This caution would also apply to lengthy investigations of the gematria of words and phrases. It should be sufficient for most to accept the existence of these remarkable patterns that have been discovered by those who have specialised in the subject, and conclude that only God could have created such a work. It will act as further confirmation that the whole of the Bible can only be the work of men under the control of the Holy Spirit, and is therefore free of error in the original script.

It should also be emphasised that this subject, intriguing as it is, should not be used as a means of evangelising, or considered as a part of the Gospel. It is more for the interest and encouragement of the believer than anything else. Even then, it should not be taken as the reason for accepting that the Bible is inspired. We should not rely upon physical manifestations before we believe the gospel, for "the Jews require a sign and the Greeks seek after wisdom" (1 Cor.1:22) Our salvation and acceptance of the Scriptures should be the result of the direct action of the Holy Spirit.

It should, however, be a challenge to non-believers.

A challenge to the non-Christian

At this point, let me address any reader who does not accept the Bible as the word of God. We have here a clear mathematical proof that only someone with the capabilities of a God-like phenomenal intellect could have possibly created the Bible with these numerical patterns. This surely proves that the Bible is a very special book that could only have been written by God.

The Christian is often asked for "proof" of his beliefs, and it would be difficult to find anything clearer than what we have set out above. We therefore have the right to ask that this evidence should be accepted by the common principles of logic and rationality, and therefore a critic should agree that the Bible was written by God. As it contains a specific message for him he should accordingly believe its contents and follow its directives.

Is this challenge likely to be accepted?

One could almost guarantee that it never is.

Some excuse, seemingly perfectly reasonable to such a reader will be proffered, the subject dropped and the interest deflected to other subjects.

Such action will only go to prove that non-Christians are not really looking for "proof"; there is plenty of that around if they would only stop, listen and open their eyes. The real prerequisite is not "proof" but the change of heart that is the necessary forerunner of spiritual insight. For "the natural man does not receive the things of the Spirit of God, for they are foolishness to him: nor can he know them for they are spiritually discerned" (1 Cor.2:14).

SUMMARY: The incredible basis of Gematria

Just to emphasise how very remarkable these Numerical Values are, the reader might like to assign numbers to the English alphabet similar to the Greek system of numbers in Fig. 1. Let him then try to form just one ordinary *word* that will have 7 as one factor in its NV. It will not be easy, but there is a chance of 1 in 7 of it complying. It is doubtful if he will be able to find any further combinations of say the first and last letters that have a factor of 7 also.

The let him find another word that goes with the first, such as an adjective with a noun, and see if he can find one that also has a factor of seven in it. Again, it is possible, but increasingly difficult, and there is still little likelihood of there being any other combinations of sevens within these words. If we were to limit the two words to have only seven letters each, we can begin to appreciate just how difficult the whole process becomes.

Panin, together with two other Hebrew scholars, spent 13 weeks trying to compose a passage with only seven features. Before he reached this number the sentence had become "nonsensical drivel". He also analysed Aesop's fables and found no numeric patterns whatsoever.

It must not be forgotten that these letters of the Hebrew (and Greek) alphabet are used to form the Bible, and they compose a complete and coherent language with correct syntax, grammar and sense. Yet, in very many places in the Bible, they also contain these beautifully ordered numerical "codes" within their words and sentences.

There is one further surprising feature. Speaking to Mr. Peter Bluer, a friend who has studied this subject for many years, he casually mentioned that, in the OT at least, this numeric pattern could only have been apparent some 1,300 years after Moses wrote the Pentateuch about 1400 BC. It was only just before the Christian era that the Hebrews adopted the Aramaic square alphabet (*EB*29:1064) and it was probably at the same time that they used the ordinary letters of their alphabet as numerals. This was a copy of the system the Greeks had adopted about 100 years before (*EB*23:611).

When Moses wrote the Pentateuch, the method of denoting numerals was quite different, and therefore none of these numeric patterns existed using their system. It was only on the adoption of the Greek method of using letters of the alphabet that these patterns could then be said to exist. Therefore, Moses could not possibly have written these patterns into his records. Surely, here is evidence of God's hand at work bringing into existence complex numeric correlations that were formed long before the key change was made that allowed them to be recognised.

That God could inspire men to write perfectly correct grammar and sentences with deep spiritual meanings which nevertheless held these incredible combinations of the factors we have set out above, surely calls forth a degree of not just admiration but indeed awe for the ability of a God who can perform such feats.

We will try to give illustration of what this is like.

Many Christians, when in great difficulties, have been told that this earthly life is like a tapestry - we only see the chaotic "wrong" side here, where all the strands of the weave are crossing over to other locations. When we get to heaven, the Tapestry will be turned over and we will see the wonderful picture on the "right" side of the Tapestry of Life in which each one of us is one of the strands He has used to form it.

We can draw on this illustration and say that in writing the Bible, God has used two different languages, and with both of them He has formed a perfect "picture" - the OT and NT of the Bible. It is when we turn this "tapestry of words" over that, far from finding a chaotic tangle of strands as we might expect, we find a whole series of pictures, each one perfect in itself. We might then stand in awe at the ability of a Weaver *who can weave pictures on both sides of his tapestry at the same time!*

Truly, He is an awesome God.

....

ADDENDUM

THE SYSTEM OF

"EQUIDISTANT LETTER SEQUENCES" (ELS)

This subject does not involve numerical values but the spacing of letters in the OT. Discovered in the 1500's, it has been revived and enlarged in the last ten years using very powerful computers. Drosnin wrote *The Bible Code* on the subject (Dros), articles appeared in the Daily Mail (4.8.85 p12 and 28/29/30.5.97) and there was a discussion on the internet between Christian Jews (www6). We summarise the topic and give some examples.

The method uses all the 304,805 letters of the Massoretic OT and sets them as one long string with no spaces. The computer steps through it, selecting letters at any required spacing and starting letter and is then asked to identify a certain word of interest. When the word has been found, the width of the block of letters on the screen is adjusted to put the highlighted letters spelling out the word(s) in a straight line. Then words having a direct relationship to the first are sought near them and these may "cross" the line of the first word. A search for a relevant date may find one nearby.

As an example, we will give code spacing that Drosnin refers to most frequently in his book. By using a large spacing distance, it has been found that the name "Yitzhak Rabin" is crossed by the words "assassin will assassinate". Nearby are "Tel Aviv" and "Amir" (the place and his assassin) and also the letters for the Jewish year 5756 that is equivalent to the year 1995-6 AD, the year of the assassination.

To illustrate the system, Fig. 4 is the computer pattern for Yitzhak Rabin's assassination, but we have used a repeated symbol for the Hebrew letters of the particular OT passage.

Drosnin claims that when he found the crossing of Yitzhak Rabin's name with "assassin", he got a letter to Rabin, but it was ignored. After the assassination, he found the name of the assassin, the place and the time coded nearby.

Very many other names and events can be found within the Hebrew OT using various spacings and starting letters. Examples produced by investigators are - the murder of the two Kennedy brothers and Anwar Sadat (the Egyptian President); World War II; the Shoemaker-Levy comet impact on Jupiter, and Drosnin gives many, many more. In some cases, these coded words may be relevant to the OT passage they are found in.

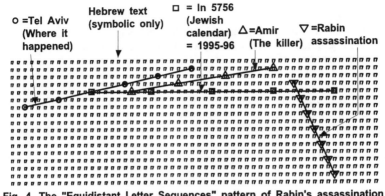

Fig. 4. The "Equidistant Letter Sequences" pattern of Rabin's assassination

This close relationship between very significant words looks very impressive, and Christians, who accept that both the OT and the NT are the direct word of God to mankind, would be delighted to find that, like gematria, there is yet further evidence in support of their belief.

However, reservations began to arise when certain combinations of "code words" were listed. For example, in view of the controversy surrounding John Kennedy's death, did Oswald (who is named as the assassin) really kill him? Similarly, the names of many "Famous Rabbis" of the Middle Ages together with their Hebrew dates and towns of residence have been found. But, as Christians, one must question why these people, who led their followers away from the true Messiah should merit a mention in the Bible as if commended by God. There are other incidents that could be queried and many have little relevance to religion. Gradually, the reservations increased as the evidence of some critics was considered. The main points are as follows.

1. The absence of vowels.

What is little appreciated is that the Hebrew text consists only of consonants; all vowels are added by the reader. This means that with any set of consonants, several words could be read into them; the fewer the number, the more words could be interpreted. As examples (in English) for BN we could have BoNe, BeeN, BiN, BaNe, eBoNy, etc. Only those with meanings to others in the same area of the text would be adopted.

This is one of the most important features of these codes for it allows a researcher to obtain any meaning he chooses by simply adding any vowels that the spelling and grammar allow in order to achieve a relevant meaning to other coded words nearby. As an example (again in English), the phrase "THe CaT SaT oN THe MaT" would appear as "THCTSTNTHMT", and could then be read as "THe CaT'S eaTeN THe MeaT"; a completely different meaning to the first.

2. Word divisions

A normal sentence in the Bible can have the spaces between the letters changed to provide a quite different sentence. Drosnin shows that "Chief of the house of the Gershonites" can be read to mean "President, but he was kicked out" - referring to Nixon (p218). This is yet another variation that can provide many words that could be relevant to a chosen subject.

3. The statistics

(a) **The choice of arrangements**. With some 300,000 words in a long sequence, one could use every word, which, of course, would use the whole OT. Using a spacing of every other letter, 150,000 letters could be searched, and if the start is the second letter, a further 150,000 letters could be searched. Using two spaces, i.e. every third letter, there would be about 100,000 letters available. Starting at the second letter there would be a further 100,000 and starting at the third letter, another 100,000 available for searching. By using longer spacings and different starting letters for each, it can be seen that the possible combinations of the 304,805 can give some 90 billion letters to choose from, all of which can be tested for any particular Hebrew consonants that the researcher is hoping to find. It can be seen that almost any word will be found with such a huge choice of letter sequences.

The codes discovered were divided into two classes -

Class A - where an analysis of the words shows that their relationship (nearness) is "statistically significant". As far as could be seen, the only case that had been analysed and said to conform to this class is that of the names of the Rabbis and their dates.

Class B - where there is an obvious relationship between words close to each other but whether they have any statistical significance has not been claimed. The Bible passage in which they were found, however, may be relevant to the subject of the codes.

The importance of these two classifications will be seen later.

It was also noted that although Drosnin refers to the whole OT, the illustrations he gives are almost all found in the first five books of the Bible - the Pentateuch. The only exceptions are a few in Isaiah and Daniel. Why this is so is not discussed and it is not clear to this author how significant this is.

(b) **Direction of reading.** As well as reading the words in the normal Hebrew (right to left) direction, words in reverse are also found. This doubles the available letter arrangements that can be used in a search for words.

(c) **Flexible language.** Hebrew is a particularly flexible language. Peter Williams, who is an expert in Hebrew, having shown how the sentence "The cat sat on the mat" (given above) could be reinterpreted, continues:

> Any reference to "Saddam", for instance, could equally well be read as "Sodom" since the consonants are simply SDM in Hebrew. Since there are two s's in Hebrew (sin and samech - not including shin and tsadhe) one could get this sequence very easily. It would be hard not to find it on a page. The chances of finding any word by ELS in Hebrew are greater than in English because you have only 22 rather than 26 letters. Further manipulation can take place by techniques such as the arbitrary doubling of letters, or aspirantization of spirants. There are also varieties of "correct" spellings of foreign words (depending on whether you want to use the vowel letters h, w, and y), and also of date formulae . There are enough ways of expressing most things that one can still truthfully claim that one has found an improbable sequence, even though the probability that you would find a sequence that said what you wanted was considerably higher.

> In short a non-context-bound reading of Hebrew, produces letter

sequences that are extremely polyvalent, and therefore able to be manipulated into a prophetic message. This is the case in Hebrew much more than in English, which has fixed spelling, more letters, and doesn't allow you to add vowels to your own suiting (WillP-CRSnet)

(d) Statistical examination. The main article that proposed the system was by three experts and appeared in Statistical Science (1994 v9 n3 p429-438). In this they claimed that the names of the early Rabbis and their dates is far above the levels of chance by millions to one. We would here mention that they have distanced themselves from the sensational claims Drosnin makes in his book.

There have been criticisms by several statisticians who have said that no statistically significant features could be found (www8), to which a reply was made (www9). It is well beyond the ability of this writer to comment on such a technical subject. Suffice it to say that in view of the criticisms that can be made of the whole method and the "predictions" it is said to give rise to, there is a very large question mark over the validity of the whole subject.

For example, on one test the experts ran, Drosnin noted:

> They looked for the same names and the same dates in the Hebrew translation of "War and Peace" and in two original Hebrew texts.
> In the Bible the names and the dates were encoded *together*. In "War and Peace" they were not. (Dros:22)

From this, it would appear that all the names and the dates *were* discovered in "War and Peace" also. The only difference was that the dates were said not to be encoded together with the names they applied to. This is much less impressive than saying that no names or dates were found in "War and Peace" at all.

In order to check how up-to-date the Bible codes could be, Drosnin asked an expert to find words relating to the news of the day. This was accomplished with ease for several days. With such flexibility, my friend Peter Bluer, commented, "You could find Mickey Mouse if you looked for it".

As a small illustration of how these codes are not quite as impressive as most think, we give just two points on the "Rabin" codes.

(i) The stepping distance required to obtain his full name is not just 20 or 50 letters but 4772 letters, which reduces the whole of the Bible to only 64 lines. This indicates just how extensive the search had to be to obtain this particular wording.

This seems to be the only case where we are given the spacing distance directly. The diagrams do not give any indication of the portion of the Bible they cover, although at the end of the book he gives the range of verses over which the main words were found. Some codes may, therefore, be spread across a large proportion of the OT in order to get words that can be associated with each other - as with the "Rabin" code.

(ii) The phrase "assassin who assassinates" is a horizontal line, and is therefore a normal phrase in the Bible. Drosnin references this to Deut. 4:42. This passage is about the "cities of refuge" that anyone who accidentally kills another person can flee to for protection from the wrath of the relatives of the slain person. The NKJV translation reads "that the manslayer might flee there who kills his neighbour unintentionally, without having hated him in times past."

Now this is in complete contrast to the interpretation that Drosnin has given to this phrase. He has turned what is clearly the context of an accidental death into a cold blooded assassination. This is indicative of the "flexibility" with which any phrase discovered can be "adapted" to the required meaning. Another example is the code related to "Einstein" which was the passage "They prophesied a brainy person" (p49). This is referenced as Numbers 11:26 (p221). The Bible verse has "they prophesied in the camp".

Considering all this, we would propose an even more powerful code - the "Alphabet Code" - for we can show that all the twenty-six letters of our alphabet contain every event (prediction?) that could take place!

....

We have shown that there is very considerable "room for manoeuvre" in obtaining a set of related words and phrases by this method, and in the opinion of this writer, the system is virtually worthless. There were two points, however, that were of interest and added to the controversy.

1. In the very few verses in Genesis 2 referring to the Garden of Eden, a total of 31 trees were found in this one passage and nowhere else in the book (Mail on Sunday 4.8.97). Strangely, Drosnin makes no reference of this, nor of finding the word "Torah" in a symmetrical pattern in the Pentateuch.

2. Christian Jews have found that in virtually every Messianic passage the name "Yeshua" (Jesus) is found, and it occurs very many times throughout the OT. Isaiah 11 is Messianic and beginning at verse 3, "Yeshua" is spelt out with every 88th letter. We have seen the significance of 8 with the name of Christ when dealing with gematria above. There is some debate between Christian Jews whether these results are statistically significant.

To complicate the controversy even further, one anti-missionary Jew claimed that the phrase "Jesus is the false Messiah" appears at least three times. However, another analysis by a Jewish Christian in the same areas found other words far more applicable to Jesus's character.

Probably more important than the codes themselves is the use to which they have been put.

Jewish interest in gematria and ELS

Judaism has long tried to stem the loss of many young Jews from the faith and usually appeal to the long history of the Jews they are deserting. This new discovery is now being used to call them back by demonstrating the uniqueness of the Torah that they have revered for thousands of years.

Many Jews are drawn to the occult and spiritism, and this ELS development has given rise to Jewish cabbalistic rabbis teaching that the text can be used for guidance, predicting the future, and opening ways to spiritual power. Gematria is also used to support "interpretations" of the OT. Thus do "the rabbinic authorities hold a monopoly on unlocking hidden truth and power" (Uri Marcus, www6).

Jewish researchers in ELS, not willing to accept that the name of Jesus appears so frequently in the OT, have claimed that this is not statistically proven (Class B above) and therefore all such discoveries are "fraudulent and deceptive, and should cease immediately." However, the vast majority of the discoveries they publicise are also of this same category (B) and by this criteria their claims should also be dismissed. Some Jews, however, have shown an interest in the discoveries by their fellow Converted Jews.

In a 1985 article on ELS in the Mail on Sunday (4 Aug. p12-13) the Jewish experts asked that it should not be given any publicity "at this early stage..as it would rock the boat, perhaps change the world before it is ready for it." They felt the discoveries "were too mind-boggling. We don't need publicity, it would cheapen the subject."

Why should they be so unwilling to publicise the fact that they had clear proof of the inspiration of the Old Testament?

The results of OT gematria has been circulated amongst the Jewish nation for centuries. To this has now been added the results of ELS. Does their original discouragement of publicity regarding gematria stem from the possibility that had they done so, then the Christians might quickly point to the fact that the New Testament *has exactly the same patterns of gematria as the Old Testament?* This would prove that the NT *also* could only be the work of God. Publicity of this fact would be less welcome and they have tried to ridicule the subject as being spurious.

There is also scant reference to gematria in the *Encyclopaedia Britannica*. There is a brief mention of a passage in Genesis concerning Jacob's ladder that is so remote that it virtually invites the reader to despise the whole subject. Similarly, the only mention in the NT is to the "number" of the "beast" being 666 ("or a variant reading 616") - little further mention of gematria being made.

Why is there such official secrecy about this subject? There are many far more abstruse subjects dealt with in the *EB* and other reference works. Yet on this, as on several other subjects, there is virtual silence.

We consider the claims made for ELS are worthless. However, this writer finds the most thought-provoking aspect of it all is that the Rabbis are using it to lead their people even deeper into the quagmire of the occult - a practice specifically forbidden by Moses (Deut. 18:9-14). This is the (spiritually) "blind leading the blind" into one of the darkest and most dangerous areas of life. One wonders why God has allowed this to take place at this particular point in time, for the very dire consequences of such actions will become apparent all in God's good time.

(5) A Christian view

With this method having been applied to the OT, it immediately prompts the question of its possible application to the NT. One problem is that a final accepted text has not been produced as we have with the OT. There is the added difficulty that the Greek text includes all the necessary vowels, reducing its "flexibility" for word choice. Some have claimed to have discovered coded words, but no research has yet been published.

The Christian is in the somewhat strange position of using gematria to demonstrate to non-believers that the Bible could only have been written by God *and yet not need such a witness for his own faith.*

Whilst many will be encouraged by physical evidence of this nature, we must insist that the True Christian does not need to rely upon such "crutches" to bolster his faith. The inner witness of the Holy Spirit should be more than sufficient. In a not dissimilar way, the Turin Shroud and the possible future discovery of Noah's Ark may cause much excitement to some, but those secure in their faith will not give such features any undue importance. As Uri Marcus, a Christian Jew who is a strong critic of ELS, commented: ·

> I submit that it's not the intensity of today's skeptics that's the problem, its the shallow faith of comfort-seeking, lukewarm lives, that no longer draw unbelievers to the truth. So they have to resort to gimmicks, even half-formulated ones like Torah codes. (www6).

He has highlighted the attraction that "gimmicks" have for the vast majority of people, and these are used by strong personalities with "charisma" to draw them to their particular brand of faith or cause. Those who misuse the Bible in any way to claim a special insight and build a following upon it will eventually have to take full responsibility for misguiding their followers.

APPENDIX 8

A CRITIQUE OF "RELATIVITY"

"If I have seen further, it is by standing on the shoulders of Giants" Isaac Newton 1676

"If I have seen further than others, it is because I peeked past the giants who were blocking the light" Pert Beckmann 1987

WHY BOTHER?

It might be thought that relativity is both too esoteric and remote from creation to warrant its inclusion in a book such as this. Let me assure the reader that the basic assumptions (and inherent contradictions) of the theory are very simple to understand, and in what follows I hope to demonstrate two aspects of relativity theory.

Firstly, there are close similarities between the way in which relativity and evolution came to reach the prominence they have at present, and that there are also similar philosophical attitudes behind both of these false theories. As biology has taken a very wrong turning in adopting evolution as its basis, so has theoretical physics adopted relativity which has spawned "paradoxes". That relativity is incomprehensible not only to the average person but to the majority of "experts" also is claimed to be a demonstration of the "brilliant mind" of Einstein who is portrayed as being far in advance of his contemporaries. Whether such accolades are warranted will be subjected to examination.

So badly has scientific investigation been derailed from a common-sense approach to the way in which mankind examines God's world that I feel relativity warrants adequate treatment to demonstrate its absurd foundations. Only when science has been put back on its tracks can it continue on its journey to find Real Truth.

Secondly, the reason that the theory was produced in the first place is intimately connected with the subject of the last appendix in this work.

THE HISTORY BEHIND THE RISE OF RELATIVITY THEORY

Before we go into any examination of the theory, it would be as well to set out how the theory arose and give a very simple explanation of the basis.

The real origin of relativity is in the famous Michelson-Morley experiment of 1887. This was an attempt to measure the speed of the earth as it swept through the aether on its fast travel around the sun. This was an important experiment that gave very unexpected results, setting in train numerous papers that tried to explained them. We will, therefore, outline how it worked and the results that were actually obtained.

The Michelson-Morley experiment

Any wave motion requires some medium through which it can travel - as water is needed to allow waves to travel across its surface. Until relativity became accepted as "proven", scientists always assumed that there was an aether that allowed light (and all other electro-magnetic waves) to be transmitted through it. On the assumption that the aether was stationary, then as objects, such as the earth, moved through it, it should be possible to detect this relative movement by its effect upon light waves. To this end, the famous Michelson-Morley experiment (Mich) was carried out in 1887. The following

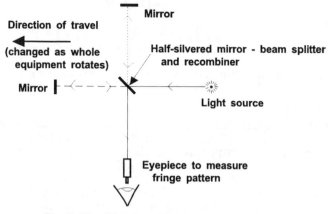

Fig. 1. The Michelson-Morley experiment

is a brief outline of how it worked.

Fig. 1 shows that the basic system. A beam of light was split by a half-silvered mirror - one half was sent in the same direction that the earth was travelling around the sun, the other half was sent at right-angles to this. On their reflection, the two beams were compared, and any interference between the returning waves was a very sensitive way of measuring if one had travelled slower than the other.

The reason why the one in the direction of travel should be slower than the one at right angles to it is as follows. Imagine two boats that can travel at 10 m.p.h. in the water of a 10 mile wide river that is flowing at 1 m.p.h. (Fig. 2). One is sent to travel across it and back again and the other started at the same time but going first upstream against the current for the same distance of 10 mile and then turning back to the starting point. Which would return first?

The first would take 10m./10 m.p.h. = 1 hr. there and 1 hr. back = 2 hrs. total. (The cross flow of the river would have little effect upon its speed - it would just aim slightly upriver each time to correct for this.)

The second boat would first have to go against the stream speed of 1 m.p.h. and therefore relative to the bank it would be travelling at only 10-1=9 m.p.h. It would therefore travel the 10 mile in 10m/9mph=1.111 hrs. For the return trip, going with the stream speed of 1mph it would then be travelling at

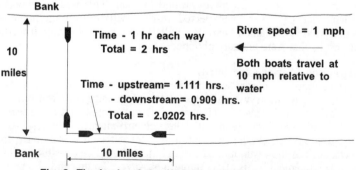

Fig. 2. The basis of the Michelson-Morely experiment

11m.p.h. relative to the bank. The time for this return trip would be 10m/11m.p.h.=0.909 hrs. The total time for both trips is 2.0202 hrs. - so it would get back later than the crossing boat. Why should this be?

The reason is that the boat going against the stream, because it is travelling slower, spends more time in this slower direction than can be made up by the shorter time when it is going with the stream. This would be even clearer if the stream were to flow at say 5 m.p.h. A recalculation would show that the boat would do the round trip in 2.666 hrs.

Applying this to the speed of light in the aether, the earth was travelling around the sun at a speed of 30 km/sec and probably even faster if the sun was also moving through space. Therefore a very significant difference in time was expected between the two directions of the light paths. The instrument could detect speeds through the aether of about 0.5 km/sec.

The experiment was carried out with meticulous care, and to the astonishment of the scientific community, virtually *no difference was detected at all!*

The most obvious inference from this experiment was that the earth was stationary relative to the aether. This possibility could not be contemplated for one moment. Fitzgerald suggested that the tube at right angles to the direction of travel got longer as it travelled through the aether by an amount that exactly counterbalanced the shorter time over this pathway, thus making the time of travel of light in the two tubes the same. Lorentz proposed alternatively that the tube pointing in the direction of travel shortened by a similar amount to give the same compensation, and provided a formula to give the amount of shortening that might take place. This formula is known as the Lorentz transformation formula, giving the amount of contraction, although as we have said, Fitzgerald had proposed a lengthening of the other tube.

Again we note the *ad hoc* provision of an "explanatory theory" to deal with the disturbing result of the Michelson-Morley experiment.

This was the generally accepted explanation, but the effects of this contraction resulted in a number of secondary effects on light, time and motion etc. Eventually, Einstein produced his Special Relativity Theory (SRT) in 1905 and widened this to become his General Relativity Theory (GRT) in 1915.

Although Einstein publicly dismissed this experiment as not being the reason for him producing his relativity theories, we will see that it was, in fact, the main stimulus.

Einstein's solution was to say that there is no such thing as the aether. This is a fundamental point in his theory. The problem that then arises is how light or any electro-magnetic wave form can travel through space if there is no medium through which it can act.

RELATIVITY THEORY.

There are two basic theories of relativity - the special and the general. The special applies to observers with uniform motion, whilst the general deals with all observers.

The special theory of relativity

The Michelson-Morley experiment failed to detect any "wind" of the aether passing our planet as we moved through space. Lorentz proposed that contraction in the direction of travel shortened the equipment which resulted in the "null" result. Einstein made two assumptions -

1. Absolute motion and absolute rest cannot be detected by any observer.

2. The speed of light (designated as "c") was the same for all observers. i.e. a stationary observer seeing a beam of light coming from a fast approaching spacecraft (velocity = v) would not see it at a velocity that was the sum of the speed of light and the spacecraft (c+v) but only at the speed of light (c).

From this Einstein deduced by his theory that -

(a) There was no aether.

(b) Objects increase in mass when they move. In fact, nothing can travel faster than the speed of light.

(c) As a corollary to this, clocks ran slower as they approached the speed of light.

A result of (c) is the well known "clock" or "twins" paradox. If the speed of an object is high (i.e. a reasonable proportion of the speed of light), any timekeeping mechanism (i.e. clock) it carries will go slower than a stationary one.

From this, if one of a pair of twins leaves the earth and travels a long time at a high speed, and then returns home, he will find that he is much younger than his twin (or so the theory contends). The same would apply to identical clocks - the travelling one would run slower than the stationary one.

The difference between the results predicted by the Classical Newtonian and relativity theories is very small as it only becomes apparent when speeds approaching that of light are involved. At all normal speeds, the difference is negligible.

The general theory of relativity

This is Einstein's interpretation of gravity and how it operates on stars and planets etc. He claimed that the mass of a body warped the space around it and it was this that gave the effect of gravity. To explain this he used a mathematical concept of the curvature of space proposed by Riemann. Einstein used this to link space, mass, time and energy.

This Riemannian space meant that the universe was curved, and that an observer, using a powerful telescope, would, if there were no obstructions, look right through space and see the back of his head!

It proposes that light has energy but no mass and that gravity is caused by energy and not simply mass. The result is that light is affected by gravity and if the attraction is strong enough, the light cannot escape from it. This is the cause of the so-called "black holes" that are said to exist in space.

A CRITICISM OF THE FOUR "PROOFS" OF RELATIV-ITY THEORY

We will be examining the internal contradictions in the special theory later but we will here demonstrate that the experimental tests claimed to "prove" that the theory is correct are badly flawed and capable of perfectly satisfactory normal classical explanations. If the scientific evidence can be shown to be false, then there is no basis for accepting either theory as correct, leaving it as a pure unsupported speculation.

There are four main experiments that have been, and still are, quoted as proving that Einstein's theories are correct. These are;

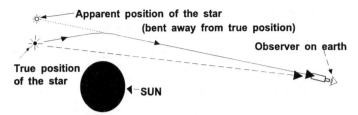

Fig. 3. The deflection of starlight passing the sun

(A) The eclipse experiments of 1919.
(B) The explanation of the precession of Mercury's perihelion.
(C) The Hafele-Keating experiment of flying atomic clocks around the world.
(D) The presence of high speed muon particles reaching the earth's surface when they have only a very short life.

Each of these can be severely criticised and we will examine them in turn.

(A) The Eclipse of 1919.

Relativity claims that light is attracted by any mass that it passes by. The amount is small and even under classical (Newtonian) physics a deflection is expected. Relativity predicts that as light passes by the sun this deflection of 1.8 seconds of arc will be twice the Newtonian deflection of 0.9. (See Fig. 3.)

Due to the brightness of the sun, this deflection cannot be seen during the day, so an attempt to measure this small deflection was made during a total eclipse in 1919 that took place in Principe off the west coast of Africa and at Sobral in Brazil. The results were reported in a memoir of the Royal Astronomical Society in 1923 (Dys).

A lengthy study of these results has been published elsewhere (Bow86) based mainly upon the criticisms of Professor Charles Lane Poor (Poor). He was the Professor of Celestial Mechanics at Columbia University and therefore well qualified to comment. I give here a sufficient description to provide an outline of the method and criticisms of the results.

The normal position of the stars were accurately recorded on seven "comparison" camera plates separately from the eclipse exposures. During the eclipse, a number of plates were exposed to record the position of the stars but many were found to be useless and only seven were of any value. On return to England, the position of the stars on the eclipse plates was then compared with their position on the normal plates.

The results were said to give a "convincing" confirmation of Einstein's theory. It was hailed as one of the most important discoveries of all time, and his fame grew even more rapidly following a prestigious meeting announcing the results held in 1919. Einstein was asked what he would have said if the had not confirmed his theory, to which he replied "Then I would have had to pity the dear Lord. The theory is correct anyway"! (Pais82:30).

However, Poor makes a number of criticisms.

(A) The telescopes.

Horizontal telescopes were used, with the starlight reflected into them by a mirror. This is not the most accurate method, which is by direct observation by a telescope. The mirror gives three times as much distortion as the same amount of distortion of a normal telescope lens.

It is interesting to note that there had been an earlier attempt to measure this

"Einstein" deflection of starlight by the famous Lick Observatory in 1919 using a normal telescope. The conclusion, quoted in the Sobral/Principe report, was:

> The final results are not yet published. Some account of a preliminary discussion has been given, but the eclipse was an unfavourable one, and from the information published the probable accidental error is large, so that the accuracy is insufficient to discriminate between the three alternatives (Dys:292).

This is surprising. Even using this more accurate method, they admit that the results are inconclusive. Yet with less accurate equipment, and a number of discarded results, the results of the Sobral and Principe measurements are said to confirm relativity.

(B) The corrections.

As starlight enters the earth's atmosphere at an angle it is bent slightly and the measurements have to be corrected for this. The problem is that the correction, which is sensitive to temperature etc. *is about 100 times greater than the small differences that the observers were looking for.* This is compounded by the fact that the tables used for these corrections are for night observations, whilst these were carried out in daylight. Not only that, but as the shadow of the moon sweeps across the surface of the earth, the air is rapidly cooled and there would be considerable turbulence generated. These conditions would have rendered the tables and standards used for normal good night conditions quite inapplicable for these observations where extreme accuracy was essential.

Poor showed that the later measurements had more deflection than the early ones as the cone of cooler air swept over the site. At one site it was noticed that the sky cleared quickly for a while just after the total eclipse. The cause was said to be the air conditions of the eclipse itself. This demonstrates the very important, indeed overwhelming, effect that the air conditions would have upon the very minute differences in measurements that were sought.

(C) The variations in the deflections.

In calculating the deflection, the experts only gave the result radially from the sun, which was the only direction they were interested in as this would have been the direction that would confirm Einstein's theory. The fact that in many instances there were large deflections to the right or left of the radial direction was completely ignored. Others, apart from Poor, had commented on this.

One supporter of relativity examined these non-axial results and came to the conclusion that they can be accounted for by the warping of the mirror during the eclipse as the air cooled. But if they can account for these quite large departures from the axial direction, does this not make the warping of the mirrors a factor that renders all the results unreliable? If it can explain one discrepancy, how do we know that it does not affect even the axial measurements? At Sobral, the images from the larger of two telescopes used were useless due to loss of focus that was blamed upon the heat of the sun on the mirror. This was therefore a significant factor.

There were seven eclipse plates and seven "comparison" plates. Therefore there were 49 possible movements for each star deflection. Fig. 4 is from Poor's plot of two of these, showing how much the images varied during the eclipse. The "direction from the sun" is the deflection that the stars should

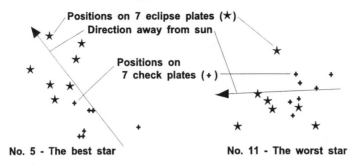

Fig. 4. The varied plots of two stars

have shown, but how varied from this ideal their positions are can be seen. There were no diagrams in the original report, so the wide variations are not immediately appreciated.

Poor points out that if the very discordant star position in the comparison plate 5 is removed, then the result would have greatly reduced the correlation with the Einstein deflection. Also, omission of some of the plates from star 11 would have reversed the direction of the deflection. This indicates how sensitive the results would be to any results "discarded" - for whatever reasons.

In summary, far from being the convincing evidence for relativity that it is portrayed, the whole experiment seems to have had poor results, many of them having to be rejected and corrections much larger than the small differences they were hoping to detect had to be applied. The final results were so varied as to be unreliable, as the Lick Observatory had admitted with their results. One cannot help feeling that the correlation with Einstein's theory was "forced" out of the wide range of chaotic results that were published.

One is left wondering whether such selection involved rejection of measurements that would have reduced the correlation even further. This could be checked by having the plates re-examined by an independent expert. However, as the results could seriously damage the standing of relativity, access to them would probably be unwelcome.

Poor provides his own suggestion for the measured curvature of light as it passed the sun. He calculated how much thin matter there would have to be around the sun to bend the passing light and what tilt it would have to have. This possible explanation was referred to in the eclipse report but brusquely dismissed with the comment: "Clearly a density of this order is out of the question." "Why?" one might ask. Thus Poor could explain the bending reported without any recourse to relativity theory. We will return to this a little later.

It is now accepted, even by relativists, that the original evidence used to support relativity was poor. Will, a convinced relativist, admitted:

> ... general relativity was initially supported by very meagre empirical evidence. For nearly forty years the validity of the theory was confirmed by data that, by today's standards, would be considered qualitative at best. Three "classical tests" formed the backbone of general relativity: the excess perihelion shift of Mercury, in agreement with the theory's prediction, but attributable at least in part to other possible causes; the deflection of light by

the sun, measured to be anywhere between one half and twice its predicted value; and the gravitational redshift, observed in spectral lines of white dwarfs again to be anywhere between one half and twice its predicted value, and moreover suspect of not a true test of relativity anyway (WillC:24).

Later he admits that the eclipse experiment "had only 30% accuracy" (WillC:51). Yet when the result of these experiments was announced in 1919 it was claimed to be "convincing proof" of relativity and given immense publicity. After a sufficient length of time for the theory to become well established, its inadequacies can now be admitted. Such is the power of the propaganda behind the theory.

Will considers that modern equipment can now accurately verify relativity. We will see if this is the case when we later examine the "flying clocks" experiment.

(B) The Precession of Mercury's Perihelion

As the planets sweep round the sun on an elliptical orbit, the shape of the ellipse has a long axis in one direction. It had been known for many years that Mercury's long axis was not fixed relative to the stars, but slowly rotated at a rate of 575 secs arc/cent. Most of this precession could be accounted for by Newtonian mechanics, but 43 secs arc/cent could not (Avil).

Einstein claimed that his theory was able to explain this precession, proclaiming "against which classical mechanics is powerless." Yet Poor was able to provide a very simple classical explanation which was again some sparse matter surrounding the sun that had refracted the light.

Although Mercury's orbit has the largest precession, all the other planetary orbits have some degree also. These could be due to material around the sun and Poor again calculated how much and at what angle it would have to be to explain these precessions. Poor showed that from this one assumption, he could explain the precession of all the other planets far more accurately than using relativity theory. What is more, *Poor found that the amount of matter and its tilt is much the same for that which explains the curvature of light past the sun.*

It has been pointed out that this matter would have become heated and therefore would have been detected. This is as may be, but we can begin to see that quite simple assumptions can explain these so-called "proofs of relativity".

There is an even better explanation - the oblateness (bulging at the equator) of the sun. Two measurements give this as 4.5 and 5.0×10^{-5}. This would cause a precession of Mercury of 44 sec. arc/c. - i.e. the actual precession is fully explained by the sun's measured oblateness (Avila).

There is yet another explanation for the precession. In 1898 Gerber claimed he could explain the precession by allowing the propagation of gravity at the speed of light, and produced exactly the same formula for the precession that Einstein presented eighteen years later (Asp82). Aspden amended and corrected Gerber's theory to give the precise value.

Finally, Moon (Moon), using Mach's Principle (the effect of the mass of the universe which we refer to later) also reached the same result as Einstein. It can be seen that there are several non-relativistic explanations for the precession. Recently, it has been found that two stars are circling each other and their precession does *not* agree with Einstein's relativity calculations. The title of the article is "Was Einstein wrong?" (Astronomy 23:54 Nov. 95)

(C) The Flying Atomic Clocks

It is a basic result of relativity that if an object moves relative to another, its mass increases and its time runs slower than for the position at rest. To check this, four very accurate atomic clocks were taken in an aircraft and flown both eastwards and then westwards. At each stage, the times given by the clocks on the aircraft were checked with ground-based clocks.

The two experts, Hafele and Keating (Haf), found that the flying clocks differed from the static clock by roughly the amount predicted by relativity - 205 nanoseconds measured gain compared with 275 theoretically (1 ns = 1 thousand millionth of a second) for the west-bound clocks, and 66 ns loss (40 theoretically) for the east-bound clocks due to the mutual cancellation of the direction of travel and gravity. The final conclusion was that the experiment confirmed Einstein's theories of relativity - both special and general.

We will not examine this experiment in great detail as we will be showing that there is a simple refutation of this evidence.

It should be noted that there were many corrections for height of the aircraft, its direction, speed, latitude etc. Not unlike the "corrections" for the eclipse, there is "room for manoeuvring" in certain assumptions that have to be made. It must be remembered in all these experiments that the difference between the classical and relative predictions is very small indeed, and it needs only a slight modification of the factors used to swing the results one way or the other.

Essen (Ess77), a world renowned expert on accurate timekeeping, pointed out that not all the data had been used, commenting "This seems a strange thing to do." When all the data was taken into account, this changed the values from 205 to 134 and from -66 to -132 ns. He complains that some factors had been ignored by the authors and concludes "I suggest that the theoretical basis of their predictions need careful scrutiny and that the experimental results given in their paper do not support these predictions."

Essen's paper appeared in the Creation Research Society Quarterly (14:46) a footnote to which said his comments had been submitted to a journal but were rejected. Criticisms of relativity, like those against evolution, are not welcomed by Establishment scientists. We refer later to the pressure put upon Essen to stop him criticising relativity.

The close scrutiny that Essen suggested was carried out by Kelly (Kell3). Hafele and Keating's articles are two fairly short papers and were obviously only a summary of many complex calculations. Kelly obtained the original detailed papers from the Naval Observatory under whose auspices the experiments has been carried out. His criticisms were severe.

Basically, the random errors of the clocks were so great that they could not be relied upon to give the necessary accurately for this experiment. They drifted badly and erratically. Sometimes the drift was corrected, other times it was not. So poor were the results that Kelly said that the clocks would have to be 100 times more accurate to obtain any useful results. Had the most error prone clock been ignored, the results would have been nearer zero change in both direction. A correction of one clock was made from 26 to 266 ns. without any explanation. Hafele in fact said in 1971:

> Most people (myself included) would be reluctant to agree that the time gained by any one of these clocks is indicative of any-

thing..the difference between theory and measurement is disturbing

This did not appear in the 1972 report that was eventually published. In fact they said that the results were "convincing qualitative results."

As with the eclipse measurements, one has the same feeling that the figures have been "massaged" to provide the values that have been previously determined to be in accordance with relativity.

Furthermore, they mentioned that they had carried out a similar series of flights in 1970 but that there had been no discernible gain or loss in these experiments. Surely this should also have been fully reported as indicating that there was *no* change in the time differences. They claimed the results were "below detection thresholds" due to speed and flying heights of the planes used but we are not told what these were. There appeared to be little difference between the conduct of the two experiments. The fact that there were two experiments carries out suggests that the method is to carry out experiments several times until a suitable result *is* obtained and then *this is the one that is reported!*

Theoretical objections

There is a fundamental aspect that has been carefully bypassed by the investigators. This was pointed out in a most interesting article by W.A. Scott Murray (Mur86). He made two major objections. The first is that the experimenters checked the moving clocks against a static clock. But it is a fundamental requirement of relativity that there is no such thing as a "static-standard" clock or reference system - *either* clock could be used as a basis. There should be no objection from relativists in using the moving clocks as a reference and claim that the earth-bound one is moving relative to them - and should therefore travel *slower* than them.

The experimenters tried to bypass this objection in their paper by saying:

> Because the earth rotates, standard clocks distributed at rest on the surface are not suitable in this case as candidates for coordinate clocks of an inertial space. Nevertheless, the relative timekeeping behaviour of terrestial clocks can be evaluated by reference to hypothetical coordinate clocks of an underlying nonrotating inertial space (Haf).

In a footnote they said:

> It is important to emphasise that special relativity purports to describe certain physical phenomena only relative to (or from the point of view of) inertial reference systems, and the speed of a clock relative to one of these systems determines its timekeeping behaviour (Haf).

Murray analyses these statements and says that the authors are making an important alteration to relativity theory, by making one of the frames (the "stationary" ground clocks) the reference frame and the moving frame (the flying clocks) the one that is observed. This completely contradicts the usual interpretation that no frame should be regarded as the "authoritative" frame of reference; i.e. the "reciprocity" of relativism has been excluded in this experiment as they claim that it only applies when *both* frames are moving. This of course completely demolishes the whole basis of relativity theory which says that neither of the observers can tell which is the one who should be considered as the reference "stationary" observer.

Their reason for inserting these comments in their paper is to try to counter the most obvious suggestion that there is a much simpler way of conducting this experiment by using several earth-bound clocks.

Einstein, in his famous 1905 paper on special relativity predicted that a clock spinning round the earth's axis would go slower than an identical clock at the pole. The speed of the equatorial clock, according to relativity, should make it run slower than the polar clock.

Hafele tries to overcome this by quoting another writer:

> Clocks at rest on the earth's surface (at average sea level) keep the same relativistic time independently of latitude differences. The effect of the different surface speed at different latitudes is cancelled to lowest order by a corresponding effect from the difference in surface potential owing to the oblate figure of the earth (Haf).

Murray then shows that this is incorrect by a separate calculation demonstrating that the oblate shape of the surface of the sea is a uniform gravitational potential and does not "cancel" the effect that different speeds at other latitudes would have on the clock rates due to relativity. Therefore, the clocks at lower latitudes *should* run slower (according to relativity).

He then points out that this experiment is being run every day. There are many accurate timekeeping clocks around the world who regularly check the time between themselves, and those nearer to the equator are travelling faster than those nearer to the poles. If there were any variation due to their different latitudes, this would have shown up by a slowing of clocks near the equator. Differences of over 1 nanosecond each day would have been easily detected, and furthermore, this would have been cumulative over a period of time. So each day, the discrepancy should become more obvious.

Murray then notes that no such discrepancy has been detected in any of the timekeeping clocks around the world. He comments "If this result puzzles you, you have my sympathy; please read on."

Those who want relativity to be correct (and students taught as such) will accept the qualifying statements in Hafele's paper to be a satisfactory explanation. But experts, such as Murray, will see the flaws and expose them in whatever periodicals will accept their articles. I might mention that the *Wireless World* that published his article is more outspoken on controversial issues than most others, having printed several critical articles and letters on relativity. (See references - Mu84, Gri, Asp82, Mu86 and 84, Ess88, McC.) I quote some of the comments they contain:

> Moreover, today's critics of special relativity are no longer die-hard, but well informed, reasoning and serious.
>
> Special relativity, which required space and time to become distorted as a consequence of the observer's motion, preserved electromagnetic theory intact at the expense of classical mechanics and common sense.
>
> That is how it all happened. It was a grand cover-up operation, and the people who pulled it off were acclaimed as heroes.
>
> Those who wrote the textbooks did not want to know.

(D) The Longer Life of Muons from Space

Muons are very high speed particles that come in from outer space and reach the earth's surface. In the laboratory, they can be generated and are found to have a life of only 2.2×10^{-6} seconds. With such a short life they should have disintegrated long before they could have reached the surface of the earth. The explanation by relativity theory is that, due to their high speed, their "clock" runs slower, and therefore they are able to reach the earth's surface before they disintegrate.

Setterfield (Sett83:42) and Barnes (Q14:219) have derived a longer life for these particles due to their speed but they emphasise that this is independent of relativity.

Quite what constitute the cosmic rays that come in with such phenomenal speeds and energies and what their origin is are still not fully known. There is therefore some doubt on whether what is recorded by instruments on earth really proves what is claimed from it. On this Professor Dingle notes:

> It needs not saying that the duration and distance of their fall are not measured by a stop-watch and measuring tape but are first inferred from a course of reasoning that includes the original Maxwell-Lorentz theory, and is "corrected" by the special relativity theory designed for the purpose of correcting it. Is it surprising that the answer comes out right? (Din:143).

The major point, however, is the same that has been raised in various ways above and discussed later. It is perfectly legitimate in relativity to consider that it is the muon that is stationary and that it is the earth that is rushing towards it. Therefore it is *our* clocks that are running slower compared with the muon's timekeeping, which as far as it is concerned is behaving perfectly normally!

This does raise the question of whether there is any real slowing of clocks or shortening of rods to the observers in high speed rockets? We will be proving that the whole theory crashes upon inherent contradictions. This does not mean that removal of relativity rules out any effect of speed upon measuring rods at least, as this was suggested by Lorentz following the Michelson-Morley experiment before relativity had been proposed by Einstein. If, however, it can been shown that there is no need for any "Lorentz transformation" formulae to explain the Michelson-Morley results, then it is legitimate to conclude that speed has no effect upon either clocks or rods.

Comment on the "proofs"

It has been admitted that the eclipse experiment was "faulty" but that there have since been experiments using interferometry that has measured deflections one thousand times more accurate than needed to prove the difference between the Newtonian and Relativistic predictions. This sounds very convincing, but this writer remains unimpressed. We have seen how the eclipse and clock experiments have been "fudged" and the alternative explanations of Mercury's precession. This raises two important issues.

(i) If scientists are so single-minded in seeking the truth in their different fields, why was there any need to falsify the results of these experiments at least? This strongly suggests that there is a "hidden agenda" to promote relativity, and adherence to "truth" is of no concern.

(ii) The serious flaws in these three "proofs" were laid bare by experts in their respective disciplines. In view of this, *this writer refuses to accept as accurate any experiment until it has been closely examined by an expert in that subject who is critical of relativity*. With such a consistent faking of the evidence in the early days, why should we accept more recent data until it has been fully examined by a critic?

We would also note that there are an increasing number of qualified scientists who are critical of relativity. Special conferences are now being held to air their views, but we fear that they can expect little publicity.

A further reason proffered for the acceptance of relativity is that it is regularly used in research laboratories and astronomy etc. and is found to give the right answers. This seems to put the subject beyond doubt. The response to this is that there are sometimes more than one classical explanation that gives exactly the same results as those "predicted" by relativity. On this, Will notes:

> General Relativity has passed every solar-system test with flying colours. Yet so have alternative theories (WillC:62).

It will often be found that many of the "proofs" quoted are actually related to other theories that relativity uses (e.g. the Lorentz transformation formula) and are not proofs of basic relativity theory.

The most common of reasons given is to quote Einstein's "discovery" of $E=mc^2$ and the existence of the atomic bomb and then say "Surely you can't deny these, so relativity must be right". The answer is that, firstly, Einstein, as we will see, did *not* discover the famous formula, and secondly, that the atomic bomb does not depend upon relativity for its existence.

A CRITIQUE OF THE THEORY.

Having shown that the four experiments that are purported to prove the correctness of the theory are far from convincing, we will now consider some of the "paradoxes" that the theory seems to revel in but which, in fact, completely undermine the theory.

The whole basis of these paradoxes is inherent in the theory and implied in its title; that there are no special points or frames in space that can be taken as a "fixed" standard. All frames can be referred to equally as a reference frame, the data from one frame moving relative to another being related to it by mathematically transforming (correcting or changing) them using the Lorentz transformation formula.

There are four main postulates that we will examine in the theory. To keep the pictures simple we will generally illustrate problems by using trains or rockets rather than the more technical "frames" that carry "observers".

1. All frames can be equally used as a reference frame (or the concept of simultaneity).

If two trains pass each other, a passenger in each train will be under the impression that they are stationary and it is the other train moving past them. According to Einstein, neither of them can determine which is the "stationary" train, and events that will be simultaneous to one passenger will not be simultaneous to the other.

Murray (Murr84) showed how Einstein switched his arguments. He took Einstein's illustration of a moving man (M) in the centre of a train passing a stationary man (M') on an embankment. Just as the two men are opposite each other, there is a flash of lightning at both the rear (A) and front (B) of the train (Fig. 5).

The flash from both ends reaches M' at the same time. To him the flashes were "simultaneous". But the man in the train (M) is moving away from A and towards B. It will therefore take the light from A longer to reach him than that from B. He will therefore see the flash from B before he sees the flash from A. Therefore, what is "simultaneous" to one observer is not simultaneous to another. Einstein's own statement on this is worth reporting:

> That light requires the same time to traverse the path A-M as for

the path B-M is in reality neither a *supposition* nor a *hypothesis* [his emphasis] about the physical nature of light but a *stipulation* which I can make of my own free will in order to arrive at a definition of simultaneity". [Murray notes that a "stipulation" - arbitrary and subject to one's own free will "in order to arrive at a definition" - does not seem quite the same thing as a natural law.] Now in reality,... M is hastening towards the beam of light coming from B, whilst he is riding on ahead of the beam of light coming from A. Hence the observer will see the beam of light emitted from B earlier than he will see that emitted from A. Observers who take the railway train as their reference-body must therefore come to the conclusion that the lightening flash B took place earlier than the lightening flash A. We thus arrive at the important result:

Events which are simultaneous with reference to the embankment are not simultaneous with respect to the train, and vice versa (relativity of simultaneity). Every reference body (Co-ordinate system) has its own particular time: unless we are told the reference body to which the statement of time refers, there is no meaning in a statement of the time of an event. [quoted in Murray].

There is, however, a gross contradiction in Einstein's argument for he has to ignore one of his own postulates. Before we go any further, the reader might like to re-read his words and see if he can detect the where Einstein contradicts his own theory. It is not difficult to spot the glaring anomaly.

The inherent contradiction is as follows:

Murray points out that if the lightening hits the front and rear at the same time, then, because Einstein claims that the speed of light relative to an observer is constant in *all* frames irrespective of their speed (postulate 3) then the light from both ends will reach the man in the centre of the train *at the same time*. (Remember that, according to Einstein, you do not add or subtract the velocities of the light and the train when dealing with the speed of light). Therefore the observer in the train should *still* see the flashes simultaneously and not at a different time as Einstein claimed. In order to say that events in different frames are not seen as simultaneous he had to ignore one of his own propositions.

Murray proves his argument by looking at the events from the point of view of the man in the train. He (M') sees the man on the embankment (M) going past him and, by the rules of relativity, is fully justified in claiming that it is the other man (M) who is moving. As he (M') considers himself stationary, he will see the flashes at the same time, but (according to Einstein's argument) the man on the train will predict that the stationary observer M will *not* see them together, which contradicts the first conclusion.

According to a strict interpretation of relativity, *both* observers should see the flashes simultaneously. Murray then notes that the two "times kept by observers M and M' must be identical in an absolute sense". Therefore, there should be no problems with time in different frames.

What Einstein effectively introduced was *a stationary aether* through which the light travelled so that the moving man on the train saw the flash from B before the flash from A reached him. But it is basic to his theory that the aether does not exist. We can begin to see the cracks in the theory even in this simple examination.

This inherent contradiction in Einstein's argument collapses his whole thesis at this point. We will find a not dissimilar line of argument operating in

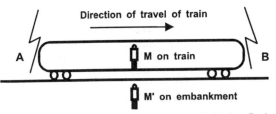

Fig. 5. The moving train and the two lightning flashes

the well known "clock (or twins) paradox".

2. Time dilation (The "clock" or "twins" paradox).

The theory says that the closer the train (or rocket) travels to the speed of light, the slower the clocks on board will run. This produces the famous "twins" or "clocks" paradox.

According to relativity, if two twins, one stationary (S) and the other moving (M) synchronised their clocks, and then one of them (M) travelled in a rocket at a speed that was a reasonable portion of the speed of light away from S, then his clock would run slower than S's clock. When he returned, he would be found to be younger than the stationary one and his clock would be behind S's. He would be quite unaware that time had passed slower, however.

This is the best known of several paradoxes that protagonists seem to revel in when exhibiting their profound knowledge and "grasp" of the theory. Yet here also is a simple contradiction in the logic used to support this idea, which is as follows.

In the scene set out above, M moves away from S, and when he returns his clock is slower than S's. But according to the basic principle of relativity, M could equally say that it was he who was stationary and it was S who moved away from him. Therefore, when S "returned" to M, it should be S's clock that was slower than M's, not the other way round. Therefore S's clock is both faster and slower than M's - which of course is impossible. *This is one of the most obvious and fundamental objections to the theory.*

How do relativists overcome this difficulty. Let us see what Einstein himself said. When this contradiction was pointed out to him he said there was "no contradiction in the foundations of the theory since C2 and not C1 has experienced acceleration." (Pai82:144).

Now there are two comments that can be made about this statement. Firstly, as soon as S is established as the "stationary" frame (by virtue of no acceleration), we then have a reference frame to which the movement of M can be related. The possibility of using M as the reference frame is thereby disallowed, which means that the claim that no frame has any more priority than any other - a basic tenet of the theory - does not apply in this situation. One frame has been given the status of a frame of reference for the movement of another, and the position is not allowed to be reciprocal.

The second more important point is that Einstein, and his followers, use the acceleration of M as the means by which it can be decided that it will be M's clock that will go slower, as his is therefore the "moving" clock. But the essential point is that the short periods of acceleration or deceleration are firstly totally insignificant and secondly, the relativity formulae take no account whatsoever of acceleration, only of the relative speed between two observers. Therefore, *the fact that one of the observers experienced some*

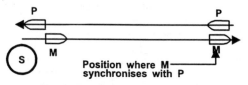

Fig. 6. The passing rockets

acceleration cannot be introduced into the formulae to give a result that will show that M's clock is specifically slower than S's. It *only* takes account of the fact that the two clocks are moving relative to each other.

Essen (Ess) notes that this insertion of "acceleration" to determine which rocket will act as the "reference frame" can be overcome by saying that the moving rocket M is passing S when they can synchronise their clocks. When it has travelled for a long enough time, a second rocket P passes by M and at that point S synchronises its clock with M. Then when P passes the stationary S they can check their clocks against each other (Fig. 6). In this case no acceleration is involved but the result should be as in the first case with only one rocket for both the outward and return journeys. As no acceleration is involved, Einstein's explanation is unacceptable, and his basic assumptions and conclusions are once again shown to be fallacious.

Thus, as with the "flying clocks" experiment above, the basic rules of the theory having to be "bent" in order to give the "right" answers.

In addition to this, Grieves (Grei) points out that two rockets, launched close to the speed of light in opposite directions, are travelling relative to each other at a speed of 2 x c, which, according to relativity, is impossible. One might ask how this question is answered by relativists.

3. The constancy of the speed of light (c)

The theory declares that no matter what the speed of a rocket was that sent a beam of light towards another rocket approaching it, or the speed of the approaching rocket, the speed of the light when it reaches that rocket will still be the same (c); i.e. the speeds of the rockets and that of the light it sends are not added together to give the speed of the light when it reaches the second rocket.

There is no problem in the speed of light being constant, whether or not there is a medium through which waves can travel. What relativity claims is that it is the same for a stationary observer as it is for an observer moving towards the source, which of course contradicts common sense.

We will be examining the Sagnac experiment in Appendix 10, but a similar experiment carried out by Kantor showed that light did *not* travel at the same speed. The experiment is shown in Fig. 7 and consists of thin glass plates on a revolving table. The speed of the rotating glasses was easily detected in the interferometer as a change in the fringe pattern. The review of the experiment in the *New Scientist* (1 November 1962 v 16 p 276) (which incidentally gave the wrong reference) said:

> If Einstein's postulate is correct there should be no interference fringes on spinning the discs...In fact an unambiguous, easily noted shift of the fringes was apparent when the mirrors [sic] were in motion. Kantor deduces that Einstein's second postulate is incorrect..if there is no alternative explanation for the observed effects,

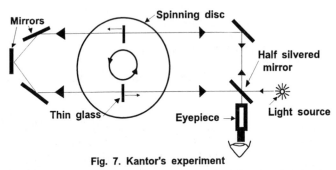

Fig. 7. Kantor's experiment

then there is a need to reconsider some basic ideas in physics.

4. The aether does not exist.

It is a fundamental requirement of relativity that the aether should not exist. The reason for this is that it would then form a framework against which motion could be detected. This contradicts the known ways of physics, for all waves need a medium through which their effect can be transmitted.

The existence of the aether has always been assumed since the discovery of electromagnetic waves, and their action delineated in Maxwell's equations. There are many experiments that demonstrate that an aether exists and we will be examining some of these in the next appendix.

Einstein's "logic"

In 1859 Fizeau found that when a beam of light was passed through moving water its speed was affected by the water. By making approximations and discarding certain small terms, Einstein claimed that this evidence could be explained by relativity theory. However, a perfectly satisfactory *classical* explanation had been found by Lorentz several years previously. Einstein's comment on this is interesting for he said that the classical explanation "does not in the least diminish the conclusiveness of the experiment as a crucial test in favour of the theory of relativity" and that relativity had been developed from the hypothesis of electrodynamics (Poor).

Poor's comment upon this is scathing:

> These two sentences of Einstein are, from one point of view, as important as any in his work on relativity; - they should be read and re-read. They give a direct insight into his methods of reasoning. Here is an experiment claimed by Einstein as a "crucial test" of his theories, yet in the very sentence in which this claim is advanced, he admits that other theories, the very theories he attempt to overthrow, can equally well explain the phenomenon. How can an experiment, equally well explained by several different theories, be a "crucial test" in favour of one of them.

It is precisely the twisting of logic portrayed by Einstein in this revealing statement that sows the seed of suspicion that we may not be dealing with a mathematical genius so much as a sleight-of-hand confidence trickster.

Criticisms by Einstein's Peers

When special relativity was first published in 1905, far from being noticed, it was virtually ignored. In fact, any reference to "relativity" was always with reference to Lorentz's formulae. Einstein was not noticed until he published his general theory in 1915. Even then, it was the "eclipse" experiments of 1919 that was to bring him world-wide fame.

There were several important physicists who did not accept Einstein's theories, amongst them Rutherford, who treated it as a joke, and Soddy, who considered it a swindle (Ess88). Others were Sir Oliver Lodge, Ernst Mach, Poincare, Max Born, Pauli, Poor and Lorentz. Pais, the foremost biographer of Einstein, referred to some of these when he said with some puzzlement:

> Why, on the whole, was Einstein so reticent to acknowledge the influence of the Michelson-Morley experiment on his thinking? Why could Lorentz never let go of the aether? Why did Poincare never understand special relativity? These questions lead us to the edge of history (Pai82:164).

Perhaps they did not accept the theory as it was both contrary to common sense and based on fallacious reasoning!

Pais provides a copy of the report that appeared in *The Times* on November 7th 1919 of the packed meeting when the results of the eclipse experiments that "proved" relativity were announced.

When the discussion started the President of the Royal Society spoke first, during which he "had to confess that no one had yet succeeded in stating in clear language what the theory of Einstein really was." When he had finished speaking, the paper briefly mentions, "At that stage Sir Oliver Lodge, whose contribution to the discussion had been eagerly expected, left the meeting" (Pai82:307).

Was this brilliant scientist perhaps disgusted at the presentation of such a contrived result, or was he already angered by the publicity given to a theory that defied common sense?

Pais makes no mention of this important incident in the Times report. Indeed, he is most careful to avoid referring too much to the many criticisms that the theory has received ever since it was first published. As we have seen, Professor Poor wrote a devastating criticism of the eclipse experiment and many other aspects, yet Pais never refers to his work. He only refers to him once, and that is only a newspaper report of his general views of the direction that science was heading - a scathing indictment which we quote later.

At one meeting, Pais records that "The task of speaking about Lorentz and Poincare fell to Born...He did not acquit himself well." His assessment of anyone who dared to criticise his hero, Einstein, is to use this patronising phrase, as though his performance was poor. In fact, he may have made an excellent speech, but that it was critical of Einstein rendered the speaker incompetent in the eyes of Pais. He does, however, give a few revealing phrases from the speech in a footnote that says:

> (Born said "The reasoning used by Poincare was just the same as that which Einstein introduced in his first paper of 1905....Does this mean that Poincare knew all this before Einstein? It is possible...) (Pai82:172).

Born was obviously suggesting that Poincare had laid the basis of some of Einstein's ideas but that this had not been adequately acknowledged by Einstein or any of his supporters.

Pais records that "Mach turned his back on relativity" (Pai82:283). Later, Einstein patronisingly wrote that Mach's absorption capacity had been "diminished by age." Einstein contended that as the whole direction of relativity Theory was in accord with Mach's ideas, he should be considered the precursor of the general relativity theory. Pais's comment on this idea was that despite Mach bluntly rejecting relativity, Einstein was trying to suggest he was actually on his side! The more prestigious his supporters, the better chance his theory stood of surviving.

In 1921, when Einstein's name had been put forward for the Nobel Prize, the task of assessing his work fell to Prof. Gullstrand. Regarding his report Pais comments, "Gullstrand's report, *highly critical of relativity*, was not a good piece of work" (Pais82:509). Again, it should be noted how a highly qualified scientist, himself a Nobel Laureate, who had criticised relativity is dismissed as giving a very "poor" report - as though Pais was marking the homework of a recalcitrant schoolboy!

Incidentally, few realise that Einstein did not receive his Nobel prize for his theories on relativity. Gullstrand's report was too damning. His Nobel prize was awarded for an earlier 1905 paper on the photoelectric effect, which was much less well known than his relativity papers that had caused such a stir. His name was proposed every year except two between 1910 and 1922, the year he received it. In reading about the award one has the feeling that it was felt that after all the hyped publicity that had surrounded him for so many years he should get a Nobel prize for *something*.

Similarly, when a vote was taken by the French Academy of Science to elect Einstein as a corresponding member, only thirteen out of one hundred voted for him, most of the thirteen being mathematicians (Lyn:xxvi).

It also appears that Max Planck, as editor of the *Physicalische Zeitschrift*, promoted Einstein by publishing his relativity papers. The aristocrat Planck was promoted as a full professor over the more talented Boltzmann who was a commoner. Boltzmann, desparing over the treatment meted to him and his work, later committed suicide (BA v 8 n 83 p 26).

Criticism of relativity has continued to this day, and has in fact slowly gained in strength over the years. This is despite the enormous barrage of publicity maintained by the mass media to give Einstein's name a prominence that far exceeds anything that has been accorded to any scientific theorist, either before or after his time.

Essen's views

One of the critics of relativity was Essen, a physicist with an international reputation. He wrote a booklet in 1971 entitled *The Special Theory of Relativity: A Critical Analysis* (Ess71), in which he highlights logical flaws in Einstein's assumptions and conclusions similar to those set out above. He shows that at one time it is held that the difference in the two clocks is only "apparent", but later this difference is classed as "real" - i.e. they do actually show different times. This switching of statements regarding whether the time difference is only apparent or real is one that can be found in several writers on the subject. It indicates that the logical arguments behind the theory, even to those professing to be "authorities" on the subject, are uncertain and often contradict the interpretations of other defenders of the theory.

Seeing Essen agreed to the publication in a creationist magazine of his letter about the "clock" experiment, I sent him an early draft of this appendix. He returned it unmarked thanking me for letting me see it. He added that he thought "there is a lot of sound (scientific) evidence in support of the theory of evolution." The word "scientific" had been crossed out! I was puzzled why he made no comment on the paper. His reticence was explained when I read his obituary; the important section of which I quote later.

Einstein and the Michelson-Morley Experiment.

As we have contended, the "null" result of the Michelson-Morley experiment of 1887 caused a shock wave to ripple through the scientific community. Yet, strangely, Einstein always claimed that he was not sure whether he even knew of the results of the experiment, and that if he did, it would not have made any difference as he had already begun thinking that the aether did not exist.

Pais notes this particularly with regard to his omitting to refer to the published papers of others saying he was "sparse" in his reference to other people's works (Pai82:95) and that he may have had difficulty in obtaining some of these papers (!).

Pais says that Einstein was "reticent" about the Michelson-Morley experiment, but does examine Einstein's claim and comes to the conclusion that he *did* know of the result. In fact, Pais records that the "Ether drift experiments were still on Einstein's mind" and that this appeared in a letter to Grossman in 1901, four years before he produced his first special theory in 1905. *This suggests that it was the Michelson-Morley experiment that was the real problem that his theories were intended to overcome.*

Why should Einstein be so reluctant to admit that he was well aware of the experiment? This is not clear, but there was a tendency to not just ignore the work of predecessors but actually use it, and attract much of the limelight to himself.

One possible explanation is that it might have been too direct to have praised Einstein for overcoming the implications of the Michelson-Morley experiment for this would have drawn attention of the public to the subject. He was therefore adulated for his "brilliant" mind that had "changed the face of science'. That his theory had overcome the problem of the MM experiment could then be treated as an incidental item, or better still, turn the whole experiment into a "confirmation" of his theory. This deflected attention from the fact that it was a "troublesome" result that generated a need for something like relativity to "explain it away".

Einstein, Poincare and E=mc^2

The brilliant mathematical physicist Henri Poincare was famous long before Einstein rose to prominence. He had written many papers on the subject of mass, energy, light etc. and was one of the few leading experts in the subject at that time. It is generally acknowledged that it was Poincare who established the relationship between mass and energy.

Pais also referred to a paper by Lorentz regarding which Poincare said it now meant that it was impossible to "determine absolute motion" (Pai82:129). This is of course a major feature of Einstein's relativity theory. The presentation dates of these two papers is interesting. Poincare delivered his on 5th June 1905, whilst Einstein sent his famous special Relativity paper to the Annalen der Physik on 30 June 1905. Did he know of Poincare's paper when he was completing his own article?

It was generally accepted that energy and mass were related and that the speed of light was the prime link. Poincare had set this out very clearly in a paper as early as 1900 giving this very equation (Whitak v2 p1). Pais relates this, saying:

> This last book [a 1904 address by Poincare], the only one of the
> four to appear before 1905, is the one Einstein and his friends read
> in Bern. I therefore believe that, prior to his own first paper on
> relativity, Einstein knew the Paris address in which Poincare
> suggested that any evidence for the lack of motion relative to the
> aether should hold generally to all orders in v/c and that "the
> cancellation of the (velocity-dependent) terms will be rigorous and
> absolute." But there is more. In *La Science et l'Hypothese*, there is
> a chapter on classical mechanics in which Poincare writes, "There
> is no absolute time; to say that two durations are equal is an
> assertion which has by itself no meaning and which can acquire
> one only by convention..." I stress that Einstein and his friends did
> much more than just browse through Poincare's writings...Of these,
> he singles out one and only one, *La Science et l'Hypothese*, for the
> following comment: "This kept us breathless for weeks"
> (Pai82:133).

At this point, the reader might like to look back at what Einstein said about
"simultaneity in time" where we discuss the train passing an observer on an
embankment. ("Events which are simultaneous...an event) and note the
similarity of Einstein's conclusion to that which Poincare had already set out
in his book. There seems little doubt that all of Einstein's main ideas, which
were to bring him world-wide fame as a "brilliant genius", had already been
presented in the works of Poincare.

It is widely thought that it was Einstein who discovered the link between
mass and energy and produced the famous equation. As with many widely
accepted beliefs about Einstein, this one is as false as many others. Byl notes
that it was hidden in Maxwell's equations and when this was set out, the
formula was $E=(3/4)mc^2$. Poincare came close to the correct formula in 1900.
Einstein's derivation of the formula in 1905 was fallacious, the correct
derivation by Planck appeared in 1907. It can be derived from special
relativity, Ive's approach or Maxwell's equations (Byle).

As Aspden has noted:

> At the outset it is stressed that experimental verification of $E=mc^2$
> is not proof of the Theory of Relativity. Einstein's theory dates
> from 1905. Einstein was not the first to theorize about the
> transmutability of energy and mass.
>
> It was textbook knowledge in 1904 that electrons and positrons
> might mutually annihilate one another and create energy. In an
> article in *Nature* by Jeans (v70 p101) this mutual annihilation was
> proposed and argued to be a "rearrangement of the adjacent aether
> structure" (Asp80:70).

Pais knew Einstein intimately near the end of his life, and asked him how
Poincare's "Palermo" paper had affected his thinking. He said that he had
never read it, so Pais lent him a copy that he possessed. It was never returned.
After Einstein's death it could not be found amongst his papers. "It had
vanished" (Pai82:171).

Even Pais has to admit that Einstein did not give enough credit to others.
He relates how Einstein had claimed that he and Lorentz were led "to develop
the theory of special relativity." Pais comments "An additional mention of
Poincare's pioneering ideas might have been gracious" (Pai82:171).

Einstein - a Plagiarist?

Several scientists have pointed out that Einstein's ideas had already been set forth by others, yet Einstein collected the credit for them. We have already discussed the work of Poincare who had already set out the main lines of a theory of relativity and presented the relationship between mass and energy. With this in mind, it is surprising that he never accepted relativity - certainly not Einstein's version. As we have mentioned, until 1919 when Einstein became famous, relativity was always associated with the name of Lorentz, whose equations Einstein had used. After that date it was referred to as "Einstein's theory".

It is obvious that there will be times when two experts, working on the same subject, will discover the same thing within a short time of each other. In reading Pais's book, he recorded several instances of this with respect to Einstein, but the number of coincidences seemed to be much higher than one might have expected. I will just list some of these that Pais mentions.

(i) Lorentz wrote of his transformations in 1904. Einstein, "aware only of Lorentz writings up to 1895 rediscovered [!] these transformations" (Pai82:p21).

(ii) "Unaware of Boltzmann's and Gibbs exhaustive treatise which had appeared earlier, he developed statistical mechanics and the molecular-kinetic theory of thermodynamics based on it" (p55).

At that time his knowledge of the writings of Ludwig Boltzmann was fragmentary, and he was not aware at all of the treatise of Josiah Willard Gibbs. Had Einstein known of Gibbs' book he would not have published his paper except for a few comments (p55).

One might ask why the peer reviewers of his paper did not realise that Einstein was repeating work already published.

(iii) "By a quite remarkable coincidence, Eq. 5.12 was discovered in Australia at practically the same time (March 1905) that Einstein did his thesis work." (p92).

(iv) "In 1905 he was blissfully unaware of Poincare's work on relativity and Brownian motion" (p94). It is not clear what Poincare had developed on the subject of Brownian motion, but this was yet another topic that Einstein wrote about in 1905 and for which he would achieve fame. That Poincare was working on *two* subjects that Einstein became famous for raises the slight possibility that there was someone on Poincare's staff informing Einstein of what his latest thinking was, which the former would present as his own discoveries. One is left pondering...

(v) "... on November 25 Einstein presented his final version..of the gravitational equations to the Prussian Academy. Five days earlier, David Hilbert had submitted a paper .. which contained the identical equation but with one qualification" (Pai82:257).

This particular incident is now said to have been resolved. A printers stamp on *proofs* of Hilbert's paper is dated Dec. 6th 1915 - 10 days after Einstein's submission on Nov. 25th (Corr). It is claimed that Hilbert's proofs were incomplete and that he subsequently added the full field equations that matched Einstein's but did not alter the date of his submission.

The sequence is complicated and there is the possibility that Einstein took a vital part of Hilbert's equations. However, it does seem that Hilbert acknowledged Einstein's work was superior and earlier than his own final version which was not published until 31 march 1916. It is interesting that in the one instance where the possibility of plagiarism by Einstein was recognised even by his supporters, he has now been exonerated.

(vi) A note on a paper by Einstein - "Herr Mandel points out to me that the results communicated by me are not new. The entire content is found in the papers by O. Klein." Pais comments: "I fail to understand why he published his two notes in the first place" (Pai82:333).

(vii) Wave properties of light. Pais mentions that Einstein had referred to a thesis on the wave properties of light by de Broglie as "a very notable publication" (p437). Pais then comments that Einstein had shown that a molecular beam should show diffraction phenomena "just as de Broglie had done". There is no evidence that Einstein had thought of the wave properties entirely independent or prior to de Broglie. On this subject Pais records a further incident.

In 1978, Pais read that, at a meeting in September 1924, Einstein proposed "to search for interference and diffraction phenomena with molecular beams." This was the classical experiment that started the whole study of quantum theory and wave mechanics. Now de Broglie's paper was not published until November of that year. Pais wondered "Could he have come across the wave properties of matter independently of de Broglie?" This would certainly have been an amazing feat and yet another achievement of Einstein.

On further investigation, Pais found that de Broglie had sent a copy of his manuscript to Langevin who had passed it on to Einstein. The latter said that de Broglie's ideas "seemed quite interesting to him" and had approved it for publication.

Knowing that de Broglie would be referring to the diffraction and interference patterns in his paper, Einstein mentioned this subject two months prior to de Broglie's paper being published. Was he again using other people's ideas without giving them credit for them? Having already read it, surely he should have mentioned de Broglie's forthcoming paper on the subject as a courtesy? No reference to this was made, leaving the audience under the impression that Einstein had thought of this himself.

What is even more surprising is that Pais's conclusion of this whole incident is:

> Thus, Einstein was not only one of the three fathers of the quantum theory, but also the sole godfather of wave mechanics (Pais82:438).

Quite how Pais could justify such a comment when Einstein had first seen de Broglie's paper and what truly original idea Einstein provided is far from clear.

It should be remembered that Pais is totally sympathetic to Einstein and his relativity theories, and therefore would be comparatively reticent in admitting that Einstein may have used the work of others. Yet even in this laudatory biography it is obvious that much of his work is far from original. A more critical biographer may have given more examples of such "coincidences". There is a need for a complete reassessment of the life and work of Einstein by a competent and impartial biographer.

THE PUBLICITY SURROUNDING EINSTEIN

This is surely one of the most amazing aspects of the whole of Einstein's life. Here we have a theoretical physicist (he was not basically a mathematician. He had to study this later in his career) dealing in a very narrow and specialised scientific subject, becoming so world-famous, that he became the accepted symbol of the pure power of human thinking at its highest pinnacle of achievement.

I will not give a lengthy recital of the way in which everything he said or did was immediately reported in the mass media. When he travelled to America, he was met at the harbour by a huge crowd of people and many reporters, and was officially welcomed by the Mayor of New York and dined with the President. In 1922 he visited Japan where he was equally idolised wherever he went. What the ordinary Japanese person in the crowd thought he was cheering for is an interesting question.

He was "wined and dined" by the great names of the world who had no obvious connection with science - Charlie Chaplin, William Randolph Hearst, lunching with Lord Rothschild and Bernard Shaw, arguing with Rockefeller about education, meeting Ghandi and Nehru, cooperating with Freud in a book about why people go to war, turning down an invitation to become president of Israel... the list goes on and on.

On one occasion, such was the "hype" of everything he wrote that in 1929 the whole of one of his papers, in which he tried to simplify and combine certain physical laws, was published in its entirety in the New York Times and displayed on the shop window of Selfridges in London. It was hailed as an "outstanding scientific advance." It was a very complex mathematical paper and it is doubtful if a single one of the readers could understand it. If it was not for their edification, why was valuable newspaper space used to present it to an uncomprehending public? One can only conclude that its sole purpose was to impress the public with Einstein's phenomenal "brainpower".

The sequel is less glamorous. The paper dealt only with minor subjects, was badly flawed and his ideas were quite valueless.

As an indication of the esteem in which he was held (by the compliant newspapermen of the day at least) was the cartoon that depicts a number of swirling planets, on one of which is fixed a memorial plaque bearing the inscription "Albert Einstein lived here". Pais used it as the frontispiece of another of his books and gave it the same title (Pai94).

Why the publicity?

When the dust has finally settled around the man and his reputation, it is legitimate to ask why it should have been raised to storm proportions in the first place.

If one stops to think about it all, we have here a theoretician, dealing with a very esoteric field of physics and cosmology, producing formulae that few can understand and presenting concepts that are not only virtually incomprehensible but even contradict common sense. Yet with all this, he is "puffed" (a newspaper word that needs no explanation) by the mass media to appear as the greatest brain ever to exist! What could possibly be the reason behind such a strange situation?

That the mass media was deliberately cranked into gear for this specific purpose should be obvious to any person who cares to examine the evidence. The way in which newspapers throughout the world fell over each other to give him front page coverage arose very suddenly. So suddenly and so excessive, in fact, that it is as if a signal had been transmitted to put a "popularity machine" into operation rather than there being a slow dawning that a great man had arisen.

The reader will no doubt draw his own conclusions. Those convinced he was indeed a genius will consider such praise well merited. I would suggest, however, that it was put into action for a quite different purpose.

At the end of my article criticising the "eclipse experiments" (Bow86) I mentioned: "one is left wondering why the mass media and the people behind it should have accorded him the phenomenal adulation he has received" (Bow86:167). Having now read the background and the muted criticisms of the theory, I think an answer might now be ventured.

The initial reaction of the scientific world was one of incomprehension, but such was the barrage of propaganda that few, whether scientists or laymen, would be prepared to go against the massive swell of popularity for this "great man". In the atmosphere generated, any criticism would appear to be churlish and rooted in jealousy. The massive publicity was indeed all part of the promotion of the man and his incomprehensible theories - theories which were ultimately an assault upon common sense and therefore needed a supporting barrage to counteract this natural reaction.

In short, it was to intimidate any opposition, particularly from professional physicists who would be competent to refute the theory. They were similarly accorded no platform on which they could publicly point out its deficiencies. To illustrate this point, we have the example of Charles Lane Poor who wrote a devastating critique of the "eclipse experiments" and other aspects of relativity, but how many professors or students have ever heard of his book, let alone read it?

There is another possible indication. The "eclipse" experiments were carried out on 29th May 1919 and read at a meeting on November 6th of the same year. Yet publication of the whole paper was not until 1923. Delay in publishing after the discussion is understandable but three years seems inordinate. Was this to allow time for the publicity machine to swing into action before the paucity of the results could be examined in detail? Having said this, Poor at least must have obtained a copy of the results beforehand as his book was published in 1922. However, like all publications critical of relativity, it was ignored by the media. As a result, his book, along with others like it, having no attention drawn to it, was allowed to gather dust on a few bookshelves, until rediscovered by creationists.

To this day, the role of massive publicity in intimidating anyone bold enough to openly oppose this false theory continues to fulfil its purpose.

As an example of very direct pressure being applied to ensure that criticisms of relativity were muted, we would quote from the obituary of Louis Essen (D. Telegraph 5 September 1997). He was a distinguished scientist known for the independence of his mind in his exploration of many interests, amongst them his collaboration with Froome in an examination of the speed of light. He was also the inventor and developer of the Caesium clock. His obituary referred to his stubborn resistance to relativity and then said:

> Essen put forward his criticisms so vehemently that he eventually came to be regarded as an anti-Establishment troublemaker. He was even warned *that his promotion prospects, and thus his pension, might be affected if he did not desist.*

And who says there is no Academic Mafia?

Was Einstein Alone?

There have been proposals that the real brains behind relativity was not Einstein but his wife Mileva. She was a bright pupil and met Einstein at the Polytechnic where they were studying together. Two factors support this suggestion. Einstein produced nothing of importance after their divorce in 1919, and she received the whole of the Nobel prize money as part of the divorce agreement. However, from my reading, there is little more than these facts and I found no reasonable evidence that she played any significant part in formulating the theory of relativity.

A more likely supporter was his friend Marcel Grossmann whom he met at the Polytechnic also. Einstein would often not turn up to lectures, and before an examination used Grossmann's neatly written notes. Grossmann's father found him his first real job in the Patents Office, and when Grossmann became a mathematics lecturer at a Zurich Polytechnical school, it was he who taught Einstein the intricacies of Riemannian tensor calculus which he then adopted as an important part of his general theory of relativity.

Certainly, Grossmann may have played a much larger part in the formulation of relativity than may be realised, particularly when it is remembered that Einstein produced little of any account after this time. It might be surprising that Einstein's knowledge of mathematics was not good, and he had to struggle with the subject to achieve some degree of mastery. It is here that Grossmann may have had far more input to the general theory at least than is perhaps realised. It is possible that he might also have read the relevant papers recently published and kept Einstein informed of the latest discoveries and theories, which Einstein might then incorporate in his papers.

Certainly, after 1915, he produced no further papers of any note and effectively lived off his name and the prestige that had been formed around him by the media.

Einstein - the Man

What sort of man was Einstein?

In examining the lives of some of those who promoted Darwin's false theories, I noted that they were generally "pillars of society" and in all their day-to-day dealings with others, were generally men of courtesy and integrity (Bow82:3). This, of course, does not excuse their activity in deliberately promoting such a false theory. Was there that same balance in the life of Einstein? Unfortunately no.

It is not only his biographers but Einstein himself who admitted that he was inadequate in his handling of social relationships. He treated his first wife very badly and seems to have had very few close companions. He also seems to have had little true affection for his second wife.

One of the most surprising facts is that he had an illegitimate daughter, Lieserl, by Mileva Maric who later became his first wife. He decided that the child should be adopted and this duly took place *without Einstein ever seeing her*. This callous disregard for those who should have been near and dear to him surfaced many times throughout his life. He seems to have had a fondness for his two boys but they were in the care of their mother. Highfield mentions that Einstein seems to have used violence against Mileva, blackening her eye on one occasion. This was mentioned in the divorce papers which are still under seal in Jerusalem (Hi:154).

One incident gives a glimpse of the contrariness of his boorish personality.

He had been out with a friend during which they had discussed something very personal that involved Einstein's second wife, Elsa. At the end of the conversation, the friend said, "Don't ever discuss this with Elsa again" and Einstein heartily nodded agreement. On arriving home, Einstein's walked through the front door and immediately repeated in Elsa's hearing all that had been said. His friend was deeply shocked at his behaviour, and on asking Einstein what made him do such a thing, he replied "We do things, but we do not know why we do them" (Pai82:209).

An even worse situation was made public in 1996. When his marriage to Mileva was failing in 1914 and he was having a secret affair with his cousin Elsa, he set out in a letter the strict conditions that Mileva was to observe in their relationships to each other. He said:

> (A) You will see to it; (1) that my clothes and linen are kept in order; (2) that I am served three regular meals a day in my room; (3) that my bedroom and study are always kept in good order and that my desk is not touched by anyone other than me. (B) You will renounce all personal relationships with me, except when these are required to keep up social appearances. In particular, you will not request: (1) that I sit with you at home; (2) that I go out with you or travel with you. (C) You will promise explicitly to observe the following points in any contact with me: (1) You will expect no affection from me and you will not reproach me for this; (2) You must answer me at once when I speak to you; (3) You must leave my bedroom or study at once without protesting when I ask you to go; (4) You will promise not to denigrate me in the eyes of the children, either by word or deed (D. Telegraph 30.10.96 p1).

A few months after receiving this letter, Mileva took her sons to Zurich and never returned to him.

In 1920, Germany was suffering from the ravages of war and the beginnings of anti-Semitism. Highfield claims that these and the jealousy of professional colleagues were the reasons behind a public rally that was organised in the largest concert hall in Berlin to attack his ideas. "With typical bloody-mindedness he went along to watch their performance from a box seat, and laughed and clapped as he was vilified from the stage" (High:194). He said that the experience was "very amusing", but later wrote an article in reply that was so bitter and anti-German that even his friends were both "surprised and embarrassed." He had obviously been very deeply hurt by the opposition to his ideas which was more widespread than he (or his supporters) cared to acknowledge.

If nothing else, it is interesting that his ideas were sufficiently unacceptable for an organisation to arise, named the Study Group of German Natural Philosophers, and arrange such a large meeting. One of the organisers was the lecturer of Mileva, Einstein's first wife. To read most accounts of the sudden rise of the fame of Einstein one has the impression that there was either wild acclaim by the experts or the silence of incomprehension as the less competent struggled to master these new theories. Yet here we have a brief mention that in Germany at least, there was a substantial body against him. That there was opposition to this degree is little known today, but with a world-wide media that had already been marshalled in his support, such events could be simply ignored, thereby becoming almost lost to future generations.

The portrait that emerges that is painted by his biographers is one of a lonely man - made lonely by his own selfish and boorish manners. He seems to have realised his own weakness in this area and concentrated on his scientific work as a compensation.

The search for "truth"

I must emphasise that some perfectly valid ideas may be proposed by non-specialists or even rogues - the validity of an idea should be examined completely independently of the source. The very first, and most important, question that should be asked of any new ideas is "Is it true?" If it is, then where it came from becomes almost irrelevant. Indeed, as I have often found, extremely surprising information can come from the most unlikely and unexpected sources.

One could go further. Real Truth is not always found in the "acknowledged authorities" referred to by orthodox specialists. These have usually been carefully "vetted" to give only the "popular" views on any one subject. To discover what the truth is, one has to hunt for a small, often impecunious, organisation that has been trying, within its limited resources, to tell the world where it has gone wrong. The early years of the Evolution Protest Movement, (now the Creation Science Movement), founded in 1932 and for decades the only organisation in the world against evolution, is a case in point.

I have mentioned the moral Victorians who nevertheless promoted evolution; i.e. the socially good promoting socially wrong ideas (Bow82:3). I have difficulty, however, in recalling anyone who is a rogue who has presented a great and universal truth that has been of undoubted benefit to the good of the world's citizens. Is this to say evil actions might come from "good" people but that real good cannot come from social misfits?

In an earlier work I gave a list of Christians (some of whom may have been nominal only) who had made notable discoveries in the last few centuries (Bow82:219). These at least could have been said to be "good" in the broadest sense, and to have given something of value to later generations.

In contrast, a study of the life of Karl Marx will show that his domestic situation was deplorable; he seduced his maid and was constantly asking Engels for money. It was he who was to produce the theoretical basis of the communist ideology that was to create such havoc amongst ordinary citizens wherever it could establish a presence.

Another such example is that of Rousseau. Famous for his view of the "Perfectibility of Man", he also wrote on the upbringing of children. Conner Cruise O'Brien noted that he had five children by his common-law wife, all of whom he sent to a foundling home. O'Brien said he was "a most villainous man" (O'BrienC).

Other not dissimilar cases could be quoted. Indeed, "By their fruit shall ye know them."

I trust I will not be thought to be using the "ad hominum" argument - i.e. denigrating the man rather than the evidence. What I am suggesting is that there may be a broad principle that good and beneficial ideas might generally come from those who seek above all else to discover the truth wherever it may lead and whatever the result may be to the seeker. I have shown that Einstein's theories are both unproven and self-contradictory. Whether the root lies within his whole personality is a subject the reader will no doubt ponder on and probably differ strongly from the tenuous link I have put forward.

....

Having written the above, I read a section of Dean Turner's "The Einstein Myth" in "The Ives Papers" (Haz) to find that I was not alone in these thoughts. He comments:

> At the beginning of this book, I praised Einstein for his consistent creative imagination. But now, I must qualify that praise by bearing upon his most serious limitations. In some major respects Einstein's imagination was uncommonly stunted. Otherwise there is no possible way to explain that the universe (reality) is finite, and that beyond it "there is nothing". By depersonalizing God, he in effect reduced nature ultimately to gross forces that are the manifestation of no intelligence, purpose, or conception whatever. In short, his view would destroy the Cosmic Scheme of Things, and thus ultimately would undermine all value and love. As he did away with God, he also did away with any intrinsic value in life (Haz:94).

His reference to "beyond it 'there is nothing' " is related to Einstein's Riemannian Space that assumes that space itself is curved and therefore there is "nothing" outside of it. Turner also notes:

> Einstein viewed ultimate reality as being totally *IM*personal [emphasis his]. His own remarks show that the ideal of a personal God, i.e., the idea of reality being ultimately personal in its nature, discomforted him enormously. Of course, no one knows the extent to which his lack of love for people was the result of his applying his philosophy, versus the extent to which his philosophy was a product of his lack of care for people. But no one familiar with the facts of his life can question that he felt awkward and not at home with close personal relations. In his own words he characterised himself as having "a marked lack of desire for direct association with men and women." He said: "I have never belonged wholeheartedly to country or state, to my circle of friends, or even to my own family" (Haz:95).

THE SCIENTIFIC REPERCUSSIONS

Far from being welcomed as a new concept, relativity came as a distinct shock to the scientific community. Most feared that they would have to unlearn all that they had "believed" in all their working lives. A significant number, however, refused to be browbeaten into submission by the hype surrounding its presentation.

Rutherford completely ignored relativity and carried on with his work (Ding:180). Prof. Blackett reported a story that Wein had been explaining to Rutherford that Newton was wrong in the matter of relative velocity and added "But no Anglo-Saxon can understand relativity." Rutherford replied "No. They have too much sense" (Ess71:2).

As we have mentioned, Sir Oliver Lodge walked out of the 1922 meeting and Poor's criticisms have never been answered.

It was noticeable that Pais rarely reported criticisms of relativity, particularly scientific evidence such as that which Poor produced. He does once refer to Poor, and then only to ridicule his views. He prefaces his remarks by saying that the introduction of relativity caused consternation in those who felt that they had to change their ideas. He continues:

> Transitions such as these can induce fear. When interviewed by *The Times* on relativity theory, Charles Poor..said "For some years

past, the entire world has been in a state of unrest, mental as well as physical. It may well be that the physical aspects of the unrest, the war, the strikes, the Bolshevist uprisings, are in reality the visible objects of some deep underlying mental disturbance, worldwide in character....This same spirit of unrest has invaded science..." (Pai82:310).

It is interesting to see the propaganda machine at work. Pais mentions that:
> The insistence on mystery never waned. One reads in *The Times* ten years later, "It is a rare exposition of relativity that does not find it necessary to warn the reader that here and here and here he had better not try to understand" (Pai82:310).

As another example, *Everyman's Encyclopaedia* (under relativity) says that most people absorb their understanding of science by their observations of surroundings. It then says:
> The judgements formed by such an observer are to a large extent subjective, and it is the business of the theory of relativity to eliminate the subjective element from physics and substitute a science that is subjective in the sense that the laws are common to all observers.

If this passage is studied carefully, it will be seen that according to the writer, the purpose of relativity theory is to "eliminate" (his word) all the normal subjective sensations that we have and which form our understanding of the world in which we live. It is only from these everyday experiences of length, place, time etc. that scientific observations can be built. To even examine a dial recording a measurement or look at a clock involves the normal senses. If we are to do away with the ordinary common sense approach to science, we can only be accepting an invitation to enter into "cloud cuckoo land"!

What relativity seeks to do is to overrule the normal faculties and substitute for it a world where incomprehensible concepts, paradoxes and contradictions to common sense are considered as constituting "the real world." And all this is on the basis of very complex mathematical theories, so that the "laws are common to all observers."

But the laws are already "common to all observers"; i.e. wherever we are, the laws of physics are the same, etc. It is not this - the universality of physical laws - that is in dispute but it is used in the quotation above in order to induce the reader to accept what is true so that what is false - the theory of relativity - may be accepted along with it.

Relativity and Mathematics.

Relativity has brought into the world of science the element of mysticism and the incomprehensibility of a mathematical theory that has no basis in the real world. To emphasise this let us give a simple illustration of how mathematics may be logically correct yet have no correspondence with the real world.

There are simple mathematical problems that can be solved where a square root has to be taken - say to determine the length of the side of a square that is 9 square inches in area. The side is obviously 3 inches long, but there is the mathematical result of -3, as this still gives an area of 9 square inches. But this latter dimension is ignored as being a theoretical artifact and having no correspondence with reality. There are of course times when a negative result is used in later computations, but in the simple case set out above it is meaningless as we do not normally measure a negative distance.

Murray gives an illustration. In relativity, you do not add the velocity of the observer (v) to that of light (c) to get the speed of light approaching the observer, but the Lorentz transformation formula is used, which gives the result as c and not c+v. He comments:

> One can scarcely refrain from murmuring "QED" in response! All that has been proved by this little exercise...is that the steps from assumed constancy of c to the Lorentz transformations and back again are free of *mathematical* (emphasis his) error; the result is just the restatement of the initial assumptions and the argument is entirely circular. Whether or not it corresponds to the working of the physical world has never been put to the test (Mur84).

Yet this is what mathematicians have done in relativistic physics. Because a mathematical theory may be logically correct and without any mathematical flaws does *not* mean that it has any relevance to reality. This would apply to the Riemannian space that Grossman suggested to Einstein for use in his theory. What evidence is there that space is curved and gravity affects the local curvature? It is a purely mathematical construction, requiring only paper and pencil, that may have no connection with reality.

Another aspect is the work of Minkowski, who provided Einstein with the idea of the "equivalence" of space and time; i.e. time could be considered, and mathematically manipulated, as if it were a fourth dimension. There is absolutely no justification for such an assumption, and its adoption brings in its train many of the "paradoxes" that relativists revel in.

This combination of Riemannian space and Minkowski's fourth dimension was strongly criticised by Callahan who was the president of Duquesne University from 1930 to 1940. In his book *Euclid or Einstein* (Haz:271), he demonstrates the fallacy of the whole basis of Riemannian geometry. He points out that it is due to a problem that has beset geometers for hundreds of years - proof of Euclid's fifth postulate; put simply, that parallel lines do not meet. In their failure to obtain a rigorous proof, some went so far as to deny its truth, and invented their own "geometry", Riemann amongst them. He postulated that *all* parallel lines meet, and from this claimed that space was finite and curved. To this was later added Minkowski's idea that time is a fourth dimension and can be used in mathematics as such. This Riemann-Minkowski combination is the basis of Einstein's mathematics.

We will not go into this subject in depth but record Callahan's rebuttal of this speculative geometry. His criticisms are available in *The Ives Papers* (Haz) which gives a condensed version of his book from which this is drawn.

Firstly, Callahan points out that the problem of Euclid's postulate is that he mixes two different propositions (parallel lines and right angles). Callahan then gives a simple proof based upon previous axioms that is entirely consistent with Euclid's rigorous system. He points out that, by their own admissions, if Euclid's geometry is correct, all others must be false.

We will concentrate on Callahan's criticisms of what he calls "metageometry"; i.e. metaphysical geometry that can only exist in mathematical formulae. It cannot even be imagined as the human brain is incapable of imagining four dimensions; it can therefore only exist in mathematical formulae.

Callahan is scathing about those who have forced the "new geometry" onto the world of physics. He agrees that there should be a regular "stock-taking" of basic concepts, but with these new theories he says:

> The mutineers against the old order have seized the ship of knowledge and nailed the flag of dissent to the mast; they have driven the defenders of all manner of orthodoxy below decks and battened down the hatches over them, and have left in their administration not a single department of science (Haz:273).

He quotes an extremely abstruse argument Riemann gives to support his theory which Callahan considers to be "pure piffle aping depth by covering itself with obscurity."

He explains this passage as only saying that we can conceive one dimension (a line), two dimensions (a plane) and three dimensions (normal space), and Riemann concludes "And it is easy to see how this construction may be continued."

Callahan comments:

> Riemann ascribes curvature to space, then space must be finite. Wonderful! So if he ascribed feet to space, space could walk; or a mouth, it could talk...There is not even a possible confirmation this time from either perception or conception. But if we ascribe it, the thing is done. What I admire about Riemann is his boldness. No intellectual difficulties stand in his way. He scorns proof. He scorns reason. Just ascribe whatever you will...This is the rubbish out of which relativists have constructed their system.

Humanism and modern mathematics

David Malcolm wrote an interesting article with this title (Malc88) which deserves wide readership. In it he exposed the false roots of modern mathematics. He is particularly critical of Cantor and "Set theory" that is so widely taught in our schools.

All humans, even children, have an intuitive realisation that $1+1=2$, $2+1=3$ etc. Cantor used set theory to show that the basis of this could be logically proven. One of his followers wrote on the subject and early in his proof said "Let S be the set of all those sets which are not members of themselves". The printing of the book was almost complete when Bertrand Russell pointed out that this was a self-contradiction. Without going into a deep analysis of the problem, suffice it to say that this rendered his rational proof of arithmetic void, and it has never yet been solved. Poincare said "Later generations will regard set theory as a disease from which one has recovered".

Goedel, and others, also tried to bring infinity into mathematics, but again, the result were self-contradictory.

The main points Malcolm makes in his article are:

(a) the infinite belongs to God but the earth is for man to explore (Ps.115:16).
(b) that mathematics is basically a religion, requiring "faith" in the basic, unprovable axioms, which is acknowledged by many mathematicians.
(c) that mathematics must be rooted in the physical, material world. Its purpose is to explain the workings of nature. When it tries to dictate how a theoretical world should behave, it is exceeding its ordained role. Many famous mathematicians have pointed this out.

He also deals with the question "Can an omnipotent God make a rock so heavy that He cannot lift it?" He shows that God cannot contradict His own nature. For example, He cannot lie (Heb.6:8). He continues by saying "Thus we also expect the creation to contain no contradictions. If we come across a contradiction, we see it as a danger signal that we have done something wrong, and we (that is mathematicians with a biblical basis) must go back and find our mistake." Malcolm limits this caution to mathematicians, but it has a far wider application than this specialist subject.

God and the infinite

One aspect struck this writer while considering Malcolm's reference to God and the infinite. Whenever the infinite is brought into mathematics (or indeed other subjects likewise) it causes problems. This is easily illustrated. One divided by infinity is zero and two divided infinity is also zero and they can therefore be equated. Multiplying both sides by infinity gives 1= 2 - which is obviously nonsense. There is no fault in the mathematics, only that it as been used unwarrantably and has included infinity. As we have said, mathematics is a good servant of science but a bad master when theories are manufactured from it. In addition, we should leave the infinite to God; only he can deal with such an entity.

....

That relativity solved the very large problem presented by the Michelson-Morley experiment was considered sufficiently important to give it the prominence it duly received. On the basis that "attack is the best form of defence", the contradictions it thereby generated were loudly presented as "progress in scientific exploration". All who did not accept this diktat were labelled "unimaginative" and considered as hidebound scientists stuck in outmoded thinking. Thus was a generation of scientists bullied into submission, and I would consider that the enormous publicity surrounding Einstein was deliberately generated in order to overwhelm any opposition, whether professional or lay.

Hannes Alfven has made a pungent comment upon the whole subject:

> Many people probably felt relieved by being told that the true nature of the physical world could not be understood except by Einstein and a few other geniuses. They had tried to understand science, but now it was evident that science was something to believe in, but nothing possible to understand. Paradoxically enough, Einstein may have been hailed by the general public not because he was a great thinker, but because he saved everybody from having to think.
>
> Soon the best-sellers among the popular science books became those that presented scientific results *as insults to common sense*. The more abstruse the better! Contrary to Bertrand Russell, science became increasingly presented as the negation of common sense. The limit between science and pseudoscience was erased. To most people it was increasingly difficult to find any difference between science and science fiction. (Alf77:5)
>
> This theory is also more dangerous because it came into the hands of mathematicians and cosmologists, who had very little contact with empirical reality. Furthermore, they applied it to regions which are very distant, and counting dimensions far away is not very easy. Many of these scientists had never visited a laboratory or looked through a telescope, and even if they had, it was below their dignity to get their hands dirty. They looked down on the experimental physicist whose only job was to confirm the high-brow conclusions they had reached, and those who were not able to confirm them were thought to be incompetent. Observing astrono-

mers came under heavy pressure from the theoreticians (Alf:6).

Alfven is a well qualified scientist who is clearly speaking from experience. It can be construed from what he claims that one result of the imposition of relativity upon the scientific establishment is to place considerable power into the hands of a few theoretical mathematicians who seem to be able to dictate what will be discovered next to prove their theories. Professor Dingle, whom we return to later, made a very similar observation:

> ..mathematics has been transformed from the servant of experience into its master...It is ironical that, in the very field in which science has claimed superiority to Theology, for example - in the abandoning of dogma and the granting of absolute freedom to criticism - the positions are now reversed. Science will not tolerate criticism of special relativity, while Theology talks freely about the death of God, religionless Christianity, and so on (on which I make no comment whatever). Unless scientists can be awakened to the situation into which they have lapsed, the future of science and civilisation is black indeed (Ding:13).

When Richard Leakey went looking for "ape-men" in Africa he announced that you needed to "look and look again until you find what you know is there" (Bow88:198). Could the same principle also be operating in the world of physics, particularly the field of atomic particles? Let us digress for a moment to briefly consider quantum theory and wave mechanics. We will find there are a number of similarities.

Quantum Theory (Q. Mechanics)

In preparation for this book, extensive reading on the subject of quantum theory was made but ultimately felt that the subject was too remote from creation to be of interest. We would mention that there have been a number of criticisms of quantum theory that have received little publicity. Gaskill contended that resonance in the atom and finite sized particle effects should be examined "so that the long-neglected field of classical mechanics may be revived. It is, I believe, our hope for the future" (Gask). We will refer to other explanations later.

Such were the parallels between the way in which they have been publicised that there seemed to be a link between the two theories, particularly in their relationship to the field of mathematics.

In both subjects, it became clear that mathematics predominated. In former times, the experimental physicist would seek the help of the mathematician to analyse and formulate the data he had collected. In both relativity and quantum theory, as Alfven and Dingle observed, the mathematician now dictated what "reality" consisted of, and set the researchers in pursuit of the evidence. In one book alone, the emphasis on mathematics as the one true guide to reality comes across very clearly. I quote from Gribben's book *In Search of Schrodinger's Cat* (Gri) in which he explains quantum theory.

> The physics is impossible, but the maths is clean and simple, familiar equations to any physicists (p174)....It sounds like science fiction, but it goes far deeper than any science fiction and it is based on impeccable mathematical equations, a consistent and logical consequence of taking quantum mechanics literally....The importance of Everett's work, published in 1957, is that he took this seemingly outrageous idea and put it on a secure mathematical foundation using the established rules of quantum theory. It is one

thing to speculate about the nature of the universe, but quite another to develop those speculations into a complete, self-consistent theory of reality (p238)....but Everett's version is science fact, not science fiction (p239).

From these abstract mathematical theories are produced a concept of "many worlds" of which only one "collapses" into reality. In a similar fashion, he shows a "Feynman" diagram of arrowed lines representing the interaction between particles. By referring to "anti-matter" and thereby reversing one of the arrows the possibility of "time reversal" is proposed and seriously discussed at length in the book. It is indeed passing wonderful the strange forms of reality that can be actually created by clever minds using only pencil and paper!

What is disconcerting is that in both relativity and quantum theory, an element of eastern mysticism has entered into science. Such are the "proven paradoxes" in the further reaches of these subjects that a mystical avenue has opened up and science is being drawn into this morass of anti-rational thinking. One book *The Dance of the Wu Li Masters* by Gary Zukov has this as its main subject stemming from quantum theory. The dangers of such a course need not be emphasised, and Turner has said:

> Controversial, unsettled matters are not presented as such, no matter how important they are - the better to keep most students pacified? Many writers pretend to understand but simply do not. Many otherwise alert students studying relativity become logically bewildered and lose confidence in their own ability to think clearly as they slip into mysticism and become the next generation of scientific priests (Haz:88).

The overall philosophical effect of both relativity and quantum theory is the removal of any stable frame of reference. Relativity removes all sense of stability or position in the universe, whilst quantum theory makes every activity ultimately indeterminate. One can see how they are paralleled by evolution which, in its removal of morals, prepares the populus for "adaptation" to violent social changes in any direction by hailing them as "the latest progress in evolution of our species as advanced animals" - or some such nonsense!

Professor Dingle's objections.

Professor Dingle, was a great advocate of relativity theory, giving talks and writing a book on the subject. He later began to think about the fundamentals and became concerned that there seemed to be a basic flaw in the arguments that were being used in its support. It was the "clock paradox" that posed the most obvious problem to the rationality of the theory. He asked a number of his professional colleagues and never received a satisfactory reply. After trying for several years and meeting a complete blockage from his peers and the media, he tried to get a more public hearing for his problem but failed to obtain an adequate response. Finally, he had to recourse to writing a book, that was published by a little known publisher, in which he set out both the unanswered questions he had posed and the inadequate replies and uncooperative reception he had received.

The title of his book is *Science at the Crossroads* (Ding), and as might be implied from the title, he accuses his scientific colleagues of unethical behaviour for they had deliberately avoided answering his simple questions about the basis of relativity. He foresaw that to continue in not facing up to facts would bring the whole field of science into disrepute and eventual disgrace. He appeared to be unaware of the power of the mass media in shaping the thinking of the general public - as it had very effectively done in the biological sciences with its promotion of evolution and the suppression of creationist evidence.

Dingle wrote his book as the opportunities to present his arguments were gradually closed to him, and he never received a satisfactory reply to his questions. As important as his criticisms were of relativity, more important is his recording of the reactions he received from his peers. It is a severe indictment of the integrity of the scientific community, not of this nation alone but the whole national consortium that refused to publish his articles critical of relativity. What was noticeable was the way in which every single one of the scientists he approached for support, many being personal friends and people of undoubted integrity, eventually refused to be drawn into the controversy. They were well aware that to side with Dingle and against relativity would raise a storm that might damage their reputation, and they therefore excused themselves on the weakest of pretexts. The powerful name given to Einstein and his theory by the mass publicity machine had done its work of intimidating the scientific world into quiet submission to accept relativity, or at least to not criticise it.

One defender stated, "Special relativity is so well established among physicists that attempts to discredit it tend not to be taken seriously" (Vella). On the other side, a critic mentioned that in all his enquiries into relativity "I found again the attitude of the master talking to the schoolboy" (Phil).

Leaky as the boat named "Relativity" clearly was, rocking it was not an activity that was to be encouraged as it was the only vessel with a certificate of sea-worthiness authorised by the Establishment.

Anyone who contends that scientists are objective and fearlessly search only for the truth in their field of science should read Dingle's book. I should point out that I have not limited this to only a few senior scientists, but to *all* those, at whatever level, who refuse to provide an answer to Dingle's simple questions that are not beyond the grasp of any sensible person.

Reading the evasive replies that Dingle received over many years raises the question of just how much integrity there is left in the scientific community.

This will doubtless raise accusations that this writer is "anti-scientific", but this is strongly denied. The vast majority of scientists are free to investigate the natural world as they desire - and can find funding. The undeniable benefits of their efforts are seen all around us. There are only two restrictions that they will meet. The first is where their researches affect the profitability of big businesses. The second is where they find evidence that contradicts evolution - *no matter how remote.* We would again refer to Halton Arp, the astronomer who showed that red-shift of light from galaxies is no indicator of their distance. This threatened the Big Bang theory which is foundational to evolution, and he was therefore denied any opportunity to research this further. We would contend that this restriction would apply to relativity also, for reasons we give below.

The Godless motive

The major effect that the theory of relativity has had is on the basic assumptions of physics. God created a world that was unified, stable and reasonably comprehensible to the human mind. Relativity destroys these concepts and replaces it with no universal time, for each "frame" has its own time that is effectively independent of any other. Thus, the unity of the universe is broken into small "worlds" of their own making.

Replace the word "frame" with "people" and one can begin to see how the fragmentation of life that is all around us is but a reflection of relativity and other similar philosophies. Morals are now reduced to "situation ethics"; i.e. if the circumstances allow an unsocial action, then it is acceptable to carry it out. There are no moral absolutes as set out in the Bible - notably the Ten Commandments: everything is "relative" - and the sense of isolation is increased.

In a strong critique of relativity, Malcolm (Malc91) quotes another critic of relativity who said:

> It is very important to realise that Einstein mostly tacitly, but nevertheless quite definitely, denies the oneness and the wholeness of the universe in the Newtonian sense. Einstein presupposes what should be called a "multi-verse", a universe with a split personality, and split in as many ways as one cares.

Malcolm comments:

> Einstein's view of reality would therefore appear to be at odds with the biblical concept of a *uni*-verse which reflects the unity of its Creator; and throughout which we suspect that universal time reigns (Malc91:65).

He notes that relativity is but one of several philosophies that are anti-Christian - e.g.

(i) Lyell used geology to remove the Flood from the Bible;

(ii) Darwin used biology to remove Man's special relationship with God;

(iii) Goedel tried to remove the basic intuition that God placed in man of the fundamentals of arithmetic and mathematics by replacing it with a purely rational proof.

(iv) Einstein removed the universal frameworks of space and time, thus denying God's record of man's progress to a final Day of Judgement.

Without labouring this point, we would hope it will be obvious how insidious is the effect of these false theories (and others) upon our concept of what this world is like and our attitude to life in general.

....

We have seen how the theory is riddled with flaws and contradictions, and can therefore be dismissed, but the failure of the Michelson-Morley experiment to detect any movement of the earth in its passage around the sun still needed an "explanation". We will be examining this question in the last appendix, but before we do so, we will show in the next appendix that there are several explanations of various unusual scientific phenomena that do not have to resort to relativity in any way, some that demonstrate that the aether most surely exists and the blindness of orthodox science to unwelcome facts.

APPENDIX 9
IS TODAY'S "SCIENCE" TRUE?

*Few things are so immutable as the addiction of groups of scientists to
ideas by which they have won fame, ideas now turned into vested interests....
One always blames the Pythagoreans who concealed the irrationality of the
square root of two. But one must accuse Pythagoras himself even more for
sacrificing a hundred oxen to celebrate the famous theorem, because, since
that time, all oxen get jittery when a new truth is discovered* (A. Landé in
Quantum Mechanics in a New Key. Quoted in Q11/3:172)

....

Towards the end of the nineteenth century, a considerable body of scientific
knowledge about the workings of nature had been amassed. Scientists were
confident that they would soon have a complete understanding of how the
universe operated - it only required the clearing up of this newly discovered
phenomena of radioactivity that had to be finalised. As we now know, this
gave rise to the whole field of atomic science and the many ramifications
arising from it.

Still today, there is an aura surrounding "science" and "scientists" in the
minds of many that implies that in their search for truth, scientists are the
custodians of real truth and are above any possibility of partisanship or
self-deception. This false attitude has been criticised by several authors (Broa;
Resn) and it is not proposed to enter into a long general diatribe against the
scientific "establishment" (some would say "mafia"), but we have reported
incidents that have affected subjects under discussion.

What we will here consider is the inability of present-day fundamental
theories that are unable explain accurately recorded experiments and events.
The reaction of establishment scientists is to blackball any worker who insists
in pursuing "awkward" subjects for he is publicising their inability to provide
an adequate explanation. We have seen how this operated in the case of
Halton Arp and his contradictory evidence about red-shifts.

Ever since science became submissive to the theory of evolution, all has
had to be interpreted from this viewpoint. As a result, there have been many
grave omissions in certain fields of study, the results of which conflict with
the present theories. The amount of evidence has become so great that one
publisher, William R. Corliss, is devoted to recording numerous anomalies
that have arisen but which mainstream scientists consistently ignore. We will
first consider his publications, then examine some alternative theories and
then some experiments that present-day science cannot explain.

"The Unclassified Residuum"

There is in this country an almost total ignorance of the work of the
American William R. Corliss who has specialised in publicising evidence that
completely demolishes this tidy view of the bounds of scientific knowledge.
For 20 years Corliss has searched through more than 10,000 volumes of
scientific magazines and periodicals to present to a wider public some 20,000
articles that are summarised and fully referenced for further investigation.
These are all papers that simply do not fit into the tidy scenario presented by
scientists, and as no easy explanations can be given, have been quietly
ignored.

He is far from being the sort of cheap, self-publicising sensationalist that
have brought this highlighting of anomalies into such disrepute. He has a few
references to corn circles and UFO's simply because there is some confusion
on what is causing them, but the majority of items are records of events, many

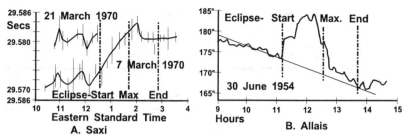

Fig. 1. Disturbance of pendulums during an eclipse

of them in serious scientific journals, that are inexplicable by present-day theories.

We give just one extract as an example. How many people, including any senior scientists, are aware that experiments with pendulums have shown that there is an alteration of their period when there is an eclipse? As this cannot be explained by present day theories of gravity it has received no publicity, yet surely on such a fundamental issue, the whole subject should have been fully investigated and reported in our leading journals. Why has there been such a silence? Fig. 1 plots the results of two separate experiments (Allais and Saxi).

Also reviewed is the Creation Science Movement pamphlet No. 236 - *The Tilt of the Earth's Axis* - and the front graph is reproduced. As we noted in that section, Corliss makes the pertinent comment "One would think that such startling data, compiled by a recognised astronomer, would be the subject of intense study in archeo-astronomic circles; instead, it is an English creationist tract that discusses the subject."

His publications were an invaluable source of information for several items within this present work.

The summaries of these articles and books are covered in different ways in several publications. They are usually presented under the main headings of Archaeology, Astronomy, Biology, Geology, Geophysics, Psychology, Physics and General. Corliss also gives his own estimate of the reliability, accuracy, interest and anomaly rating which seem very fair and objective. An adequate number of illustrations of important pictures, diagrams, graphs etc. are given to enable the reader to judge for himself the scope and importance of each item. The main publications are -

1. **Science Frontiers.** A 4 page review of books and another 4 of articles - issued every two months. Articles are briefly summarised.
2. **Catalogues.** Separate books of articles on astronomy, geophysics, Geology, Biology and Archeology.
3. **Handbooks.** Single volumes on specific subjects

These can be obtained from William R. Corliss, The Sourcebook Project, Box 107, Glen Arm, MD 21057, USA. Certainly, all main libraries should have a copy of these works for reference by any interested person. There is more than enough material to puncture any inflated image that scientists present of their calling.

To give some idea of the scope and controversial nature of the reviews, the following very brief selection is given. A number have been examined more fully in this work and its companion volume.

1. 175 grm. gyroscopes spun clockwise from above showed no weight change. When spun counter-clockwise, they lost 10 milligrams of weight.

(*Science News* 137:15, 1990. Original paper = Hayas).
2. The human ear emits a frequency of 15,000 Hz. which helps it in its signal processing. This was proposed by T. Gold just after World War II but he got nowhere. This has now been confirmed. (*Journal of Scientific Exploration* 3:103, 1989). (Gold was the proposer of a deep, non-organic source of oil, which has now been discovered (Bow91:149))
3. A very high correlation has been found between low solar activity and the irruption of earthquakes. Why should this be? (*Science News* 137:47 1990).
4. Norman and Setterfield's memorandum *The Atomic Constants, Light and Time* (See CSM pamphlets 238, 256, 262) is reviewed. Unfortunately more space is given to an American creationist's faulty criticism of this work, which has been, in turn, strongly criticised by Norman.
5. A strong correlation has been found between thunderstorms that peak in activity three days after peak levels of solar cosmic rays (*Geophysical Research Letters* 1981 v8 p521-2).

These are just a few examples of unexpected results, and those prepared to look beyond the standard text books are urged to contact Corliss.

It is often said that one crucial test of the accuracy of a theory is its ability to make correct predictions. This was checked by examining the response to the predictions of the dissident scientist Hannes Alfven. Despite their correctness, his ideas were still not accepted. Corliss comments, "If a theory is not acceptable to the scientific community, it may not gain any credit from successful predictions.... Science does not work as it is supposed to."

On the general subject of scientists unwilling to "step out of line" from accepted dogma, Corliss quotes P. Sturrock who explains why mainstream science does not clasp anomalies to its breast:

> They are uncomfortable. Your friends may doubt your judgement. You may lose the respect of some of your colleagues. You will get no funding. You will have difficulty publishing your work. Your boss may think you are wasting your time. If you don't have tenure - don't even consider it. But the reason why there should be serious consideration of at least some anomalous phenomena include the fact that the grey area of science is the crucial area. You may perhaps - without knowing it - start a scientific revolution. Also you may be honoured .... posthumously.

To read these extracts for any length of time can result in a degree of exhaustion, for the information is so contradictory of the tidy view of life that popular scientific journals generally describe to the ordinary public. One can feel somewhat overwhelmed by the amount of information provided for which no simple explanation seems possible at this time at least.

In view of this, having recommended the more enquiring reader to peruse these mind-stretching publications by Corliss, I must, like the cigarette adverts, issue a warning that they are liable to damage the complacency and confidence of orthodox scientists.

There are other theories, all with experimental support, that are well worthy of further consideration, and we will briefly consider six of them, all related to an understanding of fundamental physics which involves properties of matter, astronomical phenomena and cosmology.

ALTERNATIVE THEORIES
1. Herbert Ives

One alternative theory to relativity is the Absolute Space and Time theory produced by Herbert Ives which is based upon classical mechanics together with Lorentz shortening etc. He was a brilliant experimenter and theorist, and made several experiments that showed relativity to be in error. His work was ignored, but supporters of his views collected several of his main papers and with some other writings issued them under the title *The Einstein Myth and the Ives Papers* (Haz). Turner, a co-compiler claimed, "since Ives' Absolute Space and Time Theory yields numerical results *indistinguishable* [emphasis his] from Einstein's predictions (in the standard interpretation of Einstein) it is hard to see how Ives' could have been disproved by any experiment, although the theories of other contenders may have been. As usual, *no one seems to know of Ives' theories.* [emphasis his]" (Haz:76).

2. Harold Aspden

The theories of space and matter set out by Professor Aspden are contained in his three main works - *Science without Einstein* (Asp69), *Modern Aether Science* (Asp72) and *Physics Unified* (Asp80).

Prof. Harold Aspden contends that the theory he propounds is far simpler than the mind-bending pathway traced by relativity. He says, "it is hoped that the reader may be beginning to realise that Nature is not quite as complicated in the realm of truly fundamental physics as might appear from modern mathematical treatments" (Asp69p22).

It was the mention by Gerardus Bouw (whose work we consider later) that only Aspden had a satisfactory explanation for ball lightning (discussed below) that first stirred the interest of this author. Reading his works showed that he had met opposition to his ideas, such that he had to recourse to publishing his own books to give the subject an airing. This was precisely what Professor Dingle had to do when he found his channels of publicity blocked as soon as he began to criticise the theory of relativity.

One editor wanted to review his first book but returned it and apologised for the fact that all five persons approached were "unable" to review it. For "unable" one should read "unwilling"; unwilling, that is, to be associated with a book that was against relativity.

His theories appear to be very comprehensive and they are gradually gaining recognition. We will only briefly mention some aspects as indicative of their scope.

His basic theory is that there are three frames of reference in the universe - the E and C frames that are relevant to electromagnetism and the G Frame relating to gravity. These frames are rotating such that their node points rotate around each other. From the interaction of these frames and the few fundamental particles (electrons, positrons, muons etc.) they have within them, he derives the properties of astronomical and atomic constants, such as gravity, electron movement, magnetism etc. He also obtains Planck's constant and Shrodinger's equation.

His model has two basic particles which have specific energies, and there are two inexplicable "bumps" in the X-ray spectrum at precisely these two energies (Asp72p159).

He also gives the surprising fact that there is a high voltage difference with height in the open air. A conductor 10m. high (33 ft) will have a potential difference relative to earth of 1,500 volts. This differential voltage becomes negligible at 10,000 m (33,000 ft) (WilsH). This will be of interest when we briefly consider the work of Tesla later.

Aspden claims that the basic theory of plasma fusion is incorrect and that his theory can explain many of the anomalies that have been found (Asp80:193).

The plenum theory.

This is the concept that the aether is not a vast emptiness, but is actually packed with an extremely dense "material" or particles, within and through which ordinary matter moves easily. This is an important subject and is considered more fully in the next appendix.

He considers that the aether adjacent to the earth moves with it, extending for about 250 km (155 miles) above the surface. The slip planes between the earth's aether and that of the universe can explain the ionosphere levels and the earth's geomagnetic field (Asp69:169). Allais (All98) seems to make a similar connection between the aether rotation and the magnetic field. We would comment that to have two slipping planes of the aether would surely affect the direction of light coming in from the stars, making them vary widely depending on their angle of approach to the earth. This would be like the bending of starlight as it enters the earth's atmosphere and for which corrections have to be made. We discuss this relationship in the next appendix.

Magnetic materials

He examined magnetic materials and found that their magnetism was due to the alignment of their electron spins. This produced high stresses in the material and to resist this they had to have considerable mechanical strength. He could predict if a material could be magnetised from an examination of its physical properties.

Ball lightning.

This is usually a spinning ball of bright light that may be from a few inches to two feet or more in diameter. It can appear quite suddenly, remain stationary but usually moves, and when it hits some obstruction may burst into a spray of flashes or become two or more separate balls before eventually disappearing, often leaving a smell of burning or electric discharge. There is often a storm nearby at the time.

These appearances of ball lightning were regularly reported by ordinary citizens but the experts dismissed them as simply hallucinations or tricks of the mind. It was not until one of their own number, Prof. R.C. Jennison of the Electronics Laboratory of the University of Kent, witnessed one that the whole subject was taken more seriously. In 1963 he was in an aeroplane flying through a storm when a ball of light travelled down the central aisle of the plane and disappeared at the far end. What is striking is that physicists still have no adequate explanation for this phenomena - hence their consistent ignoring of it for many years and little reference to it even today.

Aspden's explanation is that it is a portion of the aether that is revolving as part of the forces and fundamental particles acting within his proposed electromagnetic spinning framework.

There are many more subjects covered in his books but the above should give some indication of their scope.

The opposition

I had assumed that his work was virtually unknown and was therefore surprised to see that he was sufficiently well known for the Establishment to block his ideas from spreading. This was referred to in a letter in *Electronics World and Wireless World* (May 1995 p435-7).

A letter from this author on the speed of light (September 94 p788) that referred to the barriers against unorthodox theories provoked a scathing riposte that denied the existence of any "scientific mafia". A reply to this by Caff (May 1995 p 435-7) gave concrete examples of how the Establishment had prevented the publication of threatening views. The particular passage about Aspden is worth quoting in full:

> ...there is usually no conspiracy to suppress heretical views. There is no need of one, except in specific instances, because as Charles McCutcheon wrote in the *New Scientist* (itself a notorious suppressor, but not as bad as *Nature*) on 29 April 1976, p225, "An evolved conspiracy suffices." For example, I ran into a discussion in the interval at the Royal Institution seminar to celebrate the centenary of the Michelson-Morley experiment. An American who was setting up an international conference on relativity discussed with one of the lecturers whether aether buffs [Those who claimed an aether existed and were therefore anti-relativity] should be suppressed at that conference. He also asked the lecturer *how Harold Aspden should be dealt with* [!]. They concluded that if aether believers *kept to establishment mathematics* [we have discussed above the importance of this point], they should be allowed to put their case.

> The American told me he regarded heresy in science much as he regarded heresy in religion.... Suppression is the norm rather than the exception. Even Maddox, editor of *Nature*, now says he is worried! With his track record, that is mind-blowing. Scientists have successfully resorted to false authorships and false addresses to get into *Nature*.

> The most interesting and most destructive aspect is the pandemic suppression of advances relating to the AIDS epidemic." (See Bow94 and Bow93).

It is to be hoped that there will be a relaxation of the scientific censorship in the near future. However, the reader is advised not to hold his breath...

3. Stefan Marinov

Marinov, using an "interferometric coupled-mirrors experiment" claimed he had detected the speed of the earth through the aether of 303 km/s towards a specific direction in the sky (Mari74 in Bouw92:257).

His important work has been largely ignored and his failure to get his controversial articles published in scientific journals eventually forced him to buy three pages of advertisement in the *New Scientist* in order to publicise the blockage he had experienced (Mari86).

In this "article", entitled "Marinov to the World's Scientific Conscience", he called scientists "jelly-fish" for their refusal to stand up for freedom of ideas, and gave much information on an electrical machine he had invented that appears to give energy in excess of the input but probably extracts it from the aether - as we will see later. He had taken this to conferences and had been forcibly removed, whilst no one would comment on his work for they were afraid that he would repeat their criticisms in his publications.

A study of this very technical but informative "advert", which is easily available (*New Scientist* v112 p48-50 18th December 1986), is recommended for those with the necessary technical background.

Bouw also reviews Marinov's book *Eppur Si Muove* (Mari77) and highlights a most intriguing experiment. This is illustrated in Fig. 2 and in what follows the wire is stationary in all the experiments. If the disc is spun, then a current flows through the wire. If the magnet only is spun, *there is no current.* If both magnet and disc are spun together, *a current flows!* This seems to contradict the principle of relativity which says that it is irrelevant whether the disc or the magnet move relative to one another.

Do we have here a principle that it is the rotation relative to the aether that is important? Those with access to suitable equipment might like to perform this experiment and ask questions of their scientific colleagues!

Marinov eventually committed suicide (?) on 15th July 1997 under very suspicious circumstances. The news was blocked by the authorities and only gradually leaked out. They refused to release any of his documents. Had his death been more widely publicised, those who knew of his criticisms would have started asking awkward questions which orthodox scientists knew they could not answer (Biblical Astronomer v 8 n 84 pp 25-7).

4. Joseph Newman

This is a most intriguing affair. A passing reference by Bouw that Marinov's "perpetual motion" experiment was like "Newman's machine" was noted. The reference given was *Science News* v127 1 June 1985 p342-3 and the article was very thought provoking.

Newman, "essentially self taught", considered magnetic fields are streams of gyroscopic particles travelling at the speed of light. He used this energy and in doing so, a small amount of atomic mass was converted into more spinning particles. If this destruction of matter is taken into account, the total energy balances and it is not a "perpetual motion machine". He said he knew the machine would work before he built it.

In 1979 he applied for a patent, but the American Patent Office said his invention did not work and refused his application. In 1984 he took them to court, and the judge proposed that a "Special Master" should investigate the machine, and the Patent Office appointed an experienced electrical engineer. In his report he said:

> Evidence before the Patent and Trademark Office and this court is overwhelming that Newman has built and tested a prototype of his invention in which the output energy exceeds the external input energy: there is no contradictory factual evidence.

The report was rejected by the judge who not only ordered Newman to hand his machine over to the National Bureau of Standards but also left the decision whether to grant a patent to the Patent Office - the very body he was taking to court! Newman contended that the NBS would not give him a fair deal. He therefore shipped the machine to a large hall and gave a public demonstration of it working. *The Science News* article describes it operating:

> There the machine sat: a massive permanent magnet whirling within a giant copper coil large enough to fill the back of a station wagon, ostensibly receiving energy from an array of batteries providing less than 2 milliamps of current yet producing enough energy to light up a flickering set of fluorescent and incandescent

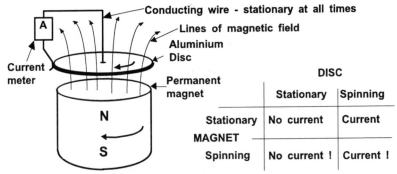

Fig. 2. The spinning disc and magnet anomaly

lights. Says Newman, "This invention speaks for itself."

He has gathered the support of a number of scientists and investors who are helping him fund his battle against the Patents Office which has lasted over five years and at that time had cost $100,000.

Another court case was due in June 1985, but I have never seen any further reports whatsoever on this most remarkable machine. As it may pose a double threat - against the scientific orthodoxy and vested interests in power generation - it is unlikely that anything more will ever be heard about it.

5. Boyer's "Stochastic Electrodynamics" (SED) or "Zero Point Energy" theory

This is not dissimilar to Aspden's theories and is a combination of classical theory and a theory of fluctuating fundamental particles of matter. This was investigated by Prof. Boyer (Boy) who found that he could derive many of the results of Quantum Theory without using their basic assumptions.

Boyer's *Scientific American* article (Boy) on the subject specifically says "Accordingly, I shall discuss the vacuum entirely in terms of classical ideas." The basic idea is that even at the lowest temperature possible, 0° Kelvin (= -273°C), a perfect vacuum still contains radiation energy. The possibility of this energy being extractable is then briefly discussed. Simple experiments have shown that a residual force between two plates close together (the Casimir effect) is inexplicable by present theories.

We will not go into the details of this theory but note that it is yet one more that depends upon the existence of the aether which, according to relativity theory does not exist.

6. Dr. Thomas G. Barnes

The creationist, Thomas Barnes, a strong critic of relativity and quantum theory, has proposed a return to a purely classical theory of the atom and has set his ideas out in several articles in the *CRSQ* (Barn:elect). His main point is the replacement of the Bohr model of the atom, which has many problems, with one that has a rotating ring electron instead of an electron circling the nucleus. From this he derives the forces of gravitation and many other phenomena without recourse to relativity or quantum theory. He has also co-founded the movement for "Common Sense Science".

Again, we see that an explanation by relativity theory does not provide any proof that it is correct. Other equally valid explanations can be provided. We leave the interested reader to examine the references to his work.

....

Having written the above, I began to wonder whether it was too remote from the aim of the book and should be removed. It was then that I saw a programme - *Equinox* (Channel 4 17.12.95) - entitled "It Runs on Water" that covered this subject in an excellent way. This encouraged me to add to this section the examples that the programme presented where some startling discoveries had been made but the results had been ignored by scientists.

Most of them, like Newman's above, had obtained much more energy output than was being used as input. This totally contradicts the First Law of Thermodynamics - that the total energy input must equal the total energy output. Energy is never lost but only changes its form, usually finishing as heat. It is for this reason that their discoveries have received scant attention and much ridicule from scientists. There are, obviously, many "weird" ideas that will never work and one can understand the reluctance of conservative scientists to have their reputations darkened by association with such cranks. But these are not just theories, they are working models, producing energy in large quantities in some cases. Yet orthodox science will have no contact with them and in fact opposes their development. The reason for this we will see at the end.

We will, therefore, briefly review the discoveries presented in this quite important programme.

A. Jim Griggs and the "hydrosonic pump"

Griggs found that "water-hammer" in a pipe produced an increase in temperature. He carried out many experiments and now produces water heaters commercially. They consist of a steel core with many holes at specific centres and angles around the rim. This is rotated rapidly, water is pumped into the casing and the water-hammer effect raises the temperature to produce hot water or steam. Griggs said that it was 108-115% efficient. A Fire Station had installed one for its hot water system and the engineer said measurements they had made showed that it was over 100% efficient. Tom Droege of Fermilab examined the system and was cautious in his conclusion but could not explain it.

B. Nicola Tesla and his high voltage systems

Tesla was well known in his day for some amazing experiments he carried out, most of them involving very high voltages. Whilst Edison was promoting the direct current generator, he developed the far more efficient alternating current generator. He invented the Tesla Coil which produced "undreamed of" voltages.

He constructed a special laboratory with a very high mast. He had several million volts pulsing at 50,000 cycles per second but there was such a surge of power that it overrode the safety circuits and the laboratory burnt down.

Callahan (Call), quoting from O'Neill's biography (O'Neill), says that he received fourteen college degrees, mainly from Europe but that now College textbooks hardly mention him. When he died in 1943 in obscurity, his papers were confiscated by the FBI. Although he patented the tuned circuit in 1897, it appears that he was tied up in court cases until his death, so he never gained financially from this discovery that is fundamental to the whole of the electronic industry. In one experiment of transmitting power over the ether he was able to turn on light bulbs 25 miles away! (Call:21f).

He was clearly an amazing genius yet he turned down a Nobel Prize. Today, there may be a resurgence of interest in his work, but his ideas do not appear to have been developed.

C. Alexandra Chernevsky and his electrical experiments

He carried out investigations in 1980 in much the same field as Tesla. He also found unexpected surges of power of the order of five times the amount of energy consumed under certain conditions. His work came to the notice of Hal Puthoff, an American physicist, who visited him in Russia and was impressed with his work. Puthoff invited him to America but he died in 1992 before he could accept the invitation.

D. James Patterson and his heat from water

A retired chemist, Patterson began experimenting with pulses of electricity through water passing over a catalyst. He generated more energy as heat than he was putting in. Thinking there was an error in his method he dropped the work for 6 years. When the controversy of heat generation arose in 1989, he re-examined his earlier work and realised that excess energy had been generated.

He passed a low voltage through a mixture of water and 1% lithium sulphate over catalytic beads of nickel and palladium coated in tin that had fine corrugations to increase the superficial area. The result was the generation of 30% more heat than the equivalent energy he was supplying. With pulsing it is now "tens of times more".

E. Stanley Meyer and his generation of hydrogen from water

Meyer's discoveries will be of particular interest to the Christian as he is clearly a man of God who has been given this vital knowledge for a specific purpose; a purpose which will be revealed in due time.

When Kuwait was invaded and an oil crisis developed in the 1970's, he was concerned that America should not be so vulnerable to actions by small oil-producing states and started looking for an alternative source of energy. He began experimenting with the electrical production of hydrogen from water. He eventually fractured the water molecules so that hydrogen was produced in abundance.

Using high frequencies and high voltages has had achieved a production of hydrogen that was 1,700% more efficient than conventional electrolysis and improvements are still being made.

He met strong opposition from the patents office and it took him three years to obtain a patent but he now has many more around the world. The efficiency of his equipment has increased considerably, and he would only demonstrate an earlier version operating that he had used to obtain the first patent.

Three times he had tried to launch his idea but each time he was ridiculed by the scientific community. However, when a British scientist visited him he was amazed at the quantity of hydrogen produced.

The opposition to change

Meyer recounted some of his experiences as the inventor of a process that would revolutionise the whole world of energy production. He said that he had refused an offer of over a billion dollars from the Arabs whose oil would be threatened, and had received many death threats, casually adding, "but I believe in the power of angels. If I didn't believe in the power of angels I wouldn't be around here too long."

He has built a car bearing the words "Water Powered Car" and over this is the claim "Jesus is Lord" - so there is no disputing where his heart lies. The engine works by using his "hydrogen splitter" like a spark plug and he is at present designing a kit for converting standard cars to run on water as his does. One can see the threat that this would provide to the whole oil industry but he appears to have secret contracts with NASA and the Pentagon. These may be more of a restriction than he realises.

One of the most pointed commentators on establishment science and the energy industry was Paul Czysz, Professor of Aeronautics at St. Louis University. Some of the statements he made were:

> If Stan Meyer's device works like he advertises, it would make energy available almost universally, almost free. That is a major, major impact.... every piston engine, every gas turbine in the world today, if it had this converter, could run on it.... What I am concerned about is the people that sell energy would be essentially bankrupt.... They are going to wipe out an entrenched power base and they may not go easily".

His suggestion that "they may not go easily" might be a slight understatement.

A challenge to present-day scientific theories?

Puthoff remarked that it was the Internet that had broken the stranglehold of orthodox scientists, by allowing "dissident" (for which read "free thinking") scientists to communicate directly with each other.

With the gathering evidence confronting the scientific establishment, there must surely come a time when the dam bursts and orthodox approved theories of space and matter have to be drastically revised. I say "surely", but the way in which the fallacious theory of evolution has been allowed to control all experiments and published results in such a wide range of disciplines for over one hundred years should teach us that truth *can* be subverted for a very much longer time than we would like to believe. It is not impossible that even these latest revelations will suffer the same fate. The control of finance and the media against unwelcome ideas is virtually total.

This raises the thorny problem of how an individual scientist might react to evidence that contradicts his basic philosophy. He may refuse to investigate one or two of those discussed above, but when they become so numerous and proven, there must come a time when a scientist is faced with a serious choice. Either he investigates one or more in his field, and suffers the opprobrium of his colleagues and even loss of his position, or he is forced to "square his conscience", banish the subject from his mind *and thereby forfeit his scientific integrity*. Difficult though the decision is - and we fully sympathise - he cannot have it both ways.

This raised once more the subject of the search for "Truth". In discussions with others on any topic, when facts are presented that are consistently brushed aside, one can gradually come to the conclusion that the defender is ultimately more concerned to defend his present position and not "lose face" than he is in the pursuit of "Truth". This attitude is far more prevalent in all spheres of life than might be imagined.

Following this digression, we will now consider why an answer to the "problem" of the Michelson-Morley experiment was so earnestly sought by the scientists who publicised Einstein's relativity theory to "explain it away".

We hope to show in the following appendix that there was in fact no "problem", and therefore no answer was needed in any case!

APPENDIX 10
GEOCENTRISM - A HERESY?

INTRODUCTION

It has been "known", of course, for several centuries, that the earth goes round the sun, for it is now obvious that the sun (helios) is at the centre of the planetary system (heliocentrism). Long gone are the days when people held to the truly Medieval superstition that the sun and planets went round the earth (geocentrism). Such is the present thinking by all reasonable people.

To even consider the possibility that the earth is the centre of not just the planetary system but of the universe will be interpreted by very many readers as a totally retrograde step that can only bring discredit upon the creationist movement in general and on this writer in particular.

Despite such a daunting prospect, surely, in the pursuit of Truth, the evidence should be examined and carefully appraised.

When first aware of this subject in 1973, the initial reaction was one of considerable scepticism. Nevertheless an open mind was kept on the topic, putting it "on the back burner" for future consideration. When interest was rekindled in 1990, further reading aroused my interest. There was a gradual progression from sceptical to interested to intrigued to ambivalent to eventually finding the evidence fairly convincing. I say "fairly convincing" as it will be seen that the universe seems to be so designed that the final proof that would determine which model is correct cannot be obtained.

As with so many things in life, assessing what is true or false will depend upon one's preconceptions of what life is all about. Such preconceptions will inevitably dictate what will be accepted as "true" according to the conceptual framework that we have each erected of our world view. The fundamental problem is that what is accepted by each individual as being true generally only increases the strength of the framework they have already erected which may itself be based upon propaganda and fallacious concepts imbibed in their youth. Such may be the case regarding geocentricity.

It can only be suggested that the reader follows through the evidence as it is presented and we trust that he will find that he progresses from the natural reaction of "utter rubbish" through "not impossible" to "very likely" - as this writer has done.

"Flat earther's?"

The startling proposition made in this appendix may raise in the minds of many the immediate charge that those who hold to it are of the same mentality as "Flat-earthers". This we would refute. The conclusion is based upon a number of verifiable scientific facts, the majority of which have been deliberately suppressed, as we will demonstrate.

Whilst on this subject of the "Flat Earth", we will digress at this point to note that there was never a time in the world's history when Europeans, at least, believed that the earth was flat. Its roundness could be seen during an eclipse, and Erastothenes had measured its circumference in 200 BC. Columbus was trying to get to the East Indies via a westerly route.

The idea that the Medieval Church was so ignorant and anti-science that it taught the earth was flat was, in fact, *invented* by two anti-Christian writers - John Draper (1811-1882) and Andrew Dickson White (1832-1918) in order to ridicule the Church. It is they who started the idea that Columbus made the journey to prove the church wrong. Ever since, this concept has been unwittingly accepted as a correct account of history and the label has been used to sneer at Christianity.

This false claim was exposed by Professor Jeffrey Russell in his *Inventing the Flat Earth: Columbus and Modern History* (Praeger 1991) which was reviewed in *CRSQ* 31/3:77. Still today, critics, such as Richard Dawkins, try to ridicule creationists by alluding to this belief - now shown to have been deliberately fabricated for this very purpose.

When a Christian is classed as a "Flat-Earther", for what ever reason, they might like to turn the tables on their accusers by gently pointing out that this was a story *deliberately fabricated* by anti-Christians in order to ridicule the Christian faith.

An acknowledgement

Before embarking upon this stormy passage, I must acknowledge the source of much that is written below. This has been obtained from the writings of the Association for Biblical Astronomy (formerly the Tychonian Society), in particular those of the present editor, Gerardus Bouw. I wish to record the debt I owe him for his excellent analysis of many highly technical papers that are relevant to the subject and his personal letters in which he has explained several points.

The society was started by Walter van der Kamp in America who doggedly held on to the scriptural evidence that the earth was at the centre of the universe. For many years he edited *The Bulletin of the Tychonian Society*. He had little support and although he had a Ph.D. in Physics he was not gifted in communicating his views. Geocentrists (and creationists?) owe him a debt for keeping the flame alight. When Gerardus Bouw took over the organisation he renamed the society The Association of Biblical Astronomers and the bulletin *The Biblical Astronomer*. Interest in the subject has grown steadily such that now it is occasionally referred to in creationist magazines. Most articles are critical for, unfortunately, the subject also has the effect of raising the blood pressure of some creationists!

Those who wish to examine this intriguing subject further should read Bouw's *Geocentricity* (Bou92) and *The Geocentric Papers* (Bou).

Before examining the evidence in earnest, there are two preliminary considerations that need to be dealt with.

1. The mental barrier.

The main objection to anyone accepting the geocentric viewpoint is the knowledge that "everyone knows" that the earth goes round the sun, spinning on its axis as it does so. The spin at least has been proved by simple scientific experiments (Foucault's pendulum etc. - described later) and there has never been anything to the contrary in the mass media or in any books.

Let us look at an example which has very close parallels - the theory of evolution. Those readers who are creationists will be aware of the surprise that people exhibit when it is seriously suggested that creation is true. Surprise can turn to shock should it then be claimed that the earth is only a few thousand years old. Yet such emotional reactions have no bearing on the fact that evolution *is* false and the earth *is* young.

It is exactly the same with geocentrism. Although most creationists may react with disbelief, this has no bearing on where the truth really lies. We should never forget that when people are firstly fed erroneous evidence and secondly prevented from hearing a fair presentation of an alternative viewpoint, then they have no option but to accept the popular ideas as absolute truth which "everyone knows". Thus, as with evolution and creation, so with heliocentrism and geocentrism - the majority believe that which has been proclaimed the longest with the loudest voice.

2. The aesthetic aspect.

In the early ages when it was accepted that the earth was the centre of the planetary system, the paths of the planets were given very complicated systems of circles within circles etc. such as will be later described in the Ptolemaic model. As further movements were observed, the ascribed paths became increasingly complex to accommodate them.

In contrast, the very much simpler system of the elliptical orbits of the planets around the sun is extremely appealing to the scientific mind. Scientists are constantly seeking tidy and simple "laws" that govern the many natural phenomena. If, from a mass of seemingly chaotic data they can derive a short formula that completely describes and predicts all these observations, they will obviously derive a very great sense of satisfaction at having discovered yet another of nature's "laws".

This deep sense of satisfaction, however, does not *necessarily* make the discovered "law" an accurate presentation of the real truth of what is actually happening. This is the elevation of mathematical models above real life experience we have discussed earlier. There may be other factors that have been ignored in deriving the "simple" scheme, which a more complicated theory may be able to accommodate. This is a parallel case to that of the structure of the atom; shown as a simple pattern of electrons around the nucleus, the detail picture is much more complex and still as yet unravelled. It may be the same regarding the geocentric viewpoint of interpreting the observed data; initially appearing to be more complex, but nearer to the truth and scientific evidence.

For Christians, what the scriptural view of this subject is will be the deciding factor and it is therefore this aspect that is dealt with before the scientific evidence.

Occam's Razor?

This states that the preferred theory is that which has to make the fewest assumptions in adequately explaining all the relevant evidence. From this, it might be argued that the heliocentric theory is simpler than the more complicated series of compounded elliptical orbits arising in the geocentric theory. The first point is that the ordinary visual evidence is that the sun goes round the earth. The second and more important point is that the results of experiments to detect this movement of the earth around the sun all ended in failure.

When this motion of the earth around the sun could not be detected, there then developed a growing number of theories and corrections that had to be applied to these experiments until the ridiculous paradoxes were reached in Einstein's Theory of Relativity. These assumptions were far more complicated than those required to explain how the sun and the universe rotate around the earth. If Occam's Razor is to be wielded, geocentricity is far more likely to survive than the multiple theories required to sustain relativity theory as we have shown above.

Creationist reservations

It is an indication of the very controversial nature of the subject that most editors of creationist publications are usually reluctant to print any geocentric articles for fear of upsetting their readership. One can sympathise with them, for over many years they have built up a good circulation and therefore they will be unwilling to lose a large section of their subscribers by publishing "ridiculous" articles about the sun going round the earth. Their caution is understandable.

As far as this writer is concerned, not having any such commercial restraints - or reputation to lose - we will throw caution to the winds and proceed to launch our small rowing boat into the raging seas of controversy!

A HISTORICAL REVIEW

1. THE BIBLICAL RECORD.

There are three passages that state that the earth is fixed in its position. These are:

Psalm 104:5 "He set the earth on its foundations; it can never be moved." (NIV)

Psalm 119:90 "You established the earth and it endures" (NIV) (AV = "abideth" - indicating permanent residence rather than just existing)

Ecclesiastes 1:4 "Generations come and generations go, but the earth remains for ever" (NIV) (AV = "abideth" again).

These are not particularly strong evidences that the earth is static and at the centre of the universe, but it must be emphasised that there are no passages that suggest that the earth is continually moving along a path. There are verses that refer to the earth being shaken, moving, reeling etc., but every single one is referring only to what God can do if he so wishes or what will happen to the earth at the "end times" when God judges the earth.

For example, Job 9:6 says: "He shakes the earth from its place and makes the mountains tremble." This passage is part of a section discussing God's great power. Clearly the earth has a "place" and God, when he wants to, can shake it such that it will make the mountains tremble.

Other passages with similar connotations are Psalm 82:5; 99:1; Isaiah 13:13 and 24:19-20; Rev. 20:11. In all these there is no mention of a path, which could easily have been described in the Hebrew. The assumption that primarily the earth is stationary is a thread running through all these passages.

One of the clearest statements of the mobility of the sun is when Joshua is fighting the five kings and needs more time to destroy them:

> ... and he said in the sight of Israel "Sun, stand thou still upon Gibeon; and thou Moon, in the valley of Ajalon". And the sun stood still and the moon stayed.... Is it not written in the book of Jasher? So the sun stood still in the midst of the heaven *and hasted not to go down about a whole day*" (Jos. 10:12-13).

There are also many references to the sun "rising" and "going down", such as:

- Psalm 104:19 "The moon marks off the seasons, and the sun knows when to go down."

- Psalm 50:1 "The Mighty One, God, the Lord, speaks and summons the earth from the rising of the sun to the place where it sets."

- Ecclesiastes 1:5 "The sun rises and the sun sets and hurries back to where it rises."

This last reference makes it quite clear that it is the sun that is doing all the moving around a stationary earth. Again, in all such passages, there is not the slightest indication of a rotating earth.

It will obviously be argued that this is merely a natural description but is not meant to be taken literally. The usual comparison is to liken it to the passage in Isaiah 55:12 where "the mountains and the hills shall break forth ..with singing and all the trees of the fields shall clap their hands". As trees cannot clap their hands then it is reasonable not to take the movement of the sun as literal. But there is a major flaw in this argument. Trees *cannot* clap their hands, but it *is* possible for the sun to go round the earth - as we shall see. The attempts to allegorise these geocentric passages with such arguments are not valid. Ultimately, it becomes a matter of personal interpretation - in which case, one point of view is as good as another. We see, once again, how the mind-set determines the interpretation.

From this brief examination of passages that refer to the sun-earth relationship, we can see that many assume the earth is stationary, whilst others do not refer to movement today, but at the time of judgement and the last days.

The fourth day
Before we conclude this brief look at scripture, we will leave the reader with one further important thought. Genesis records the fact that the earth was created on day one and then the sun on day four.

To say that the sun and moon were created on the first day but only became visible on Day 4 is an unwarranted rendering of the scriptures. We can only conclude that it has been adopted by most Christians simply to preserve heliocentrism, as the earth could then circle the sun from the very first day of creation.

We have discussed this point more fully in Section 1 on page 14, and the reader may like to refresh himself of the arguments set out there so that he may be fully convinced that the only acceptable interpretation of the Hebrew is that the sun did not exist until it was created on day four.

The importance of this is seen when we ask the question: "what was the earth doing for the first three days of creation?" It could not have been circling a non-existent sun. When the sun was eventually created on the fourth day, did the earth suddenly have to jerk into action and circle the sun? The unliklihood of this is obvious. By far the simplest understanding of the creation narrative is to accept that the earth was created first, as the most important of the heavenly bodies, and the sun was created later. We therefore contend that the sun and the whole mass of the stars began circling the earth on the fourth day. Many readers may object that the heavy mass of the sun cannot orbit around the small mass of the earth: it is the earth that must orbit around the sun. We would ask them to withhold judgement for a while for we deal with this "problem" later in this appendix, when we will show that a answer, perfectly acceptable to this writer - and we hope to the reader - can be presented.

2. THE GRADUAL CHANGE OF VIEWS.
We are today assured that we are only a minor planet revolving around an ordinary star that is one of millions in our particular galaxy; certainly not a celestial body that could possibly be of any importance. How the Medieval view that the earth was the centre of the universe was gradually changed to

today's "certainty" is well documented. Schoolchildren are taken to see the play "Galileo" and learn of the dire consequences when religious authorities try to force scientists to conform to their way of thinking.

However, as is so often the case, the popular understanding of what took place is incorrect in a number of important aspects. One of the best works on this is Arthur Koestler's *The Sleepwalkers* (Koe86), which throws considerable light upon the events of those days. For those who wish to come closer to the truth, this work is recommended, for they will find that it contradicts many popular ideas on this subject that have been built into folk-myths, books and plays. It is but one more example of a detailed investigation of original documents giving a considerably different picture to that generally accepted and recorded in popular scientific books and the mass media.

The first system proposed was that all the planets were on circular orbits around the earth. It did not take long, however, for it to be seen that the inner planets were circling the sun.

The problem with even this system was that the motions of the outer planets as seen from earth were extremely complicated. Their speed was anything but constant. Some, at certain times, slowed down, stopped, (Mars even reversed slightly) and then continued in the same direction as before. The reason for this apparent motion is that as the earth swept past a slower moving outer planet such as Mars, the latter would appear to briefly go backwards against the stationary background of distant stars.

In order to account for this behaviour, Ptolemy (around 130 AD) said that the planets were on smaller circular paths that were revolving around a point on larger path around the earth, as shown in Fig. 1A. In order to describe the paths of the moon, sun and planets accurately, more and more circles revolving around larger circles had to be provided in what became known as the Ptolemaic system. His final scheme required no less than 39 circles with another for the stars!

Surprisingly, much of early Greek wisdom, now so revered today, did not pass directly into the stream of European knowledge, but came via the translations of the Moors and Jews of the Middle East. Aristotle's *Physics* was translated through the language path of Syriac, Arabic, Hebrew to Latin. The 13 books on astronomical observations and theories written by Ptolemy, still known by its Arabic name of *Almagest*, was translated from Arabic into Latin (Koe86:107). With the works of these Greek thinkers rediscovered, they were stirred into the European pot of new concepts that was beginning to warm up.

Ptolemy's very complex system was very unsatisfying and clearly a complex concoction of orbits put together to explain the strange paths of the planets. Some other, simpler, explanation was needed but this was greatly resisted by those who taught the Ptolemaic system.

Nicolas Copernicus.

Although there had been earlier suggestions by Herakleides and others, it was Copernicus (1473-1543) who first wrote a treatise on the subject called *De Revolutionibus Orbium Coelestium - The Revolutions of the Heavenly Spheres*. He was extremely timid and fearful of the ridicule that his ideas would call forth from his academic contemporaries as he knew that he had no evidence that would support his views. Indeed it was completed in about 1530 but not published until 1543. Far from creating a furore, it was hardly noticed, and only four reprints were made in four hundred years which was a dismal

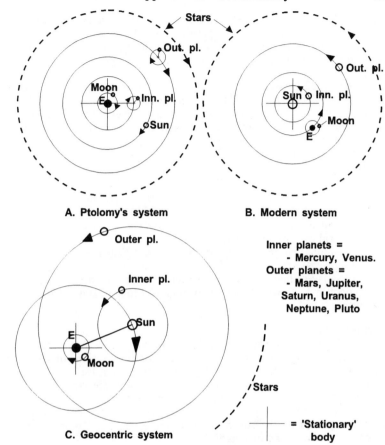

A. Ptolomy's system   B. Modern system

C. Geocentric system

Inner planets =
    - Mercury, Venus.
Outer planets =
    - Mars, Jupiter,
    Saturn, Uranus,
    Neptune, Pluto

= 'Stationary'
   body

Fig. 1. The various planetary systems.

record compared with other similar works (Koe86:194).

Koestler points out that Copernicus did not make the sun the centre, but placed this in space three times the sun's diameter away from the sun. The earth, and all the planets with it, circle this imaginary point in space, and not the sun itself. What is even more interesting is that Copernicus still used Ptolemy's circles on circles system in order to get the orbit's of the planets to conform to anything like the observations from earth. Far from reducing the 40 epicyclic paths of Ptolemy, Copernicus actually *increased* the number to 48. Thus, his system was even more complicated than Ptolemy's, a fact that is little appreciated.

Koestler calls Copernicus's work "The book that nobody read", mainly because of its "supreme unreadability". He proves this by quoting several reputable scientists who say that Copernicus employed 34 epicycles for his model. This is the figure given in the introduction as if it were the final number, but the total later reaches 48 by Koestler's reckoning. This indicates that modern scientists had not read that far or troubled to count the total orbits Copernicus eventually had to employ. It is indeed a tribute to the depth of research that Koestler undertook for this detailed but interesting book.

Koestler, in fact, considered Copernicus to be far from clever. He suggested that his main aim was to patch up the Ptolemaic system, and "the fact that the earth moves is almost an incidental matter in the system of Copernicus" (p 214).

In about 1512 Copernicus circulated a small handwritten treatise *Commentariolus* in which he set out all the major points that he was to amplify later in his major work - *Revolutions*. The ideas this small work contained spread throughout the academic world and created growing interest. Koestler claims that attacks upon Copernicus's ideas over many years came initially from the emerging Lutheran church. Bouw, however, contends that "Luther vehemently opposed" Copernicus (Biblical Astronomer v 83 n 8 p 15) and that Calvin, in his commentary to Psalm 93:1 said:

> The heavens revolve daily; immense as is their fabric, and inconceivable the rapidity of their revolutions.

This is an amazingly perceptive claim by Calvin, and we give Bouw's mathematical confirmation of it later.

The Catholic church actually repeatedly gave Copernicus, and his subsequent followers, Kepler and Galileo, very great encouragement to discuss his ideas - so long as there was no contention that the church was in error in any of its doctrines. It was this that eventually brought about the clash with Galileo.

Tycho Brahe

Brahe (1546-1601) was a meticulous observer of the astronomical bodies and made amazingly accurate measurements of the positions of stars and the motions of the planets before the days of the telescope. He devised a system, similar to Fig. 1C, that was an important variation of the Ptolemaic one. This shows the planets orbiting the sun, but the sun itself orbiting the earth. Fig. 1C is a modern proposal by the Association for Biblical Astronomy in which the stars are centred on the sun rather than the earth. Fig. 1B is the generally accepted version of the planetary system.

Johannes Kepler

Kepler (1571-1630) was Brahe's student who used his master's accurate measurements of the planets to discover, after many years of effort, the precise elliptical orbits that the planets followed around the sun. Using his orbits, Newton produced the laws that describe the laws of gravity, although he had no idea what the attractive force of gravity consisted of.

What few realise is that a careful study of Kepler's calculations by W.H. Donahue shows that he had to "massage" the accurate observations of his master, Tycho Brahe, to make them conform to his "laws" (New York Times Jan 23 1990 pC1 and C6 - quoted in Bull. Tych. Soc. n 53 Spring 1990 p 32). In addition, he is portrayed as a Christian, but a reading of his works show that he was far from such.

Galileo Galilei

Galileo (1564-1642) is presented as the archetype of scientific integrity and freedom in the stand against the overwhelming authority of hidebound religious bigotry in all generations. The real truth is a little different.

Koestler's portrait of Galileo is far from flattering, for he strips much of the myth that has been built around him over many generations of adulation for his "courageous" stand as a "scientist against the (ignorant) church". He says that the personality of Galileo has little relationship to historic facts, but is based upon partisan motives. I quote:

> It is, therefore, hardly surprising that the fame of this outstanding genius rests mostly on discoveries he never made, and on feats he never performed. Contrary to statements in even recent outlines of science, Galileo did not invent the telescope; nor the microscope; nor the thermometer; nor the pendulum clock. He did not discover the law of inertia; nor the parallelogram of forces of motions; nor the sun spots. He made no contribution to theoretical astronomy; he did not throw down weights from the leaning tower of Pisa, and did not prove the truth of the Copernican system. He was not tortured by the Inquisition, did not languish in its dungeons, did not say "eppur si muove"; and was not a martyr of science (Koe86:358).

This catalogue is very damning, but to be fair, in 1582 Galileo discovered that the regular period of the pendulum was independent of the amount of its swing (provided the swing is small). What he did not invent was the clock mechanism that could harness this to record time accurately. The candelabra in Pisa Cathedral, said to be the source of Galileo's idea was not installed until several years after his discovery. Also he did invent the thermoscope, a forerunner of the thermometer. His great ability lay in his mechanical genius in the fashioning of instruments, particularly telescopes, that had mainly been discovered by others.

Galileo, although extremely clever, nevertheless failed to get one of the forty scholarships for poor students at Pisa University. His mechanical inventiveness gave him a growing fame that resulted in his appointment at Pisa as a lecturer in mathematics, four years after they had rejected him. There is discussion why he was first rejected, but Koestler contends it was due to his "cold, sarcastic presumption" that was to cause him so much trouble throughout his life. He describes him as an arrogant genius who lacked humility (Koe86:373).

In 1597 Galileo received a book from Kepler in which he outlined Copernicus's views, and in his letter of thanks, Galileo said he had "adopted the teaching of Copernicus many years ago", and that he had written many papers in his defence but had not dared to give them any publicity for fear of ridicule. Kepler responded effusively but this annoyed Galileo and he did not write again for twelve years.

Galileo spoke much about Copernicus's theories but did not put anything into writing for many years. In a widely publicised letter on heliocentrism he wrote in 1613 he made a very pointed attack upon the final authority of the Bible when applied to matters of science. In it he also tried to shift the burden of proof onto his opponents by saying it was for them to disprove that the orbits were centred on the sun. The subtlety of this challenge is that it assumed that the Copernican system was well supported by evidence which was sufficient to establish it as a fact. Galileo was well aware that there was not a scrap of evidence that supported this claim, and therefore he tried to put this problem of lack of evidence into the court of his opponents.

In the response of Cardinal Bellarmine (1542 - 1621) to his letter his criticisms were generously excused. He wrote that the idea of the earth going round the sun was perfectly acceptable as a working hypothesis which greatly simplified the prediction of the positions of the planets. But to take the step of asserting that the earth *did* actually revolve around the sun was contrary to

Scripture. He contended that if it could be *proved* that the earth did revolve, this would require a very careful examination of Scripture, but he doubted if any such proof existed as none had been shown to him. Thus, he returned the burden of proof back to where it really belonged.

Cardinal Bellarmine was the most senior theologian of the Catholic church. His opinions were very highly respected, and he feared neither popes nor kings. He was extremely gifted and well read, yet he lived a frugal life compared with his equals. Many commented upon the "child-like quality" of his personality. He was far from being the bigoted prelate opposing the progress of science as he is often portrayed. "He was forced by the strength of Protestantism and the Augustinian doctrines of grace and freewill..to define his theological principles." and, "he gave impartial attention to Protestant works and was regarded as one of the most enlightened theologians" (*En. Brit.*). He was not, however, the head of the Inquisition that was to try Galileo in 1632 as by then he was dead.

Several years passed with Galileo nursing his annoyance at not being allowed to broadcast his views in support of Copernicus. Eventually in 1632 he had his *Dialogue* published in which three people discuss the motions of the planets and those who oppose the idea are ridiculed. He used quite preposterous arguments in trying to prove that the earth moved, which any person of ordinary common sense could see were not correct and contradicted by observation. Galileo nevertheless put them forward as "proofs", for such was his contempt for the learning of any, whether secular or clerical, who opposed him.

The publication of the *Dialogue* was delayed, and by several subterfuges, Galileo managed to have it receive the Imprimatur (the approved authorisation of the church) before it had been fully vetted. When it finally reached the church officials, they realised that they had been tricked, and the pope considered that he was portrayed as the character of the fool in the discourse. Galileo was summoned to Rome in 1632 to face the Roman Inquisition.

He began with enormous effrontery to say that the book was written as a criticism of Copernicus, but when confronted by several passages proving otherwise, his bravado eventually collapsed and he admitted that he was in error in saying that the earth travelled round the sun. His unnecessarily truculent attitude was finally made to face realism when opposed by the might of the Roman church.

Throughout the whole of the proceedings, he was treated with very great deference. He was 72, a renowned scholar throughout Europe, and was accordingly provided with luxurious accommodation during the period of the trail. He was never threatened with torture, the particular wording used being only a legal formality which could not be carried out. He knew, and so did his inquisitors, that he was lying about his "recantation", but he was treated leniently and eventually returned to his home town of Florence, where he died in 1638 aged seventy eight.

This whole famous episode has been grossly distorted by propaganda over the centuries. It hinged as much on Galileo's arrogant personality clash with the church rather than their questioning his scientific views. In fact they had done much to encourage him to discuss this contentious subject.

Ridiculed though those Catholic officials are today in their upholding of the Scriptures as being accurate wherever they touch upon scientific subjects, they were correct in their basic grasp of what should have pre-eminence and of what constituted convincing proof. Indeed, the evidence that the earth travels round the sun is still not proven today - as we shall see.

It is a strange turn of fortune, that in these two important aspects at least, they were far nearer to present day geocentrist creationists than their ecclesiastical descendants, who would consider any who hold to such doctrines as foolish and deluded.

MODERN SCIENTIFIC INVESTIGATIONS

That the earth circles the sun in space gradually seeped into society as an "accepted fact", in a similar way that the theory of evolution was to do many generations later. To doubt it was to place oneself outside not just the academic world but normal society also. And so it has been ever since. However, J.D. Cassini (1625-1712), the Astronomer Royal of France, despite being aware of Newton's planetary mechanics, nevertheless held to a geocentric universe.

There have been a number of experiments dealing with the speed of light, the motion of the earth etc. that produce results that contradict certain general preconceptions, but the conclusions that can be drawn from them present a conflicting picture of the relationships between the earth, the aether, the speed of light and other similar phenomena. In order to describe these experiments, some highly advanced physics are involved with complex formulae, and this book is not the medium to present them, neither is this writer in any way capable of such a task.

What is difficult is to know where to "draw the line" regarding the level of physics that should be delved into in order to show that the case for geocentrism is reasonable. What is here presented is for the moderately knowledgeable layman, but for those more competent who might want to go further, there will be references to more advanced ideas. Bouw's book (Bou92) gives more detail, still in a layman's language, but does give references to the very technical papers by many experts that deal with the subjects in greater depth.

Bouw is well qualified to discuss the technicalities. He has a BSc in astrophysics, a PhD in astronomy and is an Associate Professor in Mathematics and Computer Science.

Preamble

If the earth is spinning on its axis, it will have a velocity of 1,040 miles per hour (0.46 km/sec) at the equator. If, additionally, it is circling the sun, it is moving through space at the much higher velocity of 66,780 mph. (30 km/s.) What follows are various experiments designed to detect this movement, and to measure the speed of light as it travels through different media that can have a bearing on this problem.

The 18th and 19th Century saw an enormous outburst of scientific investigation by some brilliant men, their discoveries laying the foundation to the present wealth of scientific knowledge and the economic advantages that have flowed from them. Two areas of major discoveries in the 20th century were the transmission of electromagnetic waves and the working parts of the atom.

These discoveries led into a consideration of the way in which these waves are propagated through space. In order for waves to travel, they need some form of medium to transfer their energy from one place to another, in the same way that water can transmit ripples across its surface. It was therefore postulated that there was such a medium existing and it was given the name of

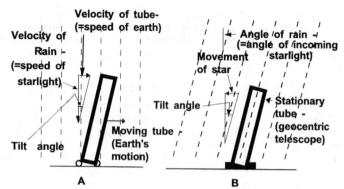

Fig. 2. The moving and stationary tubes (telescopes)

the aether - or ether in some publications.

There are two motions that the earth may have - translational (movement through the aether - around the sun) and rotational (its spin on its axis). We will examine them in this order, although they are at times part of the same investigation.

TRANSLATIONAL MOVEMENT

Bradley's "aberration" measurements.

Bradley accurately measured the direction of a star from 1725 to 1728 and found that it moved in a very small circle. He assumed that this was due to the movement of the earth through the aether. As the earth moved around the sun, its velocity of 30 km/s meant that he had to tilt the telescope slightly forward in the direction of travel to get the light from the star to pass down the centreline.

This can be explained by imagining a tube being held upright in vertically falling rain. If the tube is now moved relative to the rain, it will have to be tilted slightly forward to get the rain to fall down the centre of the tube (Fig. 2A). The amount of tilting depends upon the speed of the falling rain and the horizontal velocity of the tube. For Bradley, these were really the speed of light and the velocity of the earth, and the small angle was only 20.5 seconds of arc, giving a circle with a diameter of 41 seconds of arc.

This may appear to be proof of the motion of the earth, but there is an equally valid explanation - which is that the star, and the light from it, is moving relative to a stationary earth as shown in Fig. 2B. The amount of tilt would be exactly the same.

It should be noted that this small variation applies to all stars and should not be confused with parallax measurements of nearby stars as seen against the background of distant stars. The path for this measurement is also circular, but is at 90 degrees to the aberration measurement as shown in Fig. 3. The parallax measurement is used to calculate the distance of these nearby stars, knowing the baseline distance of the earth's orbit around the sun. The distance to the those further away are estimated using a number of assumptions and indirect methods.

Thus, Bradley's aberration measurements gave no proof of any movement of the earth. The next experiment using this approach was even more surprising.

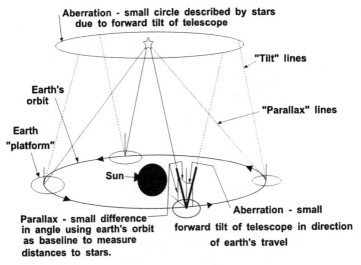

Fig. 3. Aberration and parallax

"Airy's Failure"

In the Fig. 2A above, if the rain falling down the tube were to be slowed up (say by a fan blowing upwards), the tube would have to be tilted even further. This is because the rain is falling vertically but slower but the tube is still travelling at the same speed. Therefore the ratio of horizontal speed to falling speed is greater, requiring a larger angle.

In 1871, Airy, the Astronomer Royal, repeated Bradley's measurements but filled the telescope with water, slowing the light down to 77% of its normal speed. He found that *no further tilting was needed*. Referring to Fig. 2B, we can see that the tube is stationary *and the light is already coming in at the "correct" angle* because the speed of the star is still the same relative to the stationary earth. Going slower in the tube will not affect the angle. Therefore, even if the speed of the rain is slower down the tube, no additional tipping is required. In the case of the starlight, this would be coming in at the same angle as the tilt of the telescope, so no extra tilt would be required.

The aether "drag" of light

There is an alternative explanation for this, which is that the earth is actually moving, but it is "dragging" the aether around with it as it circles the sun. Before we consider this, we should note what is happening. The most obvious conclusion that the earth is stationary is overcome by an *additional*

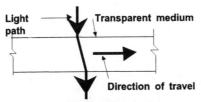

Fig. 4. Fresnell drag

hypothesis. This is, of course, yet another example of this ploy being put into operation.

Airey, in fact, was expecting no change because of an experiment performed by Arago in 1810 in which he found that light shining through a moving sheet of glass was displaced in the direction of this movement as shown in Fig. 4. This was called Fresnell Drag after the scientist who studied the subject. This dragging effect could explain why the light is reaching the telescope at an angle that is not changed when the telescope is filled with water.

What is interesting is that careful experiments have shown that probably the light is travelling through the glass at the same speed as through air, but that there is a superposition effect that makes it appear that the speed is slower. If this is the case, Bouw suggests that the actual speed of light might be infinite, but experienced this "superposition effect" in aether to give it its present speed of 299,792 km/s and lower speed still in denser mediums.

We have already discussed in the preceding appendix (p 486) the problems in the assumption that the aether is dragged by the earth in its orbit around the sun and in its daily rotation. It would surely mean that the starlight would be bent as it entered the moving and rotating aether - and star directions would vary as they came in at different angles throughout the daily cycle.

In 1892 Sir Oliver Lodge performed a dangerous experiment in which two massive metal discs 1m in diameter were spun at very high speed close to his head to see if light shining between them was affected by any drag of the aether caused by the rotating discs. None whatsoever was found (Bee).

The Michelson-Morley experiment

On the assumption that the aether was stationary, then as objects, such as the earth, moved through it, it should be possible to detect this relative movement by its effect upon light waves. To this end, the famous Michelson-Morley experiment (Mich) was carried out in 1887, which produced a null result; i.e. no movement of the earth around the sun could be detected. We have examined this whole subject in detail in Appendix 8, and shown how Einstein's relativity theory was produced mainly to overcome the apparent lack of movement of the earth through the aether.

The non-null results.

This experiment was later carried out several times by other scientists, with much the same result, the degree of accuracy being within 0.5 Km/sec. In the original Michelson-Morley and all later similar experiments, this result, surprisingly was *not* zero. A fairly small positive value was registered that seemed to vary from one location to another, all in the range of two to ten kilometres per second (MillD). Later, the experiment was carried out using laser beams and gave a result of only 1 km/s. Bouw suggested that with even more careful measurements, the true figure could be zero, placing the earth at the centre of a stationary aether.

Various criticisms have been made but refuted and careful checks made to see if there are any instrumental errors that could explain these positive results. None have been discovered.

Dayton C. Miller made many measurements in different locations and published the results (MillD). Allais, a Nobel prizewinner, analysed these results and concluded that there was a periodicity that corresponded to sidereal time, that they could determine where the earth was on its orbit around the sun, and that the earth was moving towards the Hercules constellation (Allais98). These results are still very strange and there is no easy explanation for them. Miller's latest results indicated movement of the aether that approximately accorded with the direction of star streaming which we now consider.

Star Streaming.

Very accurate measurements of the positions of stars has shown that they appear to be moving apart in one area of the sky and "closing up" in the opposite direction. This is the effect that would be seen if the sun were to be moving towards this point in the sky and the stars were "streaming" past it as it moved in space. This movement is towards the constellation of Hercules.

It is now thought that this streaming is not due to the movement of the earth so much as the stars passing the earth as they slowly revolve around the centre of the mass of stars that make up our own galaxy, known as the Milky Way.

Interestingly, galaxies appear to stream in another direction.

Surprisingly, it is reported that Marinov (Marin74) and Silvertooth have independently measured the passage of the earth through the aether as 300 km/s (Q24/4:216). This was probably obtained by using a one way measurement of the speed of light in different directions. This seems to contradict the result of the Michelson-Morley experiment, but this relied on interference between light paths that have been on a "round trip". Aspden calculated a movement through the aether of 120 km/s (Asp69:184). If this movement is correct it would surely raise problems in the observation of starlight, for there should be easily detectable difference in the spectra of stars approaching compared with those receding, but none have been found. These measurements are just some of the observations that astronomers and physicists cannot easily explain.

ROTATIONAL MOVEMENT

There are several phenomena that seem to demonstrate very clearly that the earth is rotating. We will first explain the three that are the most well known and then show that there is a perfectly good alternative explanation that would give exactly the same result.

(A) Foucault's pendulum.

In 1851 Jean Foucault swung a heavy weight in the dome of the Pantheon in Paris. The explanation given was that as the earth turned on its axis, the free

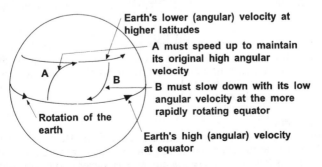

Fig. 5. The Coriolis effect

pendulum remained in the same direction in space and appeared to be slowly turning in the opposite direction inside the building. If you imagine a pendulum suspended over the north pole, then as the earth rotated anti-clockwise (eastwards) beneath it, the path of the swing of the pendulum would seem to slowly rotate in a clockwise direction at a rate of 15 degrees every hour. This seemed to be convincing proof of the earth's rotation, because the pendulum swings freely in the direction it was started on whilst the earth rotates beneath it.

This neat display of the earth turning beneath a "free" pendulum is, however, carefully contrived to ensure that it gives the "right results" - as we will see later.

(B) The Coriolis effect.

We have all seen ice skaters spinning on one spot with their arms outstretched. Then as they bring them into their body, the spin gets faster. This is because they have a certain amount of rotational energy as they spin with their arms out. As they draw them in, this energy remains the same, and as their arms are at a shorter distance from the centre of the spin, they will automatically spin faster to keep this energy of spin constant.

Let us now apply this to the movement of air masses in weather systems. Imagine a mass of air just above the equator, stationary relative to the earth as it is spinning at the same speed in an anti-clockwise direction as viewed from our north. If now this mass is drawn towards the north by a depression, it will then be on a latitude that is not spinning as fast as the latitude it was originally on. In order to maintain the same amount of rotational energy, it will have to move faster in an anti-clockwise direction to compensate for the slower speed of the earth at this latitude. It will therefore curl as shown in Fig. 5. The opposite will occur for a mass of air more northerly, also attracted to the south by a depression, but in this case it will go slower on a latitude that is rotating faster than the more northern latitude it was on. These results are said to be due to the Coriolis effect, and explain why depressions (or anti-cyclones) in the northern hemisphere always rotate clockwise. Similarly, a high mound of air in the northern hemisphere that disperses north and south will rotate anti-clockwise, forming a cyclone.

(C) The earth's bulge.

The rotation of the earth makes it wider at the equator where the speed is greatest and the centrifugal force pulls on the rocks to give the equatorial bulge. The radius at the equator is 6,378,099 metres but the polar radius is 21,468 metres less.

....

All these last three examples certainly seem to provide fairly conclusive evidence that the earth rotates on its axis. But there is a quite different explanation. This depends upon the effect of the whole of the universe which includes the enormous mass of the stars and galaxies. This brings in a principle enunciated by Mach.

Mach's Principle.

Ernst Mach is best known for giving his name to the supersonic speeds of flight - Mach 1 is at the speed of sound, etc. He also proposed an important principle which is that the mass of the universe is a major controlling factor in all relative movements of the various bodies, particularly the planetary system relative to the rest of the universe. Whether the universe rotates around the earth or the earth spins on its axis is indeterminable. It is a matter of the geometry of moving bodies and whatever reference grid we choose should give exactly the same results.

In fact, the subject of geocentricity is held in such horror by orthodox scientist, that rather than use such an emotive word, they prefer to refer to "Mach's Principle" as a code word for the same subject.

This question of determining which is the correct view raises an important philosophical point. In order to see whether the universe or the earth is rotating, we would have to go outside the universe. But this would automatically involve examining the scene from a position that was a stable reference point. But we cannot actually get outside the universe, even theoretically.

Firstly, how would we know that we are really outside of everything and that our base was truly stationary. Secondly, being outside the created universe would place us in the position of God, which is hardly achievable for mortals.

The relationship of relative rotation between the universe and the earth has been examined by various physicists mathematically, and the most advanced is by two Italian scientists.

Barbour and Bertotti

Starting with simple basic facts, these experts derived certain formulae that described the motion in general throughout the universe (Barbour - see also in Bouw's *Geocentric Papers*). From these they derived Newton's and Kepler's Laws, the perihelion precession of Mercury, the critical maximum speed of light and certain relativistic effects without invoking Einstein's Relativity. Indeed, they state they worked in a "pre-relativistic, classic framework". Their paper was published in 1977 but little further seems to have been done on this subject since then.

Part of their analysis was to have a sphere (the earth) in the centre of a much larger rotating hollow sphere (the universe). They found that the effect of the outer rotating sphere on the inner sphere due to its gravitational attraction, drag etc. produced on the inner sphere *exactly the same results that would give the Coriolis effect, Foucault's pendulum, bulging at the equators etc. Thus, there was no difference in effect whether the earth or the universe were rotating.* This is exactly in accord with Mach's Principle.

There were other interesting relationships that arose out of their "model":

(a) From their formulae they found that "The Universe is its own clock". Although not an exact parallel, one is reminded of Genesis 1:14, "And God said, Let there be lights in the firmament of heaven to divide the day from the night; and let them be for signs and for seasons, and for days, and years."

(b) Although the speed of light did not enter into their equations, they found that the "bulk of the matter of the universe" is receding (or approaching) at half the speed of light; i.e. the diameter is changing at the speed of light, which they say is "a remarkable coincidence."

(c) They derive an explanation for the precession of the orbits of the planets. They conclude they have a "natural explanation for what are otherwise "cosmic coincidences" between the parameters of the Universe and the elements of the planets."

(d) The Coriolis force is sometimes referred to as a "pseudo-force". In their.

model it becomes an actual force due to gravitational attraction by the rotating cosmos.

(e) One correspondent wrote to me and said, "The 'cosmic constant' was introduced by Einstein c 1917 to massage his General Relativity theory into line with a "static" universe, since all the solutions otherwise pointed to an expanding or contracting universe.... It was in fact an *ad hoc* hypothesis."

The authors parallel this by saying:

> By putting them (c and G) as "fundamental constants" into his local physics, Einstein may have unwittingly [!] smuggled into general relativity integrated properties of the Universe, which then, of course, show up in planetary dynamics.

Reviewing their paper, Bouw says:

> ... a lot of different and heretofore unrelated physics falls into place into a coherent whole. In other words, their geocentric model is more general and potentially more fruitful than the current heliocentric (acentric) model. In short, the geocentric model reflects reality better than does the heliocentric model.
>
> .... Barbour and Bertotti's approach promises to be able to integrate much if not all of physics into a single theoretical framework. That is the philosophy inherent in geocentricity (Bou92:317).

This subject of the effect of a rotating universe is an important explanation of geocentric theory at a fundamental level, and Bouw has more original papers on it and lists others in his *Geocentric Papers* (Bouw93B).

....

Having shown how the three "proofs" of the rotation of the earth are capable of a geocentric explanation which is also more productive, there are a few other subjects that should be dealt with.

The artificiality of the Foucault pendulum.

Richard Elmendorf has made a special study of the Foucault pendulum and has found that it is far from being the simple classic demonstration of the rotation of the earth that it is made out to be. If any long pendulum is set swinging, it will not show the gradual smooth progression of earth's rotation. It will develop a small ellipsoidal pattern, which may be clockwise or counter-clockwise, it may get "stuck" on one line, even go backwards to the expected rotation. This erratic behaviour has been the bane of physicists ever since Foucault demonstrated the first pendulum. Elmendorf quotes one physicist as saying, "Thus, if care is not taken, a Foucault pendulum can appear to turn at the wrong rate, or even indicate that the earth is turning backwards" (Elm:38 quoting p 182 of Mackay, R.S. *American Journal of Physics* v 21 p 180 March 1953)

In order to obtain the "correct" rate of turn to convince the onlookers that the earth is turning, various methods are used, the most effective means of preventing the ellipsoid movements developing being the Charron ring. This is a

Path of pendulum (exaggerated)

Rotation of earth

Centre of swing

Start point

Fig. 6. The elliptical curve of the Foucault pendulum

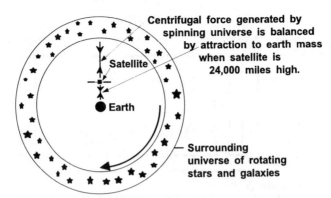

Centrifugal force generated by
spinning universe is balanced
by attraction to earth mass
when satellite is
24,000 miles high.

Satellite

Earth

Surrounding
universe of rotating
stars and galaxies

Fig. 7. The balance of forces on the geostationary satellite

ring, positioned just below the support, which the suspension wire just touches at the end of each swing. Some rings are fixed; others are loose. The most sensitive point to apply this "correcting" force is at the end of the swing, and Elmendorf wonders whether this is why in some demonstrations the point of the bob is made to touch sand as a marker of its progress. Its real use may have been to apply this small force to prevent the oscillations becoming too "wild" as they will always naturally become unless deliberately prevented.

The reason for the ellipses tending to occur is said to be due to the coriolis force. As the bob swings across the floor, the earth has turned slightly, so the bob effectively "curls" to the right by a very small amount - in the northern hemisphere. This is repeated on the return path and thus an ellipse is set up as indicated in Fig. 6.

Allais carried out many experiments on pendulums and expressed his bafflement at the varying results he obtained. He did find an unexpected 2hr 50 min correlation with the sun-moon system (All98).

Elmendorf complains that the impulse mechanisms used to keep the pendulum swinging for long periods, the various suspension systems, Charron rings etc. all have to be very carefully "tuned" to ensure that the whole system gives the "right result". He considers that the artificiality of the pendulum makes it a "fake", which in some sense it is, for it does not produce the right movements unless "encouraged" to do so.

It is agreed that the pendulum ought to perform the motion expected. However, the smooth, convincing path traced out by all the Foucault pendulums in museums around the world can only be achieved by some very sophisticated and carefully adjusted apparatus behind the scenes - a fact that the admiring public are totally unaware of.

The geosynchronous satellite.

If a satellite is launched eastwards and circles the earth at a height of 24,000 miles (38,640 km) at a precise speed, it will stay over the same position on the earth as the earth also turns eastwards. If it is faster it will spiral away from the earth to a higher orbit, and if lower, it will gradually spiral to a lower orbit.

In a geocentric system, it has been shown that the centrifugal force is a real, gravitational force induced by the spinning universe. At a height of 24,000 miles, the upward centrifugal force caused by the universe exactly balances the downward terrestial gravitational force (Fig. 7).

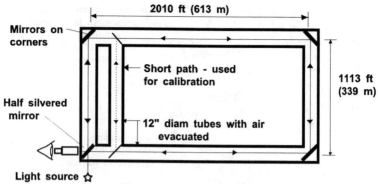

Fig. 8. The Michelson-Gale experiment

Whilst on this subject, NASA always fires its rockets eastwards in the direction of the rotation of the earth so that its rotation speed is added to that of the rocket - the "slingshot effect". The geocentric explanation is that what they are really seeking to do is to get the speed of the rocket as fast as they can *relative* to the circling universe. They therefore launch it *against* the direction that the universe is rotating. This is a perfectly justifiable explanation that gives the same result.

It is also interesting to note that the orbits for the numerous spacecraft to other planets are all calculated using the earth as the centre of the coordinates - i.e. as though the earth were the centre of the planetary system.

The Michelson-Gale experiment.

In 1925 an experiment, similar to the Michelson-Morley experiment described above, was carried out but in this case, the light was sent round a large evacuated tube laid out in a rectangular shape 2,010 ft x 1,113 ft in a field near Chicago (Fig. 8).

The Michelson-Morley experiment tried to detect the speed of the earth through the aether as it circled the sun. As we know, no speed of this order was found. The purpose of this experiment was to see if there was any measurement of the *rotation* of the earth on its axis - or if the aether was rotating around the earth. By having one length of the tube at one latitude and the corresponding length at a (slightly) different latitude, the different rate at which the earth is turning at these two latitudes should give a measure of the earth's rotation; i.e. the one nearest to the north pole will be moving slower through the aether than the one nearer to the equator.

This time a movement *was* measured and *the rotation of the earth was found to be within 2% of the predicted value.*

Therefore, from the results of these two experiments - the Michelson-Morley and Michelson-Gale, the obvious conclusion is that the sun, the planets and the whole universe rotates around the earth, and the aether rotates with it. The movement of the aether past the instrument in the Michelson-Gale experiment could of course be either the turning of the earth or, with equal validity for the geocentrist, the rotation of the universe and the aether past a stationary earth.

The Sagnac experiment.

This was carried out by Sagnac in 1913 (Sag) and was found to be able to

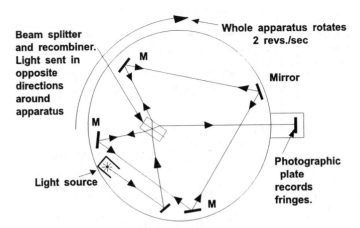

Fig. 9. Sagnac's experiment

detect rotation of an apparatus relative to the aether. Fig. 9 shows the apparatus.

In this, light is reflected in both directions from mirrors in a roughly circular pattern and any difference in the time taken could be measured by the fringe interference patterns as was done in the Michelson-Morley experiment above. The whole point of this experiment was that the mirrors and the "observer" (a recording camera) were rotated at a rate of only 2 cycles per second.

This may not appear to be very fast but was sufficient to record a time difference between the beam going with the turning of the table, and that going against it.

This experiment is particularly important for it upsets many orthodox theories and Einstein's relativity theory *cannot explain the Sagnac effect.*

The reason is as follows. Imagine a scientist in a laboratory with the reflecting mirrors, light source etc. of the Sagnac experiment. While it is stationary, he passes the light in both directions and finds no difference in the fringe measurements. Now the whole laboratory is revolved slowly; he will now see a movement of the fringes. But he is still within the laboratory and will be unaware that the whole laboratory (i.e. his "frame of reference") is turning. (We will ignore any centrifugal force he would feel; the original experiment used a camera on the rotating table to record the fringe movements). The reason that the fringes move is that the aether is a stable stationary frame of reference for the light rays that have to pass through it.

Thus, this experiment detects movement *without having to refer to any other body.* This shows that the aether exists as a frame of reference such that the speed of light can be measured against it. Yet it is a fundamental assumption of relativity that the aether does not exist.

It will be obvious that the experiment cannot determine whether it is the laboratory turning or the aether rotating around the laboratory. This is a subject we will return to later.

Recent experiments using faster rotations, lasers etc. have greatly increased the sensitivity of the results and the original findings have been fully confirmed. This discovery has been put to practical use. Laser gyrocompasses use light that is passed both ways down a fibreglass cable which has many coils to increase its sensitivity to turning. They are now regularly used as the main compass in aeroplanes and the Japanese are also installing them in some of their cars.

The equipment is also sensitive enough to detect the rotation of the aether around the earth which is not daily (24 hours) but siderial (23 hrs. 56 mins.), i.e. it is linked to the stars (See ref-Sted. Refd. in BA v 8 n 85 p 26 Summer 1998).

Dr. Kelly's memoranda.

We have referred to the work of Dr. Kelly and his criticisms of the Hafele-Keating experiment of flying clocks around the world to prove Einstein's relativity theory. The three memoranda he wrote were on the subject of the behaviour of light (Kell). In these he mentions the Sagnac experiment, Airy's failure, the Michelson-Gale experiment and the unexpected results of the spinning disc and magnet (Fig. 2 App.9). His final conclusion which he proposes (in an emphasised block) is:

> Light, generated upon the earth, travels with the earth on its orbit around the sun, but not with the spin of the earth upon its axis.

He contends that the aether travels with the earth's gravitational field, "but does not *adapt* [!] to the daily spin of the earth upon its axis." But why should it be influenced by the lateral movement of the earth but not by its rotation? His theory would allow measurement of the *slower* speed of the daily rotation of the earth, but not the *faster* movement of the earth around the sun. All this could be far better, and more logically, explained if the earth is considered at rest with the aether and the universe rotating around it - i.e. geocentricity. This may indeed be his basic concept but to claim as much is to invite the usual degree of professional ridicule. His clear presentation of much of the information we have dealt with above may nevertheless give his colleagues cause to think.

POSITIVE EVIDENCE FOR GEOCENTRICITY.

There are various astronomical observations that indicate that the earth is at the centre of the universe.

1. Varshni's quasar redshifts.

Quasars are very large and bright star-like objects that are thought to be at immense distances away. Varshni grouped 384 of them into the types of spectra they give. He found that 152 of them fell into 57 groups of very similar spectra. When he then examined the amount of redshift they each had, he was surprised to find that each quasar in each group had very similar red-shifts! It is usually assumed that increasing red-shift of the spectra indicates increasing distance from the earth as the objects move rapidly away from us. Therefore to have the same redshift would mean that they are the same distance from the earth.

This result is little short of astonishing, for it would place the earth at the centre of these "shells" of quasars (Fig. 10). If the earth were to be significantly shifted from its present position relative to them, the spectral grouping should still be the same, but the red-shifts (i.e. distance) for each quasar would be quite different to their present values and would have no correlation with the groupings as they have at present. This places the earth in a special position relative to these quasars. (This assumes that red-shift is a measure of distance, but if, as Halton Arp maintains, it is not - Section 2.2 - , then the whole of the Big Bang theory and modern cosmology is undermined in any case.)

Varshni calculated that the odds against this arrangement being pure

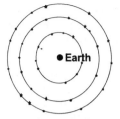

Fig. 10. Varshni's 'shells' of galaxies

chance was 3 x 10^86. Having dismissed two explanations, he concluded:

> The earth is indeed the centre of the Universe. The arrangement of quasars on certain spherical shells is only with respect to the earth. These shells would disappear if viewed from another galaxy or quasar. This means that the cosmological principle would have to go. Also it implies that a coordinate system fixed to the earth will be a preferred frame of reference in the Universe. Consequently, both the Special and General Theory of Relativity must be abandoned for cosmological purposes (Varsh:8).

He is unwilling to accept this, however, describing it as "an unaesthetic possibility", and questions whether the red-shifts are real.

Attempts were made to discredit his findings but not with any convincing success. It was also rumoured that he had changed his mind but he was still holding to it in 1989 and considered that if an analysis were to be carried out on the 2,000 or more known quasars, the result would be much the same.

Like many other phenomena, this subject is referred to as the "quasar distribution problem" by astronomers. It is obvious that there is no problem with the measurements; they can understand them perfectly. The real problem they have is that they must hold to the heliocentric, or more correctly acentric, concept of the universe to avoid rejection by their peers. Varshni's results present further evidence against their increasingly threatened model.

Having set out this evidence, we would note that Setterfield's latest paper, yet to be published, gives an explanation of stepped red-shift measurements in both galaxies and quasars which have been observed by Tifft.

As far as this writer can see, this does not nullify Varshni's evidence as the stepped red-shifts are still an indication of distance. The type of spectra would be specific to each quasar and this should not be related to its distance from the earth. Yet Varshni's investigation indicates that there *is* a connection,

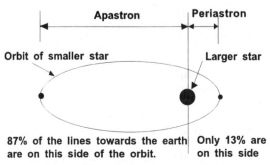

Fig. 11. The Barr "effect" in binary stars

making the earth a central point of quasars with similar spectra.

Until a physical explanation can be provided for why a particular red-shift should produce a specific spectra, then this remains evidence for geocentricity.

2. The "Barr Effect" - or the "problem" of the orientation of binary stars.

Spectral binary stars are pairs of stars rotating about each other that can only be detected from their double set of varying spectral lines. The elliptical orbit of their paths is not at a random angle to the earth. The original investigation by Barr showed that 26 out of 30 (87%) had orbits that were elongated towards the earth (Fig. 11), and a later investigation of 1,000 binaries showed that this trend was maintained (Batten).

This evidence is not compelling as there may be an acceptable explanation not yet found, but until it is, this is at least another reason for believing that the earth's position in space has particular significance relative to many other astronomical bodies.

I note in passing that this is a problem that astronomers have no explanation for and it is brushed aside as being only an "effect". There is no indication of there being any "effect" on anything: it is simply a fact of observation. Quite what could have brought about this "effect" that resulted in this preferred orientation is rarely discussed.

3. Walls of galaxies.

A galaxy is a collection of millions of stars, usually in a flat disc with a thicker centre - like a fried egg! Our sun is said to be an average star positioned about half way towards the edge of one of them.

Looking beyond the stars of our galaxy, a huge number of other galaxies can been seen. It is worth recording that modern astronomy has no adequate theory of how stars could have formed or then collected into galaxies following the Big Bang. Ignoring this major problem for a moment, it might be thought that if there had been a big explosion at the beginning of the universe, it would be expected that all the various celestial objects would be fairly randomly distributed in the space around our galaxy. Very surprisingly, this is not the case. In fact there has been found a dense cluster of galaxies, labelled The Great Wall, centred on our galaxy (or the earth!).

Later observations showed that the wall extended around the whole of the sky, but was partly obscured by the stars of our own galaxy in some areas of the sky.

This wall was eventually seen to be only the nearest of no less than seven concentric shells of galaxies, each one sufficiently dense to be called a Wall. Not only this, but the red shifts of these galaxies were collected into intervals of 72 km/sec, an observation fully confirmed later by others (Guth).

4. The uniformity of the microwave background.

This is an item that appeared in the *Encyclopaedia Britannica*, 15th edition, v 16 p 782, entitled "Microwave background radiation".

> Consider the background radiation coming to an observer on the Earth from any two opposite sides of the sky. Clearly, whatever the ultimate sources (hot plasma) for this radiation, the photons, travelling at the speed of light since their emission by the sources, have only had time to reach the earth now. The matter on one side

of the sky could not have had time to have "communicated" with the matter on the other side (they are beyond each others event horizon) that they "know" to have the same temperature approaching one part in 10^4.

If we were not at the centre of the universe, we might expect the intensity and/or the frequency of this radiation to vary in some small degree. We have discussed the efforts to find some minute variation in order to explain the formation of stars and galaxies in Section 2.2. That it is so extremely uniform presents a considerable problem to astronomers. To the geocentrist, this is precisely the result he would expect. With the earth at the centre of the universe, the radiation, whatever its source, if it was universal and galactic in origin, would then be very uniform indeed to us at the centre.

....

The examples we have set out above are only a few of a number of observations that puzzle scientists, and Bouw gives several more in his *Geocentricity* of a more technical nature. The interesting fact is that the implications of some experiments do not appear to support the implications of others, and there is no whole picture of the cosmos or of atomic physics that scientists can provide that is completely self-consistent.

In some cases, the evidence is too sparse to say that it definitely supports geocentricity, but Bouw maintains that no experiments or observations have yet incontrovertibly contradicted the geocentric proposition.

Astronomers are sometimes baffled by what they find and do not know how to handle it. They therefore tend to ignore it. One can understand their reluctance to draw the attention of students to what they cannot explain. With regard to evidence that supports geocentricity this work seeks to repair this omission in some small measure by bringing it to the attention of the wider public.

THE "PROBLEM" OF THE ROTATING UNIVERSE

There is no doubt one question that will at the forefront of many minds as they read of the whole universe spinning around the earth once every 24 hours; "Would not the stars on the fringes of space be travelling at incredible speeds and the centrifugal force be phenomenally high?". On this Bouw (Bou92:316) refers to the work of Rosser (Rosser:460) who has shown that the universe would not fall apart even if it was spinning at trillions of times per second.

In order to deal with this question, we have to delve into the fundamental nature of space, aether and matter. The subject is obviously extremely complex, both in concepts and in mathematics. What is here presented is a simplified outline of the relevant topics which can give an explanation of certain phenomena. We have already seen that much that is perceived by both scientists and the general public is contradicted by a number of facts. What follows is based upon certain concepts that arise out of highly mathematical methods that are found to fit the evidence of particle physics. They are offered for the consideration of those interested in pursuing the subject a little further. For those not inclined this way, they can go direct to the philosophical aspects.

a) Planck's constant

As physicists discovered more about the properties of the various atoms, they found that there were certain underlying basic values that seemed to link.

many of these properties together. It will be sufficient to say that they are related to Planck's constant - a measure of the smallest amount of energy that can be transmitted. Planck used this with the speed of light and the gravitational constant, and produced several other fundamental constants of length, time, mass etc. now called Planck particles (or massive superstrings). These, with his energy value, are:

Planck energy = 6.63 x 10^-34 joule.sec. (1.05 x 10^-27 ergs.sec)
Planck length = 1.616 x 10^-33 cm
Planck time = 5.39 x 10^-44 secs.
Planck mass = 2.177 x 10^-5 grms.
Planck temperature = 1.417 x 10^32 degrees Kelvin.
Planck density = 3.6 x 10^93 gm/cm^3

The time and length are incredibly small, but the mass is about the weight of a grain of sand. These fundamental values seem to link many phenomena in the world of physics. The Planck dimension, which is much smaller than an atom (10^-13 cm) is of importance, for it is considered to be the dimension of the particles that constitute the aether. These particles have Planck's density and constitute a mass that entirely fills space. This gives rise to the "plenum" (Greek for "full") theory which is like "string theory".

b) The plenum theory.

This is the concept that the aether is not a vast emptiness, but is actually packed with an extremely dense "material", within and through which the particles of matter move. The density of these material particles, even when the size of a planet or star, is insignificant compared with that of the plenum, and therefore matter is controlled by the aether. It has very little effect at the human level, but does affect it at the extreme ends of the dimensional scale - the atomic and astronomic.

It might be thought that with such high density, matter would be unable to move, but an aqualung diver can operate at great depths and pressures just as easily as near the surface. The pressure has little effect upon his movements. Similarly, we are all subject to air pressure of 15 lbs per sq. inch., yet we can all move quite freely and ignore its presence.

There is some scriptural support for this. The root (*"raqa"*) of the Hebrew for "FIRMament" (*"raqiya"*) implies "hardness" for it refers to the stretching of metal sheets by beating them - a possible reference to the stretching of the heavens described in Isaiah 42:5 and many other passages.

This dense aether controls the activity of matter (electrons, protons and muons) for as they are charged particles, they can only move in circles, hence the rotation of the electron around the nucleus etc. and the gravitational forces making the planets follow elliptical orbits. Indeed, straight line movement cannot take place in a plenum. and it is here that the infinitely dense plenum theory of Harold Aspden would operate. We have briefly described Aspden's plenum theory in the previous appendix, and it is a modification of this that Bouw has used to provide an interesting result.

With all stable masses, there is a point called the mechanical equilibrium, when its energy of rotation is equal to its gravitational energy. Bouw has used this factor, and by adding in the small mass of the material in the known universe, finds that there is a rotational speed of about 3.6 x 10^-5 radians/sec. This is extremely close to the rotation of the earth which is 7.27 x 10^-5 rad/s. i.e. *It is equal to a revolution once every two days compared with the earth's once per day!*

This is really much closer than it appears. In cosmological calculations huge numbers are involved, and to be within 100 times (10^2 logarithm) the correct value is considered to be very accurate. With the uncertainties in this calculation, using logarithmic values, 100 times would be effectively about 2%. To be only twice the value is within 0.3% of the known rotation of the earth! (Bouw95).

From this, it would seem that we have a reasonable explanation of the rotation of the universe around the earth, as it needs this rotation in order to remain stable. Were there no rotation, the universe would immediately collapse. The presence of the material universe embedded within it makes little difference to the total mass.

If this theory, or one like it, is correct, then we have a solution to the problem of the very high centrifugal forces that would be generated by a 24 hour rotation. The mass of the universe would be swamped by the very much higher density of the plenum material.

We would here mention that there is now evidence that the universe is rotating, but only very slowly (Nod). This is not related to the 24 hr. rotation that Bouw has calculated as discussed above. Godell analysed the situation of the universe which did not expand forever and found that it predicted a very faint magnetic field which has been discovered, and that this slow rotation of the universe *within* the rapidly rotating firmament could explain the red-shift of galaxies. This is yet another explanation for this phenomena (Surd. Ref. in BA v 8 n 85 p 27 Summer 1998).

SOME PHILOSOPHICAL CONSIDERATIONS.

We have travelled through some strange but, we would hope, nevertheless interesting ground in pursuing this subject. We will close with three related subjects that were noted during the extensive reading for this controversial topic.

1. THE EXISTENCE OF MATTER - AND GOD!

In his discussion of the plenum model, Bouw raised an interesting philosophical point which I present in his words for the contemplation of the reader. He headed the paragraph:

"Ex Nihilo"

> We start at the beginning with absolute nothing. The tendency is to treat "nothing" as a "thing", but its name, "no-thing" belies that. "Nothing" cannot have any properties or attributes. In particular, "nothing" cannot have length, volume, time or intelligence. It can have neither beginning nor end. It cannot have an origin and it cannot be a thing. In short, it cannot have the property of existence and so cannot exist. Since it is true that "absolute nothing" cannot exist anywhere at any time, then its inverse must also be true, that "absolute everything" must exist always and everywhere. Now do not confuse "absolute everything" with absoluteLY everything". This absolute existence must have all the inverse properties of nothingness. Whereas the nothing had no size, its inverse must be infinite in extent or omnipresent. Whereas nothing has no knowledge, its inverse must be omniscient. Whereas nothing has no existence, its inverse must have infinite existence. Whereas nothing has no power, its inverse is omnipotent. These are precisely the

characteristics of God as presented in the scripture. (Note that these characteristics require God to have a character and personality also.) Thus we have arrived at the necessary existence of God as inferred from the very existence and order built into the universe. This observation also illuminates the error of the big-bang hypothesis, namely, that the big-bang-produced universe is too small and too uncharacteristic to be realistic.

So there was nothing at all before God, and God came from nowhere because there is nowhere God could come from. Hence God is reasonable and he even invites us to reason with him, for he says: "Come now, let us reason together" in Isaiah 1:18. For God to truly be omnipresent and omniscient, he must be a plenum in the fullest sense of that word; but God is more than the material plenum of the Greek philosophers and Aspden. God is intelligent creative and all-powerful. As is taught in Romans 1:20a:

"For the invisible things of him from the creation of the world are clearly seen, being understood by the things that are made, (even) his eternal power and Godhead" (Bou92:321).

2. IS THERE AN "INFORMATION FIELD"?

Without going into technical details, there are experiments (the dual slit and electron spin measurements in Quantum Theory) that defy normal explanations for there appears to be some *instantaneous* passing of information from one part of the apparatus to the other that determines the action of each electron. Quantum Theory deals with this mathematically, but uses probability theory and cannot give a physical explanation.

There were some secular experts referring to this "information field", but I will quote from three creationist experts.

(A) Frangos pointed out that the material world is ultimately only a means of conveying information (DNA, computer programmes, speech etc.) and suggested this is a field that is behind all existence and is "an issue beyond the capability [of] an empirical scientific approach and investigation" (Fran). This has since been detected and the speed of communication through the firmament is 10^{107} cm/sec or 10^{97} times the speed of light (c 10^{10} cm/sec). Hence the "instantaneous" quantum mechanical events which have so far been consistently confirmed. These various approaches all depend upon the nature of the firmament which is the "quantum field," the "information field," etc.

(B) Prof. Herrmann has a very intricate "D (for "deductive")-world" theory in which he deals with the logic of the language that scientists use and claims that it is capable of explaining Quantum Theory, Relativity effects (of which he is critical) and many other features that seem puzzling (Herr). He considers the "supercontinuity" (The Oneness - of God?) of his model should appeal to those "who adhere to the belief that the ultimate organisation of our universe is classical in character" (Q23/2:51). His model also predicts "hyperfast information subparticles" (Herr).

(C) Gerardus Bouw briefly refers to an "advanced potential" in nature (Bouw92:310f). He notes that Gerber, using "advanced gravitational potential", showed that the spinning of the universe around the earth has the same effect as the turning of the earth on its axis - which we have discussed above. His crude theory reversed "cause and effect" and indicated that earthquakes are due to stresses that build up in the universe which are released when earthquakes take place. Bouw admits this might appear fanciful but notes that the results are indistinguishable from the usual "retarded potential". He then points out that the mathematics of radio waves require a signal to come in from infinity before it can be transmitted into space.

In considering this subject of an "information field", have the physicists here "touched the hem of God's garment" - His omniscience and omnipresence, His close control of all events?

We were unable to find much more on this fascinating topic but would suggest that this is a subject that the knowledgeable reader might like to keep in mind as I am confident that it will increase in importance over the years.

Speed of gravity effects

The speed of light has decreased about $10^{\wedge}10$. The speed of gravity is thought to be about $10^{\wedge}10$ times faster than the present speed of light (Van Fland) which suggests that they may have had the same speed at the date of creation. Setterfield proposes that this was held for the first two days, c then decreasing whilst the propagation of gravity remained constant.

3. THE WILFUL BLINDNESS OF SCIENTISTS.

One critic of relativity commented:

> I pause to note that one may scan Einstein's writings in vain to find mention of the Sagnac or Michelson-Gale experiments. The same can be said of physics textbooks and of the 1971 McGraw-Hill *Encyclopedia of Science and Technology.* ...Such an oversight in these distinguished encyclopedias constitutes a stinging indictment of professional scientific reporting (Dean Turner in Haz:44).

These are not the only encyclopaedias to omit any mention of them, and other "awkward results". The prestigious *Encyclopaedia Britannica* (a gross misnomer as it is now printed and published in America and written by international experts) makes no mention of the Michelson-Gale experiment, no reference whatsoever of Sagnac, and whilst mentioning Fresnell, his lens and other interests, ignores his "Fresnell Drag" experiment.

In this way, for very many years, have students been carefully channelled away from examining *any* evidence that contradicts the "accepted" views of the senior members of the profession. Indeed, we would ask: "How many of the readers of this book with a degree in physics have ever heard of any of these three experiments?" Two creationist friends who were highly qualified and well informed on scientific matters admitted that they had never heard of any of them.

This ignorance is a classic example of the way in which "unacceptable" evidence is ignored and eventually forgotten. The Michelson-Morley experiment was made in 1887. The Michelson-Gale experiment was in 1925. Sagnac's experiment was carried out in 1913. There was plenty of time for the importance of these experiments to have filtered down to students of the subject - yet they never reached them. Their professors probably also had never been informed of them, so how could they teach their pupils? This would have been the pattern for several generations.

In order to prove this, it is suggested that undergraduates, or anyone studying fundamental physics asks their teachers the following simple questions:

(a) Did you know that the Michelson-Morley experiment of 1887 and many later repeats have *never* produced a null result? Values from 1 to 10 km/sec have been recorded.

(b) Did you know that in 1925 Michelson and Gale detected the rotation of the earth (0.5 km/sec) within 2%, but no movement of the earth around the sun (30 km/sec)?

(c) Did you know that in 1913 Sagnac, using light on a rotating platform, easily detected the rotation, which demonstrates the existence of the aether and contradicts relativity?

(d) Have you ever heard of "Airy's failure" and can you explain it?

(e) Can you explain why the above important information has never been taught in any scientific establishment?

It will, of course, require a degree of courage to make any enquiries on these lines. To ask a knowledgeable friend might result in the raising of eyebrows. To enquire of a tutor might give rise to some opposition. To ask a professor during an open lecture would be committing professional suicide! Any enquirer must be prepared to expect only vague and evasive answers or aggressive retorts to such leading questions. Students are warned that the whole field of science is far from being the rational, objective discipline that they probably believe it to be at this present stage of their professional careers.

This ignoring of contradictory evidence is closely paralleled by the way in which students and the public in general are denied access via the mass media of any hard facts that would contradict evolution. Hence their shock when confronted by the clear evidence that it is a false theory. Is it not possible that both the public in general and fellow creationists exhibit precisely the same symptoms of shock and disbelief regarding geocentrism? This would be simply because they also have been denied information, such as the experiments listed above, that might have changed their mind. Had they known of it over a sufficiently long period they would have had time to digest its implications and accommodate it within their "conceptual framework".

Harold Armstrong, an early and very wise editor of the CRSQ, was clearly sympathetic to geocentricity and advised readers to "let these things be considered carefully and in a true Christian spirit, lest some be found fighting against God" (Q12/1:71).

When discussing the subject of geocentrism with others, I have found that ordinary Christians who have a keen interest in creation evidence generally receive it very enthusiastically. From this, I predict that this subject will experience a major leap in both interest and popularity in the evangelical Christian church amongst the ordinary members. This reaction contrasts with the sometimes heated rejection by most of those who are deeply involved in the creation movement, whether qualified or not. This strong reaction raises the possibility that they may be concerned lest their credibility, and that of the creation movement as a whole, should become tainted with such a heresy as geocentrism in the eyes of the world. In such cases, we would suggest that a desire to discover the Truth in all things should be paramount at all times - and ignore the opinion of the world.

Perhaps the day will come when "young-earth" creationists will be prepared to be vilified not only for their views on that heretical subject but also for believing that the earth is the centre of the universe. In the eyes of the world, there is not much more stigma attached to one than the other!

SOME CONCLUDING THOUGHTS

This work has ranged over many subjects, and it is hoped that the reader has been able to share the excitement experienced on discovering some of the interesting facts that support the Biblical record.

It became increasingly clear that several items would not meet with wide approval. Indeed, those who agree with all that has been written will be very few in number. It would have been very easy to have produced a "popular" work, repeating much that has appeared in other books. Research, however, showed that there was much wrong, not just with the current views of the public that have been carefully manipulated by the media to agree with evolution, but with some creationist concepts also. This is unlikely to endear the book to the wider Christian media.

For example, the decrease in the speed of light is still out of favour with many creationist organisations, and questioning the basis of creationist geology may also earn disapproval. Several subjects are far from being Politically Correct and Reformed Doctrine annoys some. To suggest any evolutionist conspiracies is to be "paranoid". To espouse geocentricity disgraces the creationist movement and is equated to dragging it back to Medieval times! One can appreciate the unwillingness of some editors, chairmen and stalwarts of creationism not to be "tarred with the same brush" as this writer will doubtless be. Yet, strangely, very many readers have expressed their appreciation of past works and of sections that have been forwarded of this.

Fully aware of all these factors operating, they have been deliberately ignored for there has been one overriding question that has dominated the composing of this book. This has been touched upon several times already in different ways, for it is the important question when examining evidence: "Is it the Truth?" - as far as can be reasonably ascertained, that is. Where there are several conflicting views, the question is: "Which is nearest to the Truth?" - not, "Which will support my view?" As will have been seen, this has resulted more than once in sections having to be completely rewritten when sound but contradictory evidence has come to hand. Similarly, wherever error has been found, this has been highlighted so that it may no longer mislead others.

Of course, this is not to claim that this book is "true", but it is the nearest reasonable approach that this author could make to that ultimate goal. Where any statement is incorrect, evidence that demonstrates this is welcomed. In view of the opposition that this work will doubtless encounter, no great sales are expected, but should future editions ever be needed, they will be corrected with the best information available. Several questions remain unanswered and these are left as a challenge to those more able, to use what is accurate in this work and then fill in the many gaps still visible in the creationist's explanation of the universe.

Blessed by God in not having to "tone down" or "trim my sails" to any winds of criticism or commercial pressures, the author leaves this book, warts and all, to the mercy of the reader. What is absolutely certain is that when the whole purpose of this wonderful creation is finally revealed to a waiting world, there will be no doubt whatsoever that:

"True Science Agreed with the Bible"

THE FINAL CURTAIN

In this work, we have tried to examine some of the evidence that supports the biblical account of creation. As we have suggested more than once, the reader is unlikely to fundamentally change his viewpoint by what he has read. If he is a Bible-believing Christian he will already be convinced of the facts of creation, and it is hoped that this volume may have been of some benefit in enlarging his understanding of the amazing world in which he finds himself, and how it came to be in its present form. For the convinced evolutionist, there may be considerable interest in a number of the topics touched upon, but no conviction that they are part of a creation by a omnipotent God. We have shown how rationalists, humanists etc. will concoct and proclaim the most ludicrous of theories rather than accept the humbling of their proud spirit that is required of all True Christians.

In surveying the whole of creation, the Flood, the Cross and the final Judgement, it can be looked upon as The Great Drama of the Universe. As we grow up from childhood, we find we are an inhabitant of a strange, demanding, frightening yet generally enjoyable world. We go to school, get some knowledge of the world, marry, have children, strive at our workplace for promotion, hopefully achieve some degree of prominence amongst our peers, get older, retire, and eventually die - leaving the stage for the next generation to make of it what they can.

Everyone, surely, at some point in their life must ask themselves "What is life really all about"!

As we go through our lives, we are like actors in this Great Drama of the Universe. We have our entry lines and having played our parts, finally leave the stage and await the Final Curtain call. The whole play is being watched by The Author and his helpers, but the house lights are down and we cannot see past the brightness of the footlights. However, at one point, the Author came onto the stage, demonstrated for us just how we should be playing our roles, and His death, though hardly noticed, was the pivotal point of the play. He left an outline of His script for all the players and He promised those who recognised who He was that they would live for eternity with Him in His glory.

Like many plays, ours will have a very dramatic conclusion. Following this, every player who has ever taken part will gather for the final curtain call. The stage will be completely filled with all the past players for this great event, and it is then that the audience will show their appreciation of the play. The house lights will go up and every player will be completely dazzled by the brilliance of the glorious spectacle before them.

And then the curtain will fall for the last time. But like all stage curtains, it will fall some distance back from the edge of the stage. Those at the front will receive their accolades and will be thrilled to be invited to dine with the author.

For those behind the falling curtain, however, *to their utter astonishment,* they will be plunged into total darkness, *and all hell will be let loose.*

In view of this scenario, may I leave the reader with just one question?

...Which side of the curtain will YOU be on?....

REFERENCES

NOTES;

Q or *CRSQ* = *Creation Research Society Quarterly*, Published by the CRS, Box 28473, Kansas City, MO 64118, U.S.A. *Creation Matters* is a supplement to the journal.

E or *CENTJ* = *Creation Ex Nihilo Technical Journal*, Published by the Creation Science Foundation, Box 6302, Acacia Ridge, D.C., Qld 4110, Australia.

ICC = *(Proceeding of) International Conferences on Creationism*. There have been three conferences - 1st. in 1986, 2nd. in 1990, 3rd. in 1994. The papers are published by the Creation Science Fellowship, Inc., 362 Ashland Ave., Pittsburgh, PA 15228, U.S.A.

SECC = *Proc. Sixth European Creationist Congress*, Evangelical College, Amersfoort, Holland. 16-19 August 1995.

SF = Science Frontiers - a synopsis of scientific articles edited by Wm. Corliss - See Appendix 9.

* = Recommended
****

Ager, D. 1973 *The Nature of the Stratigraphical Record* Macmillan London.

Ager, D. 1995 *The New Catastrophism* Cambridge Un. Press.

Airy, G. *Proc. Roy. Soc.* London v 20 p 35

Akridge, G.R. 1979 "Venusian Canopy" *CRSQ* v 16 n 3 p 188.

Akridge, G.R. 1980 "The Sun is Shrinking" *ICR Impact* No. 82 April

Akridge, G.R. et al 1981 "A Recent Creation Explanation of the 3° K background Black Body Radiation" *CRSQ* v 18 n 3 p 159-162 December

Akridge, G. R. 1982 "The Expanding Universe Theory is Internally Inconsistent" *CRSQ* v 19 n 1 p 56-9 June

Alfven, Hannes. "Cosmology: Myth or Science?" Ch. 1 p5-14 in Yourgrau, W. *Cosmology, History and Theology* Plenum Press 1977 N. York.

Allais, M. 1959 "Should the Laws of Gravitation be Reconsidered?" *Aerospace Engineering* v 18 p 46 September 1959 and v 18 p 51 October 1959

Allais, M. 1998 "Michelson-Morley-Miller: The Coverup" and "On My Experiments in Physics" *21st Century Science and Technology* Spring.

Allen, R. *Star Names: Their Lore and Meaning* Dover N.Y. 1963 (First published 1899)

Ancil, R. "The Limits of Human Thought and the Creation Model" *CRSQ* v 20 n 1 p 30-39 June 1983

Archer, G. *A Survey of Old Testament Introductions* Moody 1964

Armitage, M. "Internal Radiohaloes in a Diamond" *CENTJ* 9(1) 1995 p 93-101

Armstrong, H. "An Attempt to Correct for the Effects of the Flood in Determining Dates by Radioactive Carbon" *CRSQ* 2/4:28-30 January 1966

*Arp, Halton C. 1987 *Quasars, Redshifts and Controversies* Cambridge Un. Press.

Ashe, G. *Mythology of the British Isle* Methuen 1990

Aspden, H. 1969 *Science without Einstein* Sabberton Publications, Box 35, Southampton SO16 7RB £20. (Superseded by his *Physics Unified* but containing material not repeated in the later work)

Aspden, H. 1972 *Modern Aether Science* Sabberton

*Aspden, H. 1980 *Physics Unified* Saberton

Aspden, H. 1982 "The Ether - an Assessment" *Wireless World* October p 37-9.

Astronomy , News, October 1995 p 29-30

Austin, S. 1986 "Mount St. Helens and Catastrophism" *Proc. 1st ICC* 1986

Austin, S. 1988 "Grand Canyon Lava Flows: A Survey of Isotope Dating Methods" *ICR Impact pamphlet* No. 178 April

Austin, S., (1994) Baumgardner, J., Humphreys, D., Snelling, A., Vardiman, L., and Wise, K. "Catastrophic Plate Tectonics: A Global Flood Model of Earth History" *3rd ICC*

Avila IV, F. "Is the Precession of Mercury's Perihelion a Natural (Non-Relativistic) Phenomenon?" *1st ICC* 1986 p 175-186

Bailey, E. et al "Franciscan and Related Rocks, and Their Significance in the Geology of Western California" *Bull. 183 San Francisco: Calif. Div. of Mines and Geology* 1964.

Barbour, J. and Bertotti, B. "Gravity and Inertia in a Machian Framework" *Il Nuovo Cimento* 32B(1):1-27, 11 March 1977. A reprint appears in Bouw's "Geocentric Papers".

Barnes, T.G. 1972 "Young Age vs. Geologic Age for the Earth's Magnetic Field" *CRSQ* v 9 n 1 p 47-50.

Barnes, T.G. 1973 "Origin and Destiny of the Earth's Magnetic Field" *I.C.R. Technical Monograph* No. 4.

Barnes, T.G. 1981 "Depletion of the Earth's Magnetic Field" *I.C.R. Impact Article* No. 100, October.

Barnes, T.G. 1983 "Earth's Magnetic Age: the Achilles Heel of Evolution" *I.C.R. Impact Article* No. 122, August.

Barnes, T.G. - Electrodynamic theory - *CRSQ* v21 n2 p56-62 September 1984, v 21 n 4 p 186-9 March 1985, v 19 n 4 p 208 September 1982. Also book - *Physics of the Future* ICR 1985

*Barrow, J.D. and Tipler, J.T. *The Anthropic Cosmological Principle* Oxford University Press 1986.

**Batmanghelidj, F. *Your Body's Many Cries for Water* The Therapist Ltd., Henry House, 189 Heene Rd., Worthing BN11. £9.95 incl. p+p. Tel: 01903 236 179.

Batten, A. "The Barr Effect" *Royal Astronomical Society of Canada, Journal* 1985 v 77 p 95.

Baumgardner, J. 1994 "Computer Modelling of the Large-Scale Plate Tectonics Associated with the Genesis Flood" and "Runaway Subduction as the Driving Mechanism for the Genesis Flood" *3rd ICC* p 49-75.

Bayliss, T. In a speech at the Inst. of Civil Eng. June 1998. Reported in *New Civil Engineer* 2.7.98 p21

Beasley, G. "A Possible Creationist Perspective on the Tyrolean (Oetztaler) Ice Man" *CENTJ* v 8(2) p 179-191 1994

Beekman, G. "Hunt for the Speed of Light" *New Scientist* 13 October 1933 p 100. Also in Jolly, W. *Sir Oliver Lodge* Constable 1974.

Bergman, J. "Advances in Integrating Cosmology: The Case of the Cometesimals" *CENTJ* v 10 n 2 1996 p 202-210

Berlitz, C. *Mysteries from Forgotten Worlds* 1972 Doubleday NY.

Berthault, G. "Experiments on Lamination of Strata" *CENTJ* v 3 1988 (Previously appearing in C.R. Acad. Sci. Paris, t,303, Serie II, no. 17 1986 p 1569-1574.)

Birge, R. "The Velocity of Light" *Nature* v 134 p 771-2 1934. See also his "The General Physical Constants" *Reports on Progress in Physics* 8, 90-101 1941

Block, M. 1956 "Surface Tension as the Cause of Benard Cells...." *Nature* v 178 n 4534:650-651

Bluth, C. "Convection Currents in the Earth's Mantle: A Mechanism for Continental Drift?" *CRSQ* v 20 n 3 December 1983

Bonner, P. "Blonds in the Far East and American North West" *The Barnes Review* 1997 p3-8

*Bouw, G. 1992 *Geocentricity* Association for Biblical Astronomy. Available from the author at 4527 Wetzel Ave., Cleveland, Ohio 44109, U.S.A. In UK from B. Lamb, Quarryside, Castletown, Caithness, Scotland KW14 8SS

Bouw, G. 1993A "A Planetary Alignment at the Creation?" *The Biblical Astronomer*, v 3 n 64 Spring p23-30

Bouw, G. 1993B *The Geocentric Papers* A collection of papers on geocentrism. Available from ref. Bouw92

Bouw, G. 1995 "Massive Superstrings and the Firmanent" SECC 16-1 9 August p 11-18

Bowden, M. 1981 *Ape-men - Fact or Fallacy?* 2nd revised edition, Sovereign Publications

Bowden, M. 1982 *The Rise of the Evolution Fraud* Sovereign Publications

Bowden, M. 1986 "The Suspect 'Proof' of Relativity" *CENTJ* v 2 p 157-167.

Bowden, M. 1989 "The Speed of Light - a Critique of Aardsma's Statistical Method" (Letter) *CRSQ* v 25 March p 207-8.

Bowden, M. 1991 *Science vs Evolution* Sovereign Publications

Bowden, M. 1992 "The Trinity, Love and Suffering" Privately circulated paper.

Bowden, M. 1993 *Evolution, Revolution and Conspiracy - An exposure of the international anti-Christian forces* A privately circulated booklet.

Bowden, M. 1994 *The Medical Conspiracy - A critical examination of the medical profession in western society.* A privately circulated booklet.

Bowden, M. 1998 "Reports on the Death of Speed of Light Decay are Premature!" *CENTJ* v 12 n 1 p 48-54

Boyer, T.H. "The Classical Vacuum" *Scientific American* August 1985 p 70. Also his "A Brief Survey of Stochastic Electrodynamics" in *Foundations of Radiation Theory and Quantum Electrodynamics* A.O. Barut Ed. Plenum NY.

Bramwell, C. and Whitfield, G. "Biomechanics of Pteranodon" *Phil. Trans. Roy. Soc.* London B 267 p 503-581 1974.

*Broad, W. and Wade, N. *Betrayers of the Truth* Century London 1982

Brown, H. 1994 "Mixing Lines - Considerations Regarding their Use in Creationist Interpretation of Radioisotope Age Data" 3rd ICC

Brown, G. 1978 "European Geophysics" *Nature* v 275 n 5682 p 694-5 26 October

*Brown, W. *In the Beginning: Compelling Evidence for the Creation and the Flood.* Center for Scientific Creationism, 5612 North 20th Place, Pheonix, Arizona 85016, 6th Edition 1995

Bullinger, E. 1981 *The Witness of the Stars.* Kregel (First published 1893)

Burdick, C. 1967 "Ararat: The Mother of Mountains" *CRSQ* v 4 n 1 p 5-12 June

Burdick, C. 1975 "Discovery of Human Skeletons in Cretaceous Formation" in *Speak to the Earth.* Presbyterian and Reformed Publishing p 127f. Also in Q10/2:109

Burdick, C. 1980 "A Critical Look at Plate tectonics and Continental Drift" *CRSQ* v 17 n 2 September p 111-4

Byl, J. "On the Energy-Mass Equation" *Biblical Astronomer* Fall 1997 n 82 p 19-23

Cadush, P. Letter in *ENTJ* v 4 n 3 1981

Caesar, Julius *The Gallic War* Heinemann 1963 Reprint. Translation by H. Edwards

*Callahan, P. *Tuning in to Nature* Routledge, London 1977

Carr, B., Rees, M. "The Anthropic Principle and the Structure of the Physical World" *Nature* 12 April 1979 v 278 p 605-612

Carrigan, C. and Gubbins, D. "The source of the earth's magnetic field" *Scientific American,* Feb. 1979 v 240 n 2 p 92-101

Cassius, Dio *Roman History* Loeb Classical Library 1982

*Ceram, C. *Gods, Graves and Scholars* Gollancz 1954

Chaffin, E. 1987 "A Young Earth? - A Survey of Dating methods" *CRSQ* n 3 p 109-117 December

Chaffin, E. 1990 "A Study of Roemer's method for determining the Velocity of Light" *2nd ICC* p 47-52

Chaffin, E. 1992 "A Determination of the Speed of Light in the Seventeenth Century" *CRSQ* v 29 n 3 p 115-119 December

Chaffin, E. 1994 "Are the Fundamental 'Constants' of Physics Really Variables?" *3rd ICC.* p 143-150

Clarke, C. "Faith and Population in a Declining Civilization" *CRSQ* v 18 n 2 p 117-8 September 1981

Comins, N. and Marschall, L. "How do Spiral Galaxies Spiral?" *Astronomy* December 1987 v 15 p 7-23.

Cooke, M. 1957 "Where is the earth's radiogenic helium?" *Nature* 179:213 26 January

Cooke, M. 1966 *Prehistory and Earth Models* Parrish

Cooper, W. 1986 "The Historic Jonah" *CENTJ* v 2 p 105-116

Cooper, W. 1992 "The Early History of Man - Part 4. The Living Dinosaurs from Anglo-Saxon and other Early Records" *CENTJ* v 6 n 1 p 49-66

*Cooper, W. 1995 *After the Flood* New Wine Press

Cooper, W. 1996 "Richard Hunne" *Reformation* v 1 p 221-251. Tyndale Soc.

Cooper, W. 1997 *Paley's Watchmaker* New Wine Press

Corry, L. et al "Belated Decision in the Hilbert-Einstein Priority Dispute" *Science* v 278 p 1270-1273 14 November 1997

*Courville, D. *The Exodus Problem and its Ramifications* Vols. 1 and 2, Challenge Books, Loma Linda Cal. 1971. See also CRSQ 12/4:201, 11/1:47, 11/4 :202, 10/1:74

Cowling, T. "The Magnetic Field of Sunspots" *Month. Not. Roy. Astronomical Soc.* 1934 v 94 p 39-48

Cox, D. 1975 "The Formation of Cross Stratification: a New Explanation" *CRSQ* v 12 n 3 December p 166-173.

Cox, D. 1976A "Problems in the Glacial Theory" *CRSQ* v 13 n 1 p 25-34 June

Cox, D. 1976B "Cave Formation by Rock Disintegration" *CRSQ* v 13 n 3 p 155-161 December

Cox, D. 1977A "Kames, Eskers, and the Deluge" *CRSQ* v 14 n 1 p 47-52 June

Cox, D. 1977B "Pillars, Polystrate Formations and Potholes" *CRSQ* v 14 n 3 p 149-155 December

Cox, D. 1979 "Controversy about Ice Ages" *CRSQ* v 16 n 1 p 21-28 June

Cox, D. 1981 "On the Vertical Movements of the Earth's Crust" *CRSQ* September v 18 n 2 p 112-116

Cox, D. 1986 "Sandstone and the Flood Environment" *CRSQ* v 22 n 4 p 158-166 March

Cox, D. 1988 "Missing Mineral Inclusions in Quartz Grain Sands" *CRSQ* v 25 n 1 p 54 June

Creation 1994 v16 n3 p44 June-August "Professors: A day means a day". Creation Science Foundation (Australia)

Criswell, W.A. (Ed) *The Believer's Study Bible* (NKJV) Nelson 1991

Croft, L. *The Life and Death of Charles Darwin* Elmwood 1989

Crompton, N. "Molecular Biology of Ageing" *SECC* p 21-28

Cuenot, C. 1958 *Teilhard de Chardin* Burns and Oates (English translation 1956)

Cuozzo, J. "Neanderthal Children's Fossils: Reconstruction and Interpretation Distorted by Assumptions" *CENTJ* v 8(2) p 166-178 1994

*Custance, A.C. *Noah's Three Sons* Zondervan 1975

Dalrymple, B. "Can the Earth be Dated from Decay of its Magnetic Field?" *Journal of Geological Education*, March 1983 v 31 n 2 p 124-132.

Daly, R. *Earth's Most Challanging Mysteries* 1972 Baker

Daniken, von, E. *The Chariots of the Gods* 1969 Souvenir Press

*d'Aubigney, M. *The Reformation in England* Banner of Truth 1962

Davenas, E., Benveniste, J. et al "Human basophil degranulation triggered by very dilute antiserum against IgE" *Nature* June 1988 v 333 p 816-8. See also *Nature* v 334 p2 87-291, *New Scientist* 4 Aug. 1988 p 30-31

Davies, K. 1994 "Distribution of Supernova Remnants in the Galaxy" *3rd ICC* p 175-184

Davis, J. *Biblical Numerics* Baker 1968 (1989 printing)

Desmond, A. and Moore, J. *Darwin* Penguin 1991

Devereux, P. et al "Acoustical Properties of Ancient Ceremonial Sites" *Journal of Scientific Explorartion*, 9:438, 1995. Also Jahn, R. "Acoustical Resonances of Assorted Ancient Structures" *Tech. Report PEAR* 95002 Princeton Un. March 1995. [Ref - *SF* 102].

DeYoung, D.B., "The Water of Life" *CRSQ* v 22 n 3 December 1985.

Dillow, J. *The Waters Above: The Earth's Pre-Flood Vapour Canopy* Moody 1982. See also CRSQ 15/1:27-34.

Dingle, H. *Science at the Crossroads* Martin Brian and O'Keeffe 1972

530   References

Disputatio super Dignitatem Angliae et Galliae in Concilio Constantiano. Theodore Martin, Lovan, 1517

Dorsey, N. "The Velocity of Light" *Trans. Amer. Phil. Soc.* v 34 pt 1 p 1-110 1944

Drosnin, M. *The Bible Code* Weidenfeld and Nicholson 1997. Other books on ELS are - Jeffrey, G. *The Signature of God* and *The Handwriting of God* - Rambsel, Y. *Yeshua: The Name of Jesus Revealed in the Old Testament*

Dunham, D. et al "Observations of a Probable Change in the Solar Radius between 1715 and 1979" *Science* v 210 12 December 1980 p 1243-1245

Dyson, F.W., Eddington, A.S., Davidson, C. "A Determination of the Deflection of Light by the Sun's Eclipse of May 29, 1919" *Memoirs of the Royal Astronomical Society* 1923 n 62 p 1-43.

Eakman, B. 1990 *Educating for the New World Order* Halcyon House Portland Or.

Eddy, J. and Boornazian A. 1979 "Secular Decrease in the Solar Diameter 1863-1953" *Bull. Am. Astron. Soc.* v 11 p 437.

*Elder, Isabel *Celt, Druid and Culdee* Covenant Publishing Co. 1947

Ellis, P.B. *The Druids* Constable 1994

Elmendorf, R. *A Critical Investigation of the Foucault Pendulum* Pittsburgh Creation Society 1994

Essen, L. 1971 *The Special Theory of Relativity: A Critical Analysis* Ox. U.P.

Essen, L. 1977 "Time Coming and Going" *CRSQ* v14 n1 June

Essen, L. 1988 "Relativity - Joke or Swindle?" *Wireless World* February p 126-7

Everyman's Encyclopaedia, Dent 1978

Fange, E. 1974 "Time Upside Down" *CRSQ* June v 11 n 1 p 13-27

Fange, E. 1984 "The Archaeology of Words and the Alphabet" *CRSQ* March n 4 p 219-226

Faulstich, G. Letter - private correspondence.

Flandern, T. van *Dark Matter, Missing Planets and New Comets* North Atlantic Books, Cal. 1993

Forster, R. and Marston, P. 1989(A) *Reason and Faith* Monarch Publications

Forster, R. and Marston, P. 1989(B) *God's Strategy in Human History* Highland Books.

Forster, R. and Marston, P. 1995 *Christianity, Evidence and Truth* Monarch Publications

Frangos, A. "An Insight into the Problems of the Origins of Life and Matter" *SECC*.

Frolich, C. and Eddy, J. "Observed Relation between Solar Luminosity and Radius" *Adv. Space Research* v 4 n 8 1984 p 121-124

Gallant, R. *Bombarded Earth* John Baker London

Garstang, J. *The Story of Jericho* 1940 Hodder. 2nd edition 1948 Marshall Morgan and Scott.

Gilliland, R. "Solar Radius Variations over the past 265 years" *Astrophysical Jour.* 15 September 1981 v 248 p 1144-115 5

Gold, T. and Soter, S. 1980 "The Deep-Earth-Gas Hypothesis" *Scientific American* June v 242 n 6 p 130-7

Goldstein S. et al. "On the velocity of light three centuries ago" *Astronomical Journal* v78 n 1 p 122-125 Feb. 1973

Grazia, Alfred de (Ed.) *The Velikovsky Affair* Sidgwick 1966

Gribben, J. *In Search of Schrodinger's Cat* Wildwood House 1984

Grieve, S. "Relativity - A Critique" *Wireless World* October 1987 v 93 n 1620 p 1026-1029

Guthrie, B. and Napier, W, *Monthly Not. Roy. Astro. Soc.* December 1 1991

Hafele, J. and Keating, R. 1972 *Science* v 177 n 4044 p 166.

Hapgood, C. *Maps of the Ancient Sea Kings* Turnstone 1979

Hayasaka, H. et al. "Anomalous Weight Reduction on a Gyroscope's Right Rotations around the Vertical Axis on the Earth" *Physical Review Letters* v 63 n 25 p 2701-4 18 December 1989

Hayward, A. *Creation and Evolution: The Facts and the Fallacies* Triangle 1985 (Revised 1994)

*Hazelett, R. and Turner, D. *The Einstein Myth and the Ives' Papers* The Devin-Adair Company, Conneticutt, 1979. A collection of Herbert Ives' papers, *The Einstein Myth* by Dean Turner, a condensation of *Euclid or Einstein?* by J.J. Callahan, and papers and comments by others.

Hecht, J. "Io Spirals Towards Jupiter" *New Scientist* 23 January 1986 p 33.

Hedges, B. et al "Human Origins and Analysis of Mitochondrial DNA Sequences" Science 255:737-9 7 February 1991

Helmholtz, H. "On the Interaction of Natural Forces" *Philosophical Magazine* (London) 4th Series v 11 p 489

Herrmann, R. Articles on "D-model" *CRSQ* 22/2:84-89, 22/3:128-13 7, 23/2:47-54. Website-http://herrmannra.sma.usna.navy.mil/

Hesser, J. and Shawl. S. *Astrophysical Journal* v 217 1977

*Highfield, R., Carter, P. *The Private Lives of Albert Einstein* Faber 1993.

Hill, G. "Some Aspects of Coal Technology" *Chemical Technology* May 1972 p 296

Hislop, Rev. A. *The Two Babylons* Loizeaux Brothers 1959

*Hitchin, F. *The World Atlas of Mysteries* Pan Books 1979

Holman, Dr. R. "A Method of destroying a Malignant Rat Tumour in vivo" *Nature* v 179 May 18 1975 p 1033

Hong, S. et al 1994 "Safety Investigation of Noah's Ark in a Seaway" *CENTJ* v 8 (1) p 26-36

Hooykaas, R. *Religion and the Rise of Modern Science* Scottish Academic Press 1984 (reprint)

Hope, Lady *Our Golden Key* Seeley, Jackson and Halliday 1884

Hoyle, F. 1978 *The Cosmogeny of the Solar System* University College Cardiff Press.

Hull, E. *Deacon's Synchronological Chart of Universal History* 1890. Republished by Studio Editions London 1989 and 1991. A large wall chart of Biblical Chronology and History from Creation (4004 BC) to 1990 AD.

Humphreys, R. 1986 "Reversals of the Earth's Magnetic Field During the Genesis Flood" *1st ICC* Vol II p 113-126.

Humphreys, R. 1988 "Has the Earth's Magnetic Field ever Flipped?" *CRSQ* v 25 n 3 p 130-7

Humphreys, R. 1994 *Starlight and Time* Master Books (ICR)

Ingersoll, L. et al *Heat Conduction: With Engineering, Geological and other applications* Thames and Hudson 1955

532 References

Jastrow, R. *God and the Astronomers* Norton NY. 1978 p 115-6.

Johnson, L. "The 'Tangled' Tongue" *CRSQ* v 19 n 3 p 180-4 December 1982

Jones, A. "How Many Animals in the Ark?" *CRSQ* September 1973 v 10 n2 p102 - 108

Jones, B. "Searching for Caradog" *Archaeology Today* April 1988 p 36-9.

*Jones, J. and Gladstone, J. 1995 *The Red King's Dream* Jonathan Cape

*Jowett, G.F. *The Drama of the Lost Disciples* Covenant Publishing 1980.

*Kahn, D. *The Code Breakers* Weindenfeld 1966

Kahn, P. et al "Nautiloid Growth Rythms.." *Nature* 275:606-611 19 Oct. 1978

Kang, C. and Nelson, E. *The Discovery of Genesis* Concordia 1979

Karwell, J. "Report on the Colloquium "Chemie und Physik der Steinkohle" in *Erdol und Kohle - Petrochemie* v 18 n 7 July 1965 p 565.

Kapitsa, A. "A Large Deep Freshwater Lake beneath the Ice of Central East Antartica" *Nature* 381:684 1996

Kaula, W. et al "Dynamics of Lunar Origin and Orbital Evolution" *Rev. of Geophysics and Space Physics* May 1975 v 13 n 2 p 363-371

*Kelly, A.G. Three monographs published by the Insitution of Engineers of Ireland -

(1) *Time and the Speed of Light - A New Interpretation* January 1995

(2) *A New Theory on the Behaviour of Light* February 1996

(3) *Reliability of Relativistic Effect Tests on Airborne Clocks* February 1996

Kenyon, Sir Frederick *Our Bible and the Ancient Manuscripts* Eyre and Spottiswood 1941

Kenyon, K. *Diggin up Jericho* 1957 Earnest Benn

Kerr, R. 1991 "Coming up Short in a Crustal Quest" *Science* 254:1456-1457

Kerr, R. 1993 "Looking deeply into the earth's crust in Europe" *Science* v 261 p 295-7 16 July

*Koestler, A. 1976 *The Thirteenth Tribe: The Khazar empire and its heritage* Hutchinson

*Koestler, A. 1986 *The Sleepwalkers* Reprint Penguin Books

Koontz, R. "The Creation of Eve" *CRSQ* v 8 n 2 p 128-9 September 1971

Korff, S. "Effects of Cosmic Radiation on Terrestial Isotope Distribution" *Trans. Amer. Geophysical Union* 35:105 February 1954

Koster, J. "What was the New Zealand Monster" in *Oceans* November 1977 p 56-9. Article and photos repeated on website http://www.gennet.org/nessy.htm

Krauskopf, K. *Introduction to Geochemistry* McGraw Hill 1967

Kukla, G. and Zijderveld, J. "Magnetostratigraphic Pitfalls" *Nature* 266:774 1977

Kulling, S. *Are the Geneologies in Genesis 5 and 11 Historical and Complete, that is, without Gaps* (booklet) Immanuel-Verlag, Riehen, Switzerland 1996

Lammerts, W. "On the Rapid Formation of Beaches and a Graded Series of Flattened and Rounded Stones" *CRSQ* v 11 n 2 September 1974 p 101-3.

Laskar, J. "The Chaotic Obliquity of the Planets" *Nature* v 361 p 608 1993

Lee, J. "Hydrothermal Vents at Deep Sea Spreading Ridges: Modern-day Fountains of the Deep?" *CRSQ* v 29 n 1 p 13-18 June 1992.

Lewis, C.S. *Miracles* Fontana 1966

Lister, R. *Old maps and Globes* Bell and Hyman 1979

Lockyer, J.N. *The Dawn of Astronomy* Cassell 1894

Lubkin, G.B. "Analysis of historical data suggests Sun is shrinking" *Physics Today* Sept. 1979 v 32 p 17-19

Lynch, A. *The Case Against Einstein* Philip Allan (London) 1932

Lyttleton, R. "The Non-existence of the Oort Cometary Shell" *Astrophysics and Space Science* 1974 v 31 p 385-401 1974

"Magsat down: magnetic field declining" *Science News* 28 June 1980 v117 p407.

Malcolm, D. 1988 "Humanism and Modern Mathematics" *CENTJ* v 3 p 49-58

Malcolm, D. 1991 "Einstein's Contribution to Relativity" *CENTJ* v 5 n 1 p58-69

Malcolm, D. 1994 "Helium in the Earth's Atmosphere" *CENTJ* v 8 n 2 p 142-147

Mammel, L. Net astro reference; Group - net.astro: From - lew@ihuxr.UUCP (Lew Mammel. Jr.): Message-ID: <795@ihuxr.UUCP: Date Rcd - Fri. 2-Dec-83 23:40:50

Mammel, L. Net astro reference; Group - net.astro: From - lew@ihuxr.UUCP (Lew Mammel. Jr.): Message-ID: <800@ihuxr.UUCP: Date Rcd - Wed. 7-Dec-83 23:33:37

Marinov, L. 1974 "The Velocity of Light is Direction Dependent" *Checkosl. J. of Physics* B24:965

Marinov, L. 1977 *Eppur Si Muove* Brussels: CBDS-Pierre Libert

Marinov, S. 1986 "Marinov to the World's Scientific Conscience" *New Scientist* 18 December v 122 p 48-50

Marston, P. Letter dated 29.9.90

Masters, P. *Should Christians Drink?* Wakeman

Mazzullo, S. 1971 "Length of the Year During the Silurian and Devonian Periods - New Values" *Geol. Soc. Amer. Bull.* v 82 p 1085-6

McCausland, I. "Problems in Special Relativity" *Wireless World* October 1983

McLeod, K. "Magnetic fields in medicine: bone repair" *CRSQ* v 17 n 4 p 199 March 1981

**Mendelsohn, Dr. R. *Confessions of a Medical Heretic* 1979 Contemporary Books, Chicago. Obtainable from Gazelle Book Services, Falcon House, Queen Sq., Lancaster LA1 1RN. Tel:01524 68765.

Michelson, A. and Morley, E. 1881 "The Relative Motion of the Earth and the Luminiferous Aether" *American Journal of Science* 3rd Series v 22 Art. XXI pp. 120-129

Michelson, A. and Morley. E. 1887 "On the Relative Motion of the Earth and the Luminiferous Aether" Am. J. of Science v 24 n 203 pp. 333-345

Miller, A. *Awake my Glory* Bais Yisroel of Rugby 1980

Miller, D,. *Revue of Modern Physics* 1933 v 5 p 203

Molen, M. "Diamictites: Ice-ages or Gravity Flows?" *2nd ICC* v 2 p 177-190

Moon, P., Spencer. D. "Mach's Principle" *Philosophy of Science* 1959 v 26 p 125-134

Moore, J. *The Darwin Legend* Hodder 1995

Moore, P. *The Guinness Book of Astronomy* 4th edition Guinness 1992

*Morgan, Rev. R.W. 1925 *St. Paul in Britain* The Covenant Publishing, London.

*Morris, H. 1977 *The Genesis Record* Baker. U.K. Publisher Evangelical Press

Morris, H. 1979 "Creation and the Seven-Day Week" *ICR Impact* article No. 75 September

Morris, H. 1996 "The Geologic Column and the Flood of Genesis" *CRSQ* v 33 n 1 p 49-57 June

*Morrison, Alan. *The Serpent and the Cross* K & M Books 1994. Obtainable from 47 Elvetham Rd, Birmingham B15 2LY. £12.

Morton, G. 1982 "Electromagnetics and the Appearance of Age" *CRSQ* v 18 n 4 p227-232 March

Morton, G. 1983 "The Flood on an Expanding Earth" *CRSQ* v 19 n 4 p 219-224 March

Morton, G. 1984 (A) "The Carbon Problem" *CRSQ* v 20 n 4 p 212-9 March

Morton, G. 1984 (B) "Global, Continental and Regional Sedimentation Sytems and their Implications" *CRSQ* v 21 n 1 p 23-33 June 1984

Mulfinger, G. "Examining the Cosmogenies - a Historical Review" *CRSQ* v 4 n 2 p 57-69 September 1967

Murray, W. A. Scott 1984 "The Roots of Relativity" *Wireless World* May p 69-72

Murray, W.A. Scott 1986 "If You Want to Know the Time..." *Wireless World* December v 92 n 1610 p 28-31.

Narliker, J. "What if the Big Bang Didn't Happen?" *New Scientist* 2 March 1991 v 129 p 48-51

Needham, A. *The Uniqueness of Biological Materials* Pergamon 1965

Nelson, Byron C. Bethany Fellowship, Minneapolis 1968 (First published 1931)

Nevins, S. "Evolution: The Oceans say NO!" *ICR Impact* n 8

Nevins, S. "Continental Drift, Plate Tectonics and the Bible" *ICR Impact* n 32

Nickel, J. "Why Does Mathematics Work?" *CENTJ* v 4 p 147-157 1990

Nodland, B and Ralston, J. "Indication of anisotropy in electromagnetic propagation over cosmological distances" *Physical Review Letters* 21 April 1997 p 3043-6

Noorbergen, R. *Secrets of the Lost Races* New English Library 1980

*Norman, T. and Setterfield, B. *The Atomic Constants. Light and Time* Stanford Research Institute - An Invited Report August 1983. Available from CSM.

Oard, M. 1979 "A Rapid Post-Flood Ice Age" *CRSQ* v 16 n 1 p 29-37

Oard, M, 1984A "Ice Ages: The Mystery Solved? Part I: The Inadequacy of a Uniformitarian Ice Age" *CRSQ* v 21 n 2 p 66-76 September

Oard, M, 1984B "Ice Ages: The Mystery Solved? Part II: The Manipulation of Deep Sea Cores" *CRSQ* v 21 n 3 p 125-137 December

Oard, M. 1985 "Ice ages: The Mystery Solved? Part III: Palaeomagnetic Stratigraphy and Data Manipulation." *CRSQ* v 21 n4 p 170-181 March

Oard, M. 1992A "What is Under the Surface?" *CRSQ* v 29 n 1 p 27-8.

Oard, M. 1992B "Varves - The First Absolute Chronology - Pt 1" *CRSQ* v 29 n 2 p 72-80 September

Oard, M. 1995 "Polar Dinosaurs and the Genesis Flood" *CRSQ* v 32 n 1 p 47-56 June

O'Brien, C.C. *The Independent Magazine* 12 December 1992 p 62

O'Brien, E.M. "What was the Acheulian Hand Axe?" *Natural History* July 1984 p 20-23

O'Neill, J. *Prodigal Genius* Ives Washurn, Inc. 1944 (A biography of N. Tesla)

"Origins - How the World came to be" Eden Films and Evangelische Omroep, No. 6 of the series - *The Fossil record*

Osgood, A. "The Times of Abraham" *CENTJ* 1986 v 1 p 77-87. See also several articles by Osgood in vols. 1 and 2 on biblical chronology.

Ozanne, C. *The First 7000 Years* Exposition Press N.Y. 1970

Pais, A. 1982 *Subtle is the Lord* Oxford U.P.

Pais, A. 1994 *Albert Einstein Lived Here* Clarendon Ox. Un. Pr.

Parkinson, J. et al. 1980 "The Constancy of the Solar Diameter over the past 250 years" *Nature* 11 December v 288 p 548-551

Parkinson, J. 1983 "New Measurements of the Solar Diameter" *Nature* v 304 p 518-520 August.

Patten, D. *The Biblical Flood and the Ice Epoch* Pacific Meridian 1966

Pennisi, E. "Water, Water Everywhere" *Science News* v 143 n 8 20 Feb. 1993 p 121-5

Petersen, E. 1981 "The Necessity of the Canopies" *CRSQ* v 17 n 4 p 201-204 March

Petterson, H. "Cosmic Spherules and Meteoritic Dust" *Scientific American* v 202 p 123-13 2 Feb. 1960

Phillips. N. Letter, *Wireless World* February 1984 p 71

Plaisted, D. "Mitochondrial Eve Re-Dated?" *Creation Matters* v 2 n 6 p 6 Nov/Dec 1997. Ref. to Parsons et al, *Nature Genetics* 15(4):363-367.

*Poor, Prof. C.L. *Gravitation versus Relativity* G.P Putnam's Sons New York 1922.

Powell, C. Diane "Mechanisms for Gender Role Stasis" 3rd ICC p 423-432

Reed, J., Bennett, C., Froede, C., Oard, M. "Some Initial Thoughts Regarding Catastrophic Plate Tectonics" *CRSQ* v 32 n 3 December 1995

Resnik, D. *The Ethics of Science: An Introduction* Routledge 1998

Richards F. "Note on the age of the great temple of Ammon at Karnak" Ministry of Finance, Egypt, *Survey of Egypt* paper No. 38. Cairo 1921, reprinted 1932.

Riley, J. et al (Ed) *Chemical Oceanography* Academic Press 1965

Robson, G. "Interpreting Darwin Biography: A Footnote" *Faith and Thought* April 1997 n 21 p 9-19

*Rohl, D. *A Test of Time* Century 1995

Rosevear, D. "The Genealogies in Scripture" in *Concepts in Creationism* Ed. Andrews et al. Evangelical Press 1986

Ross, A. and Robins, D. *The Life and Death of a Druid Prince* Summit 1989

Rosser, W. *An Introduction to the Theory of Relativity* Butterworths 1964

Roy, R. 1976 "The preparation and properties of synthetic clay materials" *Colloques internationaux du C.N.R.S.*, n 105, ed CNRS Paris, 224p, 83-95

Rusch, W. "Baked Rocks" *CRSQ* v 28 n 4 March 1992 p 161-3.

Sagnac M.G. "Sur la preuve de la realite de l'ether lumineaux par l'experience de l'interferographe tournant" *Comptes Rendus* 1913 v 157 p 708-710 and 1410-1413.

Samec, R. "Effect of Radiation Pressure on Micrometeoroids, and existence of Micrometeoroids as Evidence for a Young Solar System" *CRSQ* v 12 n 1 p 7-10 June 1975

Sasaki, T. (Ed) "Collected Papers on the Carcass of an Unidentified Animal Trawled off New Zealand by the Zuiyo-maru." 1978 *La Societe Franco-Japonaise d'Oceanographie.* Tokyo

Saxi, E. and Allen, M. "1970 Solar Eclipse as 'seen' by a Torsion Pendulum" *Physical Review D*, v 3 p 3 1971

Scheven. Dr. Joachim; an early proposer of the "Carboniferous Model" and articles by M. Garton, P. Garner, D. Tyler and S. Robinhave developed this model. The major exposition is contained in several articles in the *CENTJ* v 10 part 1 1996. In this issue is his article "The Carboniferous Floating Forest - An Extinct pre-Flood Ecosystem" is on p 70-81

Scrutton, C. 1965 "Periodicity in Devonian Growth" *Palaeontology* v 7 p 552-8

*Seaman, W. *The Dawn of Christianity in the West* Chrest Foundation 1993

Seiss, J. *The Gospel in the Stars* Kregel 1972 (First published 1882)

Setterfield, B. 1983 *The Velocity of Light and the Age of the Universe - A Technical Monograph* Creation Science Association, Australia. Now out of print but the atomic properties sections are in early issues of the *Ex Nihilo* magazine - v 4 nos. 1, 2 and 3 1981

Setterfield, B. 1993 *Creation and Catastrophe* A booklet, 35 minute video and a wall chart. Distributed by Genesis Science Research, Box 318, Blackwood, SA 5051, Australia. Also by Covenant Publishing, London.

Setterfield, B. 1986 "Carbon 14 Dating, Tree Ring Dating and Speed of Light Decay" *CENTJ* v 2 p 169-188

Shirley, D. "Differentiation and Compaction in the Palisades Sill" *New Jersey, J. of Petrology*, v 28 (1987) p 835-865.

Shuker, K. "Bring me the Head of a Sea Serpent" *Strange Magazine* Spring 1995. Also on web site http://www.strangemag-.com/seaserpcarcsshuk.html

Silk, J. "Cosmology Back to the Beginning" *Nature* 30 April 1992 v 356 p 741-2.

Slichter, L. "Secular Effects of Tidal Friction upon the Earth's Rotation" *Jour. Geophysical Research* 15 July 1963 v 68 n 14 p 4281-4288

Slusher, H. "Clues Regarding the Age of the Universe" *ICR Impact* No. 19

Smith, B. "Science and Scripture" (Letter) *CRSQ* v22 n2 p96 September 1985

Snelling, A. and Rush, D. 1993 "Moon Dust and the Age of the Solar Sytem" *CENTJ* 7(1) p 2-42

Snelling, A. 1994A "Can Flood Geology Explain Thick Chalk Layers?" *CENTJ* v 8 n 1 p 11-15

Snelling, A. 1994B "Towards a Creationist Explanation of Regional Metamorphism" *CENTJ* v 8 n 1 p 51-77

Snelling, A. 1995 "Plate Tectonics: Have the Continents Really Moved Apart?" *CENTJ* v 9 n 1 p 12-20

Snow, E. "Christianity: A Cause of modern Science?" *ICR Impact* 298 April 1998. See mainly ref. www4

Sofia, S. et al. "Solar Constant: Constraints on possible variations derived from solar diameter measurements" *Science* June 1979 v 204 p 1306-1308.

Sparks, Brad. Private communications by email.

Stanton, R.L. "An Alternative to the Barrovian Interpretation? Evidence from Stratiform Ores" *Proc. Australas. Inst. Min. Metall.* n 282 June 1982 p 11-32.

Stedman, G. et al "Sideband Analysis and Seismic Detection in Large Ring Lasers" *Applied Optics* 34(24):5375, (20 August 1995)

*Steidl, P. 1979 *The Earth, the Stars and the Bible* Presbytarian and Reformed Publishing Company

Steidl, P. 1980 "Solar Neutrinos and a Young Sun" *CRSQ* v 17 n 1 June p 60-64

Steidl, P. 1987 "Comets and Creation" *CRSQ* v 23 n 4 p 153-160 March

Surdin, M. "The Rotation of the Universe" *Physics Essays* 8(3):282-4

Tacitus, *Annals* Loeb Classical Library, Harvard Un. Press and Heinemann

Tacitus, *The Agricola and the Germania* Chivers-Penguin Library edition. Rev. translation 1970

*Taylor, Ian 1991 *In the Minds of Men* TFE Publishing, Box 1344, Toronto.

Taylor, Ian 1994 "Sir Francis Bacon and the Geological Society of London" *3rd ICC* p 525-533

*Taylor, Paul *The Illustrated Origins Answer Book* Film for Christ Association 1989

Thomson, W. and Tait, P. *Natural Philosophy* 1874

Tiffin, A. *Loving and Serving: An Account of the Life and Work of J.W.C. Fegan* 1976 Trustees of the Fegan Homes

Tipler, F. *The Physics of Immortality: Modern Cosmology, God and the Resurrection of the Dead* Macmillan 1994

*Tompkins, P. *Secrets of the Great Pyramid* Allen Lane 1973

Troitskii, V. "Physical Constants and the Evolution of the Universe" *Astrophysics and Space Science* v 139 n 2 December 1987 p 389-411

Tyler, D. 1979 "Megaliths and Neolithic Man" *CRSQ* v 16 n 1 p 47-58 June

Tyler, D. 1996 "A post-Flood Solution to the Chalk Problem" *CENTJ* v 10 n 1 p 107-113

U.S. National Report to IUGG, 1991-4. *Rev. Geophys.* v33 Suppl. Am. Geophy. Union.

Unfred, D. "Flood and Post-Flood Geodynamics: An Expanded Earth Model" *CRSQ* v 22 n 4 March 1986 p 171-9

Unruh, J. "The Greater Light to Rule the Day" Reprinted in *The Biblical Astronomer* v 5 n 73 p 29-34 Summer 1995. Also *ICR Impact* n 263 May 1995

VanDecar, J. et al "Seismic Evidence for a Fossil Mantle Plume beneath South America and Implications for Plate Driving Forces" *Nature* 378:25 1995

Van Flandern, T. "The Speed of Gravity: What the Experiments Say" Meta Research Bulletin v 6 n 4. 15th Dec. 1997. See http://www.metaresearch.org

Van Till, Howard J., Snow, R.E., Stek, J.H., Young, Davis A. *Portraits of Creation* Eerdmans 1990

Vardiman, L. 1986 "The Age of the Erath's Atmosphere Estimated by its Helium Content" 1st ICC v 1 p 187-194

Vardiman, L. 1992 "Ice Cores and the Age of the Earth" *ICR Impact* n 226 April

Varghese, R. (Ed) *Cosmos, Bios, Theos* Open Court, La Salle, Illinois p2.

Varshni, Y. "The Red Shift Hypothesis for Quasars: Is the earth the center of the universe?" *Astrophysics and Space Science* 1976 v 3 p 3-8.

Velikovsky, I. 1972 *Worlds in Collision* Abacus

Velikovsky, I. 1973A *Earth in Upheaval* Abacus

Velikovsky, I. 1973B *Ages in Chaos* Abacus

Vella, A. Letter *Wireless World* February 1984 p 71.

Vidale, J. "A Snapshot of Whole Mantle Flow" *Nature* v 370 p 16-17 7 July 1994

Wacholder, Ben Zion. *Hebrew Union College Annual* v 35 1964 p 43-56, at 50 fn. 41.

Watson, David C.C. Circulated extracts of Basil's (c. 370 AD) *Hexameron (The Six Days of Creation).* Translated into French by Prof. S. Giet 1949 (Cambridge University Library 43.01.d.1.26)

Wesson, P. "The Position against Continental Drift" *Quart. Jour. Roy. Astron. Soc.* 1970 v 11 p 312-340

Whitaker, Sir Edmund, *A History of Aether and Electricity* 1953 Nelson

Whitcomb, J.C. and Morris, H. 1969 *The Genesis Flood* (Presbytarian and Reformed 1961). British Edition by Evangelical Press

Whitcomb, J.C. 1965 "The Ruin-Reconstruction Theory of Genesis 1:2" *CRSQ* v 2 n 1 May p 3-6

Wilder-Smith, A.E. 1976 *Basis for a New Biology* Telos

Wilder-Smith, A.E. 1987 *The Scientific Alternative to Neo-Darwinian Evolutionary Theory* Word for Today Publishers, Cal.

Will, C. "The Confrontation Between Gravitation Theory and Experiment" in *General Relativity: An Einstein Centenary Survey* editor S.W. Hawking Cam. Un. Press 1979.

Williams, J. *Claudia and Pudens* Rees, Longman and Co. 1848 (In Glasgow Un. Lib. "Pamphlets" Stack y8-b-5)

Williams, P. (Hebrew scholar) Personal communications.

Wilson, A. "The Sign of the Prophet Jonah and its Modern Confirmations" *Princeton Theological Review* (See *Presbyterian Review*) 1927 v 25 p 630-642

Wilson, C. 1979 *Ebla Tablets: Secrets of a Forgotten City* Master Books 3rd Ed. March

Wilson, H.A. 1937 *Modern Physics* Blackie

Wiseman, P. *Creation Revealed in Six Days* Marshall Morgan and Scott 1948

Wonderly, D. *God's Time Records in Ancient Sediments* Crystal Press Michigan 1977

Wood, B. "Jericho and the Bible" in "Did the Israelites Conquer Jericho?" *Biblical Archaeological Review* March/April 1990 p49-50 (From "The On-Line Bible CD Rom")

Woodmorappe, J. *Noah's Ark. A Feasibility Study* 1996 ICR Books.

Woods, A. "The Centre of the Earth" *ICR Technical Monograph* No. 3 1973

Wurthwein, E. *The Text of the Old Testament* SCM 1979

Young, D. *Creation and the Flood* Baker 1977

Yule, G. *The Study of Language* Cambridge U.P. 1985

WEBSITES - referred to at time of publication;

www1 - http://xroads.virginia.edu/~UG97/inherit/1925home.htl

www2 - http://earth.ics.uci.edu.:8080/faqs/old-earth.html

www3 - http://www.strangemag.com/seaserpcarcsshuk.html

www4 - http://www.rae.org/jaki.html

www5 - http://emporium.turnpike.net/C/cs/wind.htm

www6 - http://www.jewsforjudaism.org/codes/jesusfr.htm

www7 - http://www.khouse.org/ten-tribe.html

www8 - http://www.cybermail.net/~codes/report.htm

www9 - http://www.cybermail.net/~codes/tests.htm

....

X1 Details of hydrogen peroxide treatments may be obtained from International Bio-Oxidative Medicine Foundation, Box 61767, Dallas, Fort Worth, Texas 75261. For Grt. Britian, contact Sovereign Publications.

X2 Details of hydrogen peroxide ingestion - contact ECHO(UK), 13 Albert Rd., Retford, Notts DN22 6JD.

Index

By the same author‑

"APE-MEN - Fact or Fallacy?"

A critical examination of the evidence highlights the very speculative theories based upon inadequate fossil evidence, and reveals the very dubious circumstances surrounding their discovery.

Summary of Contents

PILTDOWN. The considerable body of little-publicised evidence which incriminates the Jesuit priest Teilhard de Chardin. Professor Douglas's accusation. The involvement of the British Natural History Museum.

"APE-MEN" EVIDENCE. The very speculative nature of the evidence of "ape men", and the presumptuous way in which this is presented.

EARLY HOMO SAPIENS. Their existence in deeper strata than those of "ape men". The superficial reasons given for their rejection.

PEKIN MAN. A 25 ft. high ash heap, bone tools and other evidence of human habitation of the site virtually suppressed by the experts in China. The appearance - and rapid disappearance in 13 days - of ten human skeletons. Details of the later discovery of further human skeletons delayed for five years. Ape-like skulls reconstructed with human features. Investigation of the disappearance of the fossils at the time of Pearl Harbour suggests that they were found by the Japanese and passed to the Americans after the war - only to disappear again.

JAVA MAN. Dubois's concealment of human skulls for thirty years. The faking of scientific illustrations by Dubois's supporter, Professor Haeckel. The strange circumstances of the discovery of further fossil "evidence" of Java man.

NEANDERTHAL MAN. The evidence that these were true men suffering from rickets, arthritis and syphilis.

THE AFRICAN "APE-MEN". The admission by several experts that all these fossils are simply apes with no real human features.

    OLDUVAI GORGE. L.S.B. Leakey's discoveries examined.

    EAST RUDOLF. Richard Leakey's 1470 man really a human skull. How this "awkward" fossil was quietly buried.

    HADAR (Ethiopia). D. C. Johanson's meagre collection of fossils shown to be only those of apes.

    LAETOLIL. Mary Leakey's discovery of a 6 million year old footprints are clearly those of human beings. The evidence of human tracks with those of dinosaurs in America.

    RECK'S HUMAN SKELETON. How this was found in the Olduvai Gorge and the devious means by which it was removed from the "ape-man" scene.

CONCLUSION. The inadequacy of the fossil evidence for ape-men. How the scientific establishment suppressed the publication of unwelcome evidence. The basic motive for the belief in the ape-men theories.

Demi octavo (215 x 135mm). vii + 257 pages. 66 b/w illustrations Referenced. Indexed. Four colour cover. ISBN No. 09506042 1 6. Available in Christian bookshops or direct from the publishers (p+p included)

SOVEREIGN PUBLICATIONS P.O. Box 88,Bromley, Kent, BR2 9PF

English Churchman. This is a most learned, factual and highly documented treatise on the subject of the findings, during the last two cen turies, of certain ape-like fossil fragments from which scientists have deduced that man is descended directly from the apes.

The author exposes with pitiless logic and documentation the "last-word" theories of scientists, geologists and anthropologists, consequent upon the discoveries of such things as the "Piltdown Man", exposing many of them as frauds and hoaxes - which in the case of the Piltdown findings is now universally admitted.

This is a book of absorbing interest, especially to Christian teachers of Science and R.E., since any Secondary schoolboy will tell you glibly that "Man is descended from monkeys-Science has proved it." Mr. Bowden's ex posures are quite unanswerable, . . .

International Catholic Priests Association. This is one of the most important works for years on the ape-men fossils, and it shines a bright light on four aspects. Firstly, the author shows that the ape-men fossils are dubious in the extreme. Secondly, he shows that evolutionists have concealed or minimized fossils of real men as ancient as these of their supposed ancestors, the ape-men. Thirdly, the ape-men have not been "discovered" by a huge army of scientists, but rather by a tiny group, numbered almost in single figures, travelling from hoax to hoax. Lastly, many will conclude from this work that right in the centre of this group was none other than Teilhard de Chardin . . . This book is written by a clear thinker with a scientific approach who has long studied the original books and papers, weighed one account against another, and has now given us the results in a condensed yet clear way. Everyone should have this book and make sure that their public library also has it.

Evangelical Times. In places it reads like a detective story . . . Indeed one is left with the inescapable impression that the trail of suspicion goes beyond Piltdown . . . [a book] which will be worth adding to your collection.'

Evangelical Action (Australia). Although written in a scholarly and technical manner, "Ape-men: Fact or Fallacy?" is, nevertheless, quite easily understood by the non-technical reader and I recommend it to all those who, like myself, have to provide answers to evolutionary questions.

Prophetic Witness (Review by Dr. F. A. Tatford). This is an important book, covering the whole ground of fossil evidence for evolution, and it cannot be ignored. We commend it to our readers.

Fellowship (Review by Duane T. Gish, Ph.D.-Associate Director, Institute for Creation Research, Californial. Anyone interested in the fossil evidence for the ancestry of man should have a copy of Malcolm Bowden's book .

Also by Malcolm Bowden -

"THE RISE OF THE EVOLUTION FRAUD;
an exposure of its roots"

This book demonstrates that evolution was promoted for many years before Darwin, his "Origin of Species" only appearing at the right time.

Charles Lyell - the man behind the scenes. Charles Lyell provided "millions of years" for evolution in his "Principles of Geology". His stated intention of destroying "the Mosaic account" i.e. Genesis. He quickly befriended Darwin when he returned from the Beagle voyage and the circumstantial evidence is that it was he who suggested to Darwin he should write about evolution. Darwin had no thought of it before then.

The "Beagle" voyage" Throughout this voyage, Darwin was far more interested in geology than biology. He did *not* think of evolution whilst visiting the Galapagos and seeing the various beaks of the finches. This was pointed out to him by the ornithologist entrusted with his collection *after* he had returned to England. He made many such (false) claims in his "biography" which he wrote late in his life.

The X-Club. This was a small group of only 9 people holding all the important positions in the British scientific "establishment" who conspired to force the theory upon the nation. They ensured that only evolution would be taught in our universities. Examples of the present-day barriers facing creationists for promotion etc.

The so-called "first day sell out" of "Origin of Species". This was only the normal pre-publication booking by agents. In fact, the book did not sell well, but it was the constant promotion of the theory that eventually brought it to the public's notice.

The Huxley-Wilberforce debate at Oxford. This was far from being a victory for evolutionists. Huxley did not really challenge Wilberforce with his "monkey" jibe. The powerful propaganda machine run by evolutionists has claimed this defeat as a "victory" and a "turning point" for their campaign.

The links between Evolutionists and Revolutionists. The Lunar Society consisted of a mixture of evolutionists and those who supported the French Revolution. Several links between well know evolutionists and revolutionists are traced.

Karl Marx's proposed dedication of an issue of "Das Kapital" to Darwin. This is often paraded by communist propaganda. However, it was not a letter received from Marx but from Marx's son-in-law - the unscrupulous Edward Aveling, who had written a book.

The moral implications. The repercussion of the acceptance of the theory of evolution are demonstrated in living conditions and the quality of life of those anti-Christian nations that have adopted the theory uncritically.

....

Foreword by Henry M. Morris. "Malcolm Bowden has placed the whole subject in a new perspective..a book that can make a vital contribution...I am pleased and honoured to commend it to the thoughtful study of readers everywhere."

....

222 pages, 24 b/w illustrations, referenced, 4 colour cover, ISBN 095 0604224. Available from Christian Bookshops or direct from the publishers (p+p included in price)
SOVEREIGN PUBLICATIONS, BOX 88, BROMLEY, KENT BR2 9PF

By the same author-

"SCIENCE vs. EVOLUTION"

This book covers all the major evidences, and many minor ones, said to prove that evolution had take place, but demonstrates the fallacies of each of them. It has been sectioned and referenced for easy location of each subject so that the facts can be quickly presented by creationists.

SECTION I - GEOLOGY. The many criticisms of the geological column as it is interpreted by evolutionists. Archeopteryx and the "evolution of the horse" are shown to be false links between groups and species. The ape-men "missing links" are briefly summarised.

SECTION II - BIOLOGY. Mendel's experiments refute evolution. The Peppered moth does not prove evolution. Recapitulation theory now rejected by evolutionists. Haeckel's forgeries. Darwin's Galapagos finches show only minor changes. Bird classifications - features are too varied to have evolved. Circumpolar Gulls. Whales. Duck-Billed Platypus. Bombardier Beetle. Caterpillars - Chrysalis - Butterflies. The bee. Nascent organs. Vestigial organs. The human appendix. The Golden Plover's amazing flight. Nesting habits. The Bucket Orchid.

SECTION III - PHYSICS. Chemical production of "life" is impossible. Dawkins' computer programme in his "The Blind Watchmaker" shown to be carefully designed to give the result he wants. Complexity of a "simple" cell. Radiometric dating - inaccuracies exposed. Carbon 14 dating method limitations.

RECENT DEVELOPMENTS. The decrease in the speed of light and its effects - (1) Radiometric dating (2) Astronomical observations (3) Biological effects (4) A new origin for geological strata ?

SECTION IV. THE RISE OF EVOLUTION. The propagation of evolution. Television programmes. Evolutionist's stratagies. Checking the facts. Evolutionist's catch phrases. The myths of evolution

APPENDICES. 1 - Archaeopteryx - is it a fake? **2** - The Piltdown Hoax; an update. **3** - The inadequacies of Kettlewell's Peppered Moth experiments. His famous experiment was carefully arranged to provide the results he wanted. **4** - A list of 28 deceptive strategems. An analysis of Dawkin's "tricks of the advocate's trade" in his book.

....

256 pages. 33 line illustrations. Fully referenced. Index. 4 colour cover. ISBN 09506042 3 2

Available from Christian Bookshops or direct from the publishers (p+p included in price)

SOVEREIGN PUBLICATIONS, BOX 88, BROMLEY, KENT BR2 9PF

Extracts from Reviews of "Science vs. Evolution"

Alpha Magazine April '92 by Nick Mercer, Assistant Principal of the London Bible College. Bowden showed in his earlier works..his grasp of the biological and fossil evidence..this book is something of a tour de force covering all that material and much more. He has certainly risen to every challenge from both pro-evolutionists and anti-creationists. And yet he has done this in language and concepts accessible to the intelligent non-scientist.

European Christian Bookstore Journal, March '92 by Mike Adams. The very title of this volume suggests that the theory of evolution is unscientific, and the author has lectured on this subject for more than twenty years. He comes over well. I suspect that his ruthless logic and exposure of "slogans" being used as a substitute for thought..will cure many readers from ever again thinking in cliches...we should ensure that out teenage children have the opportunity to know that "other side" that is so seldom mentioned...Mr. Bowden communicates well...He is a writer well worth reading.

Review by Dr. A.J. Monty White. ... In Malcolm's latest offering *Science vs. Evolution* he assembles a wealth of facts from virtually every scientific discipline..to show the unscientific nature of the evolutionary hypothesis... Those who have heard Malcolm speak will be aware of his quick-fire-blast-'em-with-the-facts approach. The same tactic is used in this book; no sooner is one salvo of scientific facts fired against an evolutionary view..than another salvo of yet more scientific data is launched with deadly accuracy against another dearly held belief. One is left wondering how any self-respecting scientist could possibly believe in evolution after reading this book.

Literary Review April '92 by George Stern - "Science Falling on its Face" (A reviews of all three books) Malcolm Bowden..(is) a young earth creationist..and his practical approach explodes many evolution bubbles.

English Churchman Feb. 4th. and 7th. '92 by David Watson. This comprehensive manual is a timely answer to Richard Dawkins Christmas lectures at the Royal Institution...He is adept at uncovering false analogies, straw man and the special pleading by which evolutionists deceive a gullible public.

C. Shepherd. I am writing to tell you how much I have enjoyed reading this book and I wish to congratulate you on same. The amount of research that this book has occasioned is enormous and the length of time must have been over number of years. To then have it marketed at only £7.95 can only be done by the writer working for nothing and I am sure that I can speak for many other committed Christian people to say how grateful we are to you for this help also.

I have read your previous books with keen interest, and this one is, if anything, even more complete. May the Lord bless you in the calling of your service.

Proposed book to be co-authored with Dr. R.J.K. Law.

"BREAKDOWNS ARE GOOD FOR YOU:
The myth of mental illnesses"

In an article that appeared in The English Churchman (21-28 February 1992) Dr. Law's opening paragraphs were as follows:

"When I left medicine for the Anglican Ministry, I was sent several people who sought Christian counselling. My experiences in several mental hospitals had led me to see that orthodox psychiatry was not all it was cracked up to be. One consultant psychiatrist said to me, "We can't cure these people, we can only help them to live with their illnesses." To me that was an admission of failure. Why couldn't they cure these people, I asked myself? Then it hit me. Perhaps there was nothing there to cure! I began to re-think the whole concept of mental illness and to observe closely what I was really seeing, and not what I was supposed to see as per orthodox psychiatry.

Whilst curate-in-charge of a church in Edgware in the late sixties, patients were sent to me by various clergy and from ordinary Christians. I studied them carefully and what I saw was so obvious I was amazed it had not been seen before. Actually it had been seen before, because it was there in the Bible; and also it had been acutely observed by many playwrights and novelists. But it had been obscured by the term "mental illness."

What I saw were people who were self-centred, who had no purpose or meaning in life and who were behaving irresponsibly or sinfully. It was this irresponsible, sinful behaviour that intrigued me most. I confronted them with the fact that they were behaving sinfully and challenged them to accept that fact and to behave responsibly. I told them that it was their own fault that they were as they were. They could not help their situation, but they could help their reaction to the situation.

To my astonishment, the moment they accepted the truth that their bad, irresponsible behaviour was their own fault, they first felt immediate relief, and then immediate 'healing.' After all, if it was their fault, then they could do something about i.e. Many admitted they knew it was their own fault and now that they had been found out' they were only too glad to put things right. In effect they had been brought to say, "I have sinned by my own fault, my own most grievous fault."

Suddenly it became clear. These people were not suffering from some illness which the 'Doctor' had to come and cure, but they were reacting irresponsibly, and they were covering up their bad behaviour by blaming others and making excuses. Psychiatry had given them the biggest cover-up excuse of all. "I cannot help my sinful, bad behaviour because I am mentally ill."

A humanist, O. Hobart Mowrer, who was President of the American Psychological Association, in his book "The Crisis in Psychiatry and Religion", published by Van Nostrand Press, challenged the Church to get back to its responsible duty of counselling. On p.72 of his book, he declared that psychopathology (which is another term for mental illness) was a moral problem which has gravitated into medical hands by default and complacency on the part of the Christian Ministry.

On p.60, he demands to know whether Evangelical religion had "sold it's birthright for a mess of psychological pottage". On p.157 he declared that so long as Protestant clergymen preached the gospel on Sundays and then on weekdays had recourse to secular psychotherapy for help in the management of their own lives, their message will have little force or effect in stemming the tide of personal and social disorganisation in our time."

As Dr Law is a qualified medical practitioner, has experience in psychiatry and has counselled many people, he speaks with considerable authority on the subject of "mental illnesses". He joins those who criticise the teachings of orthodox psychiatry that are accepted by many Christians.

Outline of Contents - An analysis of some Biblical personalities and their problems. How problems should be dealt with from the teaching of the Bible. How the Counsellor should deal with the Counsellee. Some illustrations from casework. Reprints of articles by other authors. Answering objections by the medical health professions. Articles dealing with specific areas of life's problems.

SOVEREIGN PUBLICATIONS BOX 88, BROMLEY, KENT BR2 9PF

A proposed publication by the same author (1999?) entitled -

"ESSAYS FOR THINKING CHRISTIANS"

Over several years, this author has circulated privately a number of papers on a wide variety of Christian topics. Many who have read them have been helped and others have been stimulated into re-examining the subjects. This book will present a number of these essays to a wider audience for their consideration.

Prayer and Worship of the Father and Son - A Reconsideration

The Trinity, Love and Suffering. The need for three persons in the Trinity: Why suffering is a necessary part of God's plan.

How Healthy is the Body of Christ? On Christian unity.

Living the Full Christian Life - When Miracles are Rare!

Is There a Purpose to Life - Or; What is Life All About? The basis of the Evangelical faith.

The Ship of Life. An allegory

Choruses - A Reconsideration

The Homecall. A poem

On Reading the First Section of "Someone Who Beckons"

A Critique of "God's Strategy in Human History"

Testimony. The unusual spiritual pilgrimage of the author to the foot of the Cross.

An Examination of Hasidic Judaism

A Critique of Modern Learning Theory

Dealing with Problems in a Christian Fellowship

"Decision Making and the Will of God" by Gary Friesen. Review.

A Travel Brochure - A Trip for All Time

"Missionaries Have No Right to Change the Beliefs of Others". The fallacy of this claim

Symbolism and the Evangelical Christian Faith

Marriage, Divorce and Remarriage. Flow chart of J. Adams' book.

...and others. 4 diagrams, 3 flow charts.

SOVEREIGN PUBLICATIONS
BOX 88, BROMLEY, KENT BR2 9PF

Join the -

Creation Science Movement

(Formerly the Evolution Protest Movement)
The oldest creation movement in the world - first formed in 1932.

BOX 888, Portsmouth PO6 2YD

As at 1998-
Membership - £6 per annum. (OAP and students - £4 per annum)

Circulates to members bi-monthly -

- The CSM *Journal* giving up-to-date details of creationist activities, news, comments, and reviews of newspapers, books and journal articles on the creation/evolution debate;

- One or two pamphlets on specific subjects.

Holds meetings throughout the U.K.

Sells pamphlets, books, cassette tapes of talks and videos on creation. Write for complete list.

CREATION EXPO
17 The Hard, Portsmouth, PO1 3DT

The first and largest permanent creation exhibition in the UK. (expected to open early 1999). Many animated computer exhibits with commentary through individual earphones. Bring along a party to the exhibition of creation evidence in the U.K.

Contact the office for opening times. Portsmouth Harbour railway station, bus and coach station immediately opposite the exhibition centre. H.M.S. Victory - Nelson's Flagship - and many other naval exhibits and tourist attractions nearby.

Notes

Notes